St. Lawrence Seaway & Power Projects

1959

REID AND BOULTON PUBLISHING CO.

PUBLISHERS

Montreal, Canada

PREFACE

Early in the summer of 1954, Canada and the United States, after years of negotiations and clearing away of legal obstacles, began the actual work of jointly constructing the vast St. Lawrence Seaway and the accompanying Power Projects. Never in the memory of living men had such a tremendous engineering feat been undertaken. It was the first time in history that two great nations, joined in peaceful cooperation, had undertaken so large a development for the betterment of mankind. Man had, at last, decided to free the great landlocked fleets of the Great Lakes and upper St. Lawrence River and provide a deep waterway from the head of the Lakes to Montreal and thence to the Atlantic Ocean.

At the same time, the mighty rapids of the St. Lawrence River were to be harnessed to work for man rather than to impede him. This was to be accomplished by the huge power dam in the Cornwall-Massena area which would provide over two million horsepower of hydro-electric energy, the output to be divided equally between the United States and Canada.

Now, as 1959 dawns, through tenacity and ingenuity, the joint forces of Canada and the United States can look back with justifiable pride to a completed task as they prepare to open the Seaway to the waterborne commerce of the world. At the same time, the generators in the huge power dam are already turning and in a very short time, their full capacity will be realized.

The entire operation will stand as a monument to international cooperation by nations in the Free World.

It has been our privilege and pleasure to record the story of these great projects. In compiling this story, we have had the cooperation of many persons and organizations and to them, we are deeply grateful. We wish to give public expression of our gratitude particularly to The St. Lawrence Seaway Authority of Canada; The Saint Lawrence Seaway Development Corporation of the United States; The Hydro-Electric Power Commission of Ontario and The Power Authority of the State of New York. At the same time, we wish to express our sincere appreciation for the support we have received from Civic bodies and the many private business firms which have been associated with the building or equipping of the Seaway and Power Projects together with those companies whose goods, services or ships will help to make the Seaway the commercial success that the original planners anticipated.

We sincerely trust that the readers of "St. Lawrence Seaway and Power Projects" will find this volume both interesting and informative.

The Publishers
Thomas H. Reid
William D. Boulton

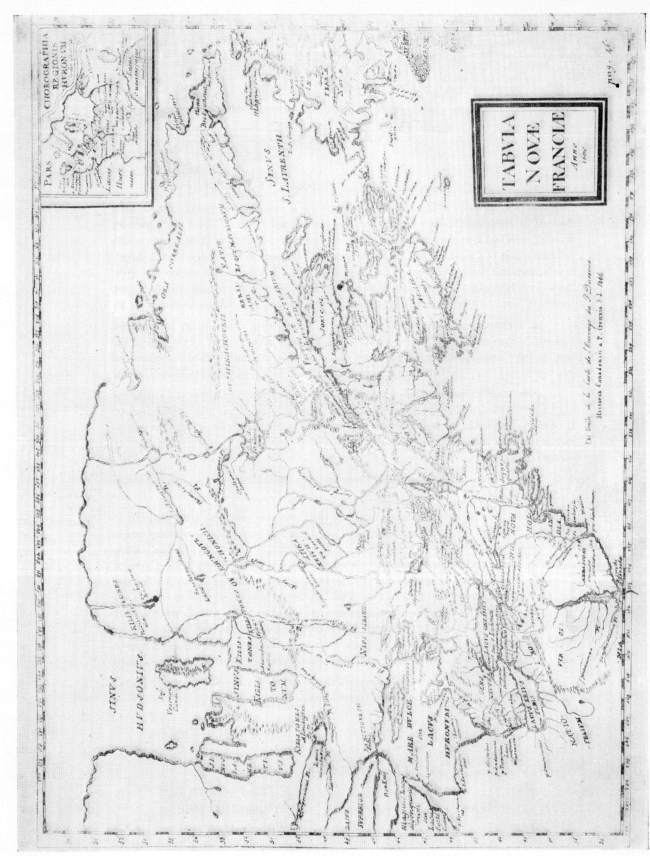

This map of northeastern North America drawn in 1660, shows an early conception of the area.

8

CONTENTS

See Index at back of book for detailed alphabetical listings

Page

Title 5

Copyright 6

Preface 7

Early Map of the Area — 1660 8

Her Majesty, Queen Elizabeth II 11

Message from the President of the United States 12

President Dwight D. Eisenhower 13

Message from the Prime Minister of Canada 14

Prime Minister John G. Diefenbaker 15

Hon. Wilber M. Brucker 16
Secretary of the Army (U.S.)

Hon. George Hees 17
Canadian Minister of Transport

B. J. Roberts 18
*President, The St. Lawrence Seaway
Authority (Canada)*

Lewis G. Castle 19
*Administrator, Saint Lawrence Seaway
Development Corporation (U.S.)*

James Stuart Duncan 20
*Chairman, Hydro-Electric Power Commission
of Ontario*

Robert Moses 21
*Chairman, Power Authority of the State
of New York*

Hon. Sinclair Weeks 22
U.S. Secretary of Commerce

Early History of the St. Lawrence River —
Chapter 1 23-32
*Discovery of the St. Lawrence River; Early
explorations and attempts at colonization*

Evolution of the Canal System — Chapter 2 33-54
*First Canal and Lock, Coteau du Lac. Early
Shallow Draft Canals — Lachine Canal, Corn-
wall Canal, Beauharnois Canal, Williamsburg
Canals, Welland Canal, Soulanges Canal.
Hydro-electric potentialities. Start of Seaway
studies; Legislative and legal problems involved*

Page

Enabling Legislation — Chapter 3 55-62
*Official Act of U.S. Congress; Official Act of
Canadian Parliament*

Executives directly associated with the Seaway
and Power Projects — Chapter 4 63-72

Relocation — Chapter 5 73-84
Towns, Railroads and Highways

Lachine (Montreal) Section — Chapter 6 85-98
*St. Lambert Lock; Cote Ste. Catherine Lock;
Jacques Cartier Bridge; Victoria Bridge; Ho-
noré Mercier Bridge; C.P.R. Bridge; Diking*

Beauharnois Section — Chapter 7 99-106
*Twin Locks at Beauharnois; Beauharnois Ship
Canal; Quebec Hydro-Electric Power Plant*

International Section — Chapter 8 107-148
*Iroquois Control Dam and Lock; Long Sault
Control Dam; Massena Intake; International
Power Dam; Inundation; Dwight D. Eisenhower
Lock; Bertrand H. Snell Lock; Wiley-Dondero
Ship Canal; High Level Bridge*

Great Lakes Connecting Channels — Chapter 9 .. 149-156
*Dredging Operations; Welland Canal and Great
Lakes connecting channels*

Shipping and Tolls — Chapter 10 157-164
*Analysis of Shipping, present and future;
Schedule of Tolls.*

Harbor facilities — Chapter 11 165-172
*Technical data concerning Great Lakes and
St. Lawrence River deep draft ports*

Commercially Sponsored Section 173-323
*Narrative description of companies directly or
indirectly associated with the Seaway and/or
Power Projects*

Contemporary Executives Section 327-413
*Executives directly or indirectly associated with
the Seaway and/or Power Projects*

Alphabetical Index and Photo Credits 414-415

HER MAJESTY, QUEEN ELIZABETH II

A Message from the President
of the United States of America.

"The St. Lawrence Seaway, with its associated Hydro-Electric Power Projects, symbolizes the accomplishments which are possible when two nations cooperate in peaceful endeavour. I am delighted that our nation is associated with our Canadian partner in this monumental development and use of the international waters of the St. Lawrence River."

Dwight D. Eisenhower

Washington
1958.

DWIGHT D. EISENHOWER
THE PRESIDENT of the UNITED STATES OF AMERICA

A Message from the Prime Minister of Canada.

"Completion of the St. Lawrence Seaway and Power Projects will mark the beginning of a great new chapter in the history of Canada, particularly in the sphere of marine transportation and hydro power production. It will focus the interest of the entire world upon this country, an interest that is bound to be reflected to the benefit of the Canadian economy in the years to come.

Because of the vastness of the St. Lawrence Seaway venture, and of its importance to every Canadian, it is commendable that its story has been recorded."

Ottawa
1958.

THE RIGHT HONOURABLE JOHN G. DIEFENBAKER
PRIME MINISTER OF CANADA.

THE HONORABLE WILBER M. BRUCKER
Secretary of the Army
United States Government

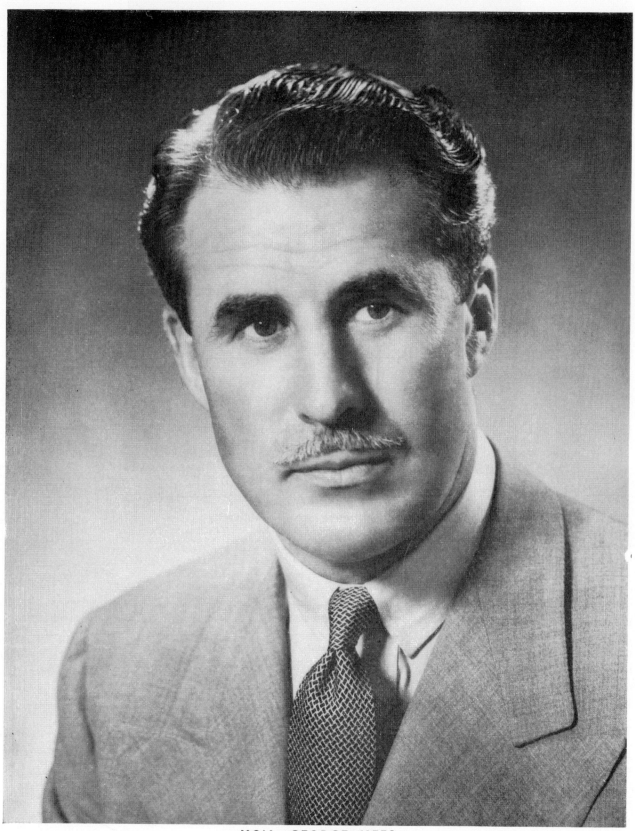

HON. GEORGE HEES
Minister of Transport
Canadian Government

BENNETT JOHN ROBERTS, C.B.E.
President
The St. Lawrence Seaway Authority

The completion of the St. Lawrence Seaway — a joint undertaking of Canada and the United States — has been anticipated by many nations in addition to ourselves. The large bulk carriers of the Great Lakes have been freed from their confinement on the inland seas of North America for passage down to the ports of the lower river. And the way has been laid open for ocean ships of considerable dimensions to trade directly with the ports of the continent's heart.

These deep-sea vessels fly the flags of many lands and some have been especially constructed over the last five years with this particular trade in view.

The enabling negotiations were well concluded; the long-made plans implemented; the work has been carried out with despatch. Ships have been using the Iroquois Lock of the Sea-

way since May of last year. Furthermore, the entire International Section has been in commercial use since July last, but necessarily to the old depth of a little over 14 feet.

Now a depth of 27 feet is available from the Atlantic to Lake Erie. Ships of well over 700 feet in length and over 70 feet beam may sail for 2300 miles, using the new water highway which has been built to circumvent the rapids of the St. Lawrence River.

Readers of this volume will find the story of the St. Lawrence Seaway and those who made it a reality a fascinating one.

B J Roberts

LEWIS G. CASTLE
Administrator
Saint Lawrence Seaway Development Corporation

Less than five years ago, the Congress of the United States legislated into existence the Saint Lawrence Seaway Development Corporation for the purpose of constructing, operating and maintaining the American portion of the St. Lawrence Seaway. Since this great project was to be a coordinated endeavor on the part of both Canada and the United States, a similar organization known as The St. Lawrence Seaway Authority had already been authorized by the Canadian government to assume responsibility for Canada's portion of the Seaway project. The United States Army Corps of Engineers were designated by our corporation as design and construction agents.

As men and equipment were massed on both sides of the border to start work on this engineering undertaking, it became more and more evident that the entire success of the operation depended on team work and cooperation on the part of all officials of the two Seaway and Power entities, contractors, equipment manufacturers and right down the line to the men in the field.

Dikes had to be built, huge locks constructed, control dams and power dams and bridges built, and channels dredged. Some were on the American side, some were on the Canadian side; some were built by the Power Authorities of the State of New York and of the Province of Ontario. It was important that all operations be accomplished on a very rigid schedule. Failure on the part of any one major operation to keep the schedule would eventually result in delay of the entire project. Fortunately, everything went as scheduled, and on July 1, 1958,

the Power Authorities blew up a temporary dike, flooding the area to form what is now known as Lake St. Lawrence. This water pool provided water depth to permit the functioning of the new United States Seaway locks for future shipping.

With the construction phase accomplished, we take this opportunity to thank all entities concerned, especially our Canadian colleagues who were most cooperative. Whenever problems arose, they were met and solved in a spirit of friendly understanding.

Thanks are also due our staff for their loyalty and devotion to duty. Their assistance has been invaluable and, to all other personnel and contractors who took part in this venture, we offer a congratulatory salute.

The St. Lawrence Seaway now stands as a tribute to man's ingenuity, skill and perseverance, but more than that, it is a symbol to the entire world of the great things that can be accomplished between nations working in peaceful cooperation for the benefit of the mankind.

JAMES STUART DUNCAN, C.M.G., LL.D.
Chairman
Hydro-Electric Power Commission of Ontario

ROBERT MOSES
Chairman
Power Authority of the State of New York

THE HONORABLE SINCLAIR WEEKS
Secretary of Commerce
United States Government

CHAPTER ONE
EARLY HISTORY OF THE ST. LAWRENCE RIVER

The discovery of Canada — Jacques Cartier landing on the Gaspe coast in the vicinity of Perce Rock, July 12th or 13th, 1534.

24

EARLY HISTORY OF THE ST. LAWRENCE RIVER

Ice-choked for four months out of every twelve, marred by thundering waterfalls and tossing rapids, and yet potentially the greatest inland waterway in the world, the St. Lawrence River and the Great Lakes beyond it have always represented one of nature's most tantalizing and frustrating bequests.

In Jacques Cartier's time, and for three centuries afterwards, it was not hard to understand the pull of the river. Goods moved by water, or not at all.

But in our modern North American society, where vast webs of steel rail and concrete highway linking the tiniest hamlets with the greatest ports form a system of high-speed ground transport beside which the waterway looks slow-moving and cumbersome, it may sometimes be hard to fathom the precise reason for ever building the St. Lawrence Seaway.

Why not, it might have been asked, dispense with further plans for improving this troublesome stretch of water, which nature never made properly in the first place? Why not move everything by land?

The reason is rooted in an elementary law of physics, a law that the fleets of shining diesels and of massive highway transports have never been able to alter, and which is as true today as it was in Cartier's time. The law is simply this: it takes less tractive effort to move a ton of goods against the friction of water than against the friction of either rail or road.

Hence, while the goods may not move as fast, and can certainly not be taken to as many places, they will move cheaper.

This single fact, together with a vast hydro-electric power potential, has preserved the importance of the St. Lawrence waterway in the life of twentieth century North America and made the building of the Seaway an economic necessity. But the river's role can never again be as vital as it was to the early explorers, the traders, the missionaries and the settlers. To them it was a lifeline: their existence depended on it.

Jacques Cartier

Cartier, who first discovered the river, really made three voyages to America.

His first Atlantic crossing, in the spring of 1534, was made in three tiny ships, the Grande Hermione of 150 tons, the Petite Hermione of 60 tons, and the Emerillon of 40 tons. He was only three weeks out of St. Malo when he sighted Newfoundland, and he entered the Gulf of St. Lawrence via the Strait of Belle Isle, pausing only to take on wood and water at a small harbor.

Seeking the fabled route to the Indies, Cartier was eventually driven out into the Gulf. He reached the west coast of New Brunswick and the Gaspé Peninsula, raised a great cross and shanghaied a pair of Indians who happened to be out fishing in Baie des Chaleurs, before making a circuit of Anticosti Island and heading for home.

It was on his second trip, in 1535, tha the Breton mariner went on up the St. Lawrence, and this time found Hochelaga, the Indian village so famous in Canadian history which stood on an island at the meeting-place of the Ottawa River and the St. Lawrence and whose modern counterpart is one of the world's great ports.

This village was a remarkable place. According to ancient writings it had fifty lodges, each one hundred and fifty feet long. It was enclosed by a fortified wooden stockade thirty feet high, and it had thousands upon thousands of Indian citizens. Whether it was really as grand as this is a point historians have argued for years. But at any rate the St. Malo captain was the first white man to visit the island which we know today as Montreal. He was the first to climb Mount Royal, and the first to gaze down in awestruck wonder on the foaming rapids of Lachine, and beyond them on the silver ribbon of the St. Lawrence reaching off into the heart of the continent. Jacques Cartier came once again to the St. Lawrence, in 1541, but accomplished nothing of importance.

After his visits the St. Lawrence Valley dozed for nearly seventy years. To be sure, hundreds of French, English, Spanish and Portuguese fishermen — more and more each summer — visited the cod-rich banks off Newfoundland. Some of them ventured into the Gulf of St. Lawrence. And a modest trade in furs developed at Tadoussac, at the mouth of the Saguenay River where a plush hotel now caters to vacationing Canadians and Americans.

But governments abroad were too involved in their various wars to worry about mastering a bleak wilderness that might or might not prove worth the taking. The fish and the furs that came from America in the late 16th century were gathered by merchants who cared little for exploration, and not at all for colonization and settlement, and whose only real incentive to probe deeper up the St. Lawrence was to discover whether the great waterway really did lead to the spices and the silks of the East. Even this attraction was not a very strong one, however, for as far as is known no white man visited the upper St. Lawrence between 1541 and the close of the century.

Samuel de Champlain

But while governments themselves were not particularly interested in putting up money for the New World they were willing to grant monopolies to the fur trade. And a turning point in history came when Henry IV of France granted one of these to Francois Grave Sieur du Pont, a naval officer, on condition that a colony of 500 be established. Pontgravé, as he was known, did only one thing to secure his place in history: he took as a partner Samuel de Champlain, and sent him to the St. Lawrence to find a better place than Tadoussac on which to base the fur trade.

Champlain came of a family of seafarers. Born in Brouage on the Bay of Biscay in 1567, he had served in the King's army. But the sea was in his blood, and he had returned to it, becoming an expert geographer and navigator, and sailing into the Spanish Main in the service of Spain. Champlain came first to the St. Lawrence in 1603. He and Pontgravé stopped at Tadoussac, and then moved on up the river in small boats toward the place where the Breton sea captain had found the great rapids.

They reached it in mid-summer and discovered as Cartier had before them that the passage was blocked. But it was here, talking to Indians, that Champlain first became captivated by the vision of what lay beyond the rapids.

It was fantastic how much information he managed to extract from these Indians, and piece together into the geography of inland North America. As they drew and gestured he was able to form pictures in his mind of the St. Lawrence and the Great Lakes, the key to the continent. He could imagine Lakes St. Louis and St. Francis; Lake Ontario, and at the end of it Niagara Falls and Lake Erie; then the narrowing of the waterway, where the motor cities of Detroit and Windsor now look across at one another; and finally Lake Huron, the great body of water which the Indians said was so vast they dared not put out upon it and whose other shore they had never seen.

By the end of it all, the explorer in Champlain had become inflamed with the urge to visit this country and discover for himself whether the waterway led to the Indies.

Lacking an interested sponsor, Champlain for the next several years spent his summers carefully mapping the eastern seaboard of America. But he never forgot the things he had learned from the Indians and their promise drew him back to the St. Lawrence in 1608, this time to establish the first settlement. He chose a site at the foot of a great rock, upstream from Tadoussac where the river narrows, and he called it Québec. Thus was born New France, a colony which ruled the St. Lawrence for more than a hundred and fifty years and

which, but for an incredible lack of interest abroad, might still be a part of the French Empire.

Champlain buried most of his companions that first terrible winter at Québec. Only he and seven others managed to stay alive until Pontgravé arrived in the summer with supplies. But he was determined to conquer this desolation of trees and rock, and so he stayed on.

For years Champlain's tiny settlement at Québec was nothing much more than a fort. But from it he set out on his famous journeys into the interior. In 1609 he followed the Richelieu River as far as Lake Champlain. Two years later found him busy on the Island of Montreal, clearing land for a settlement which he planned to call Place Royale. In 1613 he followed the Ottawa River in fruitless search for a mythical inland sea. And in 1615 he made the most famous of all his trips — up the Ottawa to Lake Nipissing and the French River and then out into Lake Huron, the great body of water which the Indians had told him about a decade earlier but which no white man had ever seen. Champlain had discovered the Great Lakes.

He had also made enemies. On his trip up the Richelieu he had run into a war party of Iroquois, blood enemies of the Hurons and Algonquins with whom he travelled, near the site of present-day Ticonderoga, New York. In the battle that followed the Iroquois were beaten. But Champlain's muskets had helped, and ever afterwards braves of the Five Nations, the most savage in the entire region of the St. Lawrence and the Lakes, hated the French, allied themselves with the English, and plotted destruction with a vicious fury.

By now, England was firmly in control along the Atlantic Seaboard. But France held the waterway that would always be the key to the mid-continent. It was inevitable that the two must someday clash.

They tangled first in 1628, when an English fleet of three ships sailed from Gravesend under the command of David Kirke and his two brothers. The Kirkes had been brought up in Dieppe, and were as much French as English, but their family had been ordered out of France by Cardinal Richelieu during one of the many wars with England and they sailed for the New World determined to even the score by taking Québec and with it control of the fur trade.

After capturing a Québec-bound French supply ship off Newfoundland the English privateers sailed into the Gulf and up the St. Lawrence. They took Tadoussac, and then moved on toward Québec.

For the centre of French power in the Americas, however, Champlain's tiny colony was pathetically weak, and the Kirkes managed to cripple it simply by butchering a herd of unsuspecting cattle. Indians at Tadoussac had told them that the little settlement grazed its cows near Cap Tourmente, offering the suggestion that if these were destroyed the conquerors would have only to wait for the town to surrender. This the Kirkes proceeded to do.

But the stubborn Champlain refused to surrender and the Kirkes, deciding that starving him out would be far easier than a military siege, sailed back into the Gulf to intercept a convoy inbound from France that Indians told them was off the Gaspé coast. The Kirkes met the French ships, captured them in a brief and almost bloodless battle and then sailed for England, confident that Champlain would get no more supplies that winter.

They were right. And when they returned the following spring Champlain and his garrison of sixteen starving men had no choice but to surrender. David Kirke wrote afterwards that the only food he found in Québec was a tub of bitter roots. Ruefully he added that he could have had thousands of beaver pelts for the amount of "victuals" he had to use up in feeding his captives.

Champlain sailed for England as a prisoner in 1629, but within three years the Kirkes discovered they might just as well not have bothered to assault Québec. For diplomacy in the Old France regained what Champlain in the New had not been able to hold. As one of the terms of the Treaty of Saint-Germain-en-Laye, signed by England and France, Cardinal Richelieu demanded and got the return of Québec. The brief period of English rule had ended, as once again the St. Lawrence River changed hands.

Religion and the fur trade together wrote the history of the St. Lawrence and the inland waterway after Champlain returned in 1633. Religion came in the garb of the priests of the Order of Jesus, who had arrived first in 1625, filled with the zeal of the Catholic Revival in France and determined to bring Christianity to the Indians. From that time on the Jesuits were supreme in the religious life of the new colony.

Their influence in creating a new society in a new land was immense, and to a great extent they filled the void in colonization efforts which neither the government in France nor the fur traders themselves seemed disposed to worry about.

Jesuits take over

In 1635, when the great Champlain died, the Jesuits started a school at Québec, which eventually became a classical college and laid the foundation of an educational system in New France. They encouraged orders of nuns to emigrate from France to staff hospitals and establish schools for Indian girls. They set up missions, not only among the friendly Hurons but also among the deadly Iroquois. They learned the languages of the tribes, and wrote dictionaries. The reports they published each year under the title "Jesuit Relations"

kept interest in the colony running high at home. And while their ultimate aim was one with which few would sympathize today — establishment of a theocracy in the New World in which the Order of Jesus would be supreme over even the civil authority — their exploits are a glorious tribute to the power of the gospel.

There were Indian wars, and unspeakable brutality. A Jesuit priest of the Huron Mission, Father Jogues, was set upon by Iroquois one August afternoon up-river from Québec. He was taken off to their lodges, and there clubbed, torn and burned for months before being rescued by the Dutch and taken back to France, only to return later and this time to meet death at the hands of the savages.

Jean de Brébeuf and Gabriel Lalemant, two other Jesuit martyrs, were captured by the Iroquois in Huron country around Georgian Bay and put to death by means of hideous tortures. Some of the tribes were cannibals, and even those who were not, enjoyed gruesome sport with captives: burning their bodies with hot coals, dragging them naked over rocks and brush, carving their flesh into ribbons, beating, burning and mutilating in insane orgies of inhumanity.

But neither Christianity nor the fur trade could be halted by Indian savagery.

On a summer day in 1641 a tiny ship sailed from La Rochelle, a French port on the Bay of Biscay. She was bound for New France, carrying forty soldiers, a single woman, and their commander. The woman was Jeanne Mance. The commander was Paul de Chomedy de Maisonneuve.

By that time the Indian settlement of Hochelaga had long since vanished, and Champlain's dream of a bustling Place Royale had remained just that. But the island at the end of deep water navigation on the St. Lawrence had begun to realize its destiny in trade. It was the jumping-off point for explorers heading up the Ottawa River or into the Great Lakes. It had no year-round settlement but it had become the natural meeting place for Indians bringing furs down the inland waterway and traders coming up the St. Lawrence in their flat-bottomed boats to do business.

Maisonneuve founds Ville Marie de Montreal

But the tiny company which sailed from La Rochelle, wintered in Québec and moved on up the river the following spring, had no interest in the fur trade. For Maisonneuve, for the saintly Jeanne Mance, and for the others, the voyage was a religious crusade, inspired by a divine call. They had been chosen to establish a sacred city on the rich meadows beneath Mount Royal, a city they had already decided to call Ville Marie de Montréal.

Father Vimont, superior of the mission at Québec and Maisonneuve's companion on the voyage up-river, spoke after the entire party had come ashore, fallen on its knees, sung hymns of thanksgiving, and raised a modest altar. "What you see is only a grain of mustard seed," he said, "but it is so animated by faith and religion that it must be that God has great designs for it."

Up until that time the two European giants had been busy carving their separate empires in America in entirely different ways.

With the English in New England the fur trade was, from the beginning, a matter of secondary importance. They came to settle. They fished for cod, farmed the land, began building little villages, and launched infant industries like lumbering, shipbuilding and distilling. They developed their own flourishing export trade with the West Indies, and each year became more prosperous and self-sufficient.

With the French along the bleak and forbidding St. Lawrence, icebound for a third of every year, it was different. First and foremost they were fur traders. Settlers and their families were extra baggage, a hindrance to the main business at hand, and that business was trade with the Indians.

Louis Hébert, the first white man to till the soil of the St. Lawrence Valley, did not arrive with his family until 1617. And even by 1635, the year Champlain died, there were only about one hundred year-round residents at Québec. The Company of New France, organized by Cardinal Richelieu and given a monopoly of the fur trade, was supposed to set up a colony numbering 4,000 by 1643. But its first boatloads of settlers had been captured by the privateering Kirkes, and it afterwards made very little progress; eventually France became weary of its foot-dragging, and wound it up, replacing it with government by the Crown.

Fur trading posts were established at Three Rivers and Fort Richelieu, site of today's Sorel. And the founding of Montreal, and with it a fort, a hospital and a school, quickened the pace of settlement a little.

But it was only a little. Civilization was moving up the St. Lawrence, but too slowly, too haphazardly. By 1660 there were only about two thousand people living in all of New France, most of them in Québec, Three Rivers and Montreal, beyond which, in the lake region, there was virtually no settlement. The Iroquois were still making trouble. To save Ville Marie, Dollard des Ormeaux and sixteen companions that same year confessed their sins and then went out to meet death at the Long Sault on the Ottawa River. Against a war party of eight hundred savages they threw up a rough stockade, and fought behind it for more than a week, without water and without sleep, until they were finally overwhelmed and slaughtered.

Canada's First Shipyard — Intendant Talon visiting shipwrights at the barn-like St. Charles mold-loft in 1672, perhaps not long before his final departure for France. The model and the actual ship beyond are typical of the period. In the background can be seen the St. Lawrence and behind that the Isle of Orleans. The main channel is hidden but the Levis shore is to be seen at the right. Seated near Talon is the shipwright, discussing the ship's draught on the plans. The men at the left are ripping long planks with the type of saw then in use.

Jean Talon

But now there came a change, as Colbert, Louis XIV's great, colonial-minded minister, decided that things must be altered, and promptly, if French power was to be extended or even maintained in America. He saw that colonization was vital; for this he chose Jean Talon. And he saw that the Iroquois must finally be mastered; for this he chose the Marquis de Tracy.

"It is much more advantageous," said Colbert, "that the inhabitants devote themselves to cultivating the land, rather than to hunting, which can never be of any use to the colony."

The chosen two who were to carry out Colbert's double-edged plan, both arrived in 1665, bringing warships, whole companies of seasoned troops, and settlers. De Tracy went straight to his work. He first built a string of forts along the Richelieu River, and then launched a campaign against the Iroquois, burning and destroying in the Mohawk Valley and creating an earnest desire for peace among the tribes of the Five Nations that was to last for twenty years.

Talon, the Intendant, also fell to with business-like efficiency. Early marriages and big families were encouraged, and bachelorhood discouraged. Model villages were set up near Québec. Strips of land running back from the river were parcelled out. Industries were established — shipbuilding, brewing, tanning, flour milling, lumbering, the weaving of cloth, the salting of fish and the extraction of fish oils. Talon examined iron deposits, laid plans for roads, and dreamed great dreams.

Over the next ten years 2,000 colonists arrived from France. Many of Tracy's soldiers settled into a life of farming. More schools, classical colleges and hospitals were set up. By 1675 the population of New France had more than trebled and a base had at last been laid for a balanced settlement.

Count Frontenac

This period, and a few years that followed it, were perhaps the greatest in the history of New France. For settlement and family life, farming and industry, were not the only things being promoted. First under Talon, and then under the Iron Governor, Count Frontenac, after Talon was recalled to France in 1672, French voyageurs carved off great chunks of inland North America and in magnificent gestures claimed it for their King. Their fur-trading empire extended deeper and

Canada's First Trade Treaty — Count Frontenac, Viceroy and Governor of New France, in council with Chiefs of Iroquois Nation at Cataraqui (Kingston), 1673.

29

deeper into the interior, until it reached from the mouth of the St. Lawrence to the mouth of the Mississippi. And if when it came to empire-building their reach exceeded their grasp; if it seems so utterly preposterous today that a handful of men could have been expected to hold a domain so immense by means of a few isolated forts and trading posts, tales of their exploits can still make the pulse quicken.

Montreal became the base for these, the most famous of the French explorers and Jesuit priests who set out to add new glory to France's North American kingdom and new converts to the Christian faith. Their names ring from the pages of history: Joliet and Father Marquette, who discovered the upper Mississippi; Dulhut, who went beyond Lake Superior; Father Hennepin, who explored the upper Mississippi; Cadillac who was later to set up trading posts at Detroit and Michilimackinac; and the greatest of them all — La Salle.

They were all of a type, these audacious Frenchmen of the late 17th century, and of a type far removed from some of the dandies who inhabited the French court at Versailles in those days. They were young men, in their twenties and early thirties mostly, and they were filled with a restless curiosity and a matchless courage.

Louis Joliet

Louis Joliet had been born in Quebec in 1645, the son of a wagonmaker. He took minor orders in his youth, but left the church to enter the fur trade and became an explorer. He had the bad luck to lose the records of his history-making Mississippi trip in the Lachine Rapids when he was returning home, but he lived to visit Hudson Bay and ended his days as a Royal Pilot on the St. Lawrence and hydrographer to the colony.

Father Marquette

Jacques Lesperance Marquette, who was born in France in 1637, was a Jesuit who became a missionary to the Indians shortly after his arrival in New France in 1666. His knowledge of six Indian languages helped him in his mission, but teaching was not enough for his eager spirit and he accompanied Joliet in the Mississippi discovery. The hardships were too great for him, however, and he died two years later, his health broken, on the shore of Lake Michigan at the mouth of the river that bears his name.

Daniel Greysolon Dulhut

Daniel Greysolon Dulhut, born in France one year before Marquette, came to Canada in 1672. He became the explorer of the south shore of Lake Superior and of the Sioux country, and developed such an influence with the Indians that he diverted much of the fur trade away from the Hudson's Bay Company. Dulhut left his name, with a slight change in spelling, to Duluth, Minnesota.

Sieur de la Salle

René Robert Cavalier, Sieur de la Salle, was formed in the same mold as these three but with an extra measure of vision and daring. He was born in Rouen in 1643, and had considered becoming a priest. But he chose the French army instead, and then gave this up to leave for New France at the age of 23. Near Montreal he obtained a seigneury, which he called La Chine for he still wondered whether the St. Lawrence and the Great Lakes led somehow or other to Asia. La Salle set up a trading post, studied Indian dialects, and began planning great journeys into the interior.

The first came in 1669 when with Father Galinée, a Jesuit priest, La Salle reached the mouth of the Niagara River, explored the shore of Lake Erie and Lake Huron, and continued northward to Sault Ste. Marie where the Jesuits had a mission.

But this was a mere appetizer, and he returned to Montreal and his seigneury with his mind full of grand ideas for consolidating the French position along the inland waterway against future inroads of the English and the Dutch from the seaboard. He favored establishing a whole chain of forts and trading posts along the Great Lakes, bringing in settlers and actually building a fleet of ships to sail on the Lakes and nail down France's hold on the commerce of the entire region.

The shipping pattern on the waterway of the Lakes and the St. Lawrence River at the time these bold and far-reaching ideas were forming in La Salle's mind was a simple one.

In the late spring French vessels arrived in convoy at Québec, bearing supplies, goods for trading and a few adventurous colonists. Some of these ocean ships reached Montreal, and all were careful to be fully loaded and clear of the St. Lawrence on the return run before too late in the fall, for then there was always the danger of ice and storms. Farther up the waterway the pattern was the same, but going in the opposite direction. Fur traders and Indians from the area surrounding the Lakes left in the spring for Montreal, Three Rivers and Québec, their canoes heavy with skins. They returned to the wilderness in the fall. When ice closed the river it also sealed off New France from the rest of the world until the following spring, and if spring came late the grim visage of starvation was real and very much a part of people's lives.

Early trading along St. Lawrence

As Europeans grew more and more fond of beaver hats, traders in the New World worked harder and harder to satisfy them. Competition had forced them to go to the Indians and to set up a few isolated trading posts, and it is a remarkable tribute to the French trader that most of the sites he picked are today busy cities.

Between Montreal and Québec fairly large boats had long been used by the traders, big flat-bottomed craft drawing little water, which carried masts and sails and could also be rowed. They were called barques and chaloupes. There were skiffs, too, equipped with oars and poles and built to travel in water too shallow for the bigger boats. And finally there were pinnaces, which sometimes had as many as three sails, and gabares, which were like big scows with sails.

Upstream from Montreal, and between the various Great Lakes, there were no canals yet to make the going easier around the rapid-strewn stretches of water and past the great falls. In fact about the only thing done to improve the inland trading route was cutting down trees along the Indian portages or carrying places.

The canoes of the Indians were beautifully designed for operating in these waters, and their basic shape has never been improved on. They were made by fitting large sheets of birch bark over a framework of wood, and then stretching the bark taut, binding and lacing it to the frame, and finally sealing the joints with a mixture of tree gum and tallow. The result was a craft strong and light, that drew very little water, could be carried easily around the rapids, and repaired with materials available everywhere.

Most times the Indians preferred two-man canoes, between fifteen and eighteen feet long. But to carry the thousands of pelts they collected each year and took down to Montreal, the fur traders soon built larger craft, wide and deep and styled after the great canoes in which the tribes travelled to war.

Under the Intendant Talon, La Salle received all the moral support he needed for his ambitious plans to strengthen the French hold on this first crude export-import trade between Europe and the St. Lawrence waterway. But of financial help there was none until the arrival of Count Frontenac, who replaced Talon in 1672.

Count Frontenac, the new Governor of Montreal, was one of the great men of the French regime. A professional soldier, who had fought in Italy, the Low Countries and Crete, he was tough, ruthless and arrogant, but he was a born leader, a man who knew instinctively how to handle Indians and whose mind travelled in channels for above the petty quarrels and jealousies of life in the colony. He shared La Salle's passion for great adventure, exploration and commercial ventures along the waterway. The two became close friends, and before long La Salle was the Iron Governor's first lieutenant in matters of exploration and trade.

The year after he arrived Frontenac had built the first French fort west of Montreal, at the point where Lake Ontario joins the St. Lawrence River and the site of present-day Kingston. Then it was known as Fort Frontenac and the year after it was built La Salle, with the Count's blessing, managed to obtain a seigneury of the lands adjoining it.

From here La Salle, a few years later, was able to begin putting into action his grand designs for opening new centres of trade and establishing the first settlers on the upper lakes. For once he had obtained the seigneury, friends and relatives lent him money. Colbert, the great French minister who had sent out Talon and de Tracy, became interested in his plans. And by late fall of 1678 his advance guard arrived triumphant at Fort Frontenac aboard a fleet of canoes and bateaux, bringing supplies, and a task force of skilled carpenters, blacksmiths and shipwrights. They pushed on to Niagara in several small sailing ships which La Salle had built at Fort Frontenac, and began building the next link in the trading chain, a fort and a portage to Lake Erie. There they were joined by La Salle himself.

It was January, 1679. Through the winter, under the watchful eyes of the Senecas who had not quite decided how to treat this invasion of their hunting grounds, a shipbuilding site was prepared farther up the Niagara River, at Cayuga Creek near the site of what later became Buffalo, N. Y. By spring a ship was well underway. And on an afternoon in early summer, as French cannon boomed and a blessing was pronounced, the first vessel ever to be built for trade on the lakes slid down the ways.

Within a few weeks the "Griffin" had been fitted out and loaded. She was about sixty tons, carried seven light guns, and was built for the fur trade, with a large hold and drawing very little water so that she could operate in shallow waters like those between Lake Erie and Lake Huron. She sailed out into Lake Erie, with La Salle in command, and the era of Great Lakes commerce had begun.

Proudly, La Salle took his new ship up Lake Erie, through the Detroit River, Lake St. Clair and the St. Clair River beyond it, up Lake Huron to Michili-mackinac where the Jesuits had a mission, on into Lake Michigan and finally, on a day in September, to the site of present-day Green Bay, Wisconsin.

But history's first laker was a doomed ship, and her first voyage was also her last. At Green Bay La Salle found some of his fur traders, and he ordered the Griffin to load the skins they had collected and sail back down the lakes. On the first day out the ship was caught in a great storm and sank, taking most of her crew with her.

La Salle was not aboard when she sank. He had gone on by canoe, to explore parts of present-day Indiana and Illinois, and to reach the supreme moment of his life when he became the first white man to sail down the Mississippi to the Gulf.

The Griffin.

Wrote Francis Parkman, greatest of the historians who have traced the development of New France: "On that day the realm of France received on parchment a stupendous accession. The fertile plains of Texas; the vast basin of the Mississippi, from its frozen northern springs to the sultry borders of the Gulf; from the woody ridge of the Alleghanies to the bare peaks of the Rocky Mountains — a region of savannas and forests, sun-cracked deserts and grassy prairies, watered by a thousand rivers, ranged by a thousand warlike tribes, passed beneath the sceptre of the Sultan of Versailles, and all by virtue of a feeble human voice, inaudible at half a mile."

La Salle died in this fabulous country he had discovered, dropped by an assassin's bullet somewhere in Texas. But he had done more to extend the French Empire of the interior than any other man. And if others like him had been in charge at the glittering court of Versailles over the century that followed, it is worth wondering whether the English would ever have burst out from their seaboard preserve to lay claim to inland America and the waterway of the St. Lawrence.

Meantime, back in Montreal, Frontenac was having his troubles. He had developed enemies, and one of them was the church, presided over at that time by François de Montmorency-Laval, the powerful first Bishop of Québec. Count Frontenac, in his fierce-aggressive drive to increase French power, tolerated many things which the church condemned.

He approved giving the Indians brandy for their furs, in order to compete with the English who were offering rum. Bishop Laval, as tough and determined a man in his own way as Frontenac was in his, did not. Frontenac believed in fighting fire with fire, and on one occasion, after the Iroquois refused to heed his warning to cease torturing French captives, he handed over two of his own Iroquois prisoners to some friendly Hurons, who promptly burned the unfortunate pair at the stake. This sort of thing Bishop Laval found intolerable.

At the same time commercial enemies were dogging Frontenac heels. There was charges of special favors to chosen friends, and of what today would be called graft. Eventually the French government grew weary of the squabbling and decided to recall the Count.

After Frontenac had been shipped home in 1682, in the interests of harmony and to soothe the ruffled feelings of the church, the colony into which he had breathed life and energy and order began, quite literally, to fall apart.

Incompetents succeeded him, men who lacked the Count's ability to deal firmly but intelligently with the Indians. The fort he had built as a buffer where Lake Ontario joins the St. Lawrence was abandoned. Knowing that the strong man was no longer in charge, the Iroquois became bolder and more daring. The fur trade with the Hurons began to fall off. And the entire colony floundered through lack of a leader.

After nine years of it, and after an abortive war carried out against the Iroquois by one of Frontenac's successors served only to harden the tribes' resolve to descend on the French and destroy them, the Iron Governor was recalled to Canada. His triumphant return came just as the first attempt was being made to improve the St. Lawrence River for navigation.

CHAPTER TWO

EVOLUTION OF THE CANAL SYSTEM

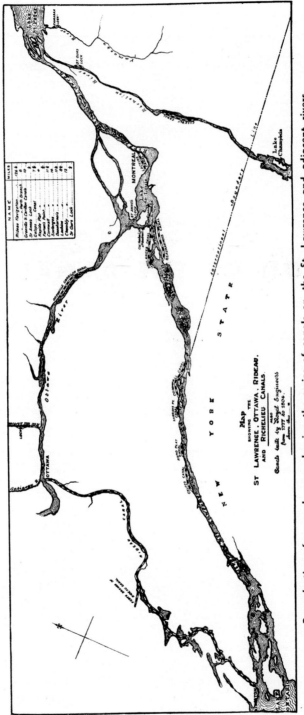

Reproduction of an early map showing the series of canals on the St. Lawrence and adjacent rivers.

GROWTH OF THE CANAL SYSTEM

Dollier de Casson was a soldier, an engineer, an explorer, and a priest. A man of fantastic physical strength and courage, he had been a captain in the French Army and had helped wage war against the Iroquois. And when in the late 1600's de Casson became Superior of Montreal's powerful Sulpician Order, he began the long chain of events that was to end three centuries later in the building of the St. Lawrence Seaway.

At the time, the fur trade was being practised with a ferocious rivalry by the French and the English, the French using Montreal as their capital. Up the St. Lawrence River from the bustling fortress at the foot of Mount Royal went muskets, brightly-colored cloth and paints, glass beads, hatchets, earrings. Back down came the skins of the beaver, bear, fox, deer, muskrat.

Because they were light and could be portaged quite easily around the rapids that marred the water route to the heart of the continent, birch bark canoes were still virtually the only means of travel between Montreal and the fort which Frontenac had built at the mouth of Lake Ontario.

Below the rapids, the Quebec shipyards established by Talon had developed into one of New France's most prosperous industries. By law, no oak, beech, cherry and elm trees could be felled by anyone until the king's shipwrights and carpenters had made their choice, and new vessels as large as 800 tons were slipping regularly into the waters of the St. Charles River.

Far to the west, too, ships were being built, for trade on the Lakes. The first had been launched by La Salle on Lake Erie, and while her history was both brief and tragic she pioneered a system of inland navigation that was to become the greatest in the world.

It was a long way from Lake Erie, however, to the place which fate had chosen for work to begin on the first of the projects that would ultimately bring deepsea ships from the ocean to the lakehead. And Dollier de Casson's plan, by modern standards, appears modest. But it was a beginning, and it concerned a small waterway called Riviere St. Pierre, which in those days cut for several miles through the lower corner of Montreal Island before it emptied into the St. Lawrence.

The Seminary of St. Sulpice owned a flour mill on this quiet little stream, a mill which usually suffered in the summertime from lack of water. Dollier de Casson's idea was to join the river with Lachine and Lake St. Louis by means of a canal about one mile long. The Sulpician had two things in mind, the same two things which centuries later were to form the foundation for the Seaway: power and navigation.

He was never able to muster much support for this first bold attempt to bypass the rapids which had blocked Jacques Cartier. Some work did finally begin, and a shallow ditch was dug 2,000 yards long. But then, on a still August night in 1689, a war party of Iroquois fell on Lachine and butchered most of the settlers. Work on the canal halted, and was not resumed until 1700 when the Sulpicians hired a Montreal contractor, Gideon de Cathologne, to finish the job.

The first Lachine Canal was to be completed by June, 1701, but money ran out, the project was abandoned, three-quarters finished, and the river ran unhindered and unconquered for the next 75 years.

During that time the French squandered and lost their empire in America. At the end of it they retained only St. Pierre and Miquelon, two small islands in the Gulf of St. Lawrence. All else lay under the Union Jack.

The daring, the boldness and the magnificent deeds had vanished with the age of La Salle and Count Frontenac. Support in France had dwindled. Louis XV had assumed the French throne, and in one of his first acts had assigned all the affairs of the colony to one of his ministers.

Corruption, graft and vicious rivalries replaced the spirit of adventure, conquest and expansion which had flourished during the late 1600's. Colonization increased a little, but in quality most of the newcomers were far below those of Talon's time. Most important of all, France refused to send an army large enough to fight a showdown with the English, a battle that was moving inexorably closer during those last years of the French regime.

The end of New France came suddenly, in 1758, after England used her great sea power to ferry armies and supplies across the Atlantic for the final onslaught. Wolfe defeated Montcalm on the Plains of Abraham. England gained control of the St. Lawrence, and inherited its problems as well.

No real progress was made toward improving navigation along the waterway until the United States War of Independence made better transport a military necessity for the British government. In the autumn of 1775, after the Canadians had made their momentous decision to snub the Revolution by refusing to send delegates to the Continental Congress at Washington, American troops swarmed across the St. Lawrence and took Montreal, capital of the fur-trading empire. They were driven back the following spring. But the Governor-in-Chief of Quebec, Sir Frederick Haldimand, had seen enough to recognize the acute problems involved in moving and supplying troops. He also foresaw the development of Montreal in trade with the Great Lakes, and while the war ruled out the chances of spending a great deal of money, Haldimand pressed for at least some improvements on the inland waterway.

The first lock canal—Coteau du Lac

For the next few years, as a result, the Royal Engineers labored over a series of small canals designed to avoid one of the most hazardous sections of the entire St. Lawrence River, a section 12 miles long joining Lake St. Francis with Lake St. Louis 30 miles west of Montreal. It was at Coteau Rapids, which bar the entrance to Lake St. Francis, that Haldimand himself several years earlier had watched 84 men drown when their boats were caught and destroyed. And it was there that North America's first lock canal was built.

It was 900 feet long and seven feet wide, and its three locks, each less than 40 feet long, were two and a half feet deep, just enough to float the flat-bottomed river boats that ferried supplies and military stores from Montreal to Kingston. Captain William Twiss, who directed construction, used Cornish miners to build masonry sides for the canal, which he predicted would become "as useful as any in the world."

Two other series of rapids disrupt the river's flow between Lakes St. Francis and St. Louis. One, Cedar Rapids, was navigable for the shallow 18th century river boats. The other, at Split Rock, was conquered by digging three small canals: the La Faucille, with one lock, the Trou du Moulin, without locks, and the Split Rock, with one lock.

By 1783, when this modest program was finished, the eastern boundaries were being drawn between Canada and the United States. And now a revolution began in the lower Lakes and the St. Lawrence Valley, a revolution that was not military but economic.

Northwestern New York and Ohio were being settled. Immigrants from New England were peopling the Eastern Townships south of Montreal. Kingston, York, Niagara and Detroit, the historic supply bases of the fur trade, were becoming the pivot points of an entirely new kind of economy.

It was an economy based for the first time on agriculture instead of animal skins. Small settlements were springing up along the wooded shores of Lake Ontario. Wheat, flour, and timber — these were the new products of the virgin interior in which the merchants of Montreal now began to be interested. Each year, more and more of these products moved down the river, and when the Grenville-Jay Treaty was signed by the United States and Great Britain in 1794, laying the ground rules for trade across the border, attention focussed again on the urgent need for improving the St. Lawrence River canal system.

In 1796, John Richardson of Montreal introduced a bill in the Assembly of Lower Canada for the construction of a Lachine canal. But he got no support. The merchants had little power in the Assembly, and the only improvements made during the next few years were on the same section of the river that had first been tackled 20 years earlier. The La Faucille and Trou du Moulin Canals were being damaged severely each spring

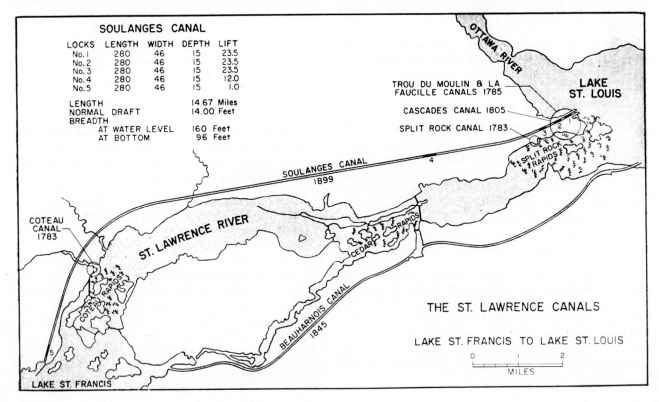

LOCKS	LENGTH	WIDTH	DEPTH	LIFT
No. 1	280	46	15	23.5
No. 2	280	46	15	23.5
No. 3	280	46	15	23.5
No. 4	280	46	15	12.0
No. 5	280	46	15	1.0

SOULANGES CANAL

LENGTH 14.67 Miles
NORMAL DRAFT 14.00 Feet
BREADTH
  AT WATER LEVEL 160 Feet
  AT BOTTOM 96 Feet

THE ST. LAWRENCE CANALS

LAKE ST. FRANCIS TO LAKE ST. LOUIS

REX WOODS

Reproduction from a painting by Rex Woods showing Captain Twiss on an inspection trip to Canada's first lock canal at Coteau du Lac in 1781.

by ice. And so they were abandoned in favor of a single new canal, the Cascades, which was built across Cascades Point. It was about 1500 feet long, with two locks 120 feet long and 20 feet wide at the lower entrance, and guard gates at the upper entrance.

The split Rock and Coteau Canals were enlarged, too, as part of this program which was completed in 1805, and brought at least some improvement over the older system.

By this time, the canoe had just about disappeared as a means of transport on the St. Lawrence. Bateaux, scows, and the new American-designed Durham boats plied between Montreal and Kingston. Commercial sloops and schooners by the hundreds were appearing on the Lakes, and John Molson, the Montreal brewer, was preparing to build his "Accommodation", the first steamboat ever to operate on the St. Lawrence.

The bateau, which carried about three tons of cargo, looked something like today's East Coast fishing dory. It was 18 to 20 feet long, flat-bottomed, and strongly built, pointed at both ends, with wall sides and a bottom inclined to bow and stern. It took four men to row and one to steer, and it carried a square sail that was hoisted when the winds were right.

The Durham boat was bigger and could carry about eight tons going upriver and 25 or 30 running the rapids on the return trip. It was a flat-bottomed craft, round at the bow, with a keel and a centerboard. Decked bow and stern, it had a wide gunwhale for the crew to stand on while they pulled it upriver or kept it amenable to the tow line. It, too, had a sail.

Durham boat about 1810.

In the decade after 1800, a merchant sending goods to York or Niagara used bateaux as far as Kingston, and his shipment was first carted by horse or oxen from Montreal to Lachine, where it was taken aboard. So that crews could help each other at the rapids, riverboats travelled in convoy, and four or five bateaux would set out together into Lake St. Louis. When they arrived at rapids that were impassable to loaded boats, their cargoes were portaged over the carrying place and the boats themselves dragged up the rapids. Then when quiet water was reached, the cargoes came back on board and the journey continued to the next rapid. The crews camped wherever nightfall found them.

It was crude, it was slow, and it was expensive. It generally took nearly two weeks to ship a cargo from Montreal to Kingston. But this was the St. Lawrence as the 19th century opened.

Dollier de Casson, the Sulpician soldier-priest, had been in his grave for more than a century before anything much was done to complete his Lachine Canal project. And action, when it finally came, was taken in response, again, to a national emergency.

For one thing, the War of 1812 had demonstrated clearly and forcibly to the Canadians the need for improvements along the entire St. Lawrence waterway, and especially at Lachine. Long convoys of barges and Durham boats heavy with military supplies and equipment for the forts along the Lakes had to run the canal system. Never had the transportation link between Montreal and the great naval shipbuilding base at Kingston, for example, appeared so meager, so inadequate and so frustrating.

Even more important, discussions were already underway across the border for the building of the New York State barge canal system. This was a threat, and a serious one, to the trade of Montreal for it would connect Lake Erie with the Hudson River, providing water access for traffic in the lakes with the Port of New York and the eastern seaboard and creating the first unbroken navigation channel to the sea.

The Lachine Canal

And so, in 1815, the government of Lower Canada finally acted. It introduced legislation for the building of a proper canal at Lachine, and voted a subsidy of £25,000 before the plan, like so many earlier and later ones, bogged down. The project's backers had been counting on London for most of the money. But the Imperial government decided instead to build the Rideau Canal, linking Lake Ontario with the Ottawa River as a defense measure. By avoiding the International waters of the St. Lawrence entirely, it felt, a military waterway to Montreal, roundabout but safe from any future American attacks, could be provided.

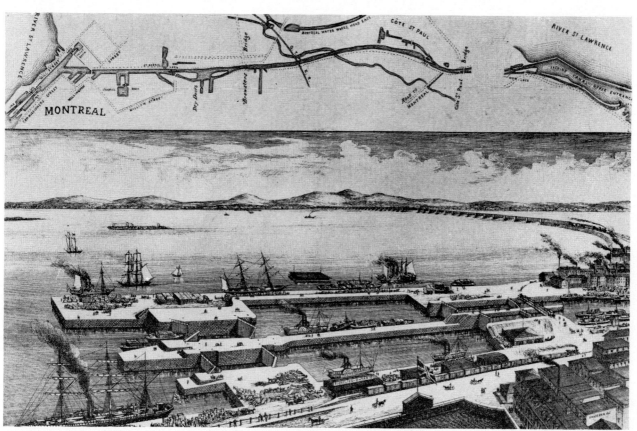

Montreal terminus of Lachine Canal, 1877.

Paddlewheels steamer shooting the Lachine Rapids 1882.

Excavating Lachine Canal near Montreal.

With London's support cut off, the Lachine project was hamstrung, until in 1819 the Assembly of Lower Canada decided that perhaps this was a job for private capital. The joint-stock Lachine Canal Company was formed, but buyers for its $600,000 worth of capital stock were disappointingly few, and two years later half of the stock remained unsold. The company appealed to the government to purchase it and a Commission was appointed which recommended that the Canal be built as a provincial undertaking. This plan was finally approved by the government. Shareholders were paid back, and on July 17, 1821, as a band played and onlookers drank beer and munched beef sandwiches, construction began.

Three years later, the Lachine Canal had progressed far enough that vessels could reach Montreal from Lachine. And in 1825, it was joined with the St. Lawrence. Some of the river's worst rapids had finally been conquered, and by a canal costing $438,000, of which the British government had contributed $40,000 on condition that government stores be allowed to pass free of tolls. It followed roughly the route of the Sulpician project; it was 8½ miles long, and its seven locks overcame the lift of about 45 feet between the harbor at Montreal and the level of Lake St. Louis. The locks were 100 feet long and 20 feet wide. But they were only five feet deep over the sills, enough for barges and not much else. Within a decade, they were to prove grossly inadequate.

Meantime, several years before they united to form a single nation, the governments of Upper and Lower Canada had mounted a joint attack on the St. Lawrence River, an attack which for the first time considered development of the entire 112-miles of water-way between Prescott and Montreal as a common problem demanding some uniform solution. Steamboats were beginning to appear now on the Lakes. The first was the Frontenac, a 700-ton, three-masted schooner, with paddlewheels, that was built near Kingston in 1816 to run between Prescott and ports on Lake Ontario. She was followed a few months later by the "Ontario" launched by the Americans at Sackett's Harbour navy yard, for service on lake Ontario. A revolution in shipping was matching the feverish economic development of the Lake region, and the St. Lawrence River rapids were clearly out of step.

Traffic was increasing rapidly, and in 1818 — with the new Erie Canal actually under construction — a joint committee from Upper Canada and Lower Canada met to study the river. It later recommended, with a sublime lack of imagination, a uniform system of canals four feet deep. No action was taken, but the mere existence of this committee can be considered a landmark on the long, tortuous road toward an improved St. Lawrence River system.

In the early 1820's, as the Erie neared completion, pressure mounted for sweeping improvements on the St. Lawrence. A St. Lawrence Association was formed, and branches of it set up in the towns along the river began bombarding the two Legislatures with demands for action.

But no action came in the 1820's. In fact, none came until 1833. By that time the Erie Canal was carrying several times as much flour and wheat as the St. Lawrence.

But 1833 was the turning point. That year, the Assembly of Upper Canada voted $280,000 to improve the St. Lawrence so as to admit vessels not of three feet draft but of nine feet. It recommended that work start immediately between Cornwall and the head of the tossing, foam-flecked waters at Long Sault which marked one of the worst series of rapids on the entire river. An American, Benjamin Wright, was chosen chief engineer of the Commission appointed to carry out the task, and the government of Lower Canada gave Wright authority to survey canals farther downriver on a scale commensurate in all respects with that in Upper Canada.

The engineers now suggested a nine-foot canal system, with standard locks 200 feet long, 45 feet wide and nine feet deep, to avoid the four distinct series of rapids hindering passage between Montreal and Prescott: the Lachine, at Montreal; the Cascades, Cedars and Coteau between Lake St. Louis and Lake St. Francis; the Long Sault, near Cornwall; and finally, the others grouped around Farran's Point, Rapide Plat, Pointe aux Iroquois, Pointe Cardinal, and Galops.

Thus was born the first ancestor of the St. Lawrence Seaway.

Cornwall Canal

The Cornwall Canal was the first of the new nine-foot links to be built.

It was to start at Dickenson's Landing, where an entrepreneur named Dickenson owned the stagecoach that carried river passengers overland past the Long Sault Rapids. It was to end at Cornwall, 11 miles to

Building the westerly section of Cornwall Canal, 1880. Long Sault Rapids are just beyond the uncompleted dike.

the east. It was to have six locks in between. And it was started, with a great burst of enthusiasm, in 1834.

Work went well at first, but suddenly and sharply, in just a few years, economic depression struck. River traffic plummeted. Upper Canada's precarious finances were strained close to the breaking point. And in 1838 work on the Cornwall Canal came to a halt.

It was more than two years before good times returned, before trade and shipping began to rise again. When the upswing did appear in 1840 it once more exposed the inadequacies of the St. Lawrence canals. And so in 1842, with the two provinces united now, work started again at Cornwall, and the first steamer sailed through the completed canal that same year.

With business booming again, the new Government of Canada began work in 1843 to bring the other canals up to the larger standards. At Lachine, three of the lower entrance locks were combined into two, and the locks arranged for a depth of 16 feet, enabling

seagoing vessels to reach the industrial sites that were developing along the banks.

Beauharnois Canal

The Beauharnois Canal, another link in the new nine-foot series, was completed in 1845 as the third attempt to overcome the rapids at Cascades, Cedars and Coteau which had first been tackled after the American Revolution. Several plans had been submitted, based on the Cornwall Canal, but the one first adopted, and which received government support, recommended short canals at each of the three rapids and use of the river between them.

A grant of $960,000 was suggested but for nine years memoranda and more plans were submitted until each argument resolved itself finally into one question: whether the canal should go north or south of the river. The chief engineer of the Board of Works settled the matter — it should go south. Moreover, it would not

View of westerly section of Cornwall Canal before inundation in 1958. Photo was taken from exact spot from which artist made drawing on opposite page, 78 years earlier.

make use of the river at all but would be 11¼ miles long, with a nine-foot draught and nine locks. In 1842, a contract was let for construction, and three years later the Beauharnois Canal was opened.

At first, the new link was not satisfactory. The upper entrance was bad, the channel was crooked, and the water was too shallow in dry weather. These faults were all corrected when two new dams built across the main channel of the St. Lawrence, just below Valleyfield, raised the water to a satisfactory level.

Williamsburg Canals

Upstream from the Long Sault, construction gangs began digging an entirely new series of canals in 1845, again as part of the nine-foot system. These were called the Williamsburg Canals, and they were needed to avoid scattered groups of rapids which were not nearly so dangerous as those downriver but, nevertheless, were hindering passage of the large sidewheelers, schooners, brigantines and barkentines, and the new propeller-driven vessels now in use on the St. Lawrence.

The first of the new series to be dug along this 30-mile stretch of the river was the Farran's Point Canal, just over a mile long and with a single lock. Following it, 10 miles upstream at Morrisburg, came the Rapide Plat Canal; it was four miles long and had two locks. Further west again two more new canals were built, one three miles long to bypass the Iroquois Rapids and the other two and a half miles long to overcome the Galops Rapids. Later, ships captains found that the Iroquois Canal lacked sufficient water for vessels going upriver, and so it was joined with the Galops to form a continuous seven and a half-mile channel with three locks, the longest of the Williamsburg series.

14' draft canal steamer after being raised passes through lock at Farrans Point, Ont.

Canaller, bound downstream, about to be lowered in one of the locks.

After lowering, lock gates open and canaller proceeds downstream.

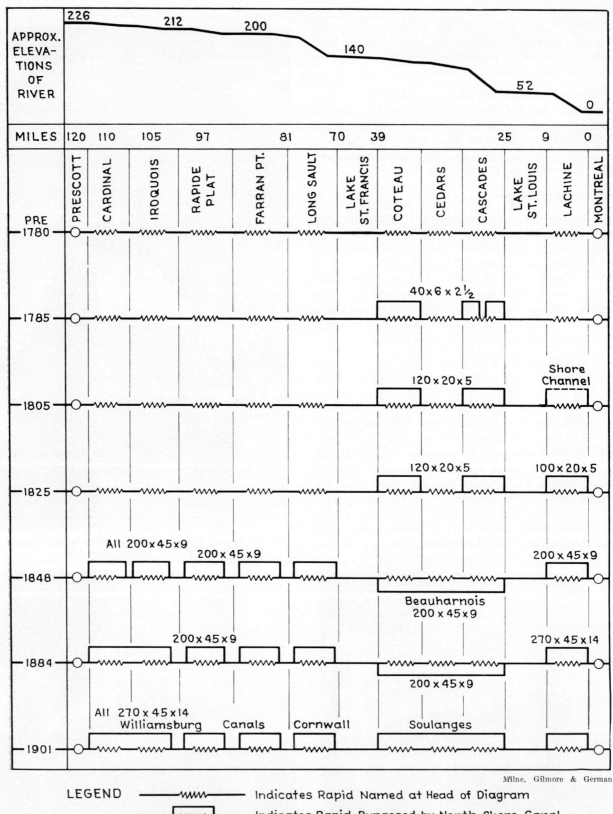

APPROX. ELEVATIONS OF RIVER

| 226 | 212 | 200 | 140 | 52 | 0 |

MILES | 120 | 110 | 105 | 97 | 81 | 70 | 39 | 25 | 9 | 0

PRESCOTT | CARDINAL | IROQUOIS | RAPIDE PLAT | FARRAN PT. | LONG SAULT | LAKE ST. FRANCIS | COTEAU | CEDARS | CASCADES | LAKE ST. LOUIS | LACHINE | MONTREAL

PRE 1780

1785

40 × 6 × 2½

Shore Channel

1805

120 × 20 × 5

1825

120 × 20 × 5

100 × 20 × 5

1848

All 200 × 45 × 9

200 × 45 × 9

200 × 45 × 9

Beauharnois 200 × 45 × 9

1884

200 × 45 × 9

270 × 45 × 14

200 × 45 × 9

1901

All 270 × 45 × 14
Williamsburg   Canals   Cornwall   Soulanges

Milne, Gilmore & German

LEGEND ⸺wwww⸺ Indicates Rapid Named at Head of Diagram

⸺wwww⸺ Indicates Rapid Bypassed by North Shore Canal

⸺wwww⸺ Indicates Rapid Bypassed by South Shore Canal

Figures given thus – 120 × 20 × 5 – are Size of Smallest Lock

Diagram illustrating development of the St. Lawrence canals system.

Opening of navigation season on old canal at Cardinal, Ont.

Prescott, Ont. Huge upper lakers could proceed no further downstream and had to transfer their cargoes of grain to smaller ships for the trip to Montreal and other Lower St. Lawrence ports. This will not be necessary after Seaway opens in 1959.

Welland Canal

While this surge of new construction was altering the face of the St. Lawrence River below Prescott, another massive canal project had been completed 250 miles to the southwest. This was designed to lower vessels, via a gigantic flight of steps, down the tremendous drop between Lake Ontario and Lake Erie, a drop of 326 feet which was concentrated in majestic fury at a single point: Niagara Falls.

It was in 1824 that William Hamilton Merritt, a bold and determined promoter, formed the Welland Canal Company to build this fantastic stairway.

Niagara Falls was already a holiday attraction. In fact, it was about this time that an obsolete British frigate, vintage 1812, was filled with wild animals one afternoon, set on fire, and sent over the cataract as the main entertainment for a picnic that was being held on the Canadian shore.

But to Merritt, Niagara represented not a potential tourist resort but an obstacle to shipping, and his plan for avoiding the falls and opening a link between Lakes Erie and Ontario called for a canal with 40 locks, each 100 feet long, 22 feet wide and eight feet deep. It was to run from the mouth of Twelve Mile Creek, at Port Dalhousie on Lake Erie, to the Welland River, and its length was to be nine and a half miles. Construction began in late 1824.

Upper Canada loaned the company $125,000 and bought $250,000 worth of stock. Lower Canada contributed $125,000. Shares were offered publicly in the two provinces and in England. But by 1827 Merritt's venture was deep in trouble: it was badly pressed for funds, and the canal was costing far more than the original estimates.

It was rescued then by Upper Canada, and through 1828 and 1829 construction was pushed forward. The company was still in financial straits, but it made fewer calls for help. On November 30, 1829, the fifth anniversary of the project, two vessels drawing seven and a half feet of water passed through. The waterway had reached Lake Erie . . .

But it was still far from complete. In 1830 more financial assistance was needed, and authority was given to increase the capital stock. Twice more, in the next three years, the company appealed for aid. It managed to borrow $250,000 from the British Government, and another $250,000 from Upper Canada. But even this was not enough. By 1834, it still required $500,000 to complete the project. And by the end of 1835 the Welland Canal Company had only $500 left in the till.

The next year a select committee of the Assembly of Upper Canada, appointed after a petition by the company, recommended that the Welland Canal be made a public work, and that the Receiver-General issue debentures for the stock outstanding. This was done three years later.

After 1841, with Upper and Lower Canada united, it was proposed that the Welland Canal locks be enlarged to the dimensions of the new ones on the St. Lawrence. This was done, and by the mid-century Canada had finished a project which, for the size of her population, was an incredible achievement: a complete set of canals and locks that permitted nine-foot draft navigation all the way from Montreal to Sault Ste. Marie.

Completion of the nine-foot system brought with it the beginnings of Great Lakes-Overseas trade.

European ports were not the first to berth ships built and loaded on the Lakes. The maiden voyage to the Atlantic was made by a barkentine bound from Cleveland for the booming California goldfields. But when the schooner Sophia cleared harbor at Kingston in 1850, bound for Liverpool, the trade which a century later was to reach more than a million tons annually and play a major part in the final decision to build the St. Lawrence Seaway had begun.

If Canada staked all her resources on this system of nine-foot canals, it was because she considered it, quite simply, a matter of economic life or death. The Canals were expected to move all the traffic, passenger and freight, to and from what is now Ontario. There were grain and lumber to be shipped out. There was an enormous volume of supplies and manufactured goods and materials for the newly-settled areas to be brought in at a reasonable cost. And it was even felt that the export and import traffic of the fast developing American Middle West might be attracted to the St. Lawrence.

Thus, when after Confederation in 1867, Canada's federal government decided to launch a new program for improving the St. Lawrence River canals, it appeared on the surface to be slightly mystifying. But by this time, a railway had been laid between Montreal and Toronto. It had been operating for more than a decade, and had siphoned off the mixed cargo that had been the cream of the canal trade. In just a few short years, progress had overtaken the canals. Apart from the bulk grain that moved from Southern Ontario to Montreal, the canals had become a distinctly secondary means of transport.

Not only had the railways taken the traffic; they also got first call on government financial support. And so, by and large, the results of all the effort and sacrifice that had gone into the nine-foot system were disappointing.

But when this second period of canal construction was begun, aimed at providing 14-foot navigation between Montreal and Lake Superior, hopes were not pitched so high as they had been for the earlier system. Specialization of traffic between rail and water was now an accepted fact. Skippers knew that canal traffic from now on would consist mainly of bulk cargoes. But they knew, too, that canals nine feet deep were very poorly equipped to hold even that traffic.

The plan developed to remedy this called for locks 270 feet long and 45 feet wide, with a draft of 14 feet, from the sea to Lake Superior. It was to take nearly a quarter of a century to complete, and most of it was to be used for nearly 60 years, until the great St. Lawrence Seaway of the modern age was finished.

All along the waterway, as the 19th century grew old, major new construction or reconstruction was launched.

At the lower end of the Lachine Canal new locks were built alongside the old, and the old ones were later enlarged, providing a double channel with a draft of 17 feet on one side and 15 feet on the other. This was finished in 1884.

Soulanges Canal

Between Lakes St. Louis and St. Francis the old nine-foot Beauharnois Canal was abandoned entirely and a new one, the Soulanges, cut through the opposite bank, largely because 14-foot navigation required a canal entrance farther to the west and this was possible only on the north shore. Started in 1892, the Soulanges was finished seven years later, its four new locks tailored to the bigger dimensions.

In the Cornwall-Williamsburg section of the river, the 200-foot locks built 40 years earlier were enlarged and deepened in stages, the canals being opened for business in 1901.

Between Lakes Ontario and Erie the Welland Canal had been enlarged and deepened to 12 feet by 1881, and five years later, with the propeller-driven steamer coming into common use, it was deepened again, this time to 14 feet.

Between Lakes Huron and Superior, through the gateway to the booming west, Canada dug the 14-foot Sault Ste. Marie Canal between 1888 and 1893. By this time, too, the United States had completed its own canal at the Sault.

Meantime, both Canada and the United States had been busy improving the channels connecting the Upper lakes. In 1875 the Canadian Government cleared parts of the Detroit River and the St. Clair River joining Lakes Erie and Huron to a depth of 16 feet, and placed navigation aids. A year later, the American Government continued the work, broadening the channel to 440 feet and deepening it to 20 feet. And in the vicinity of St. Clair Flats, where navigation was tortuous, the U.S. Corps of Engineers dredged a new channel 700 feet wide, walled it on both sides, and lighted it properly.

Just below the mouth of the St. Mary's River, connecting Lakes Huron and Superior, the Americans deepened the channel for a short distance. And in 1876 the Canadians deepened the Nebish Rapids in this area to a depth of 16 feet.

By the turn of the century the 14-foot canal system was complete, and the outcome was by no means the

Canaller going upstream, Soulanges Canal, Prov. of Quebec.

disappointment that had followed completion of the 9-foot system. For Canada now entered a period of vast expansion and immigration, which lasted to the outbreak of the first World War.

On the western plains the problem of developing strains of wheat adapted to local climatic conditions had been solved, and each year more grain moved east to the St. Lawrence ports via the St. Lawrence canals. The beginnings of industrialism had created new traffic suitable for water transport, notably coal and iron ore.

The days of sail were over now. Proud old schooners were finishing their lives as barges, their sails and rigging stripped away and their hulls towed about by upstart steam tugs. The growing trade in bulk products, ore, coal and grain, was bringing with it a need for larger ships.

By 1901, the position of the canals in the economy had changed entirely, and the vision of a deep waterway, to bring ocean shipping into the heart of North America, had for the first time taken root in men's minds.

Meanwhile, the second half of the Seaway equation was quietly taking shape.

Hydro-Electric Potentialities

Ever since the French regime small rivers in the St. Lawrence Valley had been used as a source of water power for production of flour, lumber and iron. Now, thanks to Thomas Edison, people were beginning to light their homes with electricity. A small hydro plant was generating power near Iroquois on the St. Lawrence. The river's double-edged destiny was emerging.

The United States, like Canada, has treaty rights and obligations on the St. Lawrence. The international boundary line separating the two nations follows the 45th parallel until it strikes the river, and then it follows the middle of the stream and of the Great Lakes as far as the lakehead. These waters are international. No works affecting their level — and this has always applied to the St. Lawrence Seaway for the Seaway involves development of power as well as navigation — can be undertaken without the consent of both countries.

From a purely economic point of view, early attempts to promote the Seaway's 27-foot waterway were rather daring, and probably premature. Canada was still

The first hydro electric power plant on the St. Lawrence River at Iroquois, Ont. — 1901.

an infant industrially, and the main value of a deep waterway would have been providing a cheaper export route for the principal item of traffic then in sight — western grain. In other words, when the Seaway idea first began to take root in the late 19th century, it was primarily to serve an agricultural economy. The size of the project seemed out of all proportion to Canada's resources. But the United States had a keen interest in both the navigation and the power aspects, and so from the beginning the great undertaking took on its international flavor.

Start of Seaway Studies

The first major step toward joint development came in 1895, when the Governments of Canada and the United States created an International Waterway Commission with instructions to report on the feasibility of a deep channel from the Great Lakes to the sea. But it took the next 60 years, the efforts of seven American presidents, and the defeat of a gigantic lobby before a shovel of earth was dug.

This lobby was one of the strongest and wealthiest in history, drawing support from many quarters and for many reasons: from the coal and oil companies who foresaw a substantial loss of business if enormous quantities of hydro-electric power were made available; from ports on the eastern seaboard and the Gulf coast, who pictured a deep waterway into the industrial heart of North America as a siphon, certain to drain off much of their shipping trade; from eastern business on the grounds that it would be hard hit by any drastic shift of the commercial and industrial balance toward the northwest; from Illinois, the Missouri basin, and the Mississippi valley, who feared their areas would be hurt by a restriction on the amount of water that could be diverted from the Great Lakes into the Mississippi and Missouri systems.

Eastern utilities detested the public power aspects of the Seaway plan. Eastern railroads, who had fought and lost the battle against building the Panama Canal, feared loss of business to the shipping lines. Railway unions were opposed for the same reasons as the railways themselves, and of course since locomotives burned nothing but coal in those days the mine workers lined up four-square with the opposition.

Stark warnings of tens of thousands of unemployed, of bankrupt railways, closed mines, and deserted Atlantic and Gulf ports filled the newspapers. For half a century they effectively blanketed the results of the major governmental surveys which said, without exception, that the Seaway was an economic necessity for fuller development of North America.

While the original idea for the Seaway dates back to the International Commission formed in 1895, the first comprehensive report on the St. Lawrence was not to come for another 25 years.

In the meantime, the International Waterway Commission was given the task of studying the utilization of international waters along the Canada-U.S. boundary, and its functions were later clarified and restated when the two nations signed the International Boundary Treaty establishing the International Joint Commission. The IJC was to have jurisdiction over boundary water problems and other questions or differences arising between Canada and the United States along their common frontier. Then, as now, it had six members: three from Canada and three from the United States.

Early in 1914, the United States suggested turning over to the IJC the study of navigation and power development along the St. Lawrence boundary waters.

Outbreak of World War I postponed the study, but during the 1920's the Seaway was under continual discussion, and with each passing year it appeared more and more as a practical possibility and less as a visionary's dream. This was the Golden Age. Never had confidence in economic growth been stronger. The grain trade was in its heyday, and it was still possible to envisage a Seaway built largely to haul that grain.

The first conclusive report on the improvement of the Great Lakes-St. Lawrence waterway was published in 1921. The Woodten-Bowden Commission, named after two engineers appointed by the U. S. and Canada, submitted to the International Joint Commission a favorable report for improvement of the river between Lake Ontario and Montreal.

In 1921, too, came the first formal statement on the huge power potential of the International Rapids Section. It was presented to the International Joint Commission by the publicly-owned Ontario Hydro-Electric Power Commission.

Calvin Coolidge, in his 1923 message to congress, recommended construction of the project.

By 1924, three members had been appointed by each nation to form a joint board of engineers, and the report of this board two years later confirmed the feasibility of the navigation and power development. It recommended construction of a 25-foot channel from the Great Lakes to Montreal, and full development of 2,200,000 horsepower of hydro-electric energy, at a total cost of between $625 and $650 million. The following year, a Canadian advisory committee proposed a 27-foot channel and suggested various stages of development.

The Joint Board of Engineers presented its final report in 1932, and it was this which served as the basis of the St. Lawrence Deep Waterway Treaty, signed by both governments the same year and calling for joint Canada-U.S. development of both the power and the navigation potential of the river.

In one sense, the early 1930's marked a high point on the road toward getting the Seaway built, for it was the first time that executive agreement to go ahead had been obtained on both sides of the border. But it was also a time of crushing disappointment for the project's supporters. For the treaty required ratification by Congress, a two-thirds majority in the Senate, and in March, 1934 it was defeated. The anti-Seaway lobby had won, and Presidents Roosevelt and Hoover joined Wilson, Harding, and Coolidge in defeat.

The climate of the 1930's was one far different from the 1920's. Lengthening breadlines cast long shadows across the future, no one was sure what lay ahead for traffic in grain, and industrial growth stood still.

Nevertheless, several things happened to keep the Seaway project alive during those lean depression years. The Welland Ship Canal, begun by Canada in 1913, was completed in 1932 to a depth of 25 feet, (the locks had a depth of 30 feet) extending the range of the large upper lake vessels by 247 miles, from Port Colborne to Prescott. The only barrier remaining between the lakehead and Montreal were the 14-foot canals on the St. Lawrence River, and these now took on the appearance of unfinished business.

Meantime, too, the New York State Legislature had created a St. Lawrence Power Commission to study and prepare plans for developing power in the river. And across the border, in Canada, an agreement was signed between the federal government and the Province of Ontario regarding power development at Barnhart Island, near Cornwall. Negotiations had reached the federal-state and federal-provincial level.

By 1938, the pro-Seaway forces, headed by Roosevelt in the U.S., were gathering for another attack. That year, the text of a new treaty was submitted to Canada by the United States, and when the coming of war in 1939 underlined the importance of the project both as a source of power and as a measure for national defence, hopes rose. In 1941, the two governments signed the Great Lakes-St. Lawrence Agreement, providing for joint development of the deep waterway from Montreal to the head of the lakes, and a tentative date for completion — 1948 — was even set.

Once again a treaty went to Congress, and there it stayed for ten years, neither approved nor rejected but simply pigeon-holed. With Pearl Harbor came grave shortages of steel and manpower, and in 1942 President Roosevelt shelved the project temporarily, in favor of the more important business at hand. It was revived soon after the war with both President Truman and New York Governor Thomas Dewey pushing strongly for construction. Legislative machinery was again put into motion. But again the project languished, and in 1949 Canada's Minister for External Affairs expressed

concern in the House of Commons over the seemingly interminable delays in Washington.

By the early 1950's, however, the anti-Seaway lobby was finding the going increasingly rough.

Since 1934, when the Senate rejected the first treaty, the population of the United States had increased by one-third and Canada by one-half. Gross national product had trebled, and industrial production had quadrupled. In the steel industry, as reliable a yardstick of industrial growth as it is possible to find, American production had doubled and Canadian production had increased more than eightfold.

The sharply rising curve of power demand was equally striking. Earlier proponents of the Seaway project had been somewhat embarrassed in trying to picture a possible market for 2,200,000 horsepower. Now the problem was not where to find customers but who was to be first in line. The fact that the hydro-electric power was needed, and needed urgently, on both sides of the border brought a sense of timeliness to the entire project that made a decision to proceed essential.

For the first time, moreover, outside events seemed to outstrip those affecting the Seaway itself. North America's Economy was growing up around the waterway, and the accent had changed from improving it for future growth to improving it to serve present needs.

That was so in the case of hydro-electric power. It became even more so when the decision was made to develop the vast Canadian iron ore reserves lying along the Quebec-Labrador boundary to supply the increasing demands of the steel industry in the Great Lakes area.

Twenty-five years earlier, the United States had no need to import iron ore, and in any event iron ore production in Canada was non-existent. But by the early 1950's United States requirements of imported ore were growing even faster than Canada's rapidly expanding production, and it had become clear that iron ore would be the most important single item of traffic on the Seaway.

In the face of all these facts — facts which were bolstered by the flourishing postwar growth of export-import traffic between the Great Lakes and ports overseas, and which signaled clearly that the time for the Seaway had come — the opposition forces began to crumble. But they required one final push before they toppled. And that push came from the Canadian side of the border.

On December 21st, 1951, the Canadian House of Commons passed a bill creating the St. Lawrence Seaway Authority and approving an agreement with the Province of Ontario which provided for the construction and operation of power works in the International Rapids Section. The door was left open for an American agency to co-operate and participate in the project. But Canada had given clear notice that she was tired of waiting, that she was prepared to go it alone. The Canadians sat back to see what would happen. They had only a few months to wait. In June, 1952, the U.S. Senate rejected a resolution authorizing the project and Harry S. Truman became the sixth American president to support it in vain. But this time, immediately afterwards, things began happening.

Washington and Ottawa exchanged notes. They agreed that Canada would undertake to build the navigation phase of the Seaway alone. On June 30th, by agreement with the United States, the Ontario Hydro-Electric Power Commission and the Power Authority of the State of New York applied to the International Joint Commission for permission to change the water level in the St. Lawrence so that power could be developed in the International Rapids Section. Canada formally announced her intention to build all the navigation facilities on the Canadian side from Montreal to Lake Erie, if necessary.

By October, the IJC had approved the Canadian and United States power applications. And now, facing double defeat in the form a Seaway that was not only certain to be built but that was to be all-Canadian, the opposition caved in and the United States moved promptly to retrieve its share of the project.

Early in 1953, with President Dwight D. Eisenhower just settling into the White House, two resolutions authorizing American participation in the navigation phase were introduced to Congress. In June a Senate committee approved a new bill creating the Saint Lawrence Seaway Development Corporation. Senator Robert Taft of Ohio, who fought bitterly against the Seaway under Truman, changed his mind to support it. Missouri Senator Stuart Symington reversed his state's traditional opposition. John Kennedy became the first Senator from Massachusetts in 20 years to vote for the project. The Brotherhood of Locomotive Engineers gave up the fight. And in May, 1953, Congress passed the Wiley-Dondero Act, authorizing an American agency to build

Premier Leslie Frost of Ottawa and Robert Saunders, Chairman of the Hydro-Electric Power Commission of Ontario, meet with Indian Chiefs of tribes whose reservations are located on the shores of the St. Lawrence River in both Canada and the United States.

Ceremonies near Cornwall, Ont. signifying start of the tremendous power project. Chairman Saunders of Ontario-Hydro is behind microphones. At extreme left, Premier Leslie Frost of Ontario and in the center, Gov. Thomas E. Dewey of New York and on his left, Canada's Prime Minister, Louis St. Laurent, August 10, 1954.

Gov. Thomas E. Dewey of New York addressing gathering near Massena, N.Y. at start of the huge project. At left is Chairman Robert Saunders of Ontario Hydro-Electric Commission and at right, Robert Moses, Chairman of the Power Authority of the State of New York, August 10, 1954.

L. to R.: Governor Thomas E. Dewey of New York State, Ontario's Premier Leslie Frost and Chairman Robert H. Saunders of the Hydro-Electric Power Commission of Ontario, meet near the International border for ground breaking ceremonies, August 10, 1954.

the navigation facilities required in American territory in the International Rapids Section.

Meantime, last-ditch holding actions had been underway which might have postponed the project by blocking the power development. In the summer of 1953, the U.S. Federal Power Commission had granted the Power Authority of the State of New York a licence to develop the hydro project in conjunction with Ontario. Various appeals against this decision were heard. But they were refused, and in November President Eisenhower named the New York State agency as the entity to undertake the power project on the United States side.

Only one obstacle remained, and it was cleared at the highest level on June 7, 1954, when the United States Supreme Court decided to uphold the right of the Power Authority of the State of New York to build the American phase of the power project.

A few months later, Canada's Prime Minister Louis St. Laurent, New York's Governor Thomas E. Dewey and Ontario's Premier Leslie Frost met at the International boundary near Massena, New York and Cornwall, Ontario to cut the first sod and set the great machines in motion.

The gigantic project was begun.

CHAPTER THREE

ENABLING LEGISLATION

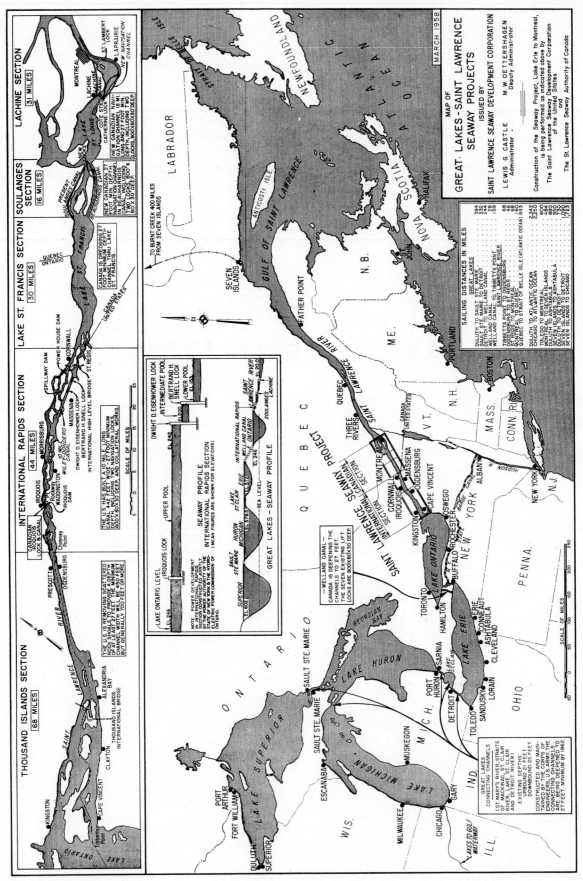

Flat and profile maps of the St. Lawrence River and Great Lakes area.

ENABLING LEGISLATION

Enabling Legislation — United States
Wiley-Dondero Act of May, 1954

(PUBLIC LAW 358—83D CONGRESS)

AN ACT Providing for creation of the Saint Lawrence Seaway Development Corporation to construct part of the Saint Lawrence Seaway in United States territory in the interest of national security; authorizing the Corporation to consummate certain arrangements with the St. Lawrence Seaway Authority of Canada relative to construction and operation of the seaway; empowering the Corporation to finance the United States share of the seaway cost on a self-liquidating basis; to establish cooperation with Canada in the control and operation of the Saint Lawrence Seaway; to authorize negotiations with Canada of an agreement on tolls; and for other purposes.

Be it enacted by the Senate and House of Representatives of the United States of America in Congress assembled,

CREATION OF CORPORATION

SECTION 1. There is hereby created, subject to the direction and supervision of the President, or the head of such agency as he may designate, a body corporate to be known as the Saint Lawrence Seaway Development Corporation (hereafter referred to as the "Corporation").

MANAGEMENT OF CORPORATION

SEC. 2. (a) The management of the Corporation shall be vested in an Administrator who shall be appointed by the President, by and with the advice and consent of the Senate, and who shall receive compensation at the rate of $17,500 per annum.

(b) To assist the Administrator in the execution of the functions vested in the Corporation there shall be a Deputy Administrator who shall be appointed by the President, by and with the advice and consent of the Senate, and who shall receive compensation at the rate of $16,000 per annum. The Deputy Administrator shall perform such duties as the Administrator may from time to time designate, and shall be acting Administrator and perform the functions of the Administrator during the absence or disability of the Administrator or in the event of a vacancy in the Office of the Administrator.

(c) There is hereby established the Advisory Board of the Saint Lawrence Seaway Development Corporation, which shall be composed of five members appointed by the President, by and with the advice and consent of the Senate, not more than three of whom shall belong to the same political party. The Advisory Board shall meet at the call of the Administrator, who shall require it to meet not less often than once each ninety days; shall review the general policies of the Corporation, including its policies in connection with design and construction of facilities and the establishment of rules of measurement for vessels and cargo and rates of charges or tolls; and shall advise the Administrator with respect thereto. Members of the Advisory Board shall receive for their services as members compensation of not to exceed $50 per diem when actually engaged in the performance of their duties, together with their necessary traveling expenses while going to and coming from meetings.

FUNCTIONS OF CORPORATION

SEC. 3. (a) The Corporation is authorized and directed to construct, in United States territory, deep-water navigation works substantially in accordance with the "Controlled single stage project, 238-242" (with a controlling depth of twenty-seven feet in channels and canals and locks at least eight hundred feet long, eighty feet wide, and thirty feet over the sills), designated as "works solely for navigation" in the joint report dated January 3, 1941, of the Canadian-Temporary Great Lakes-Saint Lawrence Basin Committee and the United States Saint Lawrence Advisory Committee, in the International Rapids section of the Saint Lawrence River together with necessary dredging in the Thousand Islands section; and to operate and maintain such works in coordination with the Saint Lawrence Seaway Authority of Canada, created by chapter 24 of the acts of the fifth session of the Twenty-first Parliament of Canada 15-16, George VI (assented to December 21, 1951) : *Provided,* That the Corporation shall not proceed with the aforesaid construction unless and until—

(1) the Saint Lawrence Seaway Authority of Canada provides assurances satisfactory to the Corporation that it will complete the Canadian portions of the navigation works authorized by section 10, chapter 24 of the acts of the fifth session of the Twenty-first Parliament of Canada 15-16, George VI, 1951, as nearly as possible concurrently with the completion of the works authorized by this section :

(2) the Corporation has received assurances satisfactory to it that the State of New York, or an entity duly designated by it, or other licensee of the Federal Power Commission, in conjunction with an appropriate agency in Canada, as nearly as possible concurrently with the navigation works herein authorized, will construct and complete the dams and power works approved by the International Joint Commission in its order of October 29, 1952 (docket 68) or any amendment or modification thereof.

CORPORATE POWERS

SEC. 4. (a) For the purpose of carrying out its functions under this joint resolution the Corporation—

(1) shall have succession in its corporate name;

(2) may adopt and use a corporate seal, which shall be judicially noticed;

(3) may sue and be sued in its corporate name;

(4) may adopt, amend, and repeal bylaws, rules

and regulations governing the manner in which its business may be conducted and the powers vested in it may be exercised;

(5) may make and carry out such contracts or agreements as are necessary or advisable in the conduct of its business;

(6) shall be held to be an inhabitant and resident of the northern judicial district of New York within the meaning of the laws of the United States relating to venue of civil suits;

(7) may appoint and fix the compensation, in accordance with the provisions of the Classification Act of 1949, of such officers, attorneys, and employees as may be necessary for the conduct of its business, define their authority and duties, delegate to them such of the powers vested in the Corporation as the Administrator may determine, require bonds of such of them as the Administrator may designate, and fix the penalties and pay the premiums on such bonds;

(8) may acquire, by purchase, lease, condemnation, or donation such real and personal property and any interest therein, and may sell, lease, or otherwise dispose of such real and personal property, as the Administrator deems necessary for the conduct of its business; and

(9) shall determine the character of and the necessity for its obligations and expenditures, and the manner in which they shall be incurred, allowed and paid, subject to provisions of law specifically applicable to Government corporations.

FINANCING

SEC. 5. In order to finance its activities, the Corporation is authorized and empowered to issue to the Secretary of the Treasury, from time to time and to have outstanding at any one time in an amount not exceeding $105,000,000, its revenue bonds which shall be payable from corporate revenues: *Provided,* That not to exceed 10 per centum of the revenue bonds herein authorized shall be issued during the first year after the effective date of this Act and not to exceed 40 per centum during any year thereafter. Such obligations shall have maturities agreed upon by the Corporation and the Secretary of the Treasury, not in excess of fifty years. Such obligations may be redeemable at the opinion of the Corporation before maturity in such manner as may be stipulated in such obligations, but the obligations thus redeemed shall not be refinanced by the Corporation. Each such obligation shall bear interest at a rate determined by the Secretary of the Treasury, taking into consideration the current average rate on current marketable obligations of the United States of comparable maturities as of the last day of the month preceding the issuance of the obligation of the Corporation. The Secretary of the Treasury is authorized and directed to purchase any obligations of the Corporation to be issued hereunder and for such purpose the Secretary of the Treasury is authorized to use as a public debt transaction the proceeds from the sale of any securities issued under the Second Liberty Bond Act, as amended, and the purposes for which securities may be issued under the Second Liberty Bond Act, as amended, are extended to include any purchases of the Corporation's obligations hereunder.

GOVERNMENT CORPORATION CONTROL ACT

SEC. 6. Section 101 of the Government Corporation Control Act is hereby amended by inserting after the words "Federal Housing Administration" the words "Saint Lawrence Seaway Development Corporation".

PAYMENTS IN LIEU OF TAXES

SEC. 7. The Corporation is authorized to make payments to State and local governments in lieu of property taxes upon property which was subject to State and local taxation before acquisition by the Corporation. Such payments may be in the amounts, at the times, and upon the terms the Corporation deems appropriate, but the Corporation shall be guided by the policy of making payments not in excess of the taxes which would have been payable for such property in the condition in which it was acquired, except in cases where special burdens are placed upon the State or local government by the activities of the Corporation or its agents. The Corporation, its property, franchises, and income are hereby expressly exempted from taxation in any manner or form by any State, county, municapility, or any subdivision thereof, but such exemption shall not extend to contractors for the Corporation.

SERVICES AND FACILITIES OF OTHER AGENCIES

SEC. 8. (a) The Corporation may, with the consent of the agency concerned, accept and utilize, on a reimbursable basis, the officers, employees, services, facilities, and information of any agency of the Federal Government, except that any such agency having custody of any data relating to any of the matters within the jurisdiction of the Corporation shall, upon request of the Administrator, make such data available to the Corporation without reimbursement.

(b) The Corporation shall contribute to the civil-service retirement and disability fund, on the basis of annual billings as determined by the Civil Service Commission, for the Government's share of the cost of the civil-service retirement system applicable to the Corporation's employees and their beneficiaries. The Corporation shall also contribute to the employee's compensation fund, on the basis of annual billings as determined by the Secretary of Labor, for the benefit payments made from such fund on account of the Corporation's employees. The annual billings shall also include a statement of the fair portion of the cost of the administration of the respective funds, which shall be paid by the Corporation into the Treasury as miscellaneous receipts.

MISAPPROPRIATION OF FUNDS

SEC. 9. (a) All general penal statutes relating to the larceny, embezzlement, or conversion, of public moneys or property of the United States shall apply to the money and property of the Corporation.

(b) Any person who, with intent to defraud the

Corporation, or to deceive any director, officer, or employee of the Corporation or any officer or employee of the United States, (1) makes any false entry in any book of the Corporation, or (2) makes any false report or statement for the Corporation, shall, upon conviction thereof, be fined not more than $10,000 or imprisoned not more than five years, or both.

(c) Any person who shall receive any compensation, rebate, or reward, or shall enter into any conspiracy, collusion, or agreement, express or implied, with intent to defraud the Corporation or wrongfully and unlawfully to defeat its purposes, shall, on conviction thereof, be fined not more than $5,000 or imprisoned not more than five years, or both.

REPORTS TO CONGRESS

Sec. 10. The Corporation shall submit to the President for transmission to the Congress at the beginning of each regular session an annual report of its operations under this Act.

SEPARABILITY OF PROVISIONS

Sec. 11. If any provision of this Act or the application of such provision to any person or circumstances shall be held invalid, the remainder of the Act and the application of such provision to persons or circumstances other than those to which it is held invalid shall not be affected thereby.

RATES OF CHARGES OR TOLLS

Sec. 12. (a) The Corporation is further authorized and directed to negotiate with the Saint Lawrence Seaway Authority of Canada, or such other agency as may be designated by the Government of Canada, an agreement as to the rules for the measurement of vessels and cargoes and the rates of charges or tolls to be levied for the use of the Saint Lawrence Seaway, and for an equitable division of the revenues of the seaway between the Corporation and the Saint Lawrence Seaway Authority of Canada. Such rules for the measurement of vessels and cargoes and rates of charges or tolls shall, to the extent practicable, be established or changed only after giving due notice and holding a public hearing. In the event that such negotiations shall not result in agreement, the Corporation is authorized and directed to establish unilaterally such rules of measurement and rates of charges or tolls for the use of the works under its administration:: *Provided, however,* That the Corporation shall give three months' notice, by publication in the Federal Register, of any proposals to establish or change unilaterally the basic rules of measurement and of any proposals to establish or change unilaterally the rates of charges or tolls, during which period a public hearing shall be conducted. Any such establishment of or changes in basic rules of measurement or rates of charges or tolls shall be subject to and shall take effect thirty days following the date of approval thereof by the President, and shall be final and conclusive, subject to review as hereinafter provided. Any person aggrieved by an order of the Corporation establishing or changing such rules or rates may, within such thirty-day per-

iod, apply to the Corporation for a rehearing of the matter upon the basis of which the order was entered. The Corporation shall have power to grant or deny the application for rehearing and upon such rehearing or without further hearing to abrogate or modify its order. The action of the Corporation in denying an application for rehearing or in abrogating or modifying its order shall be final and conclusive thirty days after its approval by the President unless within such thirty-day period a petition for review is filed by a person aggrieved by such action in the United States Court of Appeals for the circuit in which the works to which the order applies are located or in the United States Court of Appeals for the District of Columbia. The court in which such petition is filed shall have the same jurisdiction and powers as in the case of petitions to review orders of the Federal Power Commission filed under section 313 (b) of the Federal Power Act (16 U.S.C. 8251). The judgement of the court shall be final subject to review by the Supreme Court upon certiorari or certification as provided in sections 1254 (1) and 1254 (3) of title 28 of the United States Code. The filing of an application for rehearing shall not, unless specifically ordered by the Corporation, operate as a stay of the Corporation's order. The filing of a petition for review shall not, unless specifically ordered by the court, operate as a stay of the Corporation's order.

(b) In the course of its negotiations, or in the establishment, unilaterally, of the rates of charges or tolls as provided in subsection (a), the Corporation shall be guided by the following principles:

(1) That the rates shall be fair and equitable and shall give due consideration to encouragement of increased utilization of the navigation facilities, and to the special character of bulk agricultural, mineral, and other raw materials.

(2) That rates shall vary according to the character of cargo with the view that each classification of cargo shall so far as practicable derive relative benefits from the use of these facilities.

(3) That the rates on vessels in ballast without passengers or cargo may be less than the rates for vessels with passengers or cargo.

(4) That the rates prescribed shall be calculated to cover, as nearly as practicable, all costs of operating and maintaining the works under the administration of the Corporation, including depreciation, payment of interest on the obligations of the Corporation, and payments in lieu of taxes.

(5) That the rates shall provide, in addition, for the Corporation revenues sufficient to amortize the principal of the debts and obligations of the Corporation over a period not to exceed fifty years.

Approved May 13, 1954.

Canadian Law Creating the St. Lawrence Seaway Authority[1]

(15-16 GEORGE VI—CHAP. 24)
AN ACT To establish the St. Lawrence Seaway Authority

(Assented to 21st December, 1951.)

His Majesty, by and with the advice and consent of the Senate and House of Commons of Canada, enacts as follows:—

SHORT TITLE

1. This Act may be cited as *The St. Lawrence Seaway Authority Act.*

INTERPRETATION

2. In this Act.

(*a*) "Authority" means the St. Lawrence Seaway Authority established by this Act;

(*b*) "canal" means a canal, lock or navigable channel and all works and property appertaining or incident to such canal, lock or channel;

(*c*) "deep waterway" means adequate provision for navigation requiring a controlling channel depth of twenty-seven feet with a depth of thirty feet over lock sills in general inaccordance with paragraph (*j*) of the preliminary article of the Agreement between Canada and the United States providing for the Development of Navigation and Power in the Great Lakes-St. Lawrence Basin, dated the nineteenth day of March, nineteen hundred and forty-one;

(*d*) "member" means a member of the Authority;

(*e*) "Minister" means the Minister of Transport;

(*f*) "President" means the President of the Authority.

CONSTITUTION OF AUTHORITY

3. (1) There is hereby established a corporation called "The St. Lawrence Seaway Authority", consisting of a President and two other members as provided in this Act.

(2) Except as provided in section nine, the Authority is for all purposes an agent of His Majesty in right of Canada and its powers under this Act may be exercised only as an agent of His Majesty.

(3) The Authority may, on behalf of His Majesty, enter into contracts in the name of His Majesty or in the name of the Authority.

(4) Property acquired by the Authority is the property of His Majesty and title thereto may be vested in the name of His Majesty or in the name of the Authority.

4. Actions, suits or other legal proceedings in respect of any right or obligation acquired or incurred by the Authority on behalf of His Majesty, whether in its name or in the name of His Majesty, may be brought or taken by or against the Authority in the name of the Authority in any court that would have jurisdiction if the Authority were not an agent of His Majesty.

5. (1) The Governor in Coucil shall appoint the members of the Authority, who hold office during good behavior for a term not exceeding ten years and shall be paid such salaries as may be fixed by the Governor in Council.

(2) A member, on the expiration of his term of office, may be reappointed for a further term not exceeding ten years.

(3) Where a member of the Authority is absent or incapable for any reason of performing the duties of his office or the office thereof is vacant, the Governor in Council may appoint a temporary substitute member to hold the office upon such terms and conditions as the Governor in Council may prescribe.

6. The head office of the Authority shall be at the city of Ottawa or in such other place in Canada as the Governor in Council may designate.

CONDUCT OF BUSINESS OF AUTHORITY

7. (1) The President is the chief executive officer of the Authority, is charged with the general direction and control of the business of the Authority, and shall have such other powers as may be conferred on him by the by-laws.

(2) During incapacity or absence for any reason of the President or a vacancy in the office of the President, one of the other members designated by the Governor in Council, may exercise and perform all the powers and functions of the President.

(3) The exercise of the powers of the Authority is not impaired by reason of a vacancy in its membership.

8. The Authority with the approval of the Governor in Council may make by-laws not inconsistent with this Act with respect to:

(*a*) the management of the affairs of the Authority and the conduct of its business; and

(*b*) the establishment of a pension fund for the officers and employees of the Authority employed in a continuing capacity and for the members, and for their dependents, and authorizing contributions to be made to it out of the funds of the Authority.

9. The Authority may employ such officers and employees for such purposes and on such terms and conditions as may be determined by it and the officers and employees so employed are not officers or servants of His Majesty.

PURPOSES, CAPACITIES AND POWERS OF AUTHORITY

10. The Authority is incorporated for the purposes of:—

(*a*) acquiring lands for and constructing, maintaining and operating all such works as may be necessary to provide and maintain, either wholly in Canada or in conjunction with works undertaken by an appropriate authority in the United States, a deep waterway between the Port of Montreal and Lake Erie; and

(*b*) constructing, maintaining and operating all such works in connection with such a deep waterway as the Governor in Council may deem necessary to fulfil any obligation undertaken or to be undertaken by Canada pursuant to any present or future agreement.

[1]Statutes of Canada, 1951.
59702—55——2

11. Subject to this Act, the Authority, for the purposes set out in section ten, has the capacities and powers of a natural person as if it were a corporation incorporated for such purposes by Letters Patent under the Great Seal.

12. The Authority, with the approval of the Governor in Council, may lease to any person any lands, property or water power held in the name of the Authority or held in the name of His Majesty under the control of the Authority.

13. The Authority, with the approval of the Governor in Council, may, from time to time, borrow money from His Majesty or otherwise for the purposes for which it is incorporated, but the aggregate of the amounts borrowed under this Act and outstanding shall not at any time exceed three hundred million dollars.

14. The Governor in Council may entrust to the Authority the management and operation of any canals or works similar or related to the works mentioned in section ten upon such terms and conditions as the Governor in Council approves.

TOLLS

15. (1) The Authority may, subject to sections sixteen and seventeen, establish tariffs and tools to be charged by it with respect to:—

(a) vessels entering, passing through, or leaving a canal or works under its administration;

(b) passengers, goods or cargo carried in such a vessel;

(c) goods or cargo landed, shipped, transshipped or stored in a canal or on canal lands under its administration;

(d) the use of any wharf, building, plant, property or facilities under its administration; and

(e) any service performed by the Authority.

(2) The tolls that may be charged by the Authority pursuant to this section may be for the use of the canals and works administered by it as a whole or for the use of any particular part thereof or for any particular service rendered by the Authority.

(3) Every such tariff or amendement thereto shall be filed with the Board of Transport Commissioners and becomes operative from the date of such filing.

(4) Any person interested may at any time file a complaint with the Board of Transport Commissioners that there is unjust discrimination in an existing tariff and the Board shall thereupon consider such complaint and make a finding thereon which shall be reported to the Authority.

(5) Section fifty-two of the *Railway Act* applies, *mutatis mutandis*, in the case of every report of the Board of Transport Commissioners as if the same were a decision made pursuant to the *Railway Act*.

16. The tolls that may be charged by the Authority shall be fair and reasonable and designed to provide a revenue sufficient to defray the cost to the Authority of its operations in carrying out the purposes for which it is incorporated, which costs shall include:—

(a) payments in respect of the interest on amounts borrowed by the Authority to carry out such purposes;

(b) amounts sufficient to amortize the principal of amounts so borrowed over a period not exceeding fifty years; and

(c) the cost of operating and maintaining the canals and works under the administration of the Authority, including all operating costs of the Authority and such reserves as may be approved by the Minister.

17. Where the works have been constructed and are maintained and operated by the Authority to provide, in conjunction with works undertaken by an appropriate authority in the United States, the deep waterway mentioned in section ten, tolls may be established pursuant to sections fifteen and sixteen or by agreement between Canada and the United States and, in the event of such an agreement, shall be charged by the Authority in accordance with directions given by the Governor in Council.

EXPROPRIATION

18. (1) With the prior approval of the Governor in Council, the Authority may, without the consent of the owner, take or acquire lands for the purposes of this Act and, except as otherwise provided in this section, all the provisions of the *Expropriation Act* are, *mutatis mutandis*, applicable to the taking, acquisition, sale or abandonment of lands by the Authority under this section.

(2) For the purposes of section nine of the *Expropriation Act* the plan and description may be signed by the President of the Authority.

(3) The Authority shall pay compensation for lands taken or acquired under this section or for damage to lands injuriously affected by the construction of works erected by it and all claims against the Authority for such compensation may be heard and determined in the Exchequer Court of Canada in accordance with sections forty-seven to fifty of the *Exchequer Court Act*.

(4) The Authority shall pay out of the funds administered by it the compensation agreed upon or adjudged by the Court to be payable.

REGULATIONS

19. (1) The Authority may, with the approval of the Governor in Council on the recommendation of the Minister, make regulations for the administration, management and control of the works and property under its jurisdiction including:—

(a) the regulation and control of vessels navigating a canal or pertinent works;

(b) the regulation of plant, machinery or appliances for loading or unloading vessels in a canal; and

(c) the seizure, detention or sale of vessels, goods or cargo in respect of which any sum is due for tolls and is unpaid or in respect of which any provision of this Act or any regulation has been violated.

(2) A person who violates a regulation is guilty of an offense and is liable on summary conviction to a fine not exceeding one thousand dollars.

GENERAL

20. The Authority shall comply with any direction

not inconsistent with this Act with respect to the exercise of its powers or the conduct of its business given to it by the Governor in Council for the purpose of ensuring compliance on the part of Canada with any obligation of Canada to any other nation.

21. (1) Notwithstanding this Act or any other statute or law, where a person is employed by the Authority and immediately before his employment he was a contributor under a part of the *Civil Service Superannuation Act* other than Part IV, and his employment by the Authority was entered into with the consent of the Minister of the Department or Branch of the Public Service in which he was employed, he continues, while in the employment of the Authority to be such a contributor under the *Civil Service Superannuation Act*, and for the purposes of that Act his service in employment under this Act shall be counted as service in the Civil Service and upon his death or retirement therefrom, he, his widow, children or other dependents, if any, may, subject to subsection two, be granted the respective allowances or gratuities provided by that Act.

(2) Where a person to whom subsection one applies is retired from employment by the Authority for a reason other than misconduct.

(a) if before his employment by the Authority he was employed in a position to which the *Civil Service Act* applied, he may be appointed to a position to which the *Civil Service Act* applies of a class not lower than the position in which he was so employed;

(b) if before his employment by the Authority he was employed in any other position in the Public Service, he may be appointed to a position in the Public Service to which the *Civil Service Act* does not apply of a class not lower than the class in which he was so employed;

(c) if he fails to apply for or refuses appointment to a position to which he may be appointed under paragraph (a) and (b) and has not reached retirement age or become disabled or incapable of performing the duties of the position, he shall be deemed for the purposes of the *Civil Service Superannuation Act*, to have retired voluntarily from a position in the Civil Service; or

(d) if he applies for and is not appointed to such a position he shall be deemed, for the purposes of the *Civil Service Superannuation Act* to have been retired from his position in the Civil Service by reason of the abolition of office.

(3) *The Government Employees Compensation Act*, 1947, applies to officers and servants of the Authority and, notwithstanding section nine, for the purposes of that Act, but not otherwise, such officers and servants shall be deemed to be employees in the service of His Majesty.

22. The *Navigable Waters Protection Act* does not apply to works undertaken by the Authority pursuant to this Act.

23. Notwithstanding that the Authority is an agent of His Majesty, it may enter into contracts with His Majesty.

24. The accounts and financial transactions of the Authority shall be audited by the Auditor General.

LOANS AND GUARANTEES BY CROWN

25. (1) The Minister of Finance, with the approval of the Governor in Council, may, from time to time,

(a) make loans to the Authority out of money in the Consolidated Revenue Fund, or

(b) guarantee repayment of the principal of and interest on money borrowed by the Authority.

but no such loans or guarantees shall be made or given in any fiscal year except to the extent that Parliament has authorized such loans and guarantees to be made or given in that year.

(2) Notwithstanding subsection one, the Minister of Finance, with the approval of the Governor in Council, may, from time to time,

(a) make loans to the Authority out of money in the Consolidated Revenue Fund, or

(b) guarantee repayment of the principal of and interest on money borrowed by the Authority.

for the purpose of repaying money that has been borrowed under this Act.

(3) A loan or guarantee under this section shall be made or given in such manner and subject to such terms and conditions as the Governor in Council approves.

26. (1) The Minister of Finance, at the request of the Minister, and with the approval of the Governor in Council, may, from time to time, make temporary loans to the Authority out of money in the Consolidated Revenue Fund.

(2) The aggregate amount of loans outstanding under this section shall not at any time exceed ten million dollars.

(3) A loan under this section is subject to such terms and conditions as the Governor in Coucil approves and is repayable within a period not exceeding twelve months from the day on which the loan was made.

(4) A report of every loan to the Authority under this section shall be laid by the Minister of Finance before Parliament within fifteen days after it is made, or, if Parliament is not then in session, within fifteen days after the commencement of the next ensuing session thereof.

27. (1) The Minister of Finance, with the concurrence of the Minister may direct that money borrowed by the Authority under this Act shall be deposited in the Consolidated Revenue Fund to be placed to the credit of a special account in the name of the Authority.

(2) The Minister of Finance may, upon application by the Authority approved by the Minister, pay out to or for the purposes of the Authority, all or any part of the money in the special account established under subsection one.

SAVING CLAUSE

28. Nothing in this Act affects the operation of *The International Boundary Waters Treaty Act*, chapter twenty-eight of the statutes of 1911.

COMMENCEMENT

29. Each section of this Act shall come into force on a day or days to be fixed by proclamation of the Governor in Council.

CHAPTER FOUR

EXECUTIVES DIRECTLY ASSOCIATED WITH THE SEAWAY AND POWER PROJECTS

E. Reece Harrill
Assistant Administrator

SAINT LAWRENCE
SEAWAY
DEVELOPMENT
CORPORATION
EXECUTIVES

Lester W. Angell
Chief, Office of Engineering
Design, Planning and Programs

Lucius M. Hale
Director, Office of Marine
and Engineering Operations

Edward R. Place
Director of Information

Martin W. Oettershagen
Deputy Administrator

(Biographies in Executive Section)

A. G. Murphy
Chief Engineer

THE
ST. LAWRENCE
SEAWAY
AUTHORITY
EXECUTIVES

C. W. West
Member

P. E. R. Malcolm
Secretary
Director of Administration

John R. Akin
Information Officer

Jean-Claude Lessard
Vice President

(Biographies in Executive Section)

65

**The Right Hon. Louis Stephen St. Laurent,
P.C., Q.C., LL.D., D.C.L.**

Former Prime Minister of Canada — 1948-1957.

The Right Hon. Louis Stephen St. Laurent, P.C., Q.C., L.L.D., D.C.L., . . . born Compton, Que., February 1st, 1882. Educated at St. Charles College, Sherbrooke, Que., Laval University, Quebec, Que. Degrees: B.A., LL.L., LL.D. (Queen's Hon. LL.D. 1930); Univ. Manitoba, LL.D. (1935); Univ. of Montreal, hon. LL.D. (1943); Bishop's Univ. hon. LL.D. (1943); Dalhousie Univ., Hon. LL.D. (1947); Ottawa Univ., LL.D. (1947); Dartmouth Univ., Hon. LL.D. (1948); McGill Univ., hon. LL.D. (1949); Renesselaer Polytechnic Institute, Troy, N.Y.; Hon. LL.D. (1949); St. Louis, Univ., Missouri, Hon. LL.D.; St. Lawrence Univ., Canton, N.Y.; Hon. LL.D.; University of Toronto, 1950; University of Western Ontario, Northwestern University, Evanston, Ill., 1951; University of British Columbia, University of London, 1952; St. Francis Xavier University, Antigonish, N.S., 1953; University of Delhi, Peshawar University, 1954; McMaster University, 1955; Hon. D.C.L., Mt. Allison University, 1952 and Oxford University, 1953. On January 1, 1946, he was made a member of the Privy Council of the United Kingdom, and on February 7, 1955, the Freedom of the City of London was presented to him. A. Barrister. Sworn to the Privy Council and appointed Minister of Justice and Attorney General for Canada, Dec. 10, 1941. Elected to House of Commons at by-election, Feb. 9, 1942; re-elected at general election, June 11, 1945. Appointed Secretary of State for External Affairs, Dec. 10, 1946; he was chosen as leader of the Liberal Party of Canada to succeed the Rt. Hon. W. L. Mackenzie King, Aug., 1948; appointed Prime Minister of Canada, Nov. 15, 1948. Administration returned at general elections, June 27, 1949 and Aug. 10, 1953. Married May 19, 1908, Jeanne, daughter of P. E. Renault, of Beauceville, Que., has two sons and three daughters. Clubs: Garrison (Quebec); Cercle Universitaire (Montreal), University (Montreal), Rideau (Ottawa). Liberal. Address: 239 Grande Allee, Quebec City, Que.

Hon. Lionel Chevrier, Q.C., P.C., M.P.,

Former President,
The St. Lawrence Seaway Authority.

Hon. Lionel Chevrier, Q.C., P.C., M.P., . . . born in 1903 at Cornwall, Ontario. Received his primary education at Cornwall. He graduated from the University of Ottawa in 1924, after winning medals for debating and chemistry, and attended Osgoode Hall from which he was called to the Bar of Ontario in 1928. In 1938, he was created a King's Counsel. He has been Secretary to the Cornwall Board of Trade, in which capacity he was very active in promoting the St. Lawrence Seaway project. He was elected to the House of Commons in 1935, at the age of 32, and re-elected with increasing majorities in four subsequent elections for the constituency of Stormont, which he represented until his resignation on July 1, 1954. In Parliament, he took an active part in debates and in 1937, seconded the address in reply to the Speech from the Throne. In 1940 he was appointed Deputy Chief Government Whip; in 1942, Chairman of the special Parliamentary subcommittee on war expenditures; in 1943, appointed Parliamentary Assistant to the Minister of Munitions and Supply; in 1945, at the age of 42, he was appointed Minister of Transport; in 1948, he was chairman of the Canadian Delegation to the United Nations General Assembly, Paris. While holding portfolio of the Ministry of Transport he became known as the principal advocate of the St. Lawrence Seaway Project. In December, 1951, he introduced in the House of Commons the legislation which provided for the establishment of The St. Lawrence Seaway Authority and was instrumental in bringing to successful conclusion the necessary negotiations with the United States authorities. He was appointed President of the St. Lawrence Seaway Authority in July, 1954. Resigned from that post in April 25, 1957 to accept the position of President of the Privy Council in the government of the Rt. Hon. Louis S. St-Laurent. He was elected to the House of Commons for the constituency of Montreal-Laurier on June 10, 1957. In June, 1957, he was called to the Bar of Quebec. He is a member of the firm of Geoffrion & Prud'homme, Montreal. He holds the Honorary Degree of LL.D. from Ottawa University, Laval University and Queen's University. He is Honorary Colonel of the Stormont, Dundas and Glengarry Highlanders and is a Commander of the Order of St. Gregory with Star. He married Miss Lucienne Brûlé, Ottawa, in 1932 and has six children.

Honourable George C. Marler, P.C., . . . born at Montreal in 1901. He was educated at Selwyn House School, Bishop's College School, The Royal Navy College of Canada (1917-1919), and McGill University, from which he graduated in 1922 with the degree of Bachelor of Civil Law. In 1948 he received the Honorary Degree of Doctor of the University from the University of Montreal. He entered the Notarial Profession in 1923, and was formerly a senior partner of the firm W. de M. and H. M. Marler. From 1930 to 1939 he was a member of the Board of Notaries, during which period he was President of its Finance Committee and President of its Examination Committee. He is also a former President of the Notarial Association of the District of Montreal. From 1937 to 1940 he was Vice-President of the Board of Revision of Valuations, City of Montreal, and from 1940 to 1947 he was a member of the City Council of Montreal and Vice President of its Executive Committee and a member of the Montreal Metropolitan Commission. Elected in 1942 to represent Westmount-St. George in the Quebec Legislative Assembly. He represented this constituency at Quebec until July 1, 1954. From 1948 to 1950 he acted temporarily as the Leader of the Provincial Liberal party, and was Leader of the Opposition in the Legislative Assembly from 1948 until the opening of the 1953-54 session. He was appointed Minister of Transport on July 1, 1954 and was first elected to the House of Commons at a by-election on November 8, 1954, to represent St. Antoine-Westmount. He was re-elected at the 1957 general election and resigned as Minister of Transport after the defeat of the Liberal Government at that election. Member: Royal Philatelic Society of London, British North America Philatelic Society, Essay Proof Society and Royal Horticultural Society. Clubs: Montreal Club, University Club of Montreal, Montreal Reform Club, Royal Montreal Golf Club, Cascade Golf and Tennis Club, Reform Club (Quebec) and Rideau Club (Ottawa). He is married, has three daughters and one son.

Hon. George C. Marler
Former Minister of Transport,
Canadian Government.

Charles Gavsie, C.B.E., Q.C., LL.B., LL.M., . . . born in New York, N. Y., in 1906 of Canadian parents and came to Canada in 1909. His early education was received at Sydney, Cape Breton, N. S. He is an honour graduate in jurisprudence from Dalhousie University, Halifax, N. S. Following post-graduate course at Harvard College, Cambridge, Massachusetts, where he received his Master of Laws degree, he practised law in Montreal until going to Ottawa in 1941. In 1941 he joined the war-time Department of Munitions and Supply. He was general counsel first of the Department of Munitions and Supply and later of the Department of Reconstruction and Supply. For his war-time work with the Canadian Government he was named Commander of the Order of the British Empire. In 1948 he transferred to the Department of National Revenue, Taxation, as Assistant Deputy Minister and was appointed Deputy on August 1, 1951. He became a Member of the three-man Board of The St. Lawrence Seaway Authority when it was established in July, 1954. He later resigned from the post of Deputy Minister of the Department of National Revenue, Taxation, to accept the position of Vice-President of the Authority. In June, 1957, he succeeded the Honourable Lionel Chevrier as President of the St. Lawrence Seaway Authority and served until January 31, 1958, at which time he retired to practice law in Montreal. He married Sara Halparin, of Winnipeg, Manitoba. He has two sons.

Charles Gavsie, Q.C.,
Former President,
The St. Lawrence Seaway Authority.

Thomas E. Dewey,
Former Governor,
State of New York.

Thomas Edmund Dewey . . . born in Owosso, Michigan, March 24, 1902. Graduated from University of Michigan, A.B., in 1923, and from Columbia Law School, LL.D., 1925. He received the Columbia University Medal of Excellence, the Cardinal Newman Distinguished Service Award at the University of Illinois, and honorary degrees from University of Michigan, Tufts College, Brown University, Dartmouth College, St. Lawrence University, New York University, Union College, Fordham University, Alfred University, Hamilton College, Colgate University, Williams College, Columbia University, St. Bonaventure University, and Yeshiva University. In 1931 became Chief Assistant U.S. Attorney for the Southern District of New York; in 1933 U.S. Attorney; in 1934 served as Council to the Association of the Bar of the City of New York in the removal of a Municipal Court Justice. In July 1935, appointed Special Prosecutor in charge of Investigation of Organized Crime. In 1937, elected District Attorney of New York County on the Republican, American Labor and City Fusion tickets. In 1938 was the Republican Candidate for Governor, defeated by Governor Herbert H. Lehman. In 1941, as National Chairman of the 1st U.S.O. Campaign, he organized the national drive and raised $16,-000,000. In 1942 he was again the Republican Candidate for Governor and was elected by a total vote of 2,148,546 against 1,501,039. In 1944 was republican candidate for President defeated by President Franklin D. Roosevelt. In 1946, re-elected Governor by the largest majority in the history of the state. In 1948, he was again the Republican Candidate for President but was defeated by President Harry S. Truman. Re-elected Governor in 1950 he became the first in the history of the state to win three consecutive 4-year terms. Married Frances Eileen Hutt, Sapulpa, Okla., on June 16, 1928. Children: Thomas E., jr., and John M.

Hon. Bertrand H. Snell, B.A., LL.D.,
Former Congressman,
U. S. House of Representatives.

Bertrand H. Snell, B.A., LL.D., . . . born in Colton, St. Lawrence County, New York, December 9, 1870. Died in Potsdam, New York, February 2, 1958. He attended public school in Colton, State Normal School, Potsdam, and Amherst College, (B.A. 1894 — LL.D. 1929 honorary). He also received honorary degrees from Clarkson College and George Washington University. Following graduation from college, he entered the lumbering business where he was actively engaged for a number of years in the Adirondack regions. He built and operated a power plant at Higley Falls on the Racquette River in Northern New York. Served as President of the Phenix Cheese Company, now part of the National Dairy Company. In 1948 he sold the York State Oil Company, of which he was President, to the Phillips Petroleum Company. Elected to the Congress in 1914, he became Chairman of the Rules Committee and later served as Minority Leader of the House of Representatives from 1931 until his retirement in 1939. He was chairman of the Republican National Conventions in 1932 and 1936 and was generally regarded as one of the top Republican leaders of the period. Known as the Champion of the Seaway, he introduced the first seaway bill in Congress in April 1917 despite opposition from many quarters. In the years that followed he delivered many speeches for the development of the St. Lawrence Seaway. On February 7th, 1958, five days after his death, one of the St. Lawrence Seaway locks, in the International Section, was named "Bertrand H. Snell Lock" in honour of the late Congressman. On July 2nd, 1958 a plaque was dedicated to him at the Seaway. He was, for many years, active in numerous civic and charitable affairs and at the time of his death was a Director of the A. Barton Hepburn Hospital and a trustee of Clarkson College of Technology. He had previously endowed a chair of political science at Amherst College. He was also a Director of the Agricultural Insurance Company in Watertown, New York, Goulds Pumps, Inc., at Seneca Falls, New York, Northern New York Trust Company, Watertown, and was half owner of the Chazy (N. Y.) Orchards. He is survived by his wife the former Sara L. Merrick, of Gouverneur; two daughters, Mrs. Harold W. Cheel, of Ho-Ho-Kus, N. J., and Mrs. William E. Peterson, of Bronxville, and three grandchildren.

Senator Alexander Wiley . . . born in the State of Wisconsin of Norwegian immigrant parents. Rose from a small town attorney to become the second highest ranking Republican in the United States Senate, outranked in seniority only by Senator Styles Bridges, New Hampshire, who came to the Senate two years earlier than he. He is, at present, the Senior Republican Member of both the Senate Judiciary and the Senate Foreign Relations Committees. In 1947, and in 1948, during the 80th Congress, he served as Chairman of the Senate Judiciary Committee. In 1953-1954, he served as Chairman of the Foreign Relations Committee. He is the only Senator in the 108 years of statehood of his state to have occupied either such Chairmanship or both such chairmanships. First elected to the Senate in November 1938, he was re-elected in 1944, 1950, and in November 1956 by a larger percentage than ever before. His victory in the hard-fought Republican primary of September 1956, is generally regarded as the most important of all his electoral battles. He was nominated despite the fact that he refused to alter his basic position on foreign policy, in favour of strong American leadership in World Affairs. In September of 1952, he was appointed by President Truman as a delegate to the General Assembly of the United Nations. He served in the latter part of that year, as well as in 1953, by appointment of President Eisenhower at the United Nations Headquarters in New York. In 1954, he was appointed by President Eisenhower to the Inter-American Economic Conference at Rio de Janeiro. In 1955 and 1957 he represented the U.S. at Conferences of the Inter-Parliamentary Union in Helsinki and London. The Wiley-Dondero Great-Lakes-St. Lawrence Law was named in his honor and for Former Congressman George Dondero, of Michigan. In 1950 and 1951 he served on the special Senate Committee for the Investigation of Organized-Crime in Interstate Commerce (The Kefauver Committee). On the Senate Judiciary Committee he serves, at present, on the Anti-Trust and Monopoly, Juvenile Delinquency and Patents, Trade Marks and Copyrights, sub-committees. Only previous public post prior to coming to the Senate was a three-term district attorney in his home county of Chippewa from 1909-15. From 1915 to 1938 he was an Attorney in his home town. Served as member of the School Board, Operator of a dairy farm, President of the Chippewa Falls Commission Association, Director of First National Bank, Chippewa Falls. He is a 33rd Degree Mason, member of the American Bar Association, Alumni Association of University of Wisconsin, Elks, Knights of Pythias, Scandanavian American Fraternity, Sons of Norway, United Commercial Travellers, Loyal Order of Moose, The National Grange, Odd Fellows and Eagles.

Hon. Alexander Wiley,
Senior Senator — Wisconsin,
U.S. Senate.

Hon. George A. Dondero,
Former Congressman,
U.S. House of Representatives.

George A. Dondero . . . born Dec. 16, 1883, in Greenfield Township, Wayne County, Michigan. Educated in Public Schools, graduate of Royal Oak High School in 1903, and of the Detroit College of Law in 1910, with an LL.B. degree. That same year he was admitted to the Bar. He has held the following offices: Village Clerk of Royal Oak, 1905-1906; Township Treasurer of Royal Oak, 1907-1908; Village Assessor of Royal Oak, 1909; Village Attorney of Royal Oak, 1911-1921; Assistant Prosecuting Attorney for Oakland County, Michigan, 1918-1919; First Mayor, City of Royal Oak, 1921-1922. He was elected to the seventy-third Congress, and each succeeding Congress, including the 84th, a total of 12 terms or 24 years. He retired voluntarily from public life in January 1957. Member: Royal Oak Board of Education for 18 years; Methodist Church; Masonic Orders and Kiwanis International. He married the former Adele Roegner on June 28, 1913 and they have three children — Marion E., Stanton G., and Robert Lincoln.

Donald William Graham Oliver,
Comptroller,
The St. Lawrence Seaway Authority.

David William Graham Oliver . . . born in Carnoustie, Scotland, in 1900. He came to Canada at the age of 13, making his first home at Kingston, Ontario, and later moving to Montreal, Quebec. He was educated in Scotland and at the Collegiate Institute, Kingston, and followed accounting studies with Lasalle Extension University and McGill University extension classes. He joined the staff of the old Montreal Harbour Commission in 1920 and, in 1941, was appointed Treasury Officer to the National Harbours operations in Montreal. In 1943, he was loaned to Defence Communications Limited, a Crown Company, as Treasurer, and in 1952-53, he was again loaned to the International Civil Aviation Organization to assist on special financial problems. He was appointed Comptroller for the St. Lawrence Seaway Authority on August 1, 1954. Prior to this appointment he had been attending to the Seaway Authority financing with the Special Projects Branch of the Department of Transport. He is also a Director, and Secretary-Treasurer of the Cornwall International Bridge Company. He is married to the former Florence Weaver, of Montreal and they have two sons.

Raymond J. Bériault
Former Secretary,
The St. Lawrence Seaway Authority.

Raymond J. Bériault, B.A., L.PH., M.A., . . . born July 29, 1915. Educated at Fassett, Quebec, College St. Alexandre de la Gatineau, Laval University, Quebec City, Dominican Fathers' Institute of Philosophy at Ottawa and at Ottawa University. He started his business career as a teacher in secondary schools for two years and later spent four years as Investigator in the Organization Branch of the Civil Service Commission at Ottawa. He was Assistant Director of the Community Programs Branch of the Department of Education, Province of Ontario; sixteen months as head of UNESCO Technical Assistance Commission in Cambodia, Indo China. He was appointed Secretary of the St. Lawrence Seaway Authority in 1954 and resigned on May 15, 1958 to become Executive Assistant to the President and Director of Public Relations and Sales at Candiac Development Corporation. He is a former School Board Trustee for the City of Ottawa; Past President of the Ottawa-Hull Richelieu Service Club; Past-President of the Editorial Committee of "Bien-Etre Social Canadien", published by the Canadian Welfare Council; Past Vice-President of the Société Canadienne d'Education des Adultes; Past member of the Board of Administration of the Canadian Association for Adult Education. In 1950, Canadian representative to a six-week International Meeting on Adult Education, organized by UNESCO, in Salzburg, Austria, and elected President of this Meeting. In March, 1958, he lectured in Italy on the invitation of the Christian Union of Business Leaders. He authored a book entitled "Khmers", published in December, 1957. He is married and father of four children. Residence: 5277 Borden Avenue, Montreal, Que.

Robert Hood Saunders

Chairman — Hydro Electric Power Commission of Ontario
March 1, 1948 — January 16, 1955

From newsboy to lawyer and the square-collared silks of Queen's Counsel — from Alderman to Controller and then Mayor of his native Toronto, with the C.B.E. for outstanding services during the second world war. That was the career background of Robert Hood Saunders when on March 1, 1948 he was appointed Chairman of Ontario Hydro.

At that time, the demand for electricity was increasing by leaps and bounds. With new orders coming in every day, industries were still burdened by a backlog of work that could not be executed during the war. They wanted more power to speed up production. Farmers were clamouring for Hydro services. With employment at a high level, people everywhere were eager to raise their standards of living.

It was a challenging situation for Ontario Hydro and it had become an alarming one because of abnormal droughts which had affected water levels in Hydro reservoirs and headponds and reduced power production.

With characteristic initiative and energy, the new Chairman tackled the problem — both with respect to immediate needs and future requirements, which, in view of the accelerated tempo of growth and development in the Province, were scarcely less pressing.

First of all, he not only implemented a vigorous program of power conservation but at his insistent urging, all the reserve fuel-electric generation at the command of industries was brought into service. This additional resource was supplemented by temporary emergency generating stations that could be rapidly built and installed at strategic locations.

Then he directed his attention to the development programs initiated by his predecessor, to frequency standardization at 60-cycles and to the St. Lawrence power project, which had been a subject of futile discussion for more than 30 years.

Robert Saunders regarded the St. Lawrence project as vital to the people of Ontario and he "pulled out all stops" to overcome the opposition that was holding it back. Ultimately — on June 7, 1954 — the Supreme Court of the United States upheld the right of the Power Authority of the State of New York to undertake the project on the United States' side, which is now being carried out as a joint undertaking by Ontario Hydro and the Power Authority. Mr. Saunders' memory will be perpetuated by Ontario Hydro's impressive St. Lawrence power plant which will be known as "The Robert H. Saunders — St. Lawrence Generating Station.

Concentration on the St. Lawrence battle did not begin to exhaust "Bob" Saunders' dynamic energy. Major waterpower and fuel-electric plants, culminating in the 1,370,000-kilowatt Sir Adam Beck-Niagara G.S. No. 2, were constructed and placed in service during his regime as Chairman. In addition, rural programs were speeded up and like an unrolling carpet, frequency standardization covered one area after another in rapid sequence.

Looking further to future requirements, this extraordinarily versatile man was studying the possibilities of nuclear energy when death intervened. He succumbed, at the height of his career and at the comparatively early age of 52 to injuries received in a plane crash on January 15, 1955.

RELOCATION — TOWNS, RAILROADS, HIGHWAYS

CHAPTER FIVE

RELOCATION — TOWNS, RAILROADS, HIGHWAYS

RELOCATION — TOWNS, RAILROADS, HIGHWAYS

In the summer of 1954, the City of Cornwall, Ontario faced a problem which with each passing day grew larger and more delicate. At Washington the Seaway bill had been cleared through Congress. On both sides of the border the great project was about to begin. But not a shovel of earth had been turned, and no jobs had opened up.

Yet hundreds of migrant workers were streaming into Cornwall, filling the rooming houses, overflowing the taverns, tightening the squeeze on housing, and creating several rather embarrassing problems for the city fathers. And almost without exception every man arriving bore the same news: that gravediggers were needed, at ten dollars an hour, to move cemeteries from land up-river that would soon be flooded.

It was a macabre beginning for the Seaway's most poignant story, a story of villages whose time had run out, and of families who had lived all their lives along the riverfront in the certain knowledge that someday they would have to go.

Through tests with models, engineers had known for years that by filling the power pool between Iroquois and Cornwall they would inundate nearly 20,000 acres of surrounding countryside along the north shore, and 18,000 along the south. On the New York side the doomed area was sparsely populated; only about 100

farm families and some 500 cottage owners would be forced out. But along the Canadian bank of the river a social problem of immense proportions faced the Hydro-Electric Power Commission of Ontario.

There some 6,500 people living in eight different communities, and 225 farm families, would be uprooted. As well, 40 miles of mainline railway track, and 35 miles of Canada's busiest highway, would be shifted to higher ground.

But business had long ago proved that it had a heart.

In 1921, after engineers completed their first really thorough study of the power possibilities along the International Rapids, Sir Adam Beck, Chairman of Ontario Hydro, had said:

"The lands bordering the north shore of the St. Lawrence River between Cornwall and Prescott were, to a large extent, originally settled by United Empire Loyalists. The best lands in this territory, and consequently the most thickly settled, lie close along the shore of the river. They are among the earliest settled lands in the Province, and the homesteads, churches and public institutions have existed for several generations. It seems evident, therefore, that if any scheme of development on the St. Lawrence River necessitates the injury, destruction or elimination of these interests and institutions,

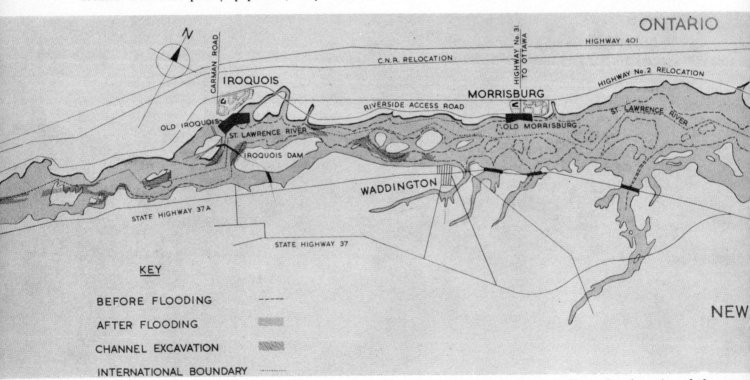

Map of St. Lawrence River after formation of the power roads and railroads. Note new locations of Iroquois, Morri

a sentimental factor is introduced which cannot be appraised as a definite cost item but to which, nevertheless, due respect must be accorded."

In the 33 years between Sir Adam's statement and the beginnings of work along the river, Ontario Hydro's attitude never changed.

"We realize," said the commission, one week after ground-breaking ceremonies in August of 1954, "that there has been genuine concern in the minds of families now living in Iroquois, Aultsville, Farran's Point, Dickinson's Landing, Wales, Moulinette, Mille Roches and part of Morrisburg. For that reason we hasten to give assurance to all of those now living in the affected area that, according to our present schedule, no flooding will take place for at least three years, and probably not for three and a half years, from this date."

The Premier of Ontario, Leslie Frost, added a footnote. "We want to make you feel that you are partners in the project, and that your problems are not overlooked in the magnitude of the problems to be faced."

Because the vast Canadian relocation job was as much a part of the power project as the generating stations themselves, its cost, too, was a part of the $600 million package which the United States and Canada had agreed to split. For this reason, all questions of rehabilitation costs and procedures had to be settled with the New York power agency. Not until then could Ontario Hydro tell citizens in the seven towns — some of them angry and all of them worried and anxious over their uncertain fate — about land procurement proposals and studies in community planning which had been in the making for more than a quarter of a century.

Agreement, however, came promptly. On August 4th, 1954, the two power entities came to terms on the methods and costs of procuring land, relocating highways, railways and other facilities in Canada.

Hydro then moved swiftly. By August 17th, it was meeting with representatives of the towns, revealing the entire relocation plan, complete with sketches, timetables and statements on policy and procedure. Separate meetings, some of them stormy, followed in each of the communities, as proposals were carried to the people themselves.

Ontario Hydro land agents then began offering each owner his choice of three different deals: rehabilitation on higher ground, under conditions determined by mutual agreement; a cash settlement; or combination of the two.

On each house, appraisers fixed a value that included a 15% bonus for inconvenience and disturbance. Land speculators were given no chance to turn a quick dollar, for Hydro examined the deed to every property before naming its price. If an owner was found to have purchased a home only recently, he was generally awarded precisely what he paid. Anyone dissatisfied with the price could, however, appeal to the Municipal Board, a neutral panel made up of local lawyers, real estate agents and other experts.

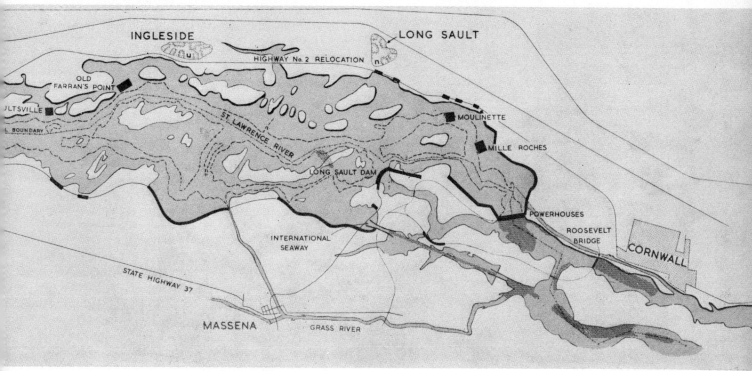

g it necessary to relocate numerous lowlying townsites,
de and Long Sault.　　　Ontario-Hydro

One by one, the houses were examined, then, to see which could be moved economically and which could not. And finally Hydro sat down to dicker.

Anyone owning a home that could be moved had to make the hard decision between the old and the new. Hydro would carry his house off to a lot, serviced and landscaped, in the new village, provide a new furnace, and repair any damage that happened on the way. Or it would buy the old home allowing the owner a vacant lot at the new site and specifying only that he build within a year or sell the land back to the commission.

For those owning the houses that could not be moved — the limit was 200 tons — the decision was easier or more difficult, depending on how you look at it. They had no choice but to sell, with Hydro paying the agreed price plus 15%. They could relocate in the new town, or they could decide to build a new life somewhere else.

Rehabilitation itself then moved forward under a long-range program of community planning, a program whose remarkable detail and enlightened policies are reflected today in the three bright new towns that have replaced the seven doomed ones, and in the relocation of much of Morrisburg.

Residential areas are laid out in loops which feed into collector streets leading, in turn, to business districts, churches, and large bright shopping centres. Houses, set well back from the street, are attractively landscaped, and none of them face directly on the highway. Schools

Capital

Policeman directs traffic as a church is moved along highway to its new location.

are cleverly placed so that no child has to cross more than one street, and can often use pathways through quiet parks green with shrubbery and trees.

Residents of the six old towns used to dump raw sewage into the river. Today, each new community boasts a filtration plant. Dial telephones provide a new luxury. Tired old railways stations have given way to sleek showplaces of glass and brick.

And each new town began life debt-free: sewers, sidewalks, streets, civic buildings, schools, all were built free of charge by Hydro.

The core of each community is a "town centre", planned carefully to cater to the demands of the motorcar age without sacrificing the man on foot. Traffic flow and parking facilities have both been arranged not only for convenient access but also to steer motorists away from the areas reserved for pedestrians. Shoppers and businessmen, as a result, stroll freely around stores, offices, restaurants and civic buildings, without having to worry about being knocked down.

Inevitably, because they are new, a certain sameness stamps some of the streets. But clever planning managed to create an individual character for each of the towns.

Fifteen miles west of Cornwall, Ingleside is a blend of villagers from Dickinson's Landing, Wales, Farran's Point and Aultsville, and is laid out on the style of the old town square. Two schools and a shopping centre border an expanse of green park and trees in the center of town, and churches of four different denominations

Capital

An old land mark being torn down to make way for the Seaway.

are set on the corners. Much of the town is set in woods, and residential streets run off to the west in a series of loops.

Long Sault, eight miles west of Cornwall and northwest of the old Moulinette, is different. Made up of villagers from Moulinette and Mille Roches, it stands on high ground, overlooking a valley. Residential streets rise in a gentle slope from the perimeter road, flanking on two sides a civic center, a shopping center and offices set down in the centre of town.

Iroquois, whose people all came from the old town of the same name which celebrated its centenary in 1957, was laid out with residential areas extending north in loops from a collector street. The business center there is at the eastern edge of town, and the new shoreline provides excellent facilities for construction of a deep water harbor.

Hydro engineers had calculated that the rising waters of the power pool would engulf only part of Morrisburg. But since the flooded area would include the entire business district and several score homes, the Commission suggested relocating these on 100 acres to the east and creating an integrated settlement. Houses, buildings, roads, and the highway, were arranged to provide the most convenient flow of cars and trucks and yet at the same time to separate the community from normal highway traffic. A shopping center built on the newest plaza lines, provides some 38 stores to replace shops on the old main street.

With a river, a vast parkland and probably a top fishing area, at their doorstep, a railway line and a super highway at their backs, it was clear that Morrisburg and the three new towns would be ideally suited for a tourist jackpot and for some types of industry once the Seaway and Power projects stood complete.

Hence when town planners prepared their sketches they earmarked whole areas as the residential and industrial areas of the future. They figured that Morrisburg's population might eventually rise from 1,800 to 12,000. New Iroquois, Ingleside and Long Sault, each of which began life with about 1,100 souls, might one day house 10,000, 7,000 and 3,000, respectively.

Putting its best public relations foot forward, as the move began, Ontario Hydro suggested but did not prescribe. It let the people themselves, through their town councils, make the rules on building restrictions, zoning and other matters of town planning.

For example, many of the families chose spanking new ranch bungalows and split-levels. But more than 500 others elected to take their homes and their memories with them.

The people of Iroquois were the first to go, and as their new community began taking shape, they chose to ignore some of the professional advice. In New

Capital

Looking down the main street in old Town of Iroquois shortly before all buildings were removed prior to area being flooded to create new Lake St. Lawrence.

Iroquois the old is mixed side by side with the new, and the small with the large. Most important, the people have precisely what they wanted. Citizens of the other new towns, on the other hand, chose the opposite tack. They chose a greater measure of town planning, and they adopted strict zoning and building regulations in an effort to achieve some uniformity in the appearance of individual streets.

Wrecking crews arrived in old Iroquois during the summer of 1955. With them came the house-moving machines, great gentle monsters capable of lifting a 200-ton home so gently that plants could be left on the windowsills and dishes in the cupboards.

With each house to be moved, once property arrangements had been completed, drawings were prepared for a new basement, a new heating system, and any alterations required. Then the house was placed on the moving list, and a superintendent arrived to mark beam locations on the drawings.

The move was to be as painless as possible, and as soon as the new basement was ready, with openings left in the walls as shown on the drawings, Hydro officials arrived to tell the family about stop-over arrangements.

Then it was time to leave a way of life which despite the promise of a new town, new stores, new schools, new everything, many hated to lose. The base-ment was cleared, and shrubs and other valuable plants dug up. TV aerials stayed where they were, but the water system, electrical connections and the furnace were all dismantled. Basement walls were drilled according to the pre-marked areas, and two long steel "I" beams went into place in the holes in the foundations under the house. They formed the main carrying beams, on which the carrying frame was built.

The house-moving machine surrounded the house, and two carrying beams were placed on the front and rear lift beams. Picked off its foundation, the house was carried to a float which had been moved into position. A tractor was then hooked onto the float, and the journey northwards began.

In the new townsite, a second house-moving machine was waiting to lift the house from the trailer, carry it to the prepared foundation, and set it gently down. After the machine was uncoupled, and rolled off, the carrying-frame was pulled from the new foundation, and blocking-in was completed. Workmen scrambled inside to begin installing water and plumbing facilities, and pre-fabricated ducts. Furnace, laundry tubs, and hot water tank were installed. Outside the house a special crew prepared the new steps and veranda.

Once work was finished inside, the house was cleaned, and the family came home again. But work continued outside. Exterior basement walls were plastered, lots graded, filled and seeded. Concrete

Ontario-Hydro

Aerial view of new Town of Iroquois with Iroquois Dam and Lock in background. Location of old Iroquois lies between the new town and the river. When flooding is completed, part of the site of the former townsite will be under water — the balance will be a port.

This was the last house to be moved under the relocation plan. It was moved from Morrisburg's Main Street and was the 525th house to be moved.

walkways were laid. Later, inspectors came to check the work and see that any walls that had been dirtied were redecorated. An outside coat of paint completed the job.

The movers had a standing bet, which no one not even the owners of one 15-room, three-storey colossus that was carted off to New Iroquois, ever collected. "Put half a glass of water on the kitchen table," they would say. "If a single drop is spilled we'll stand you and your whole family a steak dinner."

One day they put on a special demonstration. An Iroquois housewife had just finished the breakfast dishes on a bright September morning, when up rolled the moving machine. That was 9:30 a.m. An hour and a quarter later, she and her six-room bungalow were settled a mile and a half away.

The power was on, the telephone worked, water and sewage facilities had been hooked up, and new neighbors were arriving for a cup of tea.

This was to be the pattern in Iroquois for the next twelve months. A sign on the outskirts of the old town said, "We've got to go, but watch us grow" and almost everyday as someone's house rolled north, a new gap appeared on one of the old streets.

Parcelling out the choicest lots, like those in New Iroquois which border a park that runs down to the bank of the river, was done on the basis of prior right. If a homeowner had a lakefront lot in the old town, he could claim a comparable locale in the new.

Neighbors could also be chosen. In some cases families had lived side by side, happily or otherwise, for several generations. If they wanted to, they could keep it that way. If they didn't, the friendship could be dissolved quite simply, by choosing different streets to live on.

As the great upheaval began, historians moved promptly to preserve as much of Canada's past as they could from the area soon to be under water. The Ontario-St. Lawrence Development Corporation, a Crown company formed by the Ontario government in 1955, drew up plans for a museum and issued a plea for relics of the early days along the river. From attics and basements appeared dusty, hand-made bear traps, old powder horns, spinning wheels, ox yokes and hundreds of other items, including cavalry swords and muskets used by determined Canadians to repulse the American invader during the battle of Chrysler's Farm near Morrisburg in 1813.

79

The roadbed for relocation of New York State Highway Route 37B being graded and sloped.

Moving a house in the project area on the American side, to a new location intact with fire place, chimney and TV antenna.

By the summer of 1956 the entire residential district of Iroquois was on its new location. A hundred and fifty homes had been moved, another hundred torn down. And by the end of that year five miles of new streets had been paved in the new town, and a shopping centre and two new schools were being built.

With the Iroquois shift complete, the house movers and demolishers drove east to Aultsville, Farran's Point, Dickinson's Landing and Wales, whose citizens were to form Ingleside; to Mille Roches and Moulinette, nuclei of the new Long Sault; and to Morrisburg. They began work that fall, almost simultaneously in each of these areas.

Meantime, other facets of the relocation program were moving forward. Oddly enough, only some sections of the 40 miles of double-track railway line between Cornwall and Cardinal would be flooded when the power pool was filled. But to join the lengths left untouched on dry land would have produced hairpin curves entirely unsuited to trains. And so the entire section was moved north, and part of the vacated roadbed used for Ontario's new and scenic highway number two.

By summer of 1957, most of this highway diversion had been finished. By that time, too, the grisly project that drew hundreds of migrant workers to Cornwall three year earlier had finally begun. Eighteen cemeteries were moved, and most of them combined into Union Cemetery, a single new burial north of the old Wales. All the tombstones were removed and in some cases, on the request of relatives, the remains themselves were disinterred and transferred. Stone slabs were placed over all the others, to make sure they would remain forever, undisturbed.

In November, 1957, Ontario Hydro finished moving a three-storey brick and frame house into the new subdivision at Morrisburg. It was the last of the 525 houses that were shifted. Not a single pane of glass had been shattered, nor a bit of plaster cracked. Shopping centers in each of the new towns were finished in time for the Christmas trade that year, and by New Year's eve power, water and sewer services, street paving and sidewalks were all complete in Morrisburg, Iroquois, Ingleside and Long Sault. The abandoned townsites had been cleared, and while there was still work to be done on new schools, churches, and landscaping, the rehabilitation was virtually complete.

There had been grievances and, at first, some open hostility. But now that the move was over, nearly all the uprooted families were happy and most of the problems had been solved. Under fire from angry residents, for example, Ontario Hydro had agreed to salvage part of old Iroquois by dumping fill from a nearby excavation to make a 225-acre shoreline park. On Sheek Island, inside the power pool, the summer colony had managed to gain a one-year reprieve after protesting violently when it was given only a few weeks to clear out. The cottages were finally skidded across on the ice in the winter of 1957-58.

Canada's shoreline between Iroquois and Cornwall was rich in history. Along it the early French traders, explorers and Jesuit priests had cut portages. Later the Loyalists had settled, building homesteads and clearing the land for farms and towns. Near Morrisburg blood had been shed in a battle for Canadian independence. In the days before the Cornwall Canals, Dickinson's stagecoach had rattled over dusty roads, taking passengers overland past the Long Sault Rapids.

Upper New York State between Waddington and Massena contained little of this. There were no old riverfront towns to be demolished, no roots with the 18th century to be severed. Several hundred cottages, a few dozen farms, and a small number of houses in Waddington itself together with a small amount of railway and highway relocation, formed the bulk of the relocation problem facing the New York Power Authority.

Because the social problem along the American side was so much simpler the Power Authority could afford to adopt an approach that was more cut and dried. And it did. All the land along the waterfront between Barnhart Island and Waddington was simply expropriated. Wilson Hill, a strip of high ground midway between Massena and Waddington along the old shoreline, would become an island once the power pool was flooded. So a causeway was built, and this land made available to the cottage owners. But because the cost of bringing in expensive house-moving equipment to deal with a few scattered buildings would have been prohibitive the Power Authority itself took no responsibility for actually moving the houses.

Robert Moses, New York Power Authority Chairman, felt, however, that recreation should be one of the great by-products of the St. Lawrence Seaway and Power developments.

"In the construction of such large works there is a tendency on the part of engineers to postpone, minimize and even forget serious consideration of final improvements such as trimming, reforesting, landscaping, recreation, esthetics in the broad sense," he declared in 1955, as an armada of earth-moving equipment converged on the International Rapids Section. "Failure to plan and budget these items in advance may in the end lead to cutting and even eliminating this important feature of conservation and development.

"There will be no such neglect on the St. Lawrence. Power and navigation are the prime objectives, but the beauty of the river and its benefits beyond commerce, industry and utilities must be preserved and enhanced. In our zeal to begin operation, we shall not forget

Wide streets and modern dwellings are the keynote of the relocated towns. Above illustration shows lawns and roadway being graded.

This photo shows the enormous sized tires used on modern house moving truck.

Modern shopping center at Iroquois, Ont. replaces old Main Street business district.

Workman construct new street and sidewalks in a relocated town.

reforestation of huge dikes and spoil area, topsoiling and landscaping of roads, water front and parks, attractions for visitors to the power and seaway projects, recreation facilities for local people as well as visitors, promotion of high standards of zoning and building construction, and protection against eyesores, shacks, billboards and other scenic exploitations."

Earmarked for development are highways, paths, picnicking, beach and boating facilities, both on Barnhart Island and on the mainland opposite. All the land between the Seaway and the St. Lawrence, in fact, was acquired. About 2,700 acres are to be known as St. Lawrence River State Park, and turned over to the Thousand Islands State Park Commission as a magnet to attract an estimated one million visitors each year.

A scenic, riverfront boulevard runs along the new shoreline, from east of Waddington to Barnhart Island. On Barnhart itself, a roadway was built leading directly to a public parking area at the New York end of the power dam. Here, as at the Ontario end, a glass-penthouse atop a structure the size of a 10-storey building overlooks the river valley and the vast pool of impounded water. Models illustrate the hydro-electric process, and from an observation area, visitors peer in at the control room.

Elsewhere on Barnhart, construction began on driveways, car parking areas, paths, yacht basins, picnic areas, beaches, playfields and other overlooks. Parts of two grassed dikes that would rise nearly 15 feet above the level of the power pool would be made accessible as observation vantage points. At the south end of the forebay dike, parking and overlook facilities would be developed on a natural promontory 35 to 40 feet above the pool.

Ontario, too, plotted ambitious plans. Flooding of the power pool would make islands out of high ground along the old waterfront. The government-sponsored Ontario-St. Lawrence Development Corporation therefore began building a system of causeways that would link twenty of these islands in a scenic drive, connected on either end with the main land highway system and called Long Sault Parkway in honor of the rapids that would vanish forever. Docks, sand beaches, and picnicking and camping facilities would be set up in the best locations.

Never before had parkland been available along the river, for the Loyalists, when they settled, received long strips extending back from the water. Now, the public would be admitted and Ontario was making the most

of it. Three miles east of Morrisburg the battlefield at Chrysler's Farm was to become a very special place. Here, where outnumbered Canadian Militia and British Regulars defeated American troops in 1813 and helped settle Canada's destiny as a separate nation, would stand the famous obelisk memorial which for years had been given a place of honor in Morrisburg. Here, too, old houses, churches, barns, taverns and other buildings moved from the doomed towns would be renovated, rebuilt and grouped to form a little community, Upper Canada Village. Log huts, a blacksmith shop, a farmhouse, barns, all would be just as they were in the early days along the river and a museum would exhibit relics from Canada's past.

From other buildings to be demolished would come brick and stone for a walled pioneer cemetery, to be fashioned in the form of a cross. Fragile old tombstones dating from the late 18th and early 19th centuries and representing every family identified with early settlement of the district would be set into its walls.

Several years earlier frogmen working in the harbor at Kingston, Ontario, had raised the remains of a bateau, one of the flat-bottomed craft that were dragged up rapids and towed by oxen along the shallow St. Lawrence canals of the late 18th and early 19th centuries. From the relic a model was made, and then skilled craftsmen at a Kingston shipyard began the task of creating a full-sized replica for Upper Canada Village. Plans were made for a little canal, a tow path for oxen, and an 1812-size lock, to carry visitors back into history along the shoreline of the tiny community.

By the summer of 1958, as Ontario Hydro and the New York Power Authority prepared to create that shoreline by flooding their power pool, the village was beginning to take shape. The cemetery was in place. Renovation and rebuilding of the old parsonage was almost finished. Several other houses, among them Cook's Tavern, the red brick headquarters of the American invasion force, and Christ Church, from Moulinette, had been moved intact and were awaiting repair crews. Still others, including the handsome Chrysler homestead itself, lay in pieces, waiting to be reconstructed stone by stone. Research workers sifted through old records, and chipped off samples of the original paint for analysis so that fresh batches could be made.

Gone now was the old way of life along the riverfront. But in Upper Canada Village, at least, the memory of the little communities and the families which progress had displaced, would be preserved.

CHAPTER SIX

LACHINE (MONTREAL) SECTION

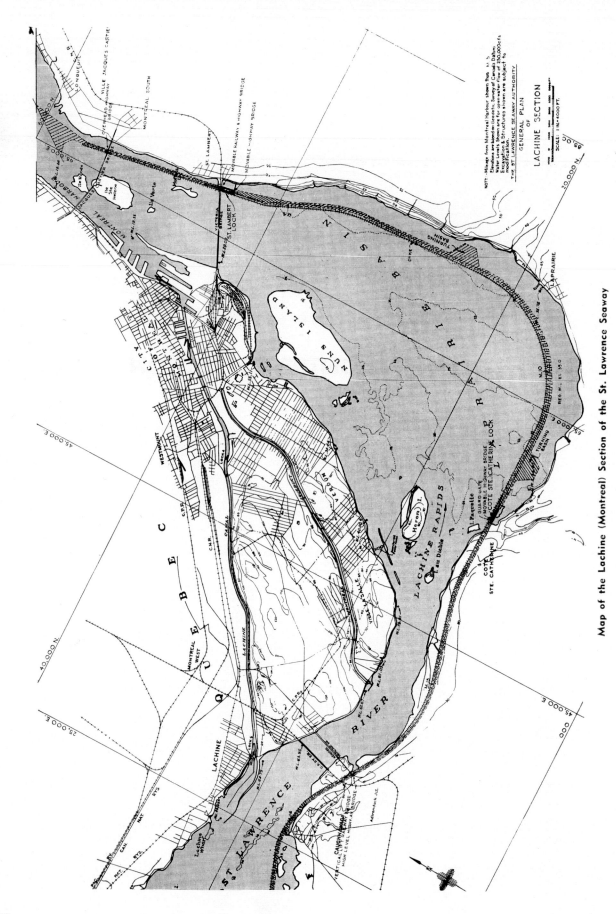

Map of the Lachine (Montreal) Section of the St. Lawrence Seaway

LACHINE (MONTREAL) SECTION

Extending some 31 miles, from the Harbor of Montreal to the head of Lake St. Louis, the Lachine Section of the St. Lawrence Seaway was, in its basic concept, a project much simpler and less grandiose than the one undertaken in the International Rapids. Nevertheless, this particular section was made complex and difficult by the massive bridge structures connecting the Island of Montreal to the South Shore and which had to be modified to provide the necessary clearance over the Seaway.

It was in this section that Canada invested more than half of her $220 million contribution to the St. Lawrence Seaway. It was only fitting that the Lachine Section should be entirely a Canadian effort as it was here that the first attempts to improve the inland waterway route had been made.

Here, on little Riviere St. Pierre, during the early days of the white man's conquest, Dollier de Casson's modest canal, one and a half feet deep, had been dug under the watchful and murderous eyes of the Iroquois. It was here, too, in 1780 and again in 1804, short side canals two to three feet deep had been built at the edge of the Lachine Rapids, enabling the freight-carrying "cannots de maitre" of the fur trading companies to move out from Montreal on their trips to posts situated hundreds of miles away to the West.

It was not until the year 1821 that construction on the first Lachine Canal proper had been undertaken. From 1843 to 1848 the channel was deepened from five feet to nine feet. Later, between 1870 and 1883, a second and last enlargement had been made to furnish 14-foot navigation throughout. Eight and a quarter miles long, the canal had a total lift and drop of 50 feet, giving access from the Port of Montreal to what is known as Lake St. Louis, which, in reality is only a widening of the St. Lawrence River at the point where the Ottawa River flows in from the northwest.

In 1947, as hopes rose that the Seaway would soon become a reality, the Canadian government established a Board of Engineers to consider whether the scheme for the improvement of the Lachine Section as recommended by the Joint Board of Engineers twenty years earlier provided the best advantage for such improvement and if not, what alternative plan it would suggest.

In 1948 the Board made public its report which contained not one, but three alternative schemes for the government to chose from. Through Lachine Rapids, classical barrier to navigation into the North American heartland, thundered an unharnessed hydro-electric potential of more than 1,200,000 horsepower, the same that Jacques Cartier had watched in silent wonder from the top of Mount Royal. Because there was power, two of the plans called for a joint hydro-navigation development by the Federal government and the Province of Quebec. The third dealt with navigation alone.

As it turned out, plan number three was chosen as Quebec, which owns the power rights along this section of the St. Lawrence, was busy elsewhere on other hydro developments.

The government made one change in the Board's recommendation. Instead of passing along Montreal's busy waterfront, as the Board had suggested and as all earlier canals had done, the decision was made to build the new Seaway canal along the opposite bank, on the south shore.

There were numerous reasons for this decision. For one thing, it would extend Montreal harbor into a new and uncluttered industrial region. A south shore canal would also avoid bringing the large Upper Lakes vessels though the treacherous St. Mary's current and the harbor area of the port, where they would have caused almost continuous traffic congestion. Finally, the south route would ease the problems of integrating existing and future rail and road communications.

The plan called for a canal to be dug 20 miles long and 300 feet wide from deep water in Montreal harbor to Lake St. Louis at Caughnawaga. In a great sweeping curve, from its entrance a short distance east of Jacques Cartier Bridge, the canal follows the south shore, partly through sections of shallow water and partly overland.

The first two miles, from just below Jacques Cartier Bridge to Victoria Bridge, and the next ten, to Cote. Ste. Catherine, run through sections of shallow water, mainly the Laprairie Basin. Along this stretch the canal is diked. Its final eight miles are overland, ending at Lake St. Louis.

Two locks start vessels on their journey westward to the Great Lakes. St. Lambert Lock, the first, is built at Victoria Bridge to overcome the difference of 15 feet between the levels of Montreal Harbor and Laprairie Basin. Cote Ste. Catherine, the second, is built 10 miles to the west, where the canal's overland section begins. It raises vessels 30 feet, the difference between Laprairie Basin and Lake St. Louis which explodes violently into the Lachine Rapids.

Provisions also were made for two turning basins, between St. Lambert Lock and Cote Ste. Catherine Lock, which allow deep sea ships and lake carriers to manoeuvre more freely in and out of the new channel.

Those were the essentials of the work at ground level. From overhead come complications.

Seaway under construction in the Montreal area at Caughnawaga. In this section, the waterway construction consists mostly of diking and digging as may be seen along the shore. The bridges are the Honore Mercier, at the top and the lower bridge is the CPR railway bridge.

Seaway specifications said that all bridges must provide clearance of at least 120 feet above water level in the new canal. To this requirement, not one of the four links between Montreal Island and the south shore measured up. The Jacques Cartier Bridge, owned by the National Harbours Board was only about 40 feet above the water, and the Victoria Bridge, owned by Canadian National Railways less than that. Farther west, the Honore Mercier Bridge and the Canadian Pacific Railway bridge, next to it, were quite low and over dry land. At this point the Seaway canal was being cut through overland. Thus it was necessary for all four structures to be raised.

Such then, was the plan for constructing this 20-mile stretch of Seaway called the Lachine Section.

It had taken 21 years to build the old 14-foot Lachine Canal, and 28 years for the Cornwall. Even the Welland Canal, until the time of the St. Lawrence Seaway the newest of the man-made cuts along the waterway, had been under construction for 19 years before it was finally completed in 1933.

But canal construction in the old days was a far different type of operation than in the mid-twentieth century. It was generally carried on in an intermittent fashion. There could be no work at all during the winter months, and in the summertime the pace of construction was geared so as not to interfere with navigation.

Not only was canal-building a long and, by the standards of those days, costly business, it also absorbed huge quantities of labor. At the peak of construction on the St. Lawrence Seaway and Power Projects about 22,000 men were at work between Montreal and the eastern end of the Welland Canal. But using construction methods in vogue even as recently as 30 years ago, it has been estimated that a work force of some 120,000 would have been necessary. And a five-year timetable for a project which in excavation alone . . . 210 million cubic yards . . . was colossal, would have been dismissed as the idea of a madman.

The difference lay, of course, in the machine . . . the bulldozers and graders and great gantry cranes, the fleets of heavy-duty diesel trucks. At one time, during the

This is where the fabulous Seaway begins — about half a mile downstream from the Jacques Cartier Bridge in Montreal harbor. View shows a cofferdam being built of earth and rock. When completed, area enclosed by cofferdam was pumped dry and construction of the entrance to the Seaway was begun.

construction period, machinery worth $75 millions was busy along the waterway, most of it engaged winter and summer alike.

It was on November 17, 1954, that the vanguard of this, perhaps the largest fleet of construction equipment ever assembled, arrived in the Montreal area. On that day also, the first blast set off in the Lachine Section marked the formal beginnings of work on the Canadian portion of the St. Lawrence Seaway. It erupted as work started on the St. Lawrence Seaway Authority's Contract Number One, awarded in October and calling for excavation of some two miles of the Seaway Channel, and construction of the protecting dike, between the Jacques Cartier and Victoria bridges.

Only about 40,000 yards of earth were moved during the first, brief construction season at Lachine. But with the following spring came the main work force.

In the shallow area above Montreal Harbor, sites were cofferdammed and then pumped out so that work could begin in the dry. Millions of cubic yards of shale and rock were drilled and blasted, and then loaded by power

showels into the heavy-duty trucks or rock-wagons. Some of it ended in disposal areas, while a great percentage was used to build dikes to protect the new 27-foot canal from the ravages of ice during the winter, and all-year round from the inflow of silt and stone which is always borne along on the waters of a great river.

This method of construction was also employed for the seven miles from St. Lambert Lock, around the bow of the Laprairie Basin where some 7.5 million cubic yards of common excavation and 3.2 millions yards of solid rock were removed.

Beginning at a point just downstream from the Jacques Cartier Bridge on the south side of the St. Lawrence River and extending 7,500 feet up-river to the Victoria Bridge, the canal leading to the St. Lambert Lock was completed eight months ahead of schedule. A total of 4,300,000 cubic yards of material was excavated and an integral part of this excavation was the building of a permanent dike on the river side of the excavation. This permanent dike of impervious material rises 60 feet above the canal bottom.

89

Above is shown the channel and dikes for the Seaway passing under the Jacques Cartier Bridge of Montreal. Work is just beginning to raise the bridge to provide 120 feet clearance between the water level of the completed Seaway and the bridge structure.

Once past Cote Ste. Catherine Lock, however, neither cofferdams nor dikes were needed, for at that point the canal became a section cut through the mainland.

By the end of November 1955, the first full construction season, contracts worth $50 millions had been awarded in the Lachine Section and the impact of man's greatest assault on the Lachine Rapids was beginning to be noticeable.

Downstream from Jacques Cartier Bridge, considerable eofferdamming had been finished and part of the site dewatered, while dikes were going up. Between the Jacques Cartier and Victoria Bridges, work was even farther along. Cofferdams had been completed, the entire contract area pumped dry, and dikes built to within five feet of their finished grade.

On the next section, west from Victoria Bridge, tenders were out for St. Lambert Lock. And westward again, in the seven-mile Laprairie Basin channel, cofferdams were finished in most places.

Contracts had been let for Cote Ste. Catherine Lock, where cofferdams stood complete and excavation was just beginning. Work was underway, too, on the overland channel running west to Lake St. Louis.

As winter set in, ice jams and high water hampered further cofferdamming in the Laprairie Basin, and freezing pumps halted work in excavation sites not clear of water. However, the below zero temperatures had no affect on rock excavation of the overland channel. West from Cote Ste. Catherine, and in the area between Jacques Cartier and Victoria Bridges, work went on as usual during the day, and at night with the help of powerful floodlights.

In March 1956, the Seaway Authority awarded its most important contract. Valued at more than $10,000,-000, it was the last of the dredging jobs in the Lachine Section. The contract entailed digging 3.3 million yards of earth and rock east of the Jacques Cartier Bridge, partly to provide a turning basin, but, more important, to make the join between Montreal Harbor and the new canal. Here would be the true entrance

Aerial view of the Jacques Cartier Bridge and approaches as raising operations near completion at southern end of the bridge. Montreal is in the background.

Jacking operations, using 450 and 500 ton capacity motor driven jacks. This operation shows the jacking going on under spans 1 and 2 at southerly end of the bridge.

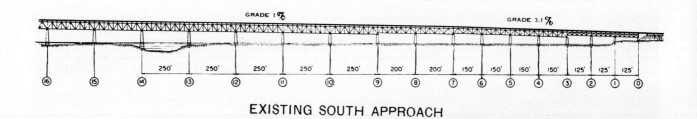

EXISTING SOUTH APPROACH

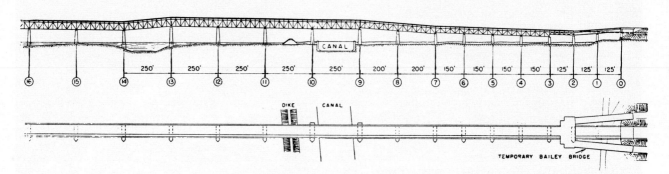

FIRST STAGE OF JACKING

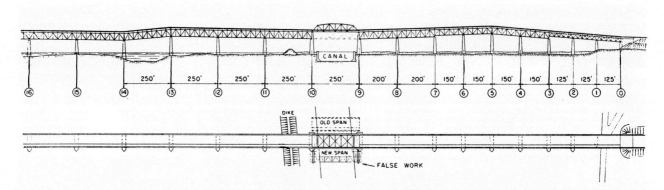

SECOND STAGE OF JACKING AND REPLACEMENT OF CANAL SPAN

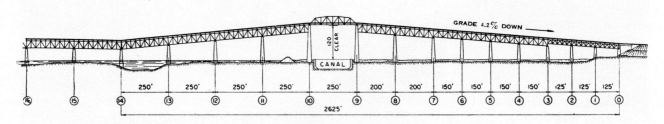

FINAL STAGE

Horizontal views of the Jacques Cartier Bridge showing the elevations at various stages of the jacking operations.

to the St. Lawrence Seaway and to the industrial heart of North America.

By late spring of 1956 construction was underway over almost the entire Lachine stretch of the canal. From deep water in Montreal Harbor to within a mile of Lake St. Louis, nine general contracts had been let, and only three others remained to be awarded. By dollar value, roughly 10% of the work had been completed with two and a half years to go.

That summer, too, construction gangs arrived to begin the delicate and difficult Jacques Cartier Bridge project. Already, one contractor was busy enlarging the bridge piers to take the added stress that would come from higher spans. Now another group arrived to start the jacking.

Largest task of its kind undertaken anywhere in the world, the Jacques Cartier bridge-raising feat was an engineering achievement of staggering complexity.

The Jacques Cartier Bridge, most easterly and also the busiest of the four bridges, presented problems to Seaway planners which were greater than any of the others. They centered around the key southern section, which would pass directly above the new canal. At a cost of nearly $7,000,000, the object was to raise the whole southern section in varying amounts so as to provide an additional clearance of 80 feet above the channel.

After carefully examining the bridge, Dr. P. L. Pratley, the Montreal Consulting Engineer who had designed the bridge twenty years earlier, decided that 50 of those 80 feet could be obtained by literally jacking up the bridge. Then, directly over the canal, for the other 30 feet, they could exchange one "deck span", with its steelwork slung underneath for a "through span", with supports above the roadway, This was all to be done, moreover, without shutting off the flow of traffic.

The contract for the job called for replacement of span number 10 by the new through-truss link; for raising 14 other spans at the southern end; and for raising the piers to suit the higher spans. Nor was that all. Height of the southern abutment was to be raised, and a new abutment built about 65 feet south of the old one. As well, a clover-leaf approach, with grade seperations, was to be built with the cooperation of the Quebec Highways Department.

In planning this delicate operation, the main consideration was to avoid too much interruption of the traffic, and to do this the new span was built in position on two runways, upstream from the old span and connected to it.

In the early hours of Sunday, October 20th, 1957, a work force of some 80 erection men and engineers gathered at the site for the crucial operation of translat-

ing the new span. That is to say, the old span was rolled out between piers nine and ten and the new span, completely finished, was rolled into position.

Both the old and new spans were mounted on roller trucks, each containing forty-two 6" diameter rollers. The trucks in turn rested on the two runways, each consisting of seven rails. The force to move the old span away and the new span into position was provided in the same way as for the raising of the bridge itself, namely, by hydraulic jacks.

On the downstream side of the bridge and at the end of the two runways, two double acting hydraulic jacks were located. These were connected to the old span by large plate-link chains. The jacks had a combined capacity of 500 tons and a stroke of 4 feet.

As soon as the signal to commence operations was received, power was supplied by electrically driven hydraulic pumps delivering oil at pressures up to 6000 per square inch. This had the effect of pulling the old span in a downstream direction and because the new span was attached to the other side, this moved also. As soon as the two spans had been moved a distance of 4 feet (the stroke of the jacks) links were removed, the jacks were retracted, reconnected and the process repeated until the entire distance of 78 feet had been moved. The total weight of the old and new spans was 3100 tons.

The time allowed for this operation was 7 hours. However, the actual time amounted to only five hours, with traffic, which was held up during the translating being resumed at 10 a.m. As flashbulbs blew and a great cheer went up, Canada's Minister of Transport, Hon. George Hees, became the first person to cross. He rode atop a huge mobile crane.

Traffic in and out from the metropolis must, under no circumstances, be halted. And so two temporary Bailey bridges were installed at the southern end, with connecting turnout platforms and temporary roads of access. Then 30 hydraulic jacks, of 400 to 600 tons capacity, and four horizontal ones, were brought to bear. Six inches at a time, the 14 spans were boosted gradually higher. With each lift the spans were supported on concrete blocks. Then, at intervals of two feet, successive concrete courses were poured on the piers. Thus it was for nearly two years, until the required neighty for each span was attained.

From each bridge came a different problem. To each, inturn, went a different solution.

The Victoria, an ancient and much maligned road-rail link two miles upstream from the Jacques Cartier, was too old and too low to bear raising. Besides, railroad trains could not climb or descend the steep grades that would result from raising the bridge. And so a new and novel approach evolved.

View of the St. Lambert Lock under construction. At the downstream end of the lock the CNR Victoria Bridge crosses directly overhead. At later stage of construction, a lift span replaced the span shown here.

St. Lambert Lock nears completion and work on lift span for the Victoria Bridge goes ahead. Motor vehicle traffic was diverted to temporary roads shown above.

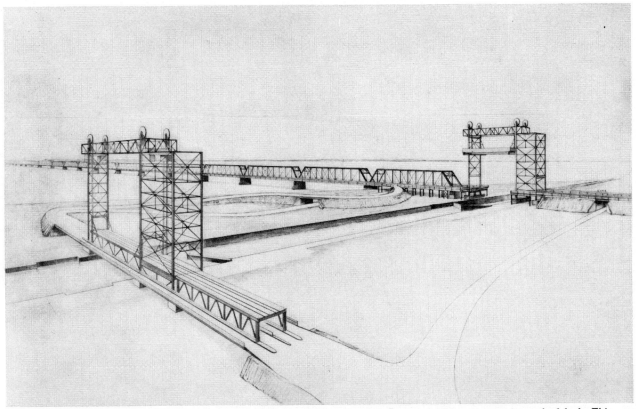

Architects drawing of the Victoria Bridge together with the diversion road and bridge at opposite end of lock. This arrangement permits free flow of traffic regardless of whether one bridge or the other is open.

At the Victoria, the St. Lawrence Seaway's first lock was to be built. To ensure an uninterrupted flow of trains, cars, trucks and busses, therefore, it was decided that there would be not one, but two new lift spans. The first would lead straight ahead from the main spans. The second, to be built to the west, would cross the upper end of the lock, linked by a diversion road running along the top of the canal dike.

When a ship bound for the Great Lakes entered St. Lambert Lock, and the first of these lift bridges rose to let her pass, motorists would drive along the dike to cross at the bridge at the upper end of the lock. Trains, however, at least until 1960, would just have to wait, because for the first year or two after the Seaway's completion, this second lift bridge would carry only a highway.

The Honore Mercier Bridge 17 miles upstream, near the Indian village of Caughnawaga, presented somewhat of a different problem. Here, the entire south end would have to be higher.

Built in 1934, the 2,900-foot long Mercier Bridge had a concrete roadway supported by 11 deck trusses, 13 concrete piers and a 400-foot continuous arch span and crosses the St. Lawrence River from the mid-western end of the Island of Montreal. The overland South approach, which consisted of twenty-five 50-foot welded steel-concrete composite deck and girder spans, had to make way for the St. Lawrence Seaway project.

The prospect of a movable bridge across the Seaway canal was definitely undesirable on account of the already too congested roadway traffic at this point. A new high-level crossing was decided upon. The raising of a portion of the existing steel bridge together with the concrete viaduct of the South approach was contemplated and found impractical.

The only alternative was to demolish the existing concrete approach and replace it with a new high-level structure, at a cost of $6 million, which would be capable of meeting future traffic needs.

Prior to the demolition of this approach, and while the excavation of the Seaway channel progressed, a temporary timber trestle and a rock-filled embankment was constructed over which traffic could be diverted.

Demolition of the concrete sections south of the main span was accomplished through the use of jack-hammers, acetylene torches, a headache ball and lastly, dynamite. The two spans adjacent to the arch were broken up with the mechanical equipment while a single push on the generator handle dropped the remaining 18 piers and the spans between them. No blast holes were drilled in the superstructure steel or concrete, but on the piers to be dynamited, vertical blast holes were drilled

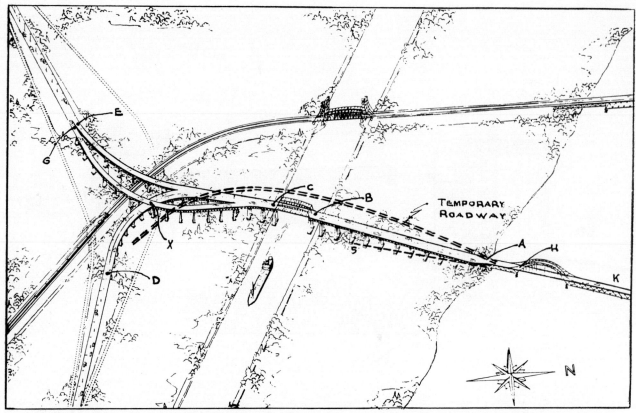

Modification of Honore Mercier (lower) and CPR Railway (upper) bridges crossing Seaway near Caughnawaga. "A" indicates point at which former south approach to Honore Mercier Bridge ("A" to "S") was demolished. "C" to "B" is the high level span over the Seaway canal. "D", "E" and "G" are new approaches for traffic coming or going in various directions. "X" is a two level cross-over. Double dotted line indicates temporary roadway used while new construction took place. CPR Railway in upper part of illustration has twin lift spans over the canal.

down the center of each pier leg. The plan was to demolish the bridge with explosives so as to break up the concrete as well as bring it down to the ground. In all, about 1,200 pounds of dynamite — 70 pounds per pier — was used. With the blast, there was a complete disintegration of the piers and the spans dropped simultaneously.

In the new section of the Honore Mercier Bridge, the continuous deck type spans are supported by reinforced concrete piers varying in height from 60 feet to 110 feet.

Simplest of the problems raised by the bridges occured at the most westerly of the four, the Canadian Pacific Railway's double-tracked Caughnawaga Bridge, erected in 1880, and adjoining the Honore Mercier Bridge to the west. It carried no road traffic, and, for this reason, it was decided simply to erect two independent lift bridges, one for each track, and built side by side over the channel to give a clearance for shipping of 120 feet from the high water level. The two bridges are identical except for secondary details such as stairs and walkways.

Each bridge consists of a 322-foot truss lift span, at each end of which is a tower having an over-all height of 140 feet 6 inches above the base of the rail. The lower

portion of each tower forms a 66-foot truss span. Leading to the towers, at each end of the bridge, is a 55-foot deck plate girder span. The over-all length of bridge is 595 feet.

Over-all, the Seaway Authority's program of bridge modification was colossal. Before it was ended, it cost in excess of $25 million. For Montreal, however, despite the inconvenience, it represented an extra dividend from the Seaway. For when the modifications were complete, including new traffic lanes on two of the four bridges — one on the Jacques Cartier built by the National Harbours Board and one of the Victoria built by Canadian National Railway — the hourly capacity between the island and the south shore would be more than doubled.

In July 1956, contractors began pouring concrete for the two new locks in the Lachine Section. At each, a high concrete hatching plant had been built, but beyond that the methods differed.

At Cote Ste. Catherine, trucks shuttled between the mixing plant and the lock structure, pouring their loads into great buckets suspended from the booms of tall, slender gantry cranes, manufactured in Lyon, France the first of their kind ever used in North America. The buckets were then lifted over the forms and the concrete lowered into place.

Cote Ste. Catherine Lock during construction in May, 1957

Looking at construction progress of Cote Ste. Catherine Lock from between legs of one of the giant gantry cranes brought to the project from France.

The $7,107,480 contract for the Cote Ste. Catherine Lock, called for the construction of the lock itself, 10,000 feet of adjacent channel with a turning basin, approach walls, an upstream regulating works and three miles of dike. The work involved excavating 4.5 million cubic yards of earth, glacial till and soft shale rock, and placing 350,000 cubic yards of concrete.

Measuring 859 feet in length with of 80 feet, concrete was poured at Cote Ste. Catherine 20 hours a day, five days a week, until the job was finished in the late spring of 1958.

The contract for the St. Lambert Lock at the entrance to the St. Lawrence Seaway, was the largest contract awarded by the Seaway Authority in terms of total volume of concrete. The lock and its approaches contains over 455,000 cubic yards of concrete and was poured in record volume of up to 4,000 cubic yards per day and 77,700 yards in a single month. The St. Lambert Lock measures 900 feet in length from gate to gate and 6,285 feet from entrance to exit which takes in the approaches.

Concrete for the approach walls was poured directly into the forms, from spouts on the rear of trucks rumbling in from the mixing plant, while for the lock momoliths themselves, a conveyor belt system with travelling stacker, was brought to bear. This "stacker" was a long pipe, leading from the conveyor which in turn ferried concrete from the mining plant.

Meantime, just as in the International Rapids Section, models were supplying the answers to key questions concerning the river in the Lachine Section. An entirely new hydraulics laboratory, in fact, had been built at Ville La Salle, near Montreal, by the St. Lawrence Seaway Authority, to house two huge reproductions of the St. Lawrence River.

One of these was called the Lachine Rapids Reach. It represented a nine-mile section of the St. Lawrence from Dorval Island to below Heron Island, where the total fall ranged from about 34 feet at high water stages to about 30 feet at low water stages.

The second, known as the Montreal Harbor model, reproduced a section from upstream of Victoria Bridge to a point two miles below the Jacques Cartier.

Surfaces were molded in concrete, and islands and navigation facilities reproduced in miniature, to stimulate the natural conditions of shores and currents.

How would the Lachine works affect the Montreal area? Would they lower the water in the Port of Montreal, or perhaps worsen flood conditions? Would they hinder harnessing of the Lachine Rapids for future hydro power in years to come?

Engineers thought they would do none of these things. But to reinforce their calculations, they built the models, which were formally opened late in 1956.

By July 1st, 1957, the St. Lawrence Seaway Authority's third anniversary, contracts worth $100 millions had been awarded in the Lachine Section, and with more than 2,500 men toiling steadily, work on this section of the Seaway had almost reached the halfway mark.

However, all had not gone smoothly for the Seaway Authority in the Lachine Section. East of Mercier Bridge, several farms and summer cottages were to be expropriated. And part of Caughnawaga, a small Indian village lay in the path of the new canal. Compared with the moving problems faced by Ontario Hydro along the International Rapids, Lachine should have been routine. But it was not, and bitterness erupted.

The Superintendent General of Indian Affairs had hired an appraiser to set values on the properties, after which negotiations began, based on these appraisals. After much haggling by the Indians, some of whom took their cases to court, the matter was settled to the satisfaction of almost everyone, with the exception of six determined braves who refused to budge from their land until the Government had paid them what they were asking. However, as men and machines lay idle awaiting a decision which could have been dragged out for months, the Seaway Authority took the bull by the horns and made

the facilities of the Exchequer Court available.

With that, for all practical purposes, the matter was settled. The six holdouts gathered their possessions and left and the giant project once again moved forward.

During the months that followed, the two locks were finished and tested. The draglines, cranes, shovels and trucks toiled along the remaining sections of the canal. With each week that passed, the canal approached nearer and nearer to completion. During the summer of 1958, the last earth dam lying across the eastern entrance to the Seaway was blasted away. And when, late in August, a series of great explosions ripped loose thousands of tons of rock downstream from Jacques Cartier Bridge, and dredges moved in to clear the Seaway's front door, the end was clearly in sight.

Across the river, the old Lachine Canal was still going strong, though its great days were nearly over. The shipping season of 1958 would not, however, be its last. Industries along its banks had been promised that the 14-foot deep link would remain open as long as they needed it.

Looking downstream from immediately above the St. Lambert Lock. The bridge in the foreground is the Canadian National Railway lift span. In the background is the Jacques Cartier Bridge and just beyond that is the Montreal entrance to the fabulous Seaway.

CHAPTER SEVEN

BEAUHARNOIS SECTION

BEAUHARNOIS SECTION

Nature did little to ease the problems of a twentieth-century construction boss when she carved the route of the St. Lawrence River.

Along the International Rapids she spread thick layers of glacial till and marine clay. One was as hard as concrete, and the other sticky as and greasy as thick paste.

Nevertheless, few places along the great waterway were left a legacy to compare with the one at Beauharnois, twenty miles west of Montreal. For this was solid rock, and not just rock of the everyday kind, but a special variety, so hard and abrasive that bits needed sharpening after only ten or twelve feet or drilling and shovel teeth wore out in a single shift.

Sandstone, this rock was called, and for more than a year it drove construction men to despair. For it rose in great layers precisely at the site chosen for two new locks which would comprise the key items in what came to be known as the Seaway's Soulanges Section.

The name Soulanges was given many years ago to a narrow, twisting, 18-mile neck of fast water joining the two great widenings in the river between Cornwall and Montreal, widenings which for some reason have always been called lakes.

Through the lake to the west, St. Francis, lies a navigation channel 30 miles long. It leads to the new Seaway and Power works in the International Rapids, and in three different places, some deepening and widening was needed to make it fit for Seaway shipping.

To the east, for 10 miles, along Lake St. Louis, the route of the Seaway strikes through water that is naturally quite deep until it reaches St. Nicholas Island. From St. Nicholas, where the channel veers in close to shore, a newly-dredged shipping lane 600 feet wide, carries vessels on to a point near Caughnawaga. There they enter the canal leading around the Lachine Rapids and into the Port of Montreal.

Soulanges thus lies athwart the shipping track between the International Rapids and Lachine, and for Seaway planners it threw up a formidable barrier; a treacherous, rock-strewn reach of river whose waters dropped 82 feet and erupted into the famous Cascades, Split Rock, Cedars and Coteau Rapids.

Beginning in 1780 with Captain Twiss and his band of Royal Engineers, many builders had dug canals and built locks to avoid those rapids. Designed for the old flat-bottomed bateaux, the canals and locks of the Engineers were six feet wide and two-and-a-half feet deep. They were replaced in 1845 by a nine-foot system,

Downstream lock of the twin locks at Beauharnois under construction. Note the cofferdam holding back the St. Lawrence River which may be seen in the background.

and this in turn gave way late in the 19th century to a 14-foot canal, the Soulanges, which was dug overland along the north shore and fitted with five locks.

Obvious for years, as the merits of a deep waterway to the mid-continent were debated on either side of the border, was the fact that the 14-foot Soulanges Canal could never be overhauled to 27-foot Seaway specifications. And so, just as at Welland far to the west, the certain knowledge that someday the discussion would end and construction begin was reflected in works completed decades before Congress and Parliament passed their respective Seaway legislation.

Between 1929 and 1932, what was then the privately-owned Beauharnois Light, Heat and Power Company and later became part of the publicly-owned Quebec Hydro-Electric Commission dug the Beauharnois Power Canal, along the river's south bank. Sixteen miles long, 27 feet deep and flanked by embankments 3,300 feet apart, this canal was designed to divert most of the waters of the St. Lawrence away from the rapids and through the turbines of a great new power house that would be built to harness, for the first time, the full drop of the river between Lakes St. Francis and St. Louis.

This the canal did, and Beauharnois came to be known the world over as one of history's most imaginative hydro-electric power developments. In time, it also became one of the largest, its capacity almost as big as the combined peak loads of two new ones built upriver

by the Province of Ontario and the State of New York.

Those who designed the Beauharnois Power Canal, however, always had more in mind than electricity. In fact, when Canada's Department of Railways and Canals first set its seal of approval to plans for diverting the river, it specified that the canal could only be built if it was tailored to Seaway standards. Someday, they, resolved, this canal will float will float foreign flag shipping and the great slender lakers; it should be dug with that in mind.

And so it was. A navigation channel 600 feet wide was dredged along its north bank. And the substructures of bridges crossing it were designed so that lift spans with clearances of 120 feet could someday be installed.

For more than a quarter of a century, no vessels save dredges sailed the Beauharnois Power Canal. But when 1954 brought final triumph in the battle for the Seaway, it was a simple matter to draft plans for completing the Soulanges section. A short side canal would be dug west of the power-house. Within it, two new locks would lower ships from the main Beauharnois Power Canal into the waters of Lake St. Louis. A swing bridge would replace the stationary span at the Melocheville railway bridge just above the powerhouse, and vertical lift spans would be installed at the two road-rail bridges: the St. Louis midway along the canal, and the Valleyfield at the upper end. Finally, a four-lane divided highway tunnel to the cut beneath the lower

Twin tunnels are directly beneath the lower lock at Beauharnois. The highway is the main road between Montreal and Valleyfield.

of the two locks would carry traffic along an important Quebec highway which followed the shore of Lake St. Louis at that point.

Estimated cost: $50 millions, to be borne, because these are Canadian waters, entirely by Canada.

Work began much later at Beauharnois than anywhere else along the Seaway. Not until March, 1956, more than a year and a half after the initial blast in the International Rapids, was the first contract awarded. To be completed by the following October, it involved clearing of the site for the two locks and their approaches, building cofferdams and service roads, excavating for the highway tunnel, and, relocating temporarily part of the New York Central railway line, which crossed the canal just upstream from its lower end.

Three months later, and both on the same day, contracts for the Upper and Lower Beauharnois Locks were awarded for completion by fall of 1958. Each of the locks would have a lift of 42 feet. They would be built in beds hewn by blasting nearly three million cubic yards of solid rock. For this reason, the two locks would not come cheap. They would cost roughly $25 millions, and thus become the most expensive of any along the Seaway.

Meantime, not actually a part of the Soulanges Section but related geographically, work to alter the contours of the river bottom above and below the canal

and thus to make room for the great ships that must clear it in 1959 was well along.

In Lake St. Louis, dredging had been underway for more than a year. Under a single contract, 3.8 million yards of overburden and rock were being lifted along a 10-mile section running from the easterly end of the Beauharnois Canal to just west of the Caughnawaga Indian Reservation.

In Lake St. Francis, three contracts had been awarded. On the most westerly, and also the largest, bucket and suction dredges were busy removing 2.7 million yards of overburden along a 10-mile stretch from Cornwall Island to Fraser Point. Farther on, at Lancaster Bar, 600,000 yards of sand, silt and clay had already been dredged. Finally, at the approach to the Beauharnois Canal itself, a third contractor was well along on his assignment of 1.1 million yards.

It had been a fairly simple matter, once the Seaway bills were passed, to sketch final plans for the Beauharnois locks. The real difficulties began only when the overburden of clay was stripped away and the terrible sandstone laid bare. In moved great fleets of churn drills and wagon drills, and from then on the digging became something of a bad dream.

Shovel teeth wore out, sometimes in less than eight hours. Grader blades were generally good for about a day. Tractor pads sometimes had to be replaced after

Aerial view of Beauharnois area. Huge power station of Hydro-Quebec is seen in left center with the Beauharnois Ship Canal directly behind it. Toward the lower right is the lower lock under construction.

The above picture above gives the reader a good idea of the type of terrain that the contractors faced as they excavated for the twin locks at Beauharnois.

working a few weeks. Worst of all was the painfully slow pace at which drills were able to penetrate this rock.

On the lower lock, if drillers averaged four feet an hour they figured they were doing well. And they were, for earlier construction jobs around Beauharnois had averaged only two. On the upper lock, to make matters worse, the contractor struck an unexpected faulted zone, and the speed of his churn drills dropped to six feet for two ten-hour shifts.

Extra large supplies of spare bits were stocked, complete sharpening facilities maintained, and extensive machine shop and garage facilities set up to replace worn out parts and keep the machines running. At the upper lock, moreover, one of the most startling pieces of equipment used along the waterway made its appearance.

It was called a jet piercer, and by using thermal energy, in the form of a searing, two-inch flame produced by a rocket type burner, it bore holes five times faster than any drill steel. As sparks flew and steam billowed out, the flame would stab into the rock at temperatures of over 4,000 degrees Fahrenheit.

One of the walls for the upstream lock at Beauharnois is shown during construction.

Mounted on tracks, the jet piercer worked by first heating the sandstone until it was white hot and then suddenly cooling it with a stream of water. The rock would shatter, escaping gases and steam would blow out the cuttings, and the flame would spear in a little deeper. If often bore as much as 125 feet in a single 10-hour shift.

By November, 1956, the three contractors at Beauharnois were digging 10,000 yards of rock a day. Excavation for the highway 720-foot tunnel beneath the upper entrance to the lower lock had been finished, and work on the tunnel itself was just beginning. By the end of that year all contracts had been awarded in the Soulanges Section of the Seaway. Work on the lower lock was about 10% complete and on the upper 13%.

Spring and early summer of 1957 brought important milestones at Soulanges. In May, the highway tunnel was partly opened to traffic as the first of its two tubes was finished. And by June excavation for the locks work had progressed to the point where the first concrete was being poured.

One after another, that summer and fall, the great concrete lock monoliths took shape and Beauharnois began to assume its ultimate appearance. At the end of 1957, the lower lock contract was 84% finished, and the upper one, lagging somewhat, 64%.

Early the following summer, both main lock structures stood complete. By late fall, the Beauhranois Power Canal had finally achieved its double-edged destiny, it provided the water power for one of the world's largest hydro-electric plants as well as the water for the locks and navigational purposes for this section of the Seaway.

CHAPTER EIGHT

INTERNATIONAL SECTION
Seaway and Hydro-Electric Power

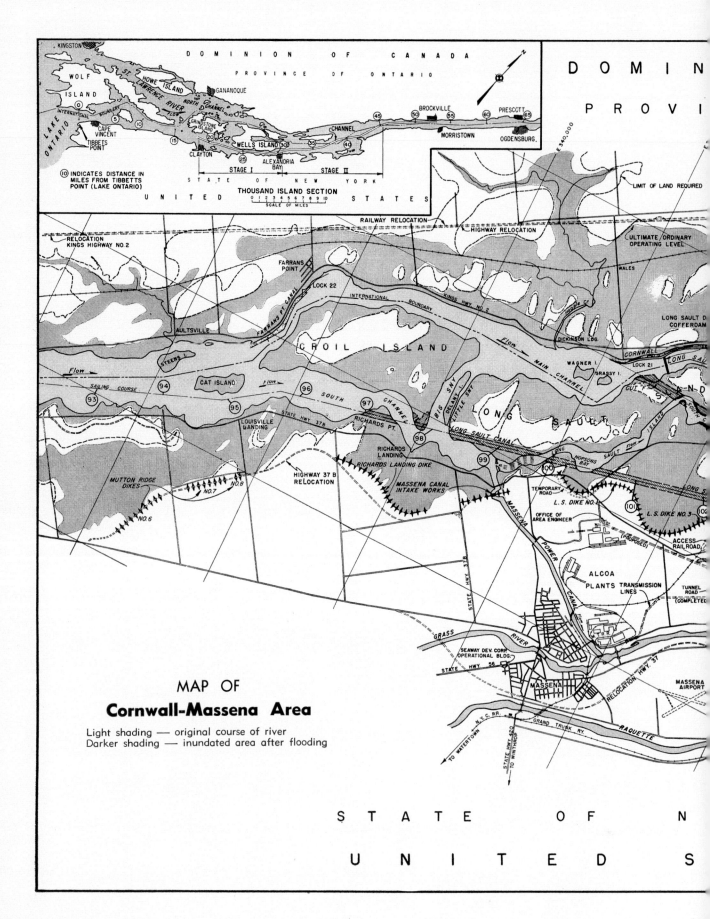

MAP OF
Cornwall-Massena Area

Light shading — original course of river
Darker shading — inundated area after flooding

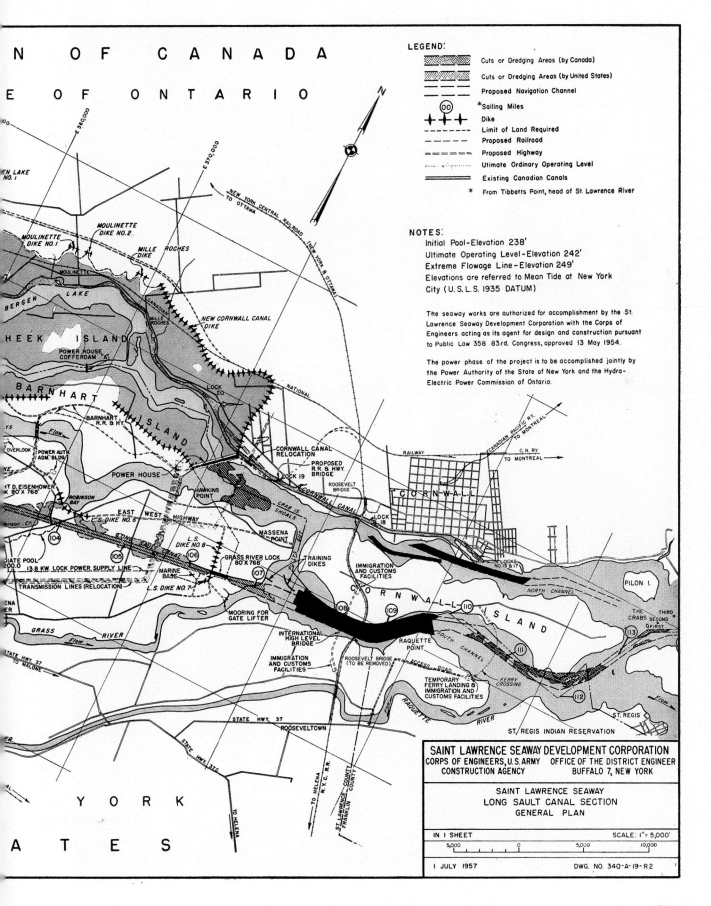

LEGEND:

- Cuts or Dredging Areas (by Canada)
- Cuts or Dredging Areas (by United States)
- Proposed Navigation Channel
- ⓄⓄ *Sailing Miles
- Dike
- Limit of Land Required
- Proposed Railroad
- Proposed Highway
- Ultimate Ordinary Operating Level
- Existing Canadian Canals
- * From Tibbetts Point, head of St. Lawrence River

NOTES:

Initial Pool-Elevation 238'
Ultimate Operating Level-Elevation 242'
Extreme Flowage Line-Elevation 249'
Elevations are referred to Mean Tide at New York
City (U.S.L.S. 1935 DATUM)

The seaway works are authorized for accomplishment by the St.
Lawrence Seaway Development Corporation with the Corps of
Engineers acting as its agent for design and construction pursuant
to Public Law 358 83rd. Congress, approved 13 May 1954.

The power phase of the project is to be accomplished jointly by
the Power Authority of the State of New York and the Hydro-
Electric Power Commission of Ontario.

SAINT LAWRENCE SEAWAY DEVELOPMENT CORPORATION
CORPS OF ENGINEERS, U.S. ARMY   OFFICE OF THE DISTRICT ENGINEER
CONSTRUCTION AGENCY   BUFFALO 7, NEW YORK

SAINT LAWRENCE SEAWAY
LONG SAULT CANAL SECTION
GENERAL PLAN

IN 1 SHEET	SCALE: 1"= 5,000'
1 JULY 1957	DWG. NO. 340-A-19-R2

Almost completed power dam is seen here with newly formed Lake St. Lawrence at its back. The international boundary divides the dam into two equal halves. The American section (left) has been named in honor of Robert Moses, Chairman of the Power Authority of the State of New York and the Canadian section (right) after Robert H. Saunders, the late Chairman of the Hydro-Electric Power Commission of Ontario.

INTERNATIONAL SECTION
Seaway and Hydro-Electric Power

Between Iroquois and Cornwall the level of the St. Lawrence River drops 85 feet. But the descent was a gradual one in pre-Seaway days, spread over 25 miles and erupting occasionally into violent and beautiful rapids, like those at the Long Sault.

Over the years, on both sides of the border, several small hydro-electric plants had harnessed bits and pieces of the gigantic power potential hidden along this turbulent reach of the river. But for more than a quarter of a century man had realized that only if he concentrated the drop at a single point could the waters plunge with maximum force against the blades of huge turbines. Not until a single giant step replaced the flight of smaller ones, engineers of the Hydro-Electric Power Commission of Ontario decided as early as 1921, would electrical energy on the massive scale of 2,200,000 horsepower become possible.

This was the heart of the power enigma. And its only logical solution would also resolve the problem of deepsea navigation. For while power generation required that the river be raised and gathered for a 25 miles, and then suddenly hurled with enormous force over the edge of a precipice, a quiet channel deep enough to float large ships was vital if the river was ever to realize its destiny as one of the world's great bearers of waterborne commerce.

And so the plan to improve navigation and develop power at one and the same time took shape. Dam the river, and build a power plant just above Cornwall, said an international Joint Board of Engineers in 1926. Let the waters rise behind the dam, until they form a great lake 25 miles long and four miles wide, a power tool that can also be used as a shipping track. Then cut channels leading into the pool at either end, and build a few locks.

Key pieces in this master concept, sketched so long ago and now finally complete, are four in number, three of them in the Cornwall-Massena area and the fourth upstream, at Iroquois. Together, and for the first time, they establish man as master of the St. Lawrence River's International Rapids.

Doubling as a dam and as a generating station, the powerhouse itself — half American and half Canadian — joins Canada's mainland with the foot of Barnhart Island. More than half a mile long, their colossal grey concrete bulk halved by the International boundary line, they funnel 110 million gallons of water per minute through the gated openings of massive intake structures, and then drop the water 87 feet into long files of giant turbines.

The powerhouses fit snugly into the north channel of the St. Lawrence River. Sealing the south channel, in a great sweeping arc between the head of Barnhart Island and the American mainland, is Long Sault Dam. As the flow of the river rises and falls its lift gates are raised and lowered. In this way the level behind the powerhouses is kept at its proper height.

Behind the powerhouses and Long Sault Dam, reaching back to Iroquois, lies the man-made lake, tranquil and slow-moving. Flooded by its waters are the series of 14-foot canals and locks which since the late 1800's had ferried vessels along the Canadian shore past the fast water of the rapids. Ships use the pool itself now. At the Cornwall-Massena end, they enter or leave it via the Wiley-Dondero Shipping Channel, a canal 10 miles long which with twin, 45-foot locks, the Dwight D. Eisenhower and the Bertrand H. Snell, was dug and blasted through the American mainland on the south shore.

Iroquois Dam, set piece at the opposite end of the power pool, takes charge of some of the more subtle features of this power-navigation scheme. Adjoining it is the pool's western shipping entrance: a single lock, on the Canadian side. But the dam itself, a gated waterway reaching from Iroquois Point in Canada to Point Rockway in the United States, regulates a very delicate aspect of the plan.

Millions of years ago, when nature shaped the St. Lawrence Valley, she laid a sharp edge of rock across the river near Chimney Point, a few miles above Iroquois. Because it permitted a certain amount of water and no more to pass round it, this simple weir controlled the entire flow of water into the St. Lawrence from Lake Ontario and thus, ultimately, from the Great Lakes watershed, far to the west.

Seaway and power planners knew that the rock ledge performed its job extremely well: not once in ninety years of careful measuring had the level of the river strayed from the range 242.5 to 249.5 feet above sea level. Until 1948 they planned to use it, together with Long Sault Dam downstream, to control the level in the power pool. That year, however, it was decided that when the Seaway was built water in the pool must be kept, at least for a while, several feet below the level needed for maximum production of power. Earth embankments flanking the dam down river must be given a chance to compact, and the entire operation must be thoroughly tested.

The rock weir and the Long Sault Dam could not be counted upon to maintain this lower level. And so, partly as a safety measure, partly to allow greater flexibility, and partly, too, to make sure that in the wintertime, water in the power pool would never be moving fast enough to form ice jams which could clog the intakes downstream, Iroquois Dam began appearing on the plans. It was to form man's substitute for the control which nature herself had furnished down through the ages. For the first decade the dam would help keep the level of the pool from rising higher than 238 feet above sea level. After that, if all was in order, the water would be raised to 242 feet.

It was from this decision that the grand design for mastering the International Rapids drew its name. To the engineers who conceived it and the contractors who built it the operation came to be known simply as the "238-242 controlled single stage project."

When man tampers with the forces of nature he must always be terribly sure of his arithmetic. And when nature assumes the form of a vast inland shipping route, a waterway whose banks are lined with many cities and towns and millions of families, tiny miscalculations can quickly bring on disaster.

The St. Lawrence is a great and powerful river—drawing physical strength from its tremendous flow and economic strength from the shipping it carries and the electricity it generates. To alter its course, to dam it here and make it run there, to replace natural controls with man-made devices proved only in the laboratory, and at all times to maintain navigation along the vital

14-foot canals that lined the Canadian side of the river, represented one of the most intricate problems ever faced by engineers.

To have solved it at all was remarkable enough. To have not only solved but also executed it within one of the tightest construction schedules on record must be counted among the greatest of man's building feats.

Consider, for example, the vast scheduling problem that faced Seaway and Power agencies during the summer of 1954, after final approval was given and the project began.

The St. Lawrence Seaway Authority (Canadian) and the Saint Lawrence Seaway Development Corporation (American) must dovetail their efforts, first so that by mid-1958 14-foot navigation could be diverted away from the old canals and through the new Iroquois, Eisenhower and Snell Locks; and second so that the entire waterway, from Montreal to Lake Erie, would open for 27-foot navigation the following spring.

Meantime, the Hydro-Electric Power Commission of Ontario and the Power Authority of the State of New York must organize and carry out a massive $600 million construction program so that the water level in the power pool could be raised to elevation 238 at precisely the time that navigation was ready for the switch.

Everything must move swiftly and with military

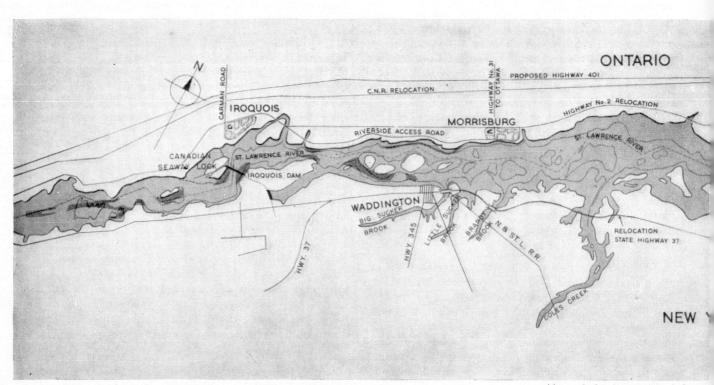

Map of the International Sectio

precision. For should any one of the pieces in the gigantic puzzle fail to meet its scheduled date of completion the entire project would falter. Production of electricity required the power pool. But the pool could not be formed until the Iroquois and Long Sault Dams were finished, until a vast relocation of people and property was complete along both shores, and until dikes were in place. And even if both powerhouses, both dams, every foot of dike and the entire relocation job was finished, flooding would be impossible unless the Iroquois Lock and the Wiley-Dondero Channel and its twin locks, the Dwight D. Eisenhower and Bertrand H. Snell, were also ready. Flooding would destroy the 14-foot canals and locks, the only other means ships had of getting through this section of the river.

Credit for the astonishing fact that over the ensuing four years virtually every deadline would be met in the International Rapids Section, and without even a modest disaster, goes, of course to the four agencies, to their contractors, and to the factories throughout Canada and the United States which fashioned equipment to operate the locks, the dams and the powerhouses.

But much of it must also go to the hydraulic study work, with models, that was conducted before and during the construction period on a scale unprecedented in engineering history.

How fast will the water flow through a section of the river after dredging is complete? What should be the length, the height and the shape of the main struc-tures? Will a particular plan for diverting the St. Lawrence during construction put ships aground in Montreal harbor, cripple Quebec's power supply, inundate the 14-foot canals, or perhaps even cause widespread flooding? From models came the answers, models at the Waterways Experimental Station in Vicksburg, Mississippi, the National Research Council at Ottawa, St. Lawrence Seaway Authority laboratories at Montreal, and above all at Ontario Hydro's Islington laboratories, near Toronto.

Ontario Hydro began investigating the power phase of the St. Lawrence in 1913. But its most intensive work started in 1952, as information was gathered and used to build its famous scale reproductions of the river. There were nine of these models, and Hydro estimates that they saved more than $5 million in construction costs.

The first three were the largest, filling an entire building. They reproduced a 35-mile stretch of the river from Ogdenburg to below the powerhouses, simulating actual river conditions and duplicating to scale the shoreline, the contours of the river bottom and the currents and turbulence of the water.

Incredible precision went into their construction. For example, because all contour measurements were made from an instrument truss that ran on machined rails along either side of models, the rails had to be dead-level. Mistakes of a fraction of an inch would represent many feet on the river.

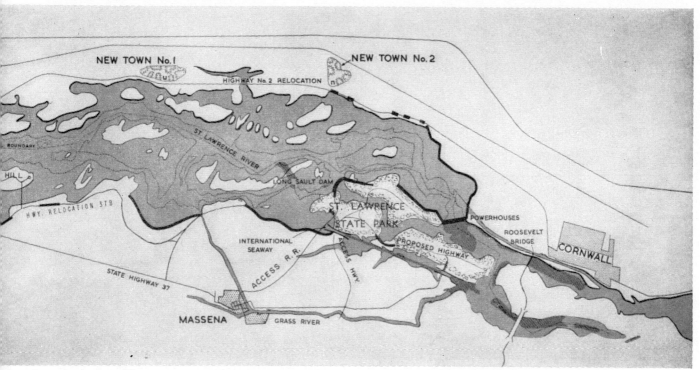

from Iroquois to Cornwall

Long Sault Rapids as they appeared when work began in 1954 to harness the river.

Cofferdam "A" constructed to seal off the river between Barnhart and Sheek Islands. When work on the power dam downstream was completed, this is the cofferdam that was later blown up to create the power pool.

Downstream from cofferdam "A", the river bed is almost dried up, permitting work to start on the power dam — summer, 1955.

Giant earth moving machines bite into Iroquois Point to clear a path for the Iroquois Lock and Canal — June 1955

An eighth of an inch vertically on the models was equal to a foot on the river itself. For this reason even the smallest foundation settlement, or heaving due to frost, could produce false results on exacting tests. And so the foundations had to be adequate. At first, as they were being built, the models looked like gigantic honeycombs. Plywood templates fitted with grooves formed the squares. Then, survey data in hand, model-men moved from template to template, marking contours. Precision sawing, according to the markings, altered the honeycomb appearance to that of the silhouette of a mountain range.

Filled with sand, to within two inches of the contour line, the cells were given a final skin of concrete. Areas representing some sections of the river had cells that could be lifted out and replaced by others reflecting the various plans for channel excavation and improvements. Then thin metal strips inserted into the concrete — 20,000 of them — gave the model river bed the precise degree of roughness as the original.

Other Hydro models helped design the dams and other permanent structures. The Long Sault Dam was tested in miniature, as were various sequences in building it. Engineers used a reproduction of the Iroquois Dam and the area around it as a guide in planning the second and critical construction stage, when water would pass between Iroquois Point and Point Rockway at a ferocious velocity. They tested the dam's sluice gates under various conditions, and tried out different cofferdam schemes to see how each would effect the river levels and existing navigation during construction.

Against the vagaries of nature the models were not entirely foolproof. They could not foresee a summer day in 1957 when a hurricane sweeping across Lake Ontario would very nearly cause a flood near the partly-finished Long Sault Dam. Nor an anxious week the following winter, when ice jams at Cornwall would bring the entire power project to the brink of a first-class disaster. But without the models, hopeless confusion, endless delays, and perhaps also catastrophe, would have been the result.

Steel facing for cofferdam behind which will be built the huge Power Dam. After the steel had been driven into the bed of the river, the cofferdam was filled with rock and earth and behind this shield, work on the Power Dam was started in the dry.

Once final clearance for the project came on June 7, 1954, in the form of the Supreme Court ruling authorizing the Power Authority of the State of New York to share in it, specific projects were parcelled out to the four agencies involved on either side of the border. With each went the responsibility for letting contracts, and for seeing that the work was done on time.

The New York Power Authority was charged with building Long Sault Dam, Iroquois Dam, its own powerhouse and eleven miles of dikes to contain the headpond. It was also to handle a modest relocation job on the American side of the future power pool, and to dredge roughly 34 million yards of earth and rock from the river above the powerhouses.

To Ontario Hydro went responsibility for its own powerhouse, for three and a half miles of dikes, for a much larger relocation job, involving 6,500 people in seven different towns, 34 miles of highway and 40 miles of railway, and for 2.9 million yards of dredging.

Except for machinery and equipment in the respective powerhouses, cost was to be an event split between the two power agencies: $300 million apiece.

Saint Lawrence Seaway Development Corporation took on the Wiley-Dondero Shipping Channel, and the Eisenhower and Snell Locks. Its Canadian partner in navigation, the St. Lawrence Seaway Authority, would pay for all of the work farther downstream, near Montreal. Its share in the International Rapids Section therefore comprised mainly Iroquois Lock.

In addition, the two navigation agencies were to share deepening and widening of the river channels north and south of Cornwall Island, below the powerhouses, and a new system of bridges and highways in the same area.

As Seaway and Power agencies deployed their forces that summer, this was the plan:

Above and below the site for the powerhouses two great cofferdams — one of them the longest in the world

The area behind the cofferdam shown on the opposite page is being dewatered for the start of construction on the 2,200,000 hp. hydro-electric dam.

— would seal the north channel of the river. Then the site would be pumped dry, and men and machines would converge on the riverbed.

Several miles upstream, meanwhile, cofferdams between the American mainland and the eastern tip of Long Sault Island would permit work to begin on lang Sault Dam. Here, engineers had decided to capitalize on a division of the river into two channels which nature created when she formed Long Sault Island. While the south half of the dam's great arc was under construction, two cofferdams and a temporary canal through the island would funnel the entire flow of the river into the north channel and through the gap between Long Sault Island and Barnhart Island. Afterwards, the completed half of the dam would handle the river while a cofferdam above Long Sault Rapids and a second temporary canal through Long Sault Island sealed off the site for the north section.

The Wiley-Dondero Canal and the dam at Iroquois both presented fewer problems, at least of a diversion nature. The first was to be tug entirely on dry land. The second would be a fully gated waterway, a string of concrete piers separated by great steel gates. Around cofferdams above and below the site for its south half the St. Lawrence could flow during first stage construction. Afterwards, the completed half of the dam could handle the river while the north section was built in the dry.

Detailed construction schedules were rushed to completion. The first season's work, it was decided, would focus on access facilities, first-stage cofferdams, and excavation to handle the river during construction. Winter was only a few months ahead. To take full advantage of the short time left initial contracts would be awarded in August. By spring, engineers would have detailed data, plans and specifications ready for the major construction contracts.

On August 10th, 1954, sod-turning ceremonies at Cornwall, Ontario, and Massena, New York, marked the official beginning of the great project. Two weeks later the Power Authority of the State of New York awarded the first contract in the International Rapids section. It was for $1,913,000, for cofferdams at Long Sault Dam.

As contractors throughout North America, during the winter that followed, awaited the chance to bid on one of history's greatest engineering feats, detailed plans were emerging from drafting rooms at Seaway and Power headquarters. In sheer bulk, the quantities involved in these plans were immense. More than 100 million cubic yards of earth and rock were to be moved, roughly a third of them from under water; nearly four million yards of concrete, 20,600 tons of structural steel and 20,000 tons of gates, hoists and cranes were to be placed.

Key items in the International Rapids section:

Powerhouses

The two powerhouses, developing 1.1 million horsepower each and adjoining each other on either side of the international boundary between the Canadian shore and the eastern end of Barnhart Island, acts as a gravity dam 3,300 feet long and 162 feet above the foundations. Thirty-two generators, each with a capacity of 57,000 kilowatts, operate under an average head of 87 feet, and are housed in powerhouses of the modified outdoor type, lacking the conventional superstructure over the generating rooms but with hatch covers for protection against the weather. Power generated at 13,800 volts is stepped up through transformers, and carried to the switchyards through cables within the powerhouse structure. First power was generated in mid-1958, and the date for full competion is the end of 1959.

Long Sault Dam

A concrete gravity curved-axsis spillway structure, 2,250 feet long and feet above its foundations, Long Sault Dam forms the main control structure for the Barnhart Island powerhouses. Thirty vertical lift gates, each 52 feet wide and 30 feet high, makes up its spillway. Fixed hoists of 175 tons capacity operate 18 of these gates. The other 12 are raised and lowered by two 275-ton travelling gantry cranes. The dam, built in two stages, had to be finished by the end of 1958.

Iroquois Dam

A buttressed gravity structure, Iroquois Dam consists essentially of a series of piers and sluiceways, 67 feet high and reaching 2,540 feet from Point Rockway in the United States to Iroquois Point in Canada. Thirty-two fixed-wheel, vertical lift gates controlling the entire flow of the river are operated by a pair of 350-ton travelling gantry cranes. This dam is needed to control and regulate the outflow from Lake Ontario and was finished by the end of February, 1958.

Iroquois Lock

Iroquois Lock, by-passing the Iroquois control dam and raising and lowering ships entering or leaving the western end of the power pool, was built on the Canadian side of the river, adjoining the dam. Its maximum lift is six feet, and it was finished early in 1958 so that shipping can be diverted away from the old 14-foot canals before these are flooded as the power pool is filled. The lock is 860 feet long, 80 feet wide, and 30 feet deep over the sills, with approach walls 3,200 feet long upstream and 1,700 feet downstream.

Wiley-Dondero Shipping Channel

Ships entering and leaving the eastern end of the power pool via the Wiley-Dondero Channel will pass through two locks. The canal itself was cut through the American mainland for seven miles and through million cubic yards. The locks, one at the eastern end of the canal and the other mid-way along it, will divide about equally the lift required to overcome an 87-foot fall at the powerhouses. Each is 860 feet long between its upper and lower gates, 80 feet wide and 30 feet deep over the sills. Each, too, has miter gates 85 feet high, and a maximum lift of 49 feet. A highway tunnel was built beneath the most westerly of the two, providing access to Barnhart Island and the American power-house. Elevation of an intermediate pool connecting the two locks is kept at about 200 feet above sea level. The canal and the two locks were ready to take shipping by July 1, 1958.

Dikes and Embankments

Since the water in the pool would be much higher than the surrounding countryside, 21 miles of earth dikes had to be built to confine it and prevent flooding. In some cases as high as 85 feet, they were fashioned from about 17 million cubic yards of compacted em-bankment, protected by some 200,000 cubic yards of riprap on the water side. Cores of glacial till dumped from areas adjacent to the dike sites would be supported by similar material compacted to a lesser extent and studded with larger stones and boulders. Sand, rock and gravel in the downstream parts of the embankments will ease drainage and ensure stability. Upstream slopes are protected by heavy riprap on a filter blanket of sand and gravel, while downstream slopes will be grassed.

Dredging

A vast program of channel improvements down-stream from Ogdensburg, New York and Prescott, Ontario, will serve two purposes. Deepening and widening in some places will provide the proper depth for ships and keep the water from flowing faster than four feet per second, the maximum for navigation purposes. In other reaches of the river the work is designed to maintain a velocity no higher than two and a quarter feet per second so that winter will bring a smooth ice sheet, and not an ice jam, above the power plant. Above the power tool, inside it, and below it, over 70 million cubic yards must be taken from the river channels and the adjoining shores, most of it by mid-summer 1958 so that 14-foot ships can use the new channels that year. The balance must be dredged before the opening of 27-foot navigation in 1959.

Massena Intake

The Massena Intake Structure, of massive rein-forced-concrete construction, will regulate the flow of water into the Massena Power Canal, handling the domestic and industrial water supply for the Village of Massena and its aluminum smelting plant. During con-struction along the river, it will also supply water for an 80,000 h.p. hydro plant at Massena, which will afterwards be closed. The intake structure, 115 feet high, has a concrete gravity section 710 feet long, an intake control section 119 feet long, and dams and dikes totalling some 4,200 feet. Motor-driven hoists operate a battery of fixed-roller gates. Scheduled for completion by the end of 1957, the intake structure houses five 10,000 gallon-per minute pumps capable of supplying water to elevated tanks at the smelter.

Early 1955 was a frantic and yet exciting time in boardrooms and engineering offices of the Seaway and Power agencies. As fast as plans and specifications could be prepared they were issued to contractors. Back came the bids. Within four months jobs worth more than a hundred million dollars were parcelled out. The van-guard of a vast armada of construction equipment rumbled into Seaway Valley — whole fleets of bulldozers, drag-lines, shovels, graders, scrapers, great Euclid trucks.

Award of the first major navigation contract came on February 11th, with acceptance of a $6,470,000 Long Sault Island for three, involved excavation of 17

Two sheet steel lined tunnels bored through the ground beneath the old Cornwall Canal, provided an underpass to expedite men and materials getting to and from the Canadian end of the Power Dam site. Note ship in old canal passing over the tunnel

bid for Iroquois Lock. Then followed a steady succession of others. By mid-June successful bidders were marshalling at Iroquois Dam, at Long Sault Dam and at both powerhouses.

To pinpoint locations, to determine topography of the surrounding terrain, the best means of access, and the speed and depth of the waters with which they would have to contend, contractors made special pilgrimages to the models of the river, and spent days studying them before moving in a single piece of equipment. In this way they developed schemes, and then tested them from the point of view of river control and continuance of existing navigation.

Meantime, preparatory work was well advanced. During the winter, two tunnels of corrugated steel pipe had been driven under the Cornwall Canal, to ferry men, materials and trucks across to the Canadian power-site. Pontoon bridges linked the American mainland with Barnhart Island.

By spring the last truck loads of earth and rock had been dumped into cofferdams above and below the two powerhouses. Cofferdam A-1, two and half miles above the construction site, was 600 feet long. Cofferdaw C-1, roughly 500 feet downstream from the site, was much larger; 4,500 feet long, its sixty steel cells anchored with 450,000 cubic yards of fill.

Late in June, as carp, bass, pickerel and muskellunge by the thousands were scooped out and moved to new quarters downstream or in the Great Lakes, great pumps began dewatering the construction site.

Six hundred and fifty million gallons were drained between the two cofferdams, leaving behind a vast vacuum into which great winds were sucked. One day in July, as shovels attacked the dry riverbed, a Dutch ship lightly ballasted and high in the water was slipping through the canal opposite the powerhouse area when a tremendous gust blew in from the west. It caught the ship's stern, and hurled it against the canal bank. Before she could be righted, her propeller was chewing into the shoreline, throwing out rocks and earth to the accompaniment of loud curses from the bridge.

By early summer, cofferdams were complete across the upper approach to Iroquois Lock, and above and below the site for the south half of Iroquois Dam. The site for stage one of Long Sault Dam had been sealed, too, and everywhere shovels, drills and trucks had moved in to begin the digging.

Moving swiftly, like the others, was the St. Lawrence Seaway Development Corporation. Contracts totalling over $11 million were awarded between December and June by its construction agents, the U. S. Army Corps of Engineers. These called for excavating more than 17 million yards of earth and rock and building dikes along the route chosen for the shipping channel and its two locks.

The first shovel of earth along this, the American portion of the Seaway, was lifted on April 11, 1955, as a Pennsylvania firm began work on the site for Eisenhower Lock.

Far to the south, meanwhile, a strange, 2,000 mile journey had begun, a journey that involved a gigantic walking dragline. Weighing 650 tons, and capable of scooping 20 tons in a single mouthful, "The Gentleman", as it was known, had left its home in the coal fields near Madisonville, Kentucky and was proceeding northwards, for a much more glamourous assignment.

More than two months were spent in moving the behemoth 18 miles overland to Pond River, the nearest water. Then, towed by river boats, it was floated down the Green River and the Ohio, up the Mississippi and the Illinois, and finally to Chicago. One highway bridge

Temporary bridge between United States mainland and Barnhart Island being swung into position on barges. Over this bridge moved men, materials and equipment for constructing the Long Sault Dam and the American part of the Power Dam.

Excavation begins for Iroquois Lock and Canal. Note rock and earth from excavation being used to create a coffer-dam to protect the project from the river upstream. Men and machines can then work in dry area.

Construction equipment being assembled preparatory to starting erection of the Iroquois Lock.

South wall of Iroquois Lock nears completion

By September, one-fifth of the excavation had been completed. Two more huge draglines, one of them from Louisiana, would arrive that fall. Meantime, halfway across the continent in St. Paul, hydraulics experts at the University of Minnesota were completing model studies aimed at developing the most suitable system for filling and emptying the locks, a system which, among other things, would avoid excessive disturbance to ships being locked through. In Buffalo, New York, and in Nashville, Tennessee, engineers and draftsmen were drawing up final plans and specifications. To prospective bidders advance notice had gone out that calls for tenders would be issued soon for the locks themselves.

Arctic marine fossils uncovered during the digging that year confirmed much of what was believed to be the early history of the St. Lawrence River. The last ice sheet, scientists estimated, must have lain nearby as recently as 7,000 years ago. As the glacier retreated it left gravel and boulders. Afterwards marine waters covered the low-lying areas. Large beds of marine clay and sand were left in some places, and beaches and bars formed round the higher hills and ridges. Still later the land rose, the sea water retreated, and the lush St. Lawrence Valley emerged as the drainage outlet for the entire area.

This legacy which nature had left below the surface made interesting study for geologists. But for contractors it was heart-breaking.

had to be removed to let the great procession pass. In another place the tow skimmed over a dam with only inches of water to spare beneath the barge. Across the Illinois Waterway more than a hundred bridges had to be navigated, some with small clearances; many of them had to be opened by specially assigned electricians and mechanics.

Great Lakes tugs, which took over at Chicago and brought "The Gentleman" down the lakes, eased it into harbor at Ogdenburg, New York, on June 6, lashed to the decks of the two big steel barges. From there a pilot skilled in navigating the fast river currents guided the big dragline on down the river to its new home.

By mid-July "The Gentleman" had settled down to business, and was chewing into the western section of the shipping channel with great gusto. Working around the clock, pausing for fresh bites every 48 seconds, he was lifting 12,000 cubic yards of earth every 24 hours.

By that time, field operations generally had eased into a two-shift, 20-hour-day clip elsewhere along the canal. Aided by weather that was hot and dry, contractors were digging some 47,000 yards of earth each day. Excavation for the two locks was to be finished first, by February, 1956, so that concrete work could begin. The westerly three-mile portion of the canal was scheduled for completion a year later, and the central six-mile section a year later againt, by spring of 1958.

Looking downstream, view shows Iroquois Lock nearing completion.

First stage of the Iroquois Control Dam being erected from the American side behind the protection of a cofferdam.

Second stage of the erection of the Iroquois Control Dam. River has now been diverted through the completed American side of the dam. New cofferdam on Canadian side will permit construction of the remainder of the dam.

Aerial view looking downstream, of the completed Iroquois Lock, Canal and Control Dam. Iroquois Lock was the first lock completed on the Seaway.

From it sprang problems. Much of the earth was either glacial till, a blend of silt and soil laced with rocks and with the density of concrete, or blue marine clay, the wet, stinking, slippery "goop" that clung like glue to buckets and earth-moving equipment.

Shovels had to work hard to dig the till. Sometimes it was blasted. And yet, ironically, it was not much good for making roads. Shot rock often had to be piled three or four feet deep on top of it to make haul roads that would hold the heavy equipment.

But on October 10th, with 6,000 men at work along the river now, the first concrete was being poured at Long Sault Dam. And Iroquois Dam began receiving it a month later, on November 11th.

To some contractors, winter's arrival in December, 1955, brought problems. To others, suprisingly, it meant relief from a nightmare. Construction of embankments was slowed, for it was impractical to use frozen material on some parts of the dikes. But elsewhere, even on days when the reading dropped far below zero, work moved ahead faster than it had for months. Weather cold enough to freeze the ground was ideal for the big "cats" that had mired down in the blue clay. They could dig and handle the stuff more easily, and use the haul roads without bogging down.

Canadian Government Tender Grenville, the first boat to pass through the Iroquois Lock.

During February, 1956, the four contractors digging the Wiley-Dondero Channel stepped up the pace and removed nearly a million yards of earth. But on March 10th all the operating engineers — the men who ran the steam shovels and the other heavy equipment — failed to report for the night shift. Pickets were posted along the entire length of the 40-mile project, bringing all work on the American side, Seaway and Power, to an abrupt halt.

Negotiations were underway. But a week passed, and then ten days, before a settlement came. Precious time had been lost, and excavation for one of the locks was already behind schedule. It would have to be made up.

On the Canadian side of the river, meanwhile, an important milestone had been reached. On February 17th, the first concrete was poured at what was to be known as the Robert H. Saunders Generating Station, in honor of the man who had chaired Ontario Hydro during the immediate pre-seaway years.

That first pour began a sequence which for two years would puzzle sightseers visiting the Cornwall-Massena area. The Canadian contractors had decided to pour concrete all through the winter using special equipment to keep finished sections warm as they cured. As soon as cold weather arrived the Americans, on the other hand, halted all concrete work. Then in the summer they doubled their work force, to catch up.

Each spring the Canadian powerhouse would seem to be advancing much faster than the American. But by fall the two would be even again, and perhaps the New York side a little ahead.

Award of the Snell and Eisenhower Lock contract in April that year brought to an end the peak period of engineering design along the International Rapids. It had absorbed the combined skills of hundreds of specialists in more than a dozen separate but interlocking fields; civil, mechanical and electrical engineering, lock design, hydraulics soil mechanics, specification writing, cost estimating, construction planning and scheduling, and many others. Now it was over. All that remained were such odds and ends as highway and railway relocation work, administration buildings, channel improvements and navigation aids.

All through that summer work pressed forward with growing intensity along the International Rapids Section. To co-ordinate plans and check progress, the different agencies met regularly. Sometimes they gathered in board rooms. More often they adjourned to the river bank.

There were sidelights to ease the burden of the tight schedule. Archeologists, one day in July, hurried to Sheek Island, where an Ontario Hydro engineer had turned up a very old arrowhead. Working carefully, under the direction of Dr. Norman Emerson of the University of Toronto, the scientists soon discovered not only arrowheads but pipes, drills, knives, whetstones, adzes, choppers and other relics of an Indian civilization they estimated to be 3,500 years old probably the ancestral tribe of the Iroquois. Chunks of pottery were found, pottery with designs printed in exactly the same way as on other chunks that had been discovered years earlier in Siberia.

The find was important, for it established another possible link between the North American Indian and the ancient peoples of Asia. As the search went on, Ontario Hydro sent one of its best bulldozer operators to the island, an artist who startled the team of dedicated diggers by scalping a precise three or four inches from the surface without disturbing the earth beneath.

By September a gasping hole measuring ninety feet deep, over a hundred feet wide, and thousands of feet long had replaced apple orchards and cottages at the site of Iroquois Lock.

Working night and day, and resting only on Sundays, power-shovels, drills and fleets of 22-ton trucks labored to clear rocklife glacial till from the downstream approach. With each passing day the approach wall upstream grew longer and higher. Designed to moor ships waiting to enter the lock, the wall would be over 3,000 feet long. Now, more than half of it had been built to a final height of 47 feet. A towering, 275-ton gantry crane swung in great buckets of concrete, each weighing nearly ten tons, and walls six feet wide at the top and fattening outgradually to 34 feet at the bottom grew more and more massive.

Beside the excavation stood the mixing plant, its tall white tower outlined against the sky. In June it had begun churning the vast quantities of concrete needed for the lock; before it was finished 600,000 tons would be in place. An endless belt ferried tons of crushed stone from stockpiles into the hopper on top and then sand and cement, each carefully weighed and measured, were tipped into the mixers. Afterwards the mixers wheeled to spew liquid concrete into great buckets carried by trucks that rumbled in below.

Trucks would load and then thunder down into the great cut, to the foot of the gantry crane. Then the crane would lift the bucket, and pour its contents into the forms for the wall.

That fall brought one of the few, and perhaps the most serious public disagreement among the four agencies building the combined power-navigation project.

Roosevelt Bridge, linking Canada with the United States by rail and by road, had two spans. One joined the Canadian shore with Canadian-owned Cornwall Island. The other, from Cornwall Island to the American mainland, was too low for vessels approaching and leaving Grasse River Lock in the new south shipping channel. It was to be taken down. That much was agreed.

An aerial view of the Cornwall-Massena area of the International Section. At the left is the Wiley-Dondero Ship Channel with the Snell Lock at the lower left and the Eisenhower Lock about midway in the Channel. Just above center is the Long Sault Control Dam and just below and to the right of center is the Power Dam. Note the dry areas behind the Power Dam and along the Channel and Locks. Then compare with picture on next page.

This is the same area shown in the picture on the opposite page. It was taken two days after the temporary dike was blown up and the area inundated to create the huge power pool. One day after this picture was taken ships began using the Eisenhower and Snell locks and the Wiley-Dondero Shipping Channel. Cornwall is at the right.

Late in 1955, following conferences at the Pentagon in Washington, Canadian and American seaway officials had announced agreement on an elaborate system of bridges, roads and railway lines to replace the south channel span. Key item, a new railway-highway bridge across Polly's Gut, would link the U. S. mainland with the western tip of Cornwall Island, clear of the new shipping channel. Contractors would move several miles of railway, and build three other bridges, two of them crossing Snell Lock, to funnel trains, cars and trucks to the Polly's Gut span.

Plans and specifications were rushed to completion. Calls were issued for tenders. By June, 1956, several railway and highway relocation contracts had actually been awarded. Then, suddenly, plans were changed. New York Central, it was announced in September, wanted to abandon its line between Massena and Cornwall. Accordingly, instead of four new bridges only one would be necessary. And it would span the new south shipping channel in a great high-level arc, just above the site of the old span that was to be removed.

Reaction from Robert Moss, Chairman of the Power Authority of the State of New York, was swift and hot. The new bridge could never be finished in time for the power-navigation deadline of summer, 1958, he charged. It would delay the entire project for a year.

Nonsense, said Lewis Castle, Administrator for the St. Lawrence Seaway Development Corporation. "Ships travel under bridges. They do not go through them."

And with that, the matter was settled. Plans moved into higher gear, and contracts were awarded in November. They called for a bridge designed not only to fill today's needs but also tomorrow's increase in car and truck traffic between the two nations. The bridge would be one-third of a mile long, with a two-lane highway and a walkway for pedestrians. To be ready for traffic by July 1, 1958, it would form a $7 million join project. Canada would pay for the substructure, and the United States the superstructure, in an arrangement harmonizing perfectly with the theme of a bronze plaque which was to be given a place of honor on it. Reads the plaque, mounted originally on the old span by Kiwanis International on July 14, 1936:

"This unfortified boundary line between the Dominion of Canada and the United States of America should quicken the remembrance of the more than century-old friendship between these two countries, as a lesson of peace to all nations."

That same fall, Canadian-American joint planning settled another problem that had been pending in the Cornwall Island area. Like so many others, it reflected the fact that navigation and power are closely interwined in the International Rapids section, so much that the effects of works done for one almost invariably spill over onto the other.

Before ships could use the new Seaway route south of the Island and below Snell Lock, the channel must be deepened, widened and straightened, not only to float the larger vessels but also to slow down the river's flow to no more than four feet per second.

International High Level Bridge over the South Channel of the St. Lawrence River from U.S. main land to Cornwall Island on the Canadian side. Cost was shared by the United States and Canada.

Dwight D. Eisenhower Lock facing downstream, is shown here prior to the Channel being filled to its proper depth. Snell Lock is seen at the downstream end of the Wiley-Dondero ship Channel. Entrances to the highway tunnel beneath the lock are shown at the bottom of the picture.

Steel lined vehicle tunnel under Eisenhower Lock during construction. When lock is completed, the part of tunnel shown above will be directly below ships passing through the lock.

But enlarging the channel south of the island and leaving untouched the one north of it would draw more water down the south side. And this, according to the agreement between Canada and the United States, could not be done. Partly because Canada might one day built a second deep waterway, north of Cornwall Island, dredging was not to disturb the old division of waters.

Both channels therefore had to be dredged. And the resulting reduction in the velocity of the water would flatten the slope of the river, all the way from Lake St. Francis up to the tailrace at the powerhouse. It would only amount to a foot or so, but translated into the difference in head this would mean a gain in power of nearly 20,000 horsepower.

For this reason, even though the two navigation agencies were to do the actual work, the power authorities would share the $35 million cost of dredging required around Cornwall Island. Contracts for the north channel were let in the fall of 1956, and for the south channel

the following spring. Much of the work was to be finished by July 1, 1958, in time for 14-foot navigation through the new Seaway. The balance would be completed in time for 27-foot shipping in 1959.

Late in 1956, with factories in many parts of Canada and the United States busy now fabricating lock ridges, electrical equipment, and operating machinery, the first half of Long Sault Dam was finished. Above and below it cofferdams were removed. One gate was raised. The river began to flow. Then four more lifted. The south channel had been diverted.

As the third construction season ended Seaway and Power authorities were breathing easier. The St. Lawrence River flowed smoothly now through the completed south halves of Iroquois and Long Sault Dam. Powerhouses on both sides of the border stood half finished. Dredging, too, had reached the midway mark. Massena Intake was three-quarters complete, and would soon take water. At Iroquois Lock 65% of the work had been

Eisenhower Lock during the construction period.

Looking up from the bottom of the Eisenhower Lock as it neared completion, the walls form a huge canyon.

finished, with excavation almost complete, the approach walls more than half finished and concrete being poured on part of the lock structure. Work on the great shipping channel and its two locks was on schedule, and "The Gentleman" had gone home to Kentucky. Dike-building, too, was on time, as was relocation of towns, highways, railways, and utilities. With any luck, another year would bring to an end the bulk of the heavy construction.

All through the winter, where it could, work moved forward, and the coming of spring in April, 1957 brought one of the toughest of engineering assignments, The south half of Long Sault Dam had been finished. Now it must handle the entire flow of the river. The north channel must be sealed, so that work could begin in the dry on the balance of the dam.

Cut "F", a second temporary canal, had been dug through Long Sault Island to help funnel water from the north channel into the south. To complete the diversion a new cofferdam must span the gap between the island and the Canadian mainland, just above the awesome Long Sault Rapids.

So that rock for the base of the cofferdam would stick and not be swept downstream in the boiling waters, an overhead cableway was strung across the channel, and fitted with a skip. From it boulders were hurled into the riverbed a hundred feet below. Then, beginning at the Canadian shoreline and using finished sections as

a roadway, trucks rumbled in to dump millions of yards of fill on top of the rock.

Work moved ahead swiftly — for a time. But as the gap narrowed between mainland and island the river was forced through an opening that grew steadily smaller. The completed sections of the cofferdam, moreover, had raised the level of the water upstream, creating a falls at the gap. At least all but the final one hundred feet were sealed. But now water raced through the gap at fifty feet per second. As fast as they could be dumped, earth and rock were swept downstream.

The overhead crane was brought to bear. But this time it was useless. Great boulders weighing several tons apiece crashed into the riverbed from a hundred feet and were torn away like pebbles.

Growing more and more desperate, as the day appointed for closing the gap passed, the contractor finally discovered several lengths of steel in a local scrap yard. These were welded together into fantastic shapes, and then steel cables were lashed to them and fastened at the other end to trees along the bank. Then, with a prayer, the shapes went into the river. They held. Boulders were tossed in behind them. They stayed. Then came more rock, and earth. The gap was closed.

Summer of 1957 brought long weeks of hot, dry weather along the river. Bulldozers and shovels that had bogged down in the sticky clay had a field day making up time on the Wiley-Dondero channel. At the power-

The four illustrations on this page show the Eisenhower Lock being filled with water. All other locks on the Seaway are filled in the same manner. There are about 40 ducts, 20 on each side. These are fed from a huge viaduct running through the base of each lock wall. Picture at upper left shows water starting to enter; upper right shows about half the ducts flowing; lower left shows three-quarters of the ducts flowing and at lower right, all ducts in action. It takes about seven minutes to fill lock. Procedure is reversed for dewatering lock.

Artist's drawing of Dwight D. Eisenhower Lock with landscaping completed.

houses work moved ahead on a 24-hour basis. Near Massena, flatcars bearing the first transformers, built in Switzerland, began arriving. By July, Ontario Hydro had poured nearly 65% of the concrete needed for its power-house. And at stage two of Long Sault Dam great cranes running on tracks round the curved circumference lowered the first buckets of concrete.

Earth moving had begun in 1955. By summer of 1957, one of history's largest concentrations of excavating equipment had dug 90 million yards. On the American side of the river alone, 135 shovels and draglines, 400 crawler tractors, 730 trucks, and eight dredges were at work.

It was ideal construction weather — most of the time. Once that it wasn't, brought a day of crisis to the New York Power Authority.

At the time the completed half of Long Sault Dam was handling about nine-tenths of the entire flow of the St. Lawrence — the 14-foot canals used the rest — and most days eight of its thirteen gates were opened to let the water through. But on June 29th the tail end of a hurricane swept across Lake Ontario. Within five hours the flow at Long Sault Dam had risen from 250,000 to 300,000 cubic feet per second. Engineers were helpless.

If the completed half of the Iroquois Dam was closed upstream, the little town of Cardinal behind it would swiftly be flooded. And yet if the flow continued to rise Long Sault Dam would no longer be able to handle it. Water would rise behind the dam, flooding lock number 21 and a section of the 14 foot navigation channel lying opposite on the Canadian side of the river.

By two o'clock the following morning, as gale force winds screamed down the St. Lawrence Valley, 12 gates were wide open at the dam and a gantry crane stood poised over the 13th and last. More than two million gallons of water were streaming through every second. Warnings had gone out to all ships to tie up. Officials had calculated that the level of the river at the canal should be no higher than 204 feet above sea level. It reached 204.33. And then, as engineers weary after 19 hours at their posts prepared for disaster, nature relented. The flow began dropping and the crisis passed.

For tourists it was a circus that summer, with at least half a dozen different rings.

Cornwall and Massena together had handled more than half a million visitors during the 1956 construction season. In 1957 twice that many came. On the Canadian side, Ontario Hydro ran special indoctrination movies,

133

An artist's drawing of the completed Bertrand H. Snell Lock.

Aerial view of Bertrand H. Snell Lock showing ships moving downstream.

Massena Intake serves to divert water for the use of the Village of Massena and also to supply water for the operation of a power station built at Massena a number of years ago. View shows southern portion of Intake nearing completion with cofferdam in place to divert water while construction starts on northern section.

Completed Massena Intake and wildly churning water pouring through after the level of the outside water has
been raised for the Power Pool.

and gave visitors a free bus ride to the Canadian end of the powerhouse.

On the New York side, an observation and parking area on the northern rim of Eisenhower lock, and an overlook presenting a splendid view of the Long Sault Dam spillway under construction, attracted most of the sightseers. Since April, when cofferdams were placed above them, the Long Sault Rapids had vanished. For centuries a colossal 100 million gallons of water had thundered down a 90-foot grade every minute. Now the rapids were gone, leaving the naked, boulder-strewn bed of the river. Tourists dressed in bright sport shirts and laden with cameras poked about in the curious potholes, and staggered off bearing old cannon balls, anchors and other relics of an age long past.

On August 28th, tripped from eight-ton buckets, the last mass concrete was placed at Iroquois Lock. It marked completion of the 1200-foot chamber itself and its two approach walls, 3200 feet long upstream and 1700 feet downstream. Almost immediately, a program was launched to ready the lock for 1958 shipping. With gates and other gear installed, engineers raced the calendar to complete testing before winter. Each piece of machinery had to be examined thoroughly before a gallon of the water lapping outside against sets of stop-logs was allowed into the chamber. Massive gate fenders, 47 feet high, fender booms, and other major parts were operated, and as electrical equipment was installed, the entire working of the lock, with lights, heating apparatus and pumps, was tested "in the dry".

Late in November engineers finished the final test, and Canada's Minister of Transport, Hon. George Hees, arrived to move the lever on the control panel and opened the sector gates. Into the lock chamber sailed C.G.S. Grenville, a Canadian government lighthouse tender. She was raised, and passed through the upper gates. The Seaway's first major goal had been reached — on time.

Others were nearing completion. As 1957 drew to a close only 90,000 yards of the original 17 million remained to be excavated in the big ditch ten miles long, 442 feet wide and 27 feet deep which in a few months would float the shipping of the world. Except for installation of fenders, the canal's mooring cells were complete, and concrete bases had been poured for several of the navigation aids. Winter arrived late in November, but it found the Eisenhower Lock 92% complete and the Snell over 85%. Operating machinery was going welded. both, and the great miter gates were being welded. Bricklayers and painters were at work, and the concrete batch plant was being taken down, an unmistakable sign that things were coming to an end.

Black bars recording work completed had, in fact, approached the 100% mark in construction shacks

Long Sault Dam — Stage I of construction, shown at upper right completed, work on Stage II gets underway. Note curvature of the dam.

throughout the area. In December, as the last cells of the Stage Two cofferdams were removed, Ontario Hydro's permanent operating staff took over Iroquois Dam from the contractor. That month, too, as the north half of Long Sault Dam was completed far enough to take water, the cofferdam above Long Sault Rapids was breached. Canny bulldozer operators, with the full weight of the St. Lawrence at their backs, carved a tiny channel in the cofferdam. The river, pent up for months, trickled through, slowly at first and then faster. Very soon it had covered the rapids.

Downstream, Ontario Hydro continued pouring still more concrete into its immense Robert H. Saunders generating station. But it was also installing turbines, generators, trash racks, headgates, and headgate hoists. Its neighbour next door, too, was busy on the final stages. Nearly all the concrete was in place at the Barnhart Island generating station. Generator rotors weighing 267 tons apiece were being assembled in the erection bay, and 150-ton runner assemblies, — containing the turbine blades themselves — were being lowered into position.

Dredging had paused for the winter, but channel improvements in many places were now over 90% complete, and the sub-structure for the new high-level bridge had been finished. During the summer Iroquois Dam had been finished to the point where it could assume control of the river's flow. As a result, the new shipping channel through Galop Island — the rock weir that had formed the natural control — was reached in October.

With so many major contracts complete or nearly so, the work force along the riverfront was rapidly dwindling. By year's end just over 7,000 men remained on both the navigation and power phases, compared with a peak of over 14,000.

The worst moment for the two power agencies however, still lay ahead.

Late in January, 1958, as if to prove that nature still held full control, ice suddenly jammed where the river narrows just below the powerhouses. Channel deepening and widening, by lowering the velocity of the water and permitting a smooth ice cover to form, would prevent such things once the Seaway was complete. But dredging in the Cornwall channels was far from finished that winter.

The ice backed up rapidly, rising fast and putting tremendous pressure on the huge downstream cofferdam. Fifty-feet below the level of the cofferdam's base workers were suddenly in peril.

Ontario Hydro, which had just finished its last big concrete pour, quickly cleared men and machines from its entire working area. Stop-logs were thrust into openings leading to the generators. And the ice continued to rise.

Engineers decided that if it went much higher pres-

sure on the cofferdam would become too great. One or two cells would have to be breached. This would flood the area behind the dam, setting the New York side of the project back months, perhaps even a full year. But if the dam was not breached it might be destroyed entirely, a matter much more serious.

The dam was too big for dynamite. And so the ice continued to rise, steadily and inexorably. It was only five feet below the top of the cofferdam. And there it halted. The dam was saved.

That was January. Two months later, as work moved ahead swiftly, the cofferdam was no longer needed. For three years it had served as a valuable causeway. Tourists by the thousands had come to its lookout, to gaze across at the army of men and machines at work on the powerhouse. Still others had driven across it, to reach Barnhart Island and the American mainland for an inspection of the Long Sault Dam and the canal and locks beyond. Truckloads of cement had rolled across it, during an American strike in mid-1957 that might have held up the project.

Then in March, 1958, the cofferdams' usefulness was at an end. In little more than three months the first power would be generated. Water would foam into the tailrace area. By that time, much of the cofferdam must be out of the way.

Delicate and involved, "Operation Breaching" began on March 31st, aimed at funnelling 300 million gallons of water into the tailrace area to equalize pressure on both sides of the cofferdam and permit its removal. Fill material in cell 28 was scooped out. A gang of workers armed with acetylene torches scrambled inside to cut big slots below the water level in the downstream face of the cell. Upstream, on the dry face of the cofferdam, nine more slots were cut. And then temporary seals were

Long Sault Dam — tunnels which carried the river flow through during the completion of Stage II of the dam, shown being filled with concrete.

The completed Long Sault Dam with the newly formed Lake St. Lawrence behind it. Temporary construction supply bridge facing the dam, has since been removed.

pushed down in front of the openings on the water side.

When the time came to flood, a piledriver working in reverse withdrew the long steel piles that formed the cell. In rushed the St. Lawrence. Stage one leading to eventual flooding of the power pool had been completed.

Meantime, the coming of spring had brought annual deliverance to the St. Lawrence. Commerce was moving again on the river, and as the shipping season opened a little canal vessel called the "Calgarian" made history by becoming the first commercial ship ever to use a Seaway lock.

She approached Iroquois a few minutes before 3.00 P.M. on May 22nd. A wire-rope fender lay across the entrance, suspended from a steel boom. If the master of the vessel suddenly lost control of his ship this boom would sheer apart. The cables, designed to absorb in 70 feet the shock of a 40,000 ton ship moving at three miles per hour, would then guard the lock gates by putting tension on huge drums set deep in the walls.

As the "Calgarian" approached, slowly and under control but watched carefully from the western control tower, a traffic light winked green just outside the gate fender. The fender lifted, then, the gates opened, and the ship eased into the chamber itself, grey-white and immaculate. There, as upstream gates closed behind her, she was secured to mooring bollards. Downstream gates, automatically controlled and looking like great black half oil-barrels, swung noiselessly open, slowly at first, then a little faster, and finally slower again before coming to rest. Within a few minutes, 20 million gallons of water had surged through the open gates, lowering the ship to the level of the river below. Then the "Calgarian", 254-feet long, built for a snug fit in the old locks and looking a bit overwhelmed in the immense

new quarters, cast-off, slipped out of the lock, and returned to the 14-foot canals.

While this was taking place above ground the real work was going on far below, in the base of deep concrete walls where more than a quarter of a mile of cable gallery line either side of the lock chamber at Iroquois. Like immense boa-constrictors, black-coated electrical cables weighing nine pounds to the foot lay in steel racks along the tunnel walls. There, too, lay the operating machinery, sealed off from the weather and fitted with heating apparatus to maintain the atmosphere at the precise degree of dryness necessary for the best operating conditions.

Pilot generators had governed the machinery operating each major piece of machinery at Iroquois Lock as the "Calgarian" passed through. One, for example, had controlled the amount the electricity being fed to the gate-operating machines, moving them at the desired speed. The lock gates themselves had been opened and closed by sector gears whose teeth were engaged by a pinion-wheel which was turned by a shaft powered by this machinery deep in the bowels of the lock. This pinion and sector gear moved a steel strut, which in turn pushed and pulled the gate levers closed and open.

Six hundred horsepower of electrical energy had been required to operate the gates, fenders, pumps and other gear. Ordinarily this would come from conventional power lines. But twin, eight-cylinder diesels stood ready to generate the power needed in case of emergency.

As May blended into June of 1958, and ships from Rotterdam and Hamburg, from Oslo and London, passed through Iroquois Lock, the great seaway-power project approached a dramatic climax in the International Rapids Section. For now the powerhouses were nearly finished,

Aerial view, looking toward Canada, shows power dam under construction. By a series of cofferdams, the construction site is sealed off from both upstream and downstream. Actually the power dam extends from easterly tip of Barnhart Island, U.S.A., to the Canadian mainland.

Long Sault Dam was complete, and the Wiley-Dondero Shipping Channel and its two locks almost so. It was time to fill the pool.

Trees, brush and stumps, hydro poles, fences, buildings – everything more than a foot high and two inches wide, that could float down to the powerhouses and cause trouble – was stripped from the 38,000 acres to be flooded along the Canadian and American shore.

As if to hide its scars under a final blaze of color, the doomed land had produced acres of bright yellow mustard. Down along the river bank diesel engines throbbed softly as ships slipped through the old canals, each one for the last time. Workers, alone in a valley empty of trees and fences and cattle, salvaged lumber from a wrecked building that had once been a hatchery. It was left to the last by Hydro, so that a final brood of chicks could be born.

A stranger passing through might have thought the world had gone mad. Far inland, on the edge of green meadows, truckloads of sand were being bulldozed into beaches, for bathing. Rows of tall pylons marked a channel across dry land. Two miles from the nearest water a sign freshly painted over a new quonset hut read "Long Sault Marina". The rowboats outside were for hire after July 1st, when the backyard would become a yacht basin.

A sidewalk crumbling and overgrown with fieldgrass and weeds was all that remained of Mille Roches. Aultsville's tombstone was a single pile of broken red brick and rubble. And in some places there was nothing left at all.

All along the front from Iroquois to Cornwall last-minute preparations were underway. Thirty tons of explosive lay buried in the cofferdam above the powerhouses. Telephone and hydro crews busied themselves removing all lines except a few needed to operate the old canals. Busloads of sightseers roared over deserted roads for a last look, and on Sheek Island archeologists dug in desperate haste for final relics of the lost Indian culture. It too, would soon be buried forever, for the pool would soon be filled. Experts in hydraulics, meanwhile, checked and rechecked their figures.

During the flooding, Montreal harbor and hydo-electric plants downriver at Beauharnois must not under any circumstances be deprived of their usual supply of water. The level of Lake Ontario must not be lowered drastically. And finally shipping through the International Rapids Section of the river must not be suspended for an hour longer than absolutely necessary.

Working with models, engineers had calculated that Montreal harbor needed water at the rate of 240,000 cubic feet per second to maintain navigation. Their original flooding plan therefore invovled opening Iroquois Dam to funnel a collosal 130,000 c.f.s. into the pool. Of this, 240,000 c.f.s. would pass on downriver, via Long Sault Dam. The balance, their figures showed, would raise the water behind the dams to the level required for shipping and generation of power. And while sucking 310,000 c.f.s. through Iroquois would certainly lower the water level in Lake Ontario the drop would nowhere be greater than roughly two and one-half inches.

Work on Canadian end of Power Dam goes ahead behind protection of downstream cofferdam.

Heated concrete is placed on American side of dam
during winter months. Steam is piped to all areas of
structure to allow work to proceed.

Looking along the center line of the Power Dam,
showing the location of the generating units.

Illuminated by extensive batteries of floodlights, construction of the Power Dam goes on 24 hours a day.

Lower bracket and rotor for generator unit being assembled in erection bay at Canadian side of Power Dam.

267 ton generator rotor has been assembled in erection bay and is shown being hoisted and moved to its place in the unit.

150 ton runner assembly being lowered into position for one of the units.

Miles of cable trays will carry for control and power distribution. This is cable control tunnel between power plant and switchyard.

Satisfied, the two agencies had handed their plan to the St. Lawrence River Joint Board of Engineers, a body appointed by the International Joint Commission to look after such things. After checking with the downstream interests, the Joint Board had countered with a proposal slightly different. True, it said Montreal must have its 240,000 c.f.s. but the Ottawa River will be supplying a portion of this. Only 210,000 c.f.s. needs to be passed through Long Sault Dam during the flooding, leaving 100,000 c.f.s. for the pool. This will fill it in 65 hours instead of 96. Navigation will be resumed almost a full day sooner, a fact which means thousands of dollars in pocket for shippers.

This, then, was the skeleton plan. As the appointed day approached its details were sketched in.

Shortly before the end of June engineers would visit the Ottawa River, to measure the flow and decide whether last minute adjustments should be made in the flooding plans to protect Montreal harbor.

At 8:00 a.m. on June 30th all shipping would be cleared from the 14-foot canals. Special crews standing ready along the river bank would then have 24 hours in which to remove power, lighting and telephone lines serving the old canals and locks, to take out the old lock gates, and to lay permanent trash booms across the river.

At precisely 4:00 a.m. on July 1st the lift gates at Iroquois Dam woud rise, allowing 310,000 c.f.s. to stream into the power pool every second. At 6:00 a.m. engineers downstream would begin closing gates at Long Sault Dam. At 8:00 a.m. a tremendous geyser of earth and rock would rise upstream from the powerhouse, as two holes one hundred feet wide were blown in the cofferdam. The detonating team would then leave its bunker on Sheek Island, and drive across the last remaining bridge to the mainland as a tidal wave twenty feet high roared down the dry riverbed to hurl itself against the powerhouse.

All day and long into the night before the blast, as ships dropped anchor above and below the critical area and the people of Cornwall danced in the streets, hundreds of workers scrambled to salvage lock gates and anchor them on long ropes, remove lock machinery, take down poles and wires, and set pontoons in place beneath bridges that would be towed away on the rising waters. Others ranged the countryside, destroying anything that might float down and cause trouble at the intake structure. Bonfires burned late along the new riverbed.

The following morning on the dot of eight o'clock, as a crowd of 10,000 watched from the dike flanking the Canadian powerhouse, Dr. Otto Holden, Ontario Hydro's chief engineer, pressed a button at the bunker on Sheek Island. A great cloud of earth rose from the cofferdam, and boulders shot 1,000 feet into the air. Then, with a roar, came the river, muddy and foam-flecked as it seethed through two great gaps ripped in the dam.

Engineers had expected the water to reach the powerhouses within twenty minutes, in a tidal wave twenty feet high. But not until nearly an hour after the blast did it arrive, in a wave six feet high. Fifteen minutes later, however, the river was eight feet deep behind the intake structure, piling up dead branches, small logs, and a little band of muskrats who swam gamely but could make no headway against the force of the current and at last were sucked through the intake.

By nightfall more than twelve feet of water covered land that had been dry, and the following morning, as the level continued to rise about two inches every hour, Hydro crews put out in rowboats to check for any leaks in the dam.

Three days after the blast, precisely as the Joint Board of Engineers had predicted, the first shipping moved through the new American locks and into the power pool. Flotillas of ocean ships and canallers, each about 100 vessels strong and loaded with iron ore, grain, paper, and package freight, had gathered above and below the pool, waiting for it to be filled. They raised steam now, and formed into queues. The first ones through, on the fourth of July, were a Canadian cargo vessel bearing newsprint, the Humberdoc, and an American canoe piloted by a 70-year old paddler from Northfield, Massachusetts.

There was still dredging to be done before ships drawing 27 feet of water could use the river. But the dream that had formed in the early days of the century had come true. The International Rapids had been conquered.

S.S. "Humberdoc", the first freighter to go through the Eisenhower Lock, July 4, 1958.

142

A last look at what had been the Long Sault Dam. When the temporary cofferdam was breached, this area was completely inundated.

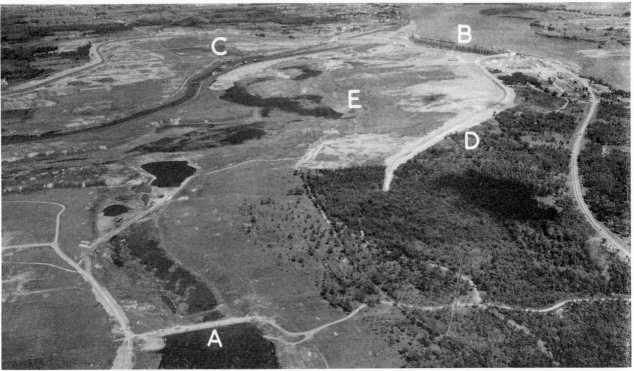

July 1, 1958 inundation area: In this aerial picture, the main forebay area is shown with Cofferdam A in the foreground and the powerhouse in the right background. The blast occured at (A) which was the temporary cofferdam between Sheek and Barnhart Islands. Water rushed down the channel (E) to the powerhouse (B). In the centre background, Cornwall dike above (C) can be seen stretching from the north end of the powerhouse and Barnhart Island dike (D) is visible at the extreme right extending from the south end of the powerhouse. Just below (C) can be seen the Cornwall Canal which was covered deep at the bottom of the resulting power pool.

July 1, 1958 — Cofferdam A-1, upstream from the Power Dam is blasted to initiate inundation of the unwatered area.

Water rushes over the remains of blasted cofferdam A-1, as it pours in to fill the previously unwatered area upstream from the Power Dam and eventually create Lake St. Lawrence.

Water beginning to rise behind Power Dam 1½ hours after blasting of Cofferdam.

This is how it looked 8½ hours after the blast.

Water has now risen to 238 feet above sea level.

Dramatic aerial view of power project. Note the Cofferdam in front of power dam has been breached and water has entered tailrace. Upstream dam has not been breached yet and vast area behind the dam is dry. See photo below.

After Cofferdam A upstream was blasted, flooding the area to form the huge power pool, this is what the area looked like.

During flooding of the area, Chairman Robert Moses of N.Y. Hydro chats with Gov. Averill Harriman of New York State.

Gov. Harriman of New York looks on as Premier Frost of Ontario points out water rising in power pool immediately after blast, July 1, 1958.

On President Eisenhower's visit to the St. Lawrence Seaway and Power Projects, July 11, 1958, Robert Moses, Chairman of New York Hydro is flanked by the President and John Foster Dulles, U.S. Secretary of State.

HISTORIC "FIRST" AT EISENHOWER LOCK. Passenger cruise ship SS SOUTH AMERICAN (right) of the Georgian Bay Line leads its sister ship SS NORTH AMERICAN into Dwight D. Eisenhower Lock on September 6, 1958 with 900 passengers aboard both vessels. These were the first cruise ships to transit the American portion of the St. Lawrence Seaway. The SOUTH AMERICAN was chartered by Cleveland Press and Cleveland Chamber of Commerce and the NORTH AMERICAN sponsored by Chicago Association of Commerce and Industry.

CHAPTER NINE

GREAT LAKES CONNECTING CHANNELS

GREAT LAKES CONNECTING CHANNELS

Officially, construction of the St. Lawrence Seaway began on November 17th, 1954, when the first bundles of dynamite shook loose several tons of earth and rock on the south shore of the St. Lawernce River, opposite Montreal Island.

Unofficially, construction of the Seaway began more than forty years earlier, not on the St. Lawrence and not as an international affair but with a very definite eye to the future.

The year was 1913. It was the end of an era when people worried more about baseball than bombs. In North America 1913 was a boom year. Jobs were plentiful, business was expanding, and the New World was the envy of the Old. Times were good, so good that Canada launched the most ambitious inland waterway project in her history; the Welland Ship Canal.

The Welland Canal was to run for 28 miles, from the eastern end of Lake Erie to the western end of Lake Ontario. Seven locks, far larger than any built to that time, would lower ships in gentle stages down the 326-foot drop past mighty Niagara. The two lakes would then be joined by the world's most up-to-date man-made ditch.

Not until twenty years later was the Welland actually finished. In between times came the first war, when construction was halted entirely, and the 1920's, when it moved along at a quite leisurely pace. But with the canal's completion in 1933 the first link in the Seaway stood ready for service. To its locks and their specifications — 859 feet long by 80 feet wide by 30 feet deep over the sills — would be patterned each of the seven new ones which a quarter of a century later would appear downstream in the St. Lawrence River itself.

Only a minor amount of work was needed at Welland to bring the canal up to the Seaway standards. Already 27 feet of water are available along 17 of its 28 miles. Deepening the balance from 25 to 27 feet could be done, it was decided without disrupting traffic in any way.

By summer of 1956, three excavation contracts had been let on the Welland, and two of them have been completed. By a year later the final three contracts had been awarded. Five hundred men were at work, and about $21 millions were being spent to ready this most westerly Seaway link for the opening in 1959.

According to the bills passed both in Washington and on Parliament Hill in Ottawa, the St. Lawrence Seaway goes no farther than the western end of the Welland Canal. It provides 27-foot navigation to Lake Erie. And there it ends.

But its job no more ends at Lake Erie than does that of a super-highway crossing a state line. Beyond, to the west, lie the three other Great Lakes — Huron, Michigan and Superior — helping make up the largest concentration of fresh water on earth. On either shore, for hundreds of miles, stretch sections of the world's greatest industrial area, an economic collossus whose thousands of parts mesh and interlock to such a degree that they can never be separated by an arbitrary line on a map. In the United States alone, 58 million people live in the 17 states econimically contiguous to the Great Lakes and making up roughly the entire mid-continental area from the Appalachians to the Rocky Mountains.

Ore and coal, newsprint, grain and gasoline, an endless variety of the produce of other continents — and all in quantities totalling more than a hundred million tons a year — are waterborne on the Great Lakes, sometimes using what legally is the Seaway and sometimes not.

Vitally important economically, their ownership shared by both nations, what have come to be known as the Upper Lakes were, nevertheless, considered outside the proper scope of the joint, cost-shared St. Lawrence Seaway. Just as Canada alone dredged the St. Lawrence below Montreal to make it fit for deep-draft navigation, and built and paid for the Welland Canal, the United States by herself shouldered the task of improving to Seaway standards the waterway west from Lake Erie to Lake Superior.

Linking Lake Superior with Lake Huron, the St. Mary's River winds southeast for about 70 miles dropping 22 feet along the way. Most of the fall is centred at the sites of two cities, one in Michigan and one in Ontario and each called Sault Ste. Marie. Here the United States owns four locks. Canada has one.

By contrast, from a navigation standpoint, Lakes Huron and Michigan are really a single body of water. Connecting them and leading to Chicago, the Straits of Mackinac are broad and deep. Between the two lakes there is no perceptible flow, and their surfaces are at the same level.

Lake Huron empties, however, in a much more complicated fashion. To reach Lake Erie, ship masters steer an 87-mile course along an often tortuous channel through the St. Clair River, Lake St. Clair and the Detroit River. Here, although the water drops about eight feet between the two lakes, the fall is gradual, and the rivers free flowing throughout their entire length. No locks have ever been necessary.

The Great Lakes themselves, of course, are deep enough to float the largest ships. Even Erie, the shallowest, goes down 210 feet while Superior, the deepest, finds bottom in some places at 1300 feet. The supreme test of a lake captain's skill comes, however, when he enters the connecting channels. These are narrow, twisting and shallow, studded with reefs and shoals and laced with tricky currents. No voyage from the lakehead ever becomes routine, even though the volume of traffic that moves through these channels is staggering.

During fifteen recent years, for example, cargoes through the St. Mary's River were never less than 92 million tons a season. One year they reached 133 million tons, more than Panama and Suez and four times more than the Seaway itself was expected to handle, at least for a start. Moving east there was grain. Moving west there was coal. There were oil products, forest products, and limestone. Most of all there was iron ore.

No other commodity has become so important to Great Lakes shipping as iron ore. From the vast range of Mesabi, it flows out of Duluth in an endless stream to feed steel mills in the South Chicago area, in Detroit, along the shore of Lake Erie and in the Youngstown-Pittsburgh area. All of the iron ore from Lake Superior to United States ports passes down the St. Mary's River to Lake Huron. Part of it is siphoned off through the Straits of Mackinac to South Chicago. The rest moves on through the St. Clair River, Lake St. Clair and the Detroit River, to Detroit, Cleveland and to other ports on Lake Erie.

Three-quarters of the 30,000 ships that pass through the "Soo" locks each season have carried iron ore, and if no other goods moved on the lakes, iron ore alone would long ago have been important enough to warrant improvements along the connecting channels. As it turned out, ore was supported by coal and by products of farm and forest until by the mid-1950's nearly 25 per cent of the total waterborne commerce of the United States, including all ocean ports and inland waterways, was borne on the Great Lakes.   ....

The United States began improving the channels connecting these lakes more than a century ago. It was during the summer of 1856 that the Corps of Engineers first attacked the problem, digging a 14-foot shipping track through Lake George in the lower St. Mary's River. Thirteen years later a channel 11-1/2 feet deep was open for business between Lakes Superior and Huron, and by the turn of the century, with the first large locks operating in the St. Mary's River, controlling depths of 18 feet were available all the way from Lake Superior to Lake Erie.

Sparked mainly by the iron ore of Mesabi, more digging during the first few decades of the twentieth century furnished shipowners with a far better channel in the upper lakes than they had in the St. Lawrence River itself. As Congress debated for the last time the merits of the Seaway, in fact, deep-draft loaded ore car-

Dipper dredge "Midland" shown just as the bucket leaves the water while dredging in the Cornwall, Ont. area.

riers were sailing from Duluth to Cleveland through channels deepened to 25 feet. Not quite so roomy, controlling depths upbound were only 21 feet, but then ships were lighter on the return run, and drew less water.

In most places vessels have always used the same stretch of water to pass each other going different ways through these channels. But here and there are separate routes. In the lower St. Mary's River, the West Neebish Channel carries traffic downbound, and the Middle Neebish upbound, past Neebish Island. Similarly the Livingstone Channel, in the lower Detroit River, is reserved for ships steaming westward from Lake Huron to Lake Erie, while Amherstburg Channel is used by vessels heading east.

By June, 1955, the United States had laid out $96 million to improve the waterway between Lakes Erie and Superior. In the decade following, assuming Congress voted the money, it was to spend another $150 million.

For one thing, the fact that the Seaway was no longer just a dream but would soon bring 27-foot navigation westward to Lake Erie had generated a clamor for comparable facilities all the way to the lakehead.

Just as important as the Seaway, moreover, were the inflexible economics of the shipping business. These had bred radical changes in vessel design. Ships were getting bigger, and faster. Before World War II, the largest in the American Great Lakes fleet averaged about 600 feet long and drew between 21 and 22 feet of water. During the war and after it, nearly fifty new ones entered the trade, a few of them as long as 710 feet and drawing almost 27 feet.

Except when the water was unusually high, none of these new ships could take on a full cargo. By 1954, for example, nearly a third of the U.S. lakers had maximum allowable drafts of more than 24 feet. But at low water the controlling safe draft, always a little less than the actual depth of the channel, was only 22.3 feet. Thus for most of the season these ships were forced to load at reduced drafts. It costs very little more to operate a ship fully loaded than partly loaded, so this meant a major out-of-pocket loss to shipowners and, in turn, to the businessmen and the farmers who used the waterways.

Realizing that with each passing year the need for further improvements to the connecting channels was becoming more urgent, The Public Works Committees of both the U.S. House of Representatives and the Senate had adopted resolutions in 1953, authorizing the Board of Engineers for Rivers and Harbors to review earlier reports on the channels, find out what should be done and how.

Studies were launched by the Corps of Engineers, studies which ended in a report suggesting that chan-

Dipper dredge "Monarch" dredging the channel about four miles east of Cornwall, Ont.

The Paraiso, claimed to be the world's largest dipper dredge, is lowered in the Eisenhower Lock on its journey from the Panama Canal to the South Cornwall Channel.

nels be provided with controlling safe drafts of 25.5 feet at low-water. This, said the Corps, would permit most of the fleet to carry full loads about 88 per cent of the time during the entire navigation season. In Great Lakes trade alone, without even considering the benefits to shipping entering and leaving the waterway via the St. Lawrence Seaway, it would generate transportation savings of nearly $10 millions a year.

The report of the Corps was accepted by the Board of Engineers for River and Harbors. Govenrors of the eight states bordering the lakes greeted it enthusiastically. In 1955, backed by a favorable recommendation of the Secretary of the Army, it arrived in Congress. There it was passed, to be signed on March 21, 1956 by President Eisenhower.

The Blatnik Act, as the report is called now, provided for a vast, seven-year program to reshape the face of the connecting channels. Under it a single new lock, the Poe, would be built to replace an older one of the same name at Sault Ste. Marie. Much more important, roughly 45 million yards of earth and rock would be dredged in the channels. Work began in the spring of 1957, and if Congress each year voted the necessary money, would probably be finished by about mid-1964.

Within the overall plan to provide a safe draft of 25.5 feet when the ruling level reaches what hydraulic engineers call the "low-water datum plane", shipping routes were to be dredged to depths ranging anywhere from 27 to 30 feet.

The precise amount would depend, in each case, on circumstances. Every foot of channel had been studied to determine the allowance needed between the actual depth and the safe draft. Because of the constant danger of rock being turned up and ripping a ship's hull, an extra clearance was allowed in rock bottom over that in soft bottom. Engineers checked the fluctuations of the lake levels above their respective datum planes. They allowed for the "squat" of vessels when underway, and for their "scend" due to waves in exposed locations.

Out of their calculations came the plan, which called for dredging about 130 miles of channel, ranging from 300 feet to 1,200 feet wide.

In the St. Mary's River, between Lakes Superior and Huron, 63 miles of channel would be deepened. Shoals would be removed from Gros Cap to Crab Island, and anchorage areas carved out at Point Iroquois Shoal and in Lake Nicolet.

Dredges working in the Straits of Mackinac, between Lakes Michigan and Huron, would remove shoals between Mackinac Island and Round Island, and also remove Poe Reef Shoal.

Farther down the waterway, in the St. Clair River, 46.2 miles of channels were earmarked for attention. In

Lake St. Clair, dredges would deepen 17.2 miles. In the Detroit River, which leads into Lake Erie, 32 miles of channel were to be deepened. And east of the Detroit River Light, 8.7 miles would be deepened, and the Pellee Island Shoal would be removed.

Most of the work would be done in sheltered waters. But at the west end of Lake Erie, at and below the mouth of the Detroit River, and at the foot of Lake Huron approaching the head of the St. Clair River, the channel areas to be dredged would be exposed to storm waves from the open lake. Areas to be dredged at the upper end of the St. Mary's River would also be exposed to waves.

But the main problem, with which engineers expected to wrestle in scheduling and completing their work, was neither storm nor fast-running water. Instead, it was traffic.

If shipping traffic spreads evenly through the Great Lakes season, simple arithmetic shows that a vessel will slip through the St. Mary's River every 13 minutes, through the Detroit River every fifteen minutes, and through the St. Clair River every seventeen minutes. This posed delicate dredging problems. Schedules must be arranged so as not to interfere with the traffic. Drilling and blasting, moreover, must be carried on with the utmost care, to guard against rocks and earth being thrown into the shipping lanes, where every inch of depth was vital.

Added complications arose from the fact that neither the West Neebish nor the Livingstone Channels, each downbound, was wide enough to take traffic while dredging, sweeping and clearing were going on. Hence they would have to be closed while the dredges fell to.

This would mean, in turn, that top priority must be given to deepening the western ends of the Middle Neebish and Amherstburg channels. Only then would it become possible to open these two upbound routes for two-way traffic during the time that the downbound ones were sealed off from commerce.

That was the plan, and Congress voted $5 millions in 1956 to begin the work. By 1960, it was estimated the upbound Middle Neebish and Amherstburg channels could be completed to a minimum controlling depth of 25 feet, and in the shipping season that followed they would handle two-way traffic at that depth. Work in the other channels could then be completed from Lake Erie to Lake Superior in time for navigation in 1964.

There would be an inevitable lag between opening of the St. Lawrence Seaway and completion of the Upper Lakes connecting links. But then, the world had waited half a century for the Seaway; another few years upstream was not too hardly crucial.

The dredging called for in this vast program would be by far the largest ever undertaken on the Great Lakes.

That it would be worth every penny was confirmed in the report of the U.S. Corps of Engineers. This report considered only Great Lakes traffic, and it showed that the huge traffic in such bulk commodities as iron ore, stone, coal, grain and petroleum products would continue at least at their existing rates well beyond the economic life span of the improvement plan, which was placed at 50 years.

All of these bulk materials, moreover, would continue to move mainly by ship, since they are the type of product ideally suited to waterborne transportation.

Iron ore, the report estimated, would continue to be shipped from Lake Superior at about 81 million tons annually. Coal traffic was expected to increase from 52 million to 62 million, stone from 22 million to 35 million.

Prospects for a special program to modernize the Great Lakes fleet also appeared bright. Shipowners had said that if the connecting channels were not improved, it was unlikely that many more ships of the largest class would be built; replacements, they predicted, would generally be limited to vessels between 600 and 650 feet long. With deeper channels, on the other hand, more ships of the 650-700 foot class would be laid down, and from these would come large savings in transportation costs.

Even more important, the Seaway in its broadest sense — the fabulous deep waterway from the Atlantic to the head of the Great Lakes — would finally be a fact.

A dredge at work on a Seaway Channel.

CHAPTER TEN

SHIPPING AND TOLLS

SAILING DISTANCES BETWEEN LAKES AND SEAWAY POINTS

	DULUTH	MILWAUKEE	CHICAGO	SAULT ST. MARIE	DETROIT	TOLEDO	LORAIN	CLEVELAND	BUFFALO	PORT COLBORNE	PORT WELLER	OGDENSBURG	IROQUOIS LOCK	EISENHOWER LOCK	SNELL LOCK	BEAUHARNOIS LOCKS	ST. CATHERINE LOCK	ST. LAMBERT LOCK	MONTREAL HARBOR	QUEBEC
SEVEN ISLANDS	1861	1703	1768	1466	1135	1128	1071	1051	913	891	864	647	637	613	609	559	539	531	527	367
QUEBEC	1494	1336	1401	1099	768	761	704	684	546	524	497	280	270	246	242	192	172	164	160	0
MONTREAL HARBOR	1334	1176	1241	939	608	601	544	524	386	364	337	129	110	86	82	32	12	4	0	160
ST. LAMBERT LOCK	1330	1172	1237	935	604	597	540	520	382	360	333	116	106	82	78	28	8	0	4	164
ST. CATHERINE LOCK	1322	1164	1229	927	596	589	532	512	374	352	325	108	98	74	70	20	0	8	12	172
BEAUHARNOIS LOCKS	1302	1144	1209	907	576	569	512	492	354	332	305	88	78	54	50	0	20	28	32	192
SNELL LOCK	1252	1094	1159	857	526	519	462	442	304	282	255	38	28	4	0	50	70	78	82	242
EISENHOWER LOCK	1248	1090	1155	853	522	515	458	438	300	278	251	34	24	0	4	54	74	82	86	246
IROQUOIS LOCK	1224	1066	1131	829	498	491	434	414	276	254	227	10	0	24	28	78	98	106	110	270
OGDENSBURG	1216	1058	1123	821	490	483	426	406	268	246	217	0	10	34	38	88	108	116	129	280
PORT WELLER	997	839	904	602	271	264	207	187	49	27	0	217	227	251	255	305	325	333	337	497
PORT COLBORNE	970	812	877	575	244	237	180	160	22	0	27	246	254	278	282	332	352	360	364	524
CLEVELAND	833	675	740	438	108	96	28	0	176	160	187	406	414	438	442	492	512	520	524	684
LORAIN	816	658	723	422	91	72	0	28	197	180	207	426	434	458	462	512	532	540	544	704
TOLEDO	781	622	688	385	54	0	72	96	254	237	264	483	491	515	519	569	589	597	601	761
DETROIT	726	568	633	331	0	54	91	108	261	244	271	490	498	522	526	576	596	604	608	768
SAULT ST. MARIE	394	349	414	0	331	385	422	438	592	575	602	821	829	853	857	907	927	935	939	1099
CHICAGO	808	85	0	414	633	688	723	740	893	877	904	1123	1131	1155	1159	1209	1229	1237	1241	1401
MILWAUKEE	743	0	85	349	568	622	658	675	828	812	839	1058	1066	1090	1094	1144	1164	1172	1176	1336
DULUTH	0	743	808	394	726	781	816	833	986	970	997	1216	1224	1248	1252	1302	1322	1330	1334	1494

SHIPPING AND TOLLS

On a chill December day in 1957, as tugs hooted a greeting, the largest ocean-going dry cargo ship ever built in Canada coasted down freshly-greased ways at one of the great yards that line the waterfront in east-end Montreal. She was christened the Alexander T. Wood.

That same week, in New York, officials of one of the world's largest shipping lines announced plans for opening a trade route between the North American ports of Chicago, Milwaukee, Detroit, Toronto and Montreal, and the South American ports of Aruba, Curacao, La Guiara and Maracaibo. For this, they said, they would use at least six and possibly as many as nine 9,000-ton freighters.

At about the same time, in Germany, a group of shipowners was busy plotting the first Montreal voyage of a new 5,600-ton freighter which had just finished fitting out. And in harbor at Port de Bouc, France, the hulls of two sleek, 7,500-ton motorships destined for Great Lakes trading were taking shape.

In Oslo and Rotterdam, in London and in Hamburg, in all the world's great ports, the men who build ships and the men who run them were preparing for the 1959 opening of the St. Lawrence Seaway.

Consider the facts which sparked their plans:

The eight states adjoining the Seaway on the American side contained 35% of the population of the United States. Over one-half of the value added to products by manufacturing throughout the entire nation was attributable to the industries of those states.

Statistics on the Canadian side were equally impressive. Over 60% of Canada's people lived in Ontario and Quebec, the two provinces adjoining the Seaway. Nearly 80% of Canada's manufacturing and processing capacity was located there.

Perhaps the richest in the world, these regions were now to be finally linked with the sea by a deep waterway, an intricate system of locks and canals which would upset all the established transportation patterns, both on water and on land.

The 21 locks of the old canal system between Montreal and Lake Ontario had a controlling depth of 14 feet. They could handle vessels no longer than 253 feet and with beams not exceeding 44 feet. Out of them grew a special breed of ship, called the canaller, whose deadweight capacity was less than 3,000 tons. Seagoing vessels of the general cargo type could carry about 1,500 tons.

By contrast the new Seaway locks were immense. They could handle ships as long as 730 feet with beams of up to 74 feet. Large bulk carriers with a deadweight of over 25,000 tons would now be able, as a result, to leave the Great Lakes. For the first time, they could sail to Montreal. They could go even further, to the Lower St. Lawrence and the ports there. Ocean-going

ships carrying general cargo, moreover, could be handled in sizes up to about 9,000 tons deadweight in service between the Great Lakes and overseas ports.

The implications of this change were threefold. In the first place, it would no longer be necessary to transship cargoes into small canallers. That would save money. So would the fact that large ships could operate for the first time in the river, because it costs less per ton of capacity to run a big ship than a small one. And finally, the smaller number of locks — seven instead of twenty-one — could save shipowners up to $1,000 per trip in vessel time.

What would all this mean?

The St. Lawrence Canals were handling roughly ten million tons of cargo between mid-April and mid-November in the years just prior to the Seaway's opening. About one-third of this was in grain, while iron ore, petroleum and petroleum products, and coal and coke accounted for about 15% each, and woodpulp, pulpwood and general cargoes for most of the balance.

What precise pattern would form on the completed Seaway no one could really be sure as construction entered its final stages. Tolls had been recommended, but never tested. How much traffic they would attract and how much they would turn away — these were the great imponderables.

But earlier estimates provided some yardsticks to gauge the impetus shipping would receive along the river by reason of the cuts in transportation costs. At least five of these had been prepared and published by, among others, Canada's Department of Trade and Commerce and the U.S. St. Lawrence Seaway Development Corporation.

No one of these estimates agreed with any of the others, but the range within which most calculations fell was a fairly narrow one. It called for traffic of between thirty and forty million tons for the first few years, rising to between forty-five and fifty-five millions by 1970. One estimate, made by the U.S. Department of Commerce, was far higher than any of the others, but its forecast of at least 58 million tons and at most 84 millions was based on petroleum and iron ore shipments much bigger than most other experts considered possible.

Of all the products that the new deep waterway would carry, grain shaped up among the largest.

In the years just before the Seaway, about half of Canada's grain exports had moved into world markets through either Vancouver and other British Columbia ports, or Port Churchill, on Hudson Bay. The other half had been waterborne on the Great Lakes, moving out of Fort William and Port Arthur aboard huge lake ships. Some of the grain had sailed only as far as Midland and Port McNicol on Lake Huron's Georgian Bay, travelling from there by rail to Montreal, Three Rivers, Sorel and Quebec City on the St. Lawrence, and to

Halifax and Saint John on the Eastern seaboard. But most of it had moved farther down the waterway, to cities like Port Colborne, Kingston and Prescott, before being trans-shipped either into the fleet of small canallers capable of navigating the 14-foot St. Lawrence canals or, again, into boxcars.

Also taken to market in a variety of ways was the harvest of the American mid-west. About a quarter of it moved out of Duluth in the holds of the great lakers, sailing to Buffalo on Lake Erie or Oswego on Lake Ontario, and there either transferred to barges and ferried down the Erie Canal to Albany and New York, or moved directly by rail to Baltimore. More than 40% moved south, by rail and by the Mississippi River, to New Orleans, Galveston and oher Gulf Coast ports. About 20% was shipped out of Seattle and other Pacific coast ports, and less than 15% travelled east by rail from Chicago all the way to Baltimore and Philadelphia.

The St. Lawrence canal system itself had carried between three and four million tons of grain. With the Seaway, and delimination of trans-shipment costs, this would rise to ten million, and perhaps even higher, transportation experts predicted.

Trans-shipment had meant unloading the great 500,000-bushel capacity lake carriers and reloading the grain into boxcars or 100,000-bushel canallers. It meant higher rates for sending products by rail or by small ship. And so by eliminating cargo transfers and slashing rates for part of the trip covered earlier on land or through shallow-draft canals, the Seaway would cut grain shipping costs in two ways.

For example, it cost eight cents to carry a bushel of wheat from Fort William to Toronto aboard a laker, a trip of some 900 miles. But it had cost another eight cents to take it on by rail or canal ship to the Port of Montreal, 300 miles away. Experts therefore estimated that the Seaway would save someone — farmer, shipper or buyer — between three and five cents on every bushel. In the grain business, where harvests are measured in the hundreds of millions of bushels, those would be handsome savings, large enough to funnel into the St. Lawrence all the Canadian spring and fall grain that had moved to eastern ports part way by rail.

For the first time, moreover, products grown in the American mid-west would move on the St. Lawrence. Wheat, oats, barley and other grains are all of low value per unit of weight. They are ideal for mechanized bulk handling, and are practically self-trimming in the holds of ships. Even for short distances, water transport has always been preferred — so long as the price was right. But until the Seaway, largely because of trans-shipment but partly, too, because there were few ocean ships in the lakes looking for grain to top off cargoes of other goods, the price was too high and grain moved to market through other channels. For a century and a half, Canada had beckoned to the middle-west to direct some of its trade through the St. Lawrence. Now it would do just that.

If grain was to be important on the Seaway, iron ore would be equally so.

Past economic development had produced North America's heaviest concentration of steel mills on and adjacent to the south shore of Lake Erie. There in the glow of the open hearth lay the core of America's industrial greatness. Fed by the vast Mesabi range, its growth had spawned the largest iron ore trade in the world. Ore in fantastic quantities moved aboard large bulk carriers from the western end of Lake Superior to the huge industrial markets of the east and their hub city, Cleveland. Rarely had it ever moved between Lake Erie and the Sea.

Now this was to be altered. The great iron ranges of Northern Minnesota and Michigan were still decades away from exhaustion. But the tremendous growth of the steel industry had meant that they could no longer maintain their predominant position. Increasingly, the iron riches of a long trough, straddling the Quebec-Labrador border north of the Lower St. Lawrence port of Sept Iles, would be called upon to meet the expected demand.

It was, in fact, discovery of this Canadian ore at a time when the United States needed it that finally tipped the balance in favor of building the Seaway. Until then the St. Lawrence had been, economically, a Canadian river. True, Ohio coal moved to Montreal and the Lower St. Lawrence, and return shipments brought Canadian woodpulp and newsprint into the mid-west. But the main job of the St. Lawrence lay for years in ferrying Canadian grain to world markets, and much of the long-standing American opposition to deepening the waterway had always focussed on that point.

But when the Labrador ore fields were found, and developed largely with American capital, the enticing prospect of shipments to U.S. steel mills in the Lake States proved irresistible. At one stroke the potential traffic was raised by at least half. Opposition swiftly changed to active support. Small canal ships began taking Labrador ore through the old canals in 1954. That year they carried 300,000 tons. With the Seaway's completion, ten million tons were expected to move west.

Grain and iron ore — one moving east and the other west — were expected to develop a two-way traffic amounting to 20 million tons, or roughly two-thirds of all the cargo moving along the Seaway during the first few years after its completion. Moreover, the possibility of an integrated trade took shape. Eastward from the lakehead, via an enlarged fleet of bulk carriers, would come grain, most of it to unload at Montreal, but some, perhaps, to move farther down the river, for plans were being laid to build new elevators so that ocean vessels could load at ports like Baie Comeau and Seven Islands. Back from Seven Islands, in the holds of the same inland fleet, would come the iron ore and from Baie Comeau, newsprint.

The glamor of the Seaway, of course, had always been fixed not on such mundane things as grain and iron ore but on the vision of foreign flag shipping lying at anchor off ports in the mid-continent, the vision of a vast increase in direct trade between the heartland of North America and countries far away.

This too, there would be.

No one, of course, would ever see the "Queen Mary" or the "United States" steaming in the Great Lakes, or any of the new super-tankers which could carry enough oil on a single trip to run Canada's entire economy for a day. These great ships draw too much water for the Seaway. Only a handful of the world's ports were deep enough to berth them and in any event, so far as passenger liners were concerned, no owner depending so heavily on speed would stay long in business if he wasted his ship's time being locked through canals.

But for most shipping, for the vast fleet of vagabond tramps that wander the oceans of the world and for package freighters sailing on fixed schedules over regular routes, the Seaway's 27-foot channel would be deep enough and would generate a sharp increase in trade.

Great Lakes-Overseas trade was actually a comparatively recent phenomenon. Regular, scheduled sailings were pioneered by Norway's Fjell Line in 1933. Oranje, of Holland, joined the service five years later, but trade grew slowly during the lean 1930's, and then of course halted entirely with the outbreak of war.

Re-established in 1945 by the same two European lines, it grew at a fantastic rate during the decade that followed. Driving alongside the Soulange Canal, near Montreal, a motorist could almost smell the salt water by the summer of 1954, as time and again he swept past another trim, stubby little foreign freighter.

That year the flags of more than a dozen overseas lines were seen on the Great Lakes, and 120 foreign ships shuttled back and forth from Europe carrying more than 780,000 tons of cargo. Three years later nineteen lines were in the trade, ferrying almost one million tons.

Reflecting both the products and the needs of the massive industrial empires of Detroit, Chicago, Toronto, Buffalo, Toledo, Cleveland, Milwaukee and Hamilton, their cargoes were incredibly varied. On any given day at the peak of the shipping season iron and steel products, automobiles, machinery, electrical equipment, clay and earthen products, glass, wines, liquor — a fantastic assortment of the goods essential to modern living — could be found moving up and down the waterway.

As the date approached for the Seaway opening, experts predicted that Great Lakes-overseas trade would certainly treble within a few years. Some economists were even more optimistic: they maintained that some day cargoes totalling closed to 25 million tons would move to distant continents via the St. Lawrence.

The Seaway would still have its faults as a world trade route, they admitted, faults such as the round-about entrance to the St. Lawrence estuary and the twisting pattern of the Great Lakes. But despite these limitations a sharply increased trade was foreseen over the old routes and probably, too, extensions to the east and west coasts of South America, the East coast of Africa, the Middle East, India and perhaps Indonesia and other East Indies Islands.

Trade with Northern Europe would still account for the bulk of the overseas business, for it was here that the advantages of the St. Lawrence would always be greatest. The water haul from most lake ports to Northwestern Europe, for example, is actually shorter than the combined railway-ocean shipping routes involved in transport from the lakes via U.S. Coastal ports.

Aside from grain, iron ore and assorted overseas cargoes, the Seaway would also handle a large and growing volume of other products, among them coal and coke, crude oil and petroleum products, pulpwood, woodpulp and paper. These alone, in fact, would probably account for 25% of the Seaway tonnage, or around seven or eight million tons.

The logic of economics, moreover, was working more and more in favor of water transport. Industries were growing larger, and requiring bigger flows of raw material and finished products. With each passing year, more commodities were being shipped in quantities large enough to be classed as bulk cargoes. Traffic possibilities were emerging which could hardly have taken into account as recently as, say, 1950.

The key factor, of course, would be tolls.

In both the Wiley-Dondero Act, authorizing American participation in the Seaway, and the St. Lawrence Seaway Authority Act, authorizing Canadian participation, it says clearly that the great project must pay for itself. Not only operating costs, but interest and amortization of capital must be recovered from tolls to be charged the users of the Seaway. The Canadian and American acts in setting a deadline for repayment are similar — the entire expense of building the deep waterway must be paid for out of tolls within 50 years, or by A.D. 2009.

Lionel Chevrier, president of Canada's St. Lawrence Seaway Authority until he left in 1957 to re-enter politics, outlined the immense difficulties facing the two tolls committees that had been formed, one in Canada and one in the United States.

"If we could estimate either the number of ships entering the Seaway, or the aggregate ship tonnage or the aggregate cargo tonnage," he said, "simple arithmetic would then give us a uniform rate, whether by ship passage, by ship measurement or by cargo tonnage. Unfortunately, it is far from being that simple.

"The Seaway being a canal on which tolls are to be charged, comparison is immediately suggested with Panama and Suez. Physically the resemblance is there but economically it will be, I suggest, quite different, and we should be wary of drawing any parallels between toll policies. Panama and Suez are so located with respect to the great land masses of the world that they provide routes saving many thousands of miles over the nearest alternatives. At the same time, they can be by-passed. Ships entering them in one direction are not obliged to return by the same route. This situation is reflected in their toll charges. On the Panama Canal, for example, light vessels are charged 80% of the toll of loaded vessels.

"The Seaway's geographic position is quite different. It will afford a route to the Great Lakes for the ships of the world. But it is not a meeting point of many different trade routes. It cannot form a part of a triangular route which a vessel can use only once before returning to its starting point. Vessels entering the Seaway must leave by the same route, a fact which will almost certainly require a different toll policy on light vessels than used on either Panama or Suez. The objective of that policy must be to encourage vessels to enter the Seaway, for traffic can only develop if ships are on hand.

"Another geographic feature of the Seaway is that it is paralleled by rail and highway routes, which will offer competition for certain types of local traffic and, in combination with ocean routes from the Atlantic ports, for overseas traffic. Perhaps, then, we can visualize the Seaway's economic position most clearly by likening it to a toll highway. Just as a toll highway, it will offer certain definite advantages for the movement of traffic, provided these are not defeated by too restrictive a toll policy, in which case traffic would take to the competing routes.

"The Seaway administration cannot be blind to the effect of its toll policy on its traffic. All the more so, since its annual costs are largely outside its power to vary with the traffic offering. This, I believe, will be the best assurance that the toll policy will be fair and reasonable to all traffic. The Seaway must act as any progressive business under competitive conditions and price its services so as to develop the maximum volume of traffic. Rates low enough to attract business and yet high enough to pay the costs — the two halves of the perennial pricing dilemma, and yet about the only guideposts available to the United States Tolls Committee and the Canadian Tolls Committees as they opened public hearings in mid-1957 in Washington, Chicago and Ottawa".

Seaway agencies in both countries had agreed that a composite rate — one charge on the registered tonnage of each ship, and a second and higher one on the actual cargo being carried — would be better than the system at Panama and Suez, where all ships are subject to uniform toll rate regardless of whether or not they are loaded. Now, shipowners, shipping agencies, and in fact anyone with an interest in the subject, was invited to state his case.

Over the weeks that followed a steady procession of companies and other organizations arrived to present their views. Some wanted high tolls. Some wanted no tolls, contending that the waterway had always been free and should remain so. Most fell somewhere in between.

The toll structure recommended by the American and Canadian committees several months after hearings ended measured up to what most shipper had expected. It set out several different rates, depending on how far a ship was going.

Shippers using the entire Seaway, from Montreal to Lake Erie, would be assessed a basic six cents per gross registered ton of the ship, plus 45 cents for each ton of bulk cargo and 95 cents for each ton of general cargo.

That was the package deal. A vessel sailing between Montreal and Lake Ontario, and not using the Welland Canal into Lake Erie, would pay only four cents per gross registered ton, and a slightly lower rate on its cargo — 40 cents per ton of bulk and 90 cents per ton of general.

Since a vast volume of shipping, such as iron ore, moves through the Welland alone, and never comes near the St. Lawrence River, a separate rate was set for this, the most westerly of the Seaway's seven locks. There the charge was to be two cents per gross registered ton, plus two cents on each ton of bulk cargo and five cents on each on of general cargo.

The tolls committees set up special split rates for ships going only partway through the Welland or partway up river between Montreal and Lake Ontario. They also defined bulk and general cargoes. The first would include such items as grain and grain products, loose or in sacks, ores and minerals, liquids in ships' tanks, pulpwood, poles and logs, woodpulp, waste paper, iron and steel, and scrap and pig iron. To compete against railways and truckers, for traffic in America and Canadian domestic package freight, the Seaway authorities would classify this, too, as bulk cargo. All other products would move through the waterway under the higher general cargo charge.

The two committees have calculated these rates, the charge per gross ton designed to pay all operating and maintenance costs and the charge on cargo to meet interest payments and retire the debt — on the assumption that traffic totaling 225 million tons would move between Montreal and Lake Erie as soon as the Seaway opened. Thereafter, they figured, it would gradually rise, reaching by 1968 the workable capacity of the waterway, 50 million tons. For the Welland Canal, considered separately, upbound and downbound tonnage was estimated at 40 million tons in 1959, and 60 million by 1968.

These estimates were reflected in the rates suggested by the committees. They decided that for the first ten years it could well be that revenue would fall short of costs. But any deficit during that first decade would be made up once traffic hit the peak in 1968, and the entire cost of the project — $471 million — would be cleared, on schedule, by the year 2008.

Whatever its cargo or its destination every ship using the St. Lawrence waterway to be guided by the most comprehensive system of marine traffic cops ever developed, at seven locks between Montreal and Lake Ontario.

To make this work the Seaway had been divided into several divisions, with radio despatchers established at four major locks — Cote Ste. Catherine, Beauharnois, Eisenhower and Iroquois. A ship approaching any of these would radio its position from about 20 miles out. The despatcher would then plot the position, and if a line-up had formed at the lock tell the captain to anchor. Once a ship passed through a lock it would move into another control area, its movements plotted by models on charts almost yard by yard every minute it was inside the 115-mile waterway.

SCHEDULE OF TOLLS
Subject to change in the manner prescribed by law.

PART 1. Definitions.

1. "Vessel" means any watercraft of whatever description which is used, or is capable of being used, or is intended to be used as a means of transportation by water.
2. "Pleasure craft" means a vessel however propelled that is used exclusively for pleasure and does not carry passengers.
3. "Cargo" means all goods aboard a vessel except those carried as ship's fuel or stores or crew and passengers' effects whether carried as revenue or non-revenue freight or carried for the vessel owner.
   (a) For purposes of assessment of tolls, the following commodities ars classified as *bulk cargo:*
      (i) Grain and grain products, including flour and mill feed, loose or in sacks.
      (ii) Ores and minerals (crude, screened, sized or concentrated, but not otherwise processed) including ore concentrates in sacks, sand, stone and gravel, coal and choke.
      (iii) Liquids moving in ships' tanks.
      (iv) Pulpwood, poles and logs, loose or bundled.
      (v) Woodpulp, loose or in bales.
      (vi) Waste paper.
      (vii) Iron and steel scrap and pig iron.
      (viii) Domestic package freight.
   (b) All commodities not included in the above defini-bulk cargo are classified as *general cargo.*
4. "Passenger" means any person being transported through the Seaway and who has paid a fare for passage.
5. "Ton" — unless otherwise stated, shall mean a unit of weight of 2,000 pounds.
6. "Toll" means the total assessment levied against a vessel, its cargo and revenue passengers for complete or partial transit covering a single trip in one direction.

PART 2. Tolls.

All vessels or craft using the Seaway, except units certified as working for the Authority or the Corporation, shall pay a toll for passage as prescribed below:
(b) For partial transit of the Seaway, the charges will be as follows:
   (i) for the Montreal to Lake Ontario Section, 15 percent per lock of the toll assessed for complete passage, but the value not to exceed the charge for complete passage;
   (ii) for the Lake Ontario to Lake Erie Section, 50 percent of the toll assessed for complete passage;
   (iii) for pleasure craft $2.00 per vessel per each lock transited;
   (iv) for all other vessel $4.00 per vessel per each lock transited.
(c) Tolls for the Montreal to Lake Ontario Section to be payable 71 percent in Canadian funds and 29 percent in the United States funds. For other than through passages, payments for passages through locks in Canada to be made in Canadian dollars and payments for passages through locks in the United States to be paid in United States dollars.
(d) All tolls for the transit of the Welland Canal will be payable in Canadian dollars and will accrue to the St. Lawrence Seaway Authority.
(e) Cargo weight and description shall be indicated on the ship's manifest or similar document, copy of which will be supplied for toll purposes, with the proviso that the Seaway entity shall have the right to make such inspection and verification of the cargo which it considers necessary for the purposes of determining tolls payable.

TOLLS

	Total Passage	Montreal to Lake Ontario	Lake Ontario to Lake Erie (Welland Canal)
(a) The toll for transiting the Seaway is a composite one, comprising:			
(i) charge per gross registered ton, as per national registry of the vessel, applicable whether the vessel is wholly or partially laden, or is in ballast	6¢	4¢	2¢
(ii) charge per ton of cargo as evidenced by ship's manifest or similar receipt or document, as follows:			
— bulk cargo	42¢	40¢	2¢
— general cargo	95¢	90¢	5¢
(iii) passenger	$30.00	$14.00	$16.00
(iv) pleasure craft — through passage for each section — minimum charge subject to the provisions of items (i) and (ii)	$60.00	$28.00	$32.00
(v) all other vessels — through passage for each section — minimum charge subject to the provisions of items (i) and (ii)	$7.50	$3.50	$4.00

163

CHAPTER ELEVEN

HARBOR FACILITIES

HARBOR FACILITIES

QUEBEC

BERTHS — 40
... **Length of Berthing** — 34,240 feet
... **Minimum Depths** — From 20 to 40 feet
... **Shedded Berths** — 12 (Sheds "A" and 29 are each two-berth sheds)
... **Open Berths** — 28

TRANSIT SHEDS — 10 (2 are two-storey)
... **Floor Area** — 766,000 square feet

GRAIN ELEVATORS — 1
... **Storage Capacity** — 4,000,000 bushels
... **Receiving Capacity** — 25,000 bushels per hour from cars, 40,000 bushels per hour from vessels
... **Shipping Capacity** — 90,000 bushels per hour to vessels, 20,000 bushels per hour to cars
... **Number of Grain Berths** — 4
... **Number of Marine Towers** — 3

REFRIGERATED WAREHOUSE
... **Capacity Main Warehouse** — 528,000 cubic feet
... **Capacity Fish House** — 1,000,000 pounds

TERMINAL RAILWAY
... **Trackage** — 23 miles, serving all deepsea berths
... **Switching Locomotives** — 3 diesel-electric locomotives, 550 H.P., 80 tons
... **Rail Connections** — Canadian National Railways and Canadian Pacific Railway

CRANES
... **Floating Crane** — 75-ton capacity
... **Three Locomotive Cranes** — Up to 38-ton capacity

REPAIR FACILITIES
... **Dry Docks** — One dock 1,150 feet by 120 feet wide at entrance. Can dock largest ship afloat. One dock 624 feet by 61½ feet wide at entrance by 25¾ feet over sill
... **Marine Railway** — 284 feet by 60 feet wide, lifting capacity 2,000 tons, for vessels up to 17-foot draught
... **Complete machine shop, other repair facilities and salvage equipment available**

BUNKERING
... **Oil** — Fuel-oil pipelines at all important berths. Diesel oil at 1 berth only
... **Coal** — Available at several coal wharves

TOWING FACILITIES
... **A fleet of harbour and salvage tugs is available**

THREE RIVERS

BERTHS — 21
... **Length of Berthing** — 9,000 feet
... **Minimum Depth** — 30 feet
... **Shedded Berths** — 8
... **Open Berths** — 13

TRANSIT SHEDS — 8
... **Floor Area** — 236,000 square feet

GRAIN ELEVATOR
... **Storage Capacity** — 5,000,000 bushels (including annex)
... **Shipping Capacity** — 40,000 bushels per hour to ships, 10,000 bushels per hour to railway cars
... **Receiving Capacity** — 20,000 bushels per hour from ships, 8,000 bushels per hour from railway cars
... **Number of Grain Berths** — 1
... **Number of Marine Legs** — 1

TERMINAL RAILWAY
... **Trackage** — 5 miles
... **Operation** — By Canadian Pacific Railway

BUNKERING
... **Coal** — Delivered direct to ships at 4 coal berths
... **Oil** — Delivered direct to ships at 2 berths

MONTREAL

BERTHS — 112
... **Length of Berthing** — Approximately 10 miles
... **Minimum Depths** — 62 berths, 30 to 35 feet. Remainder, 25 to 29½ feet, except 600 linear feet at less than 25 feet.
... **Shedded Berths** — 31
... **Open Berths** — 81

TRANSIT SHEDS — 31 (19 are two-storey)
... **Floor Area** — 2,400,000 square feet

GRAIN ELEVATORS — 4
... **Storage Capacity** — 15,162,000 bushels
... **Receiving or Shipping Capacity** — 1,250,000 bushels per 13-hour day
... **Number of Grain Berths** — 27 (5 open, 22 chedded)
... **Number of Marine Legs** — 10, located at 6 berths

REFRIGERATED WAREHOUSE
... **Capacity** — 3,000,000 cubic feet

TERMINAL RAILWAY
... **Trackage** — 62 miles, serving nearly all berths
... **Switching Locomotives** — 8 diesel electric locomotives, 660 H.P., 100 tons
... **Switching Capacity** — 1,500 cars to or from berths per day
... **Rail Connections** — Canadian National Railways and Canadian Pacific Railway

CRANES
... **Floating Cranes** — Rated capacity, 75 tons. Can lift 90 tons with restricted outreach
... **Diesel Caterpillar Crane** — 30-ton capacity
... **Ten Locomotive Cranes** — 10-ton to 30-ton capacity

REPAIR FACILITIES
... **Floating Dry Dock** — 25,000-ton capacity, length 600 feet, draught 27½ feet
... **Three Graving Docks** — Dimensions of the largest are: Length 400 feet, entrance width 50 feet, depth over sill 15 feet 3 inches
... **Complete repair facilities and salvage equipment available**

BUNKERING
... **Oil** — Delivered direct to vessels at a number of berths; also delivered by tanker to vessels at any berth in the harbour
... **Coal** — Delivered direct to vessels at a number of coal berths

TOWING FACILITIES
... **A large fleet of harbour, canal, and ocean-going tugs, ranging from 650 to 1,000 H.P., is available**

TORONTO

BERTHS —
... **Length of Berthing** — 12 miles
... **Minimum Depths** — 27 feet

TRANSIT SHEDS — 10
... **Floor Area** — 383,500 square feet

GRAIN ELEVATORS — 3
... **Storage Capacity** — 9,500,000 bushels
... **Receiving or Shipping Capacity** — 7,500 bushels per hour at two elevators and 35,000 bushels per hour at one elevator
... **Number of Grain Berths** — Number of berths available for grain depends on the size of the vessel

REFRIGERATED WAREHOUSE
... **Capacity** — 2,500,000 feet

TERMINAL RAILWAY
... **Trackage** — 34 miles serving port area
... **Rail Connections** — Canadian National Railways and Canadian Pacific Railway

CRANES
... **Floating Cranes** — 2 — 25-ton and 50-ton capacity
... **Locomotive Crane** — None operating. If desired, arrangements can be made between shipping line and railway
... **Mobile Cranes** — A number available with capacity up to 18 tons

REPAIR FACILITIES
... **Floating Dry Dock** — 900-ton capacity
... **Complete repair facilities and salvage equipment available**

BUNKERING
... **Oil** — Bunkering pipes on dockside. Ships move to the berts for bunkering.
... **Coal** — Available at coal docks

TOWING FACILITIES
... **A fleet of harbour and salvage tugs is available from 140 H.P. to 260 H.P.**

HAMILTON

BERTHS — 40 (4 under construction)
... **Length of Berthing** — 36,000 running feet
... **Minimum Depths** — From 16 feet to 27 feet
... **Shedded Berths** — 7
... **Open Berths** — 33 (4 under construction)

TRANSIT SHEDS — 8
... **Floor Area** — 306,000 square feet. Frost-proof areas 306,000 square feet

GRAIN ELEVATORS — 1 planned Capacity 1,000,000 bushels

TERMINAL RAILWAY
... **Trackage** — 6 miles
... **Rail Connections** — Canadian National Railways, Canadian Pacific Railway, Toronto, Hamilton & Buffalo Railway

CRANES
... **Floating Crane** — Rated Capacity, 75-ton (under construction)
... **Other types** — Crawler type capacity 280-tons.

REPAIR FACILITIES
... **Marine Railway** — Capacity 100-tons
... **Complete platework and engine repair facilities available**

BUNKERING
... **Oil** — By tank truck
... **Coal** — By dockside crane

TOWING FACILITIES
... **5 tugs, ranging from 150 to 750 H.P. are available**

DULUTH, MINNESOTA

BERTHS — 3 (Public Marine Terminal, under construction)
... **Length of Berthing** — 1,000 feet
... **Minimum Depths** — 25 feet (to be increased to 27 feet)
... **Shedded Berths** — 2
... **Open Berths** — 1

TRANSIT SHEDS —2
... **Floor Area** — 180,000 square feet
... **Frost-proof areas** — 180,000 square feet

GRAIN ELEVATORS — 7
... **Storage Capacity** — From 1,200,000 bushels to 6,000,000
... **Shipping Capacity** — From 40,000 bushels to 75,000 bushels per hour
... **Number of Grain Berths** — 8
... **Number of Marine Legs** — 5

REFRIGERATED WAREHOUSE
... **Capacity** — 1,779,032 Cubic Feet

TERMINAL RAILWAY
... **Trackage & Operation** — Eight railroads have terminus at this port and operated under reciprocal agreements. Service to Public Marine Terminal to be on a joint basis

CRANES
... **Floating Cranes** — 2 — Rated Capacity 35-tons
... **Locomotive Cranes** — Number owned by private interests, ranging from 5 to 45 tons.
... **Other Types** — Two 65-ton SWL gantry cranes to be operating at the Public Marine Terminal

REPAIR FACILITIES
... **Graving Docks** — Located in Superior, Wis.
... **Diver service available for salvage work**

BUNKERING
... **Oil** — By self-propelled oil barge
... **Coal** — Service at coal docks

TOWING FACILITIES
... **A fleet of four diesel tugs of 1250 H.P. and one steam tug of 600 H.P. available**

CLEVELAND, OHIO

BERTHS — 24
... **Length of Berthing** — Approximately 7,282 running feet
... **Minimum Depths** — 21 feet

TRANSIT SHEDS — 6
... **Floor Area** — 265,000 square feet

GRAIN ELEVATORS — 2 (privately owned)
... **Storage Capacity** — 990,000 bushels
... **Unloading Capacity** — 12,000 bushels per hour
... **Grain Berths** — Each elevator has berthing space for one vessel

REFRIGERATED WAREHOUSE — (not on docks, located in the City)
... **Capacity** — 12,000,000 cubic feet

TERMINAL RAILWAY
... **Trackage** — about 40 miles
... **Rail Connections** — New York Central, Baltimore and Ohio, Erie, Pennsylvania, and the Nickel Plate

CRANES
... **Floating Cranes** 10 to 40-ton capacity
... **Locomotive Cranes** — 30 to 50-ton capacity
... **Other Types** — up to 100-ton capacity

REPAIR FACILITIES
... **Graving Docks** — 2 at Lorain, Ohio, 25 miles west of Cleveland Dock No. 1 has a capacity of 574 feet and Dock No.2 has a capacity of 733 feet. Both have a depth of 12 feet 6 inches over sill
... **Repair facilities and diving equipment available**

BUNKERING
... **Oil** — Available at oil dock at maximum rate of 800 barrels per hour. Also available to vessels at any berth by fuel barge
... **Coal** — Available at the rate of 1,800 tons per hour at coal docks

TOWING FACILITIES
... **A fleet of four diesel tugs with rated H.P. of 1,000 each available for harbor and lake towing**

ROCHESTER (CHARLOTTE) HARBOR, New York

BERTHS — 2
... **Length of Berthing** — 5,735 feet long
... **Minimum Depth** — 20 feet

TRANSIT SHEDS — 2
... **Floor area** —

TERMINAL RAILWAY
... **Rail Connections** — New York Central Railway and Baltimore & Ohio Railroad

CRANES
... **Type** — Stationary cranes available on order

BUNKERING
... **Oil** — Delivered direct to vessels by tank trucks at Municipal terminal
... **Coal** — Coal Bunker facilities available at Genesee Docks.

SAULT STE. MARIE, MICHIGAN

BERTHS — 2
... **Length of Berthing** — Approximately 600 feet each
... **Minimum Depths** — 19 feet
... **Open Berths** — 2

BUNKERING
... **Coal** — Can be obtained at Kemp's coal dock

TOWING FACILITIES
... **Two tugs, 100 H.P. and 1100 H.P. available**

GREEN BAY, WISCONSIN

BERTHS —
... **Length of Berthing** — 400 feet
... **Minimum Depth** — 22 feet
... **Open Berths** — 26

TRANSIT SHEDS
... **Frost Proof Areas** — Waterfront warehouses 725,000 square feet

GRAIN ELEVATORS —
... **Storage Capacity** — 1,150,000 bushels
... **Shipping Capacity** — 20,000 bushels per hour
... **Number of Grain Berths** — 2

TERMINAL RAILWAY
... **Trackage** — 5 miles
... **Rail Connections** —

CRANES
... **Floating Crane** — 1 — Rated Capacity, 20-tons
... **Diesel Caterpillar Cranes** — 10 with rated capacity of 10 to 20 tons
... **Other Type** — 40-ton stationary crane on order

REPAIR FACILITIES
... **Ship repair and floating derrick facilities available**

BUNKERING
... **Oil** —Delivered direct to ship from dock
... **Coal** — Coal bridge to ship direct

TOWING FACILITIES
... **1 steam tug of 450 H.P. available**

OGDENSBURG, NEW YORK

BERTHS —
... **Length of Berthing** — 2,000 feet
... **Minimum Depths** — 21 feet
... **Open Berths** — 2,000 feet

TRANSIT SHEDS
... **Floor Area** — 104,500 square feet

GRAIN ELEVATORS
... **Storage Capacity** — 900,000 bushels
... **Shipping Capacity** — 8,000 bushels per hour
... **Grain Berth** — 600 feet
... **Number of Marine Towers** — 1

TERMINAL RAILWAY
... **Trackage** — 1 mile
... **Rail Connections** — Rutland Railway & New York Central

CRANES

...**Types** — 2 crawler types

BUNKERING

...**Oil** — Pipe line on dock
...**Coal** — Delivered by crane motor

CHEBOYGAN, MICHIGAN

BERTHS — 3

...**Length of Berthing** — 2,200 lin. feet
...**Minimum Depths** — 18.5 feet
...**Open Berths** — 3

TERMINAL RAILWAY

...**Trackage** — 1,000 lineal feet
...**Rail Connections** — New York Central and

CRANES

...**Floating Crane** — 1, rated capacity 100 tons
...**Other Types** — 2 crawler cranes, rated capacity 25 tons

REPAIR FACILITIES

...**Full facilities for repairing above water line**
...**Complete equipment for Marine Salvage**

BUNKERING

...**Coal** — Crane and conveyor

TOWING FACILITIES

...**One 500 H.P. tug.**

TOLEDO, OHIO

BERTHS

...**Length of Berthing** — 1,000 running feet
...**Minimum Depths** — 24 feet
...**Open Berths** — 1

TRANSIT SHEDS

...**Floor Area** — 420,000 cubic feet. Increasing warehouse by 1/3. 6 acres open storage
...**Frost-Proof Areas** — 25,000 cubic feet

GRAIN ELEVATORS — 3

...**Storage Capacity** — on waterfront, 8, 175, 488 bushels. In switching district, 23 million bushels.
...**Shipping Capacities** — 15,000-30,000 per hour per elevator.
...**Number of Grain Berths** — 4
...**Number of Marine Towers** — 1

CRANES

...**Floating Cranes** — 3. 1 - 6 ton; 1 - 1 ton derrick scow; 1 - 3 ton stiff-leg derrick.
...**Locomotive Cranes** — 2. 1 - 12 ton; 1 - 25 ton.
...**Other Types** — 2. Stiff-leg, 40 tons; A-frame, 80 tons.

REPAIR FACILITIES

...**Graving docks** — 2. No. 1 - 14 ft. over sill; 103 ft. at coping & 541 ft. long at coping. No. 2 - 15.3 ft. over sill; 95 ft. entrance width at coping; 656 ft. long at coping.
...**Any type of hull, deck, or machinery repair can be handled.**
...**Floating derricks, barges, diving gear are available locally. Other salvage equipment available on call.**

BUNKERING

...**Oil** — Available at 6 refinery & terminal wharves; also by tanker & tank truck.
...**Coal** — 7 coal loaders. Average coal bunkering rate per hour is 3,000 short tons.

TOWING FACILITIES

...**2 diesel powered tugs available. Others available on call.**

DETROIT, MICHIGAN

BERTHS — 6

...**Length of Berthing** — 1,800 running feet
...**Minimum Depths** — 23 feet at one terminal, 21 on the other
...**Shedded Berths** — 4
...**Open Berths** — 2

TRANSIT SHEDS — 3

...**Floor area** — 45,346 square feet

GRAIN ELEVATORS

...**No public elevators. It is possible to have grain products handled and stored at a private elevator during periods when the company is not using their own facility to capacity. Arrangements & charge made directly with the private elevator.**

REFRIGERATED WAREHOUSE

...**Capacity** — 2,000,000 cubic feet

TERMINAL RAILWAY

...**Trackage** — 3 miles
...**Rail Connections** — With all railroads.

CRANES

...**3 electric Gantry** — 25 - 40 tons; 5 locomotive diesel 35-40 tons; caterpillar 10 tons; mobile crane 2 - 15-25 tons; lima crawler - 1 - 30 tons shear Leg - 1 - 85 tons

REPAIR FACILITIES

...**1 Floating dry dock** — 10,000 tons, 750 feet long, 84 feet wide.
...**Limited salvage equipment available and other necessary equipment can be arranged for.**

BUNKERING

...**Oil** — Tug and barge on river while vessel is either under way or alongside.
...**Coal** — bunker at dock.

TOWING FACILITIES

...**7 diesel tugs ranging from 800 to 1600 HP.**

OSWEGO, NEW YORK

BERTHS — 9

...**Depths** — 14-21 feet l.w.d.
...**Shedded Berths** — 3
...**Open Berths** — 6

TRANSIT SHEDS — 2

...**Floor Area** — 12,400 square feet & 34,390 square feet.

GRAIN ELEVATORS — 1

...**Storage Capacity** — 1,000,000 bushels
...**Shipping Capacity** — 45,000 bushels
...**Marine Towers** — 2

TERMINAL RAILWAY

...**Rail Connections** — Delaware, Lackawanna and Western and New York Central

CRANES

...**Mobile cranes of almost any capacity can be leased locally**

BUNKERING

...**Oil** — No. 1 Diesel fuel bunkered at coal dock. Delivery by truck for other grades of fuel
...**Coal** — at coal dock

KINGSTON, ONTARIO

BERTHS — 6 main berths and numerous smaller ones
...**Length of Berthing** — 5,755 ft. at main berths
...**Minimum Depths** — 13½ feet

GRAIN ELEVATORS — 1
...**Storage Capacity** — 2,500,000 bushels
...**Receiving or Shipping Capacity** — 35,000 bushels per hour
...**Number of Grain Berths** — 1
...**Number of Marine Legs** — 2. Loading spouts, 6

TERMINAL RAILWAY

...**Canadian National Railway & Canadian Pacific railways service docks.**

CRANES

...**cranes and shear legs to 100 tons at Kingston Shipyards Ltd. dock.**

REPAIR FACILITIES

...**Dry Docks** — 2 - maximum length 379 ft. width 50 ft.
...**Complete repair facilities and salvage equipment available**

BUNKERING

...**Oil** — Bunker "C" and diesel oil stored for large ships and readily available
...**Coal** — loaded from lighters or at wharf

TOWING FACILITIES

...**Tugs available. Necessary to handle ships in rough weather at the Elevator, not otherwise.**

PORT ARTHUR, ONTARIO

BERTHS

...**Length of Berthing** — approx. 4½ miles
...**Minimum Depths** — 25 ft. alongside principal wharves at low lake levels.
...**Open Berths** — 1
...**Shedded Berths**

TRANSIT SHEDS

...**Floor Areas**

GRAIN ELEVATORS — 16
...**Storage Capacity** — 52,490,000 bushels
...**Shipping Capacities**
...**Number of Grain Berths** — 14

REPAIR FACILITIES

...**Dry Dock** — 1. 746 ft. overall, depth over sill 16.5 ft.
...**Complete facilities for ship repairs available.**

BUNKERING

...**Oil** — Diesel oil available only in barrels
...**Coal** — loaded at coal dock

TOWING FACILITIES

...**Tugs available**

TERMINAL RAILWAY

...**total miles 343.6**
...**Connections** — Canadian National & Canadian Pacific

PORT OF MILWAUKEE, WISCONSIN

BERTHS — 103 @ 500 feet each.
...**Length of Berthing** — (Total Running Feet) 51,000 ft.
...**Minimum Depths** — 21 ft. 30 ft. in Outer Harbor Slips
...**Shedded Berths** — 7
...**Open Berths** — 96

TRANSIT SHEDS — 7
...**Floor Area** — 529,085 square feet.
...**Frost-proof Areas** — 40,000 square feet.
...**Grain Elevators** — 6,900,000 (Storage capacity — Number of bushels) 8,000 to 10,000 Bushels per hour — Shipping capacities.
...**Number of Grain Berths** — 3
...**Number of Marine Towers** — 0

REFRIGERATED WAREHOUSE

...**Capacity** — (In cubic feet)
...**Cooler** — 942,340 cubic feet.
...**Freezer** — 1,550,210 cubic feet.
(1,191,000 can be converted to cooler space)

TERMINAL RAILWAY

...**Trackage** — 10.8 mi. (Number of miles serving deep sea berths)
...**Railroads** —
C&NW
C.M.St.P.&P.
Soo Line
Chesapeake & Ohio

CRANES

...**Floating Cranes** — 0
...**Locomotive Cranes** — 2. 30-ton each.
...**Other Types of Cranes** — 7. 2 5-ton semi-portal; 3 25-ton gantries; 1 20-ton mobile; 1 90-ton gantry.

REPAIR FACILITIES —

...**Floating Dry Dock** — 0
...**Graving Docks** — 0

SALVAGE EQUIPMENT

...**Adequate** — by marine contractors.

BUNKERING

...**Oil** — Pump, tank car, or tank truck.
...**Cool** — Traveling bridge crane-100 tons per hour. Rail & truck connection.

TOWING FACILITIES

..**2 Diesel Electric 1,000 H.P.**

COMMERCIAL SECTION

A dredging scene at Sorel, Quebec, from a painting by Franklin Arbuckle, A.R.C.A.

MARINE INDUSTRIES LIMITED
The Pathway to Progress

The history of dredging is almost as old as man's first venturing out on the rivers and seas in frail craft, first to explore and then for either trade or on military expeditions. When early man had progressed beyond the rafts, hollowed-out tree trunks and coracles to craft of heavier draft, and began transporting goods by water, he found it necessary to build wharves and docks.

The great harbors of Alexandria, Tyre, Carthage, Massalia — now the modern Marseilles — and the Roman port of Ostia and the Athenian port of Peiraeus would not have been possible without dredging. While it is true that many of the great ports of both antiquity and modern times have been built on the sites of natural harbors, they would not have been able to grow to greatness without continual enlargement — in which dredging played a major part.

The huge, mechanically-powered dredges of today are a far cry from the primitive equipment in use until even comparatively recent times. The Dutch, who are among the great maritime people in the world, at an early stage in their history, used a cloth bag attached to a long handle to dredge their harbors and canals. When one considers how much of the work was done by manual labor, the achievements of the old canal builders and the naval engineers who were responsible for the deepening and maintenance of harbors are indeed outstanding.

Yet all of these magnificent achievements and other engineering marvels pale almost into insignificance beside the St. Lawrence Seaway and Power Projects. Stated one of Canada's leading industrialists in a study of this project, which has attracted world-wide attention:

"The St. Lawrence Seaway and Power Project is one of those undertakings, so imaginative in conception and so vast in scope, that descriptive adjectives must but detract from its grandeur.

One of Marine Industries' derricks employed on the St. Lawrence Seaway and Power Projects.

"Yet plain truth it is that never before in the history of mankind has a single engineering scheme embraced within a single grand design so many interlocking parts of a continent's life. It is a venture which not only sets the scene for things historic yet to come; it consummates, it completes, it crowns the history of four centuries past. It is the final fulfilment of a dream originally formed by men who knew nothing of steamships and hydro-electric power, men whose fathers had hailed the spectacle of fire propelling wood over water as an eighth wonder of the world, men whose grandfathers had believed, indeed, that the world was flat.

"But they were men, these early pioneers, who, like the great of all times and countries, refused to be limited by the present or daunted by the unknown. Few were the technical resources at their command; their vision and daring it was that more than quadrupled the size of the civilized world. It is only against the background of their vision and their work that the grandeur of the St. Lawrence Seaway and Power Projects can be appreciated."

The size of the Project meant that only those companies with years of experience and skill could even contemplate participating successfully in it. It was a big job calling for men with big ideas, with the know-how to handle any problem that might conceivably arise. And the biggest dredging company, the leader in its field which had, over many years, developed underwater excavation of great quantities of earth and rock to a highly specialized degree, was Marine Industries Limited, of Montreal and Sorel, Quebec.

The Dredging Division of Marine Industries has enjoyed a steady growth and expansion from the time when Dredging Contractors Limited of Vancouver obtained a contract for dredging and land reclamation at Wolfe's Cove Terminal at Quebec City. In 1926, Dredging Contractors entered into partnership with Manseau Shipyards at Sorel, later forming a new company called General Dredging Contractors Limited. At this time there was great activity throughout Eastern Canada in new port construction and harbor improvements. To meet this expanding business, the new company also took over the plants and business of Sorel Iron Foundries, Beauchemin & Fils, Limitée, and Sorel Mechanical Shops, Limited, all of which, in 1937, were consolidated into Marine Industries Limited.

1759, it is today the site of a great deep-water terminal which can accommodate ocean liners of any tonnage. This project, which was started in 1926, was completed in 1932, and involved the creation of more than 400 acres of waterfront property at Wolfe's Cove and it is today one of the most valuable pieces of real estate in the area.

From 1926 to the end of 1957, Marine Industries' dredging equipment has removed many millions of cubic yards of various kinds of material, including shale, boulder clay, hard-pan, rock and glacial till. In addition to projects in Canada, the company's equipment and services have been utilized in harbor deepening and channel improvement in Bermuda and British Guiana.

Marine Industries' dredging fleet over the years has played an important role in deepening and widening the St. Lawrence River Ship Channel, which now becomes an integral part of the Seaway. Meeting with such conditions as solid and broken rock, hard-pan and boulders, the project has entailed the excavation of approximately 72,000,000 cubic yards of material.

The Wolfe's Cove Terminal job was only the first of many major projects undertaken by Marine Industries. An historic landmark where General Wolfe and his troops stormed the rocky, forbidding heights to win a decisive battle over the forces of General Montcalm in

Another major project was the preparation of a site for the Seigniory Club at Lucerne-in-Quebec. Here an enclosed yachting basin was created and low-level ground built up to above the highwater levels. At the same time, about a half-mile of river front was deepened to a uniform grade right up to the shore line. Low-lying swampy shore land in the area was filled in as a mosquito-control measure.

Elevator dredge doing its job despite heavy seas and high wind.

One of the more notable dredging feats undertaken by Marine Industries was the dredging of the Beauharnois Power Canal, which supplies the water for one of the largest hydro-electric power plants in the world.

The Beauharnois Power Canal stretches 18 miles from Lake St. Francis to Lake St. Louis, just west of Montreal. Marine Industries' dredging fleet removed over 11,000,000 cubic yards of boulder clay and 25,000,-000 cubic yards of marine clay, and one of the most important problems overcome was the disposal of this material ashore.

Another outstanding job undertaken by the company was a land reclamation contract at Limoilou, Quebec, for the Anglo-Canadian Pulp & Paper Mills Limited. Almost 2,000,000 cubic yards of material were pumped out by the Marine Industries' dredge "General Wolfe" of the confluence of the St. Charles and St.. Lawrence Rivers. To reclaim the ground on which Anglo-Canadian's plant was erected involved some 300 acres of tide flat improvement. The unique method developed by Marine Industries in this dredging operation saved valuable time and enabled the mill to start production a full year earlier than would have been possible otherwise.

Up to the end of the 1957 season, approximately 6,600,000 cubic yards were excavated on St. Lawrence Seaway contracts. Included were the turning basin in the Montreal Harbor, which will allow the largest Upper Lakes' ships on leaving the canal to enter this great port; deepening and cutting the channels in both Lake

St. Louis and Lake St. Francis; dredging the entrances at Beauharnois and channel improvements and relocation at Cornwall Island.

All contracts are of an interesting nature to Marine Industries Dredging Division, but one of the most interesting was the excavation of hundreds of thousands of cubic yards from the St. Lawrence River for the account of the Montreal Pipe Line Company. The problem was to bring the pipe of the Portland, Maine-Montreal

The "Manseau 107", one of Marine Industries' powerful fleet of dipper dredges.

177

pipeline across the river to the site of the oil refineries in Montreal East. In this job, one of every type of Marine Industries dredging equipment was called into play, together with all the necessary ancillary equipment, such as tugs and scows. A dipper dredge was used to excavate and to strip the overburden from the rock which was encountered; drillboats were used to prepare the rock for blasting, and dipper and ladder dredges were used to excavate the rock.

The riverbed now being ready, one of the company's ladder dredges was used to pull the pipe, in one continuous piece, 10,000 feet across the river. The Pipe Line Company's engineers and crews welded the 150-foot lengths ashore and as each section was welded to the next, Marine Industries' ladder dredge placed it in the bed and pulled the whole line across almost two miles of river. The line now being connected at both ends, a M.I.L. suction dredge was used for the delicate operation of filling in and covering over the pipe to supply a ten-foot protective cover against the ravages of ice in the winter and the passing traffic during the navigation season.

Over the years, in excess of 4,000,000 cubic yards have been excavated on various projects of the Department of Public Works, extending from Matane to Montreal and also in the Maritimes.

Marine Industries' equipment, employed on behalf of Saguenay Terminals Ltd., excavated around 1,000,000 cubic yards in connection with the construction of a new wharf at Port Alfred, Quebec, in 1947 and in 1949. The company's dredges have also been active for many years on behalf of the National Harbours Board, dredging some 4,000,000 cubic yards in the harbors at Quebec, Three Rivers and Montreal.

When Quebec Iron & Titanium Corporation called, through its contractors, Fraser-Brace Co., for tenders in connection with the building of a new wharf at Sorel, it was handled expeditiously by Marine Industries. Other major contractors who have availed themselves of the company's services have been E. G. M. Cape & Co., Foundation Co. of Canada Ltd., Key Construction Co., Angus Robertson Ltd. and Canit Construction, to name but a few.

Mention was made previously of a harbor-deepening and channel-improvement contract in Bermuda. In this job, some 1,500,00 cubic yards of coral rock and 2,000,-000 yards of coral sand were excavated. This contract, carried out in the early days of the war, was on behalf of the United States Government which recognized the company's efficiency in handling even the most difficult of jobs, and was necessitated by the American Government's decision to build a U.S. Naval-Air Base on the Island.

In order to efficiently handle jobs of the magnitude cited, Marine Industries has one of the largest and most up-to-date dredging fleets in North America. The company not only operates the largest private fleet of dredges in Canada but is also the only Canadian company equipped to design, build and operate its own dredges. The company's shipyards, technical staff and skilled workers are available for not only the company's own maritime

The "Hydro-Quebec", a hydraulic suction dredge, known as the most powerful in the world, built for Beauharnois Light, Heat and Power.

operations but can also handle any shipbuilding or ship-repairing problems efficiently and expeditiously.

The shipyard, located at Sorel — the company's head office is in Montreal — covering over 100 acres and with a water frontage of 3,500 feet, maintains the world's largest marine railway, capable of transferring up to 12,000 ton ships from six separate berths to a launching platform; ample mooring and fitting out facilities; a 150-ton shear leg; and a complete, modern machine shop, mould loft, joiners' and pipe shops, plate and angle shop, tool room and power and gas plants. An efficient combination of derricks, cranes, trucks, tractors and other equipment takes care of material and equipment through all operations.

Ships built by Marine Industries Ltd. have sailed every ocean and are familiar sights in every major port in the world and it is worthy of note that, during the war, the company set a record by delivering one 10,000-ton freighter a week during the shipping season.

New improvements and economies are continuously being brought to bear on dredging projects by Marine Industries. A striking example of this is the development of hydraulic dredging as the most efficient and economical means of excavating material of any kind. It performs three operations in one: removes, raises and places the excavated material all at the cost of a single operation. Another feature is the excellent performance of the company's drillboats which execute rock removal where drilling is done faster and more economically than by any other method in use today.

In the years ahead, Marine Industries sees a challenge and an opportunity for its Dredging Division. Canada is growing in all directions and there is no section of our economy which will not be benefitted by this expansion. As one of the leading trading nations in the world, much of the produce of our fields and forests and mines and factories must move by water. And there is little doubt that much of it will be transported along the Seaway. We have already built new wharfage facilities or had to enlarge existing facilities along the St. Lawrence and there is no doubt that with the opening of the Seaway more facilities will have to be built or added.

The St. Lawrence Seaway and Power Project was not conceived with the idea of solely benefitting one region of Canada. It will be of advantage to the entire Canadian economy. It will leave its mark on the furthermost ports of the Great Lakes and reach beyond. The wheatfields of the Prairies, the mining developments in the North, the new industrial complexes that are springing up almost magically from coast to coast — all these will be benefitted by the Seaway.

When the St. Lawrence Seaway becomes an operating reality, there will still be no let-up for one phase of the project. There will still be a need for dredging to widen the ship channel and its approaches and to further expand and develop harbor facilities. As it has in the past, Marine Industries expects to continue to play a major part in this great inland waterway, making its contribution toward the greatness of Canada.

Electric hydraulic dredge designed and built by Marine Industries shipyards at Sorel, Quebec.

179

THE J. P. PORTER COMPANY LIMITED

Dipper dredge "Delver" deepening Port Weller Harbor during severe winter ice conditions.

As one travels the scenic highway which parallels the St. Lawrence Seaway and Power Projects the sights that meet the eye never fail to amaze. For here indeed is the engineering "masterpiece" of the century . . . a tribute to the Governments of Canada and the United States who turned this dream of long years ago into reality. But what of the many contracting firms charged with the actual construction of the giant deep waterway? Should not a major portion of the tribute be paid to them for a tough job well done?

One of the most important jobs on the St. Lawrence Seaway was the task of enlarging and deepening the existing channels from Montreal to Lake Erie. A large portion of this work was undertaken with dredging equipment. Dredging at any time is not the easiest of jobs but on this project it was particularly difficult due to the presence of large quantities of glacial till and also because of the necessity of removing extremely thin layers of rock from certain sections of the Welland Canal.

These obstacles and many others as well were faced by the J. P. Porter Company Limited during their Seaway operations. This firm, a marine construction company specializing in dredging work, is playing an active part in the building of the St. Lawrence Seaway and Power Projects and has been awarded three dredging contracts in the Welland Canal area alone.

The first of these involved the removal of some 320,000 cubic yards of clay and broken rock from Port Weller Harbor with their Diesel-Electric Suction Dredge SHUNIAH. Although this dredge was able to remove most of the material, which interfered with Seaway-depth navigation, from the harbor, it encountered, in certain sections, solid rock which it could not excavate.

Some time after the SHUNIAH had finished its work, the St. Lawrence Seaway Authority called for tenders for the removal of the 37,000 cubic yards of rock which remained above the required Seaway grade. The Porter Company was again low bidder and proceeded to remove this rock, which extended an average of only 8 inches above grade, with their 8 cubic yard dipper dredge DELVER and their drillboat J.P.P. No. 8, which is equipped with two 6 inch pneumatic drills.

This rock contract, with its extremely shallow "cut", was by no means easy but J. P. Porter Company handled it with the same efficiency which has gained for them the reputation of being one of the foremost dredging concerns in Canada.

The Porter Company obtained its third Welland Canal dredging contract in August of 1958 and will be undertaking it during the Fall months with their 5 cubic yard Clamshell Dredge HAMILTON 56. This project contains a large number of small scattered dredging areas and extends for a distance of ten miles along the southerly end of the Canal.

The first Seaway dredging work undertaken by the Porter Company was at Chimney Island, three miles east of Prescott, Ontario. This Channel Improvement contract was awarded to Canadian Dredge and Dock Company Limited by the Ontario Hydro Electric Power Commission and Canadian Dredge, in turn, sublet approximately 500,000 cubic yards to the Porter Company. Porter's work at Chimney Island, incidentally, included the actual removal of a large portion of the Island.

At Cardinal, Ontario, the Porter Company participated with Canadian Dredge in a joint venture dredging contract awarded by the Ontario Hydro Electric Power Commission. This channel enlargement project involved the removal of 2,000,000 cubic yards of material and the Porter Company contracted to carry out their portion of the work with their dipper dredge FUNDY, an eight cubic yard machine.

Dredging the upstream approaches to Iroquois Lock in the International Section of the Seaway was another project in which J. P. Porter joined forces with the Canadian Dredge and Dock Company. Here, another of their 8 cubic yard dipper dredges, the DIGBY, was employed.

The removal of Iroquois Point, located just west of the new dam at Iroquois, Ontario, called for a combination of "dry" excavation and dredging. The "dry" work was undertaken by Iroquois Constructors Limited, the prime contractor, while the dredging, which amounted to approximately 600,000 cubic yards, was sublet to the J. P. Porter Company. Dredges FUNDY and DIGBY were assigned to this work.

Several miles downstream from Iroquois, in the vicinity of Morrisburg, the Porter Company again entered into a joint venture with Canadian Dredge and Dock to carry out channel improvements for Ontario Hydro. The dredging at this section, which will exceed a million cubic yards, consists of the removal of sections of the bank of the old St. Lawrence Canal, as well as the removal of portions of Ogden and Canada Islands, and is scheduled to be completed in late 1959.

The most easterly of the Porter Company's Seaway dredging contracts is located on the Beauharnois Power Canal in Quebec. It involves the removal of approximately 30,000 cubic yards of Potsdam sandstone from the approach to the Upper Beauharnois Lock for United Waterways Constructors Limited who are the prime contractors for the construction of the Upper Lock. This work is scheduled for completion in November of this year.

The glacial till referred to above has been encountered on almost all of the Porter Company's contracts between Chimney Island and Morrisburg and its presence has reduced the production of all of the large dipper dredges by as much as 50 per cent. Glacial till is an extremely dense mixture of sand, clay and boulders and has a weight of the same order as concrete. The toughness of this "earth" may be gauged from the fact that many of the Seaway contractors operating on shore found it necessary to drill and blast, prior to excavation with large power shovels.

The J. P. Porter Company Limited has been associated with some of the largest dredging, land reclamation and marine construction projects in Eastern Canada. Included among these projects are wharf construction contracts at Pictou, Nova Scotia, Summerside, Prince Edward Island, Ste. Anne des Monts, Quebec and Sept Isles, Quebec; land reclamation contracts in connection with the Burlington Skyway and dredging contracts at Fort William and Hamilton in Ontario, at Rimouski and Seven Islands in Quebec, at Dingwall, Sydney, Halifax and Brooklyn, in Nova Scotia and at Port aux Basques in Newfoundland.

The J. P. Porter Company is particularly proud of its up-to-date equipment which includes thirteen dredges, three drillboats, twenty-two tugs and workboats and numerous scows and ancillary units.

Officers of the Company are: B. K. Boulton, President and Managing Director; W. A. Kalls, Vice-President and Secretary-Treasurer; R. E. Heard, Assistant Secretary-Treasurer; H. G. Rindress, Chief Engineer and D. Lauder, General Superintendent.

20" Diesel-Electric Suction Dredge "Shuniah".

S.S. T.R. McLagan passing Detroit, Mich. This giant bulk carrier has a carrying capacity of 25,000 tons of cargo.

CANADA STEAMSHIP LINES LIMITED

The story of the growth of the small company which commenced operations with one vessel on the Richelieu River in 1845, into the giant transportation system that is Canada Steamship Lines Limited today, is one which parallels the economic growth of the St. Lawrence River and Great Lakes areas served by the Company.

Throughout the years, as circumstances warranted, vessels and related activities were acquired, with the result that today the Company operates Canada's largest fleet of ships, is the country's largest shipbuilder, operates scheduled passenger, freight and truck services and is developing a rapidly growing general engineering service.

The fleet is made up of 61 units, of which 17 are huge upper lake bulk freighters which transport millions of bushels of grain and millions of tons of coal and iron ore each year; 21 are especially designed for the package freight trade which operates on scheduled sailings between ports extending from Quebec City on the lower St. Lawrence River to Fort William and Port Arthur at the head of the Great Lakes and provides rail connections to Western Canada; 16 are St. Lawrence canal size vessels which handle grain, coal, iron ore and miscellaneous cargoes; 4 are self-unloading carriers especially equipped to deliver coal and stone ashore with the ship's own machinery and 3 passenger steamers which provide luxury pleasure cruises on the St. Lawrence and Saguenay Rivers.

To service and operate in conjunction with the fleet, the Company owns two large grain transhipping elevators located at Kingston and Midland, Ontario, numerous package freight terminals equipped with

T.S.S. St. Lawrence cruising on the Saguenay River.

View of freight handling with modern equipment on a C.S.L. package freighter.

Ships for commerce, for safety of navigation and for national defence; all ready for launching on the same day at Davie Shipbuilding, Lauzon, Quebec.

modern mechanical handling equipment and, through a subsidiary, the Century Coal Company, provide fast bunkering service at various ports along the waterway system.

The magnificent Manoir Richelieu located at Murray Bay, Quebec, and the beautiful Hotel Tadoussac at Tadoussac, Quebec, are resort hotels operated in conjunction with the passenger cruise ships Richelieu, St. Lawrence and Tadoussac and provide unsurpassed holiday facilities for thousands of guests each year.

The Company's shipbuilding subsidiaries, the Davie Shipbuilding Company with plant at Lauzon, Levis, Quebec, and the Canadian Shipbuilding and Engineering Company with yards at Kingston, Midland, Collingwood and Port Arthur, Ontario are equipped with the most up-to-date machinery to produce new construction of all types — naval and merchant marine — and to handle necessary ship repairs. The industrial engineering

divisions of the companies are producing many items of custom design fabrication and industrial equipment for Canadian industry and enjoy the same high reputation for workmanship as does the shipbuilding division.

The Kingsway Transports Limited has become one of the country's major trucking systems and provides the shipping public with a speedy service between many major cities in eastern Canada and to the three prairie provinces. Service to Lyndhurst, N.J. and other points in the United States is also in operation. Fine modern terminals are operated to safely handle and speed the dispatch of freight by truck.

The head office of the company is located in the Canada Steamship Lines Building at 759 Victoria Square, Montreal, from which Mr. T. R. McLagan, President and General Manager, directs the many varied interests of the Company. Branch offices are located in many of the principal cities of Canada, United States and Great Britain.

M.V. Metis, modern bulk freighter — capacity 3,000 tons.

The S.S. Fort Henry, one of the largest and most modern of the package freighters in the C.S.L. fleet.

IRON ORE COMPANY OF CANADA LIMITED

The first white men who were able to get a look at the seacoast of northeast Canada called it "the land God gave to Cain". For the past four centuries the world has been content to leave it at that. But now, one of the greatest private mining undertakings in history has changed all that.

The Iron Ore Company of Canada has created an industry, a community, and a mass transportation system deep in the stark and forbidding sub-Arctic north, on the ancient plateau of the Quebec-Labrador frontier, more than 200 miles from the nearest established settlement.

To get the full meaning of what the discovery of iron ore means to the economic future of Canada, one must go back to the middle of the 19th century, around which time accounts of explorations into the interior were beginning to appear in print. However, it was not until the turn of the century that any part of the outside world had a hint of what this northeast corner might mean to the whole North American future.

At that time, Albert Peter Low, a Montreal-born geologist in the service of the Canadian Government, had at his disposal enough accurate information to start an article for the Engineering Magazine with this sentence: "The present high value of iron and steel, and the consequent activity in the search for and development of new sources of iron ore make this a fitting time to call attention to the iron-bearing deposits of the Labrador Peninsula."

Low, later to become Deputy Minister of Mines, wrote not from hearsay, but from actual experience. From 1892 through 1899, Low, working as a geologist for the Canadian Geological Survey, ranged some 7,100 miles ... by canoe, boat, dog sled and foot ... through the country east of Hudson Bay and on through to Ungava Bay and the Quebec-Labrador frontier.

He traced a belt of iron-bearing rocks 300 miles long and 50 miles wide through the heart of the country. And along the east coast of Hudson Bay he reported another 300 mile strip of iron formation.

However, it took 50 years after Low's reports to bring men in numbers to this part of the country. Low himself said, because of the lack of a railroad, no fuel and no available power, "it seems as if this area, along with many others, may long remain one of the undeveloped resources of the country."

In 1929 and again in 1933 more deposits of iron ore were discovered. However, it was not until 1936 that a company, the Labrador Mining and Exploration Company, was formed by Canadian interests and was granted a concession of 20,000 square miles by the New-

foundland government. After three years of hard and constant work, six of the currently recognized ore bodies in the Quebec-Labrador region had been found. But at this point work was suspended due to the economic difficulties of operating in so remote a region.

It was not until 1942 that this veritable wilderness began to take on a new appearance. In that year Hollinger Consolidated Gold Mines Limited obtained an option to purchase control of Labrador Mining and Exploration. A new company, Hollinger North Shore Exploration Company Limited, was formed to hold concession rights on 3,900 square miles in Quebec adjoining the Labrador border.

In 1942-43, the M. A. Hanna Company of Cleveland, Ohio, joined forces with the Hollinger interests and under the leadership of Jules R. Timmins of Hollinger Consolidated and George M. Humphrey of Hanna, work got under way with extra vigour to push back the frontier for the soon-to-come development of iron ore.

By the end of 1950 approximately $10,000,000. had been spent on exploration and the proving of some 400,000,000 tons of direct-shipping iron ore. However, this was only the beginning.

To raise the enormous amount of capital needed and to assure a market for the large tonnages of ore that must be produced to support the project, the original Canadian concession companies and Hollinger Consolidated Gold Mines joined forces with Republic, National, Armco, Youngstown, Wheeling and Hanna to form the Iron Ore Company of Canada.

With George M. Humphrey at the helm, Iron Ore Company of Canada took over the task of raising the money, opening the country and developing the ore. Hollinger-Hanna Limited was formed to manage the affairs of the companies affiliated with the iron ore project.

Together with the financing provided by the partners and the $150,000,000. loaned by 19 American and Canadian insurance companies, the project represents one of the largest mining undertakings ever attempted by private capital.

The arrival, on October 2, 1950 of a small, insignificant looking coastal steamer at the port of Sept Iles marked the beginning of a new era for this "land of Cain". For it was this little vessel which carried the first construction equipment that would soon be clearing the brush for the first construction camp.

The job ahead was indeed a big one for the builders. But they made their deadline. In the four years alloted to them they built dormitory housing for construction gangs, private homes, a 25,000 horsepower hydro-electric plant furnishing power for the new railway and terminal facilities in the area, for the Gulf Pulp and Paper Company and for the town of Sept Iles.

A 357 mile railroad, heading north out of Sept Iles and stretching to the Silver Lake yards in the heart of the ore mining district, was constructed. It is one of the longest stretches of railroad construction on this continent in this century and the only one in history built by airlift.

The function of the Quebec North Shore and Labrador Railway is to haul iron ore economically and efficiently. It took five years of careful surveying to select the route, after which construction crews had their work cut out for them laying tracks through solid rock, over swirling rivers and muskeg... and all this in a country where 50 below temperatures are not uncommon during the dead of winter.

In December, 1953, working out of the ultimate railroad midpoint known as Oreway, track-laying crews made more than two miles a day for ten straight days in 30 below zero weather.

Back in Sept Iles docking facilities large enough to receive raw materials as they arrived were constructed. Today, Iron Ore Company of Canada ships through its enlarged docking area over 10,000,000 tons of ore a year.

Two new townsites were built... one at Sept Iles and the other at what was formerly known as Knob Lake, since rechristened Schefferville, in honor of the Bishop of Labrador. Schefferville is a modern well-planned community of houses, stores, schools and churches.

As if this was not enough, construction crews had to prepare open-pit mines for operation, construct crushing, screening and loading facilities and while all this was going on, geologists were still out exploring ore bodies.

But the most spectacular story of all was the giant airlift... the largest civilian operation of its kind in history and one of the most amazing demonstrations of efficient aircraft use ever put on record.

Almost without major exception, every man, machine, part, or pound of food on the entire project went up the line by air. There was literally no other way to reach much of the interior. Everyone and everything depended on the humble airplane.

The airlift was operated by Hollinger-Ungava Transport, an Iron Ore Company affiliate based at Mont Joli on Quebec's South Shore. From October, 1950 to December, 1953, HUT carried a total of 138,700 passengers and flew 170,343,000 pounds of freight for a total of 15,263,190 ton miles. And all this without so much as a scratch to a crewman or passenger despite the adverse weather conditions so common to this part of the country.

The development of iron ore by the Iron Ore Company of Canada has proved a boon to the economy of both the Province of Quebec and Labrador. Purchases from suppliers alone amounted to $22.3 million in 1957, while duties under the Quebec Mining Tax Act paid by Iron Ore Company and Hollinger North Shore for the 1957 taxation year, was estimated at more than $800,000.

By the end of 1957, Iron Ore Company had built 465 housing units plus schools, water and sewage and other facilities in the town of Schefferville in Quebec. As is the case in Sept Iles, these houses are available to employees at a nominal rental and can be purchased under the special Company housing plan.

In the Sept Iles area, the Company provided the only hospital in the area at considerable expense, and has operated it for the benefit of the community for the past seven years. In addition, Iron Ore Company has subscribed $150,000 towards the construction of a new hospital in Sept Iles... $200,000 towards a recreation centre, also in Sept Iles... $50,000 towards the building of a technical college at Haute River near Sept Iles... $500,000 to a community centre in Schefferville and $40,000 to Montreal's McGill University.

Royalties paid to the Newfoundland Government in 1957 by the Iron Ore Company and Labrador Mining and Exploration Company was estimated at $625,000. Payments under the Social Security Assessment Act totalled approximately $75,000 to the end of 1957.

Total capital expenditures by Iron Ore Company to the end of 1957 amounted to $289,000,000. most of which was spent in the Province of Quebec. Capital expenditures in Newfoundland reached the sum of $81,000,000.

Statistics show that from 1954 to 1957 the production of iron ore, mined and shipped, has risen steadily. In 1954, Iron Ore Company mined 658,000 tons in Quebec and 1,460,000 tons in Labrador. In 1957, 8,385,000 tons were mined in Quebec and 4,635,-000 tons in Labrador. In 1954 the Company shipped 580,000 tons of Quebec ore and 1,201,000 tons of Labrador ore compared to 8,009,000 tons from Quebec and 4,427,000 from Labrador in 1957.

With the groundwork laid and production at its peak, Iron Ore Company of Canada awaits, with anticipation, the inauguration of yet another behemoth in the world of construction... the billion dollar St. Lawrence Seaway and Power Developments. When the Seaway starts operating, existing Great Lakes ore carriers will come to Sept Iles to help deep-water vessels move enormous tonnage of iron ore, speedily and economically, over an inland waterway to the Great Lakes steel-making centres which have more than 75% of the blast furnace capacity of Canada and the United States.

LaSalle Hydraulic Laboratory — Ville LaSalle.

Interior of experimental Laboratory — Ville LaSalle.

NEYRPIC CANADA LIMITED

Delving a little deeper into the facts about the St. Lawrence Seaway and Power Projects we come up with many an unsung hero. These are the people who laid the foundations for the giant deep waterway and about whom we hear very little. We are well aware of the visual work that has been done and about the continuous advances being made along the Seaway route, but are we thoroughly informed about some of the background firms?

One of the major firms that dealt with the St. Lawrence Seaway is The LaSalle Hydraulic Laboratory, located in Ville LaSalle, a suburb of Montreal, Quebec. They are a division of Neyrpic Canada Limited, and base their experience on the long established reputation of Sogreah in Grenoble, France, created by Neyrpic in 1906.

The Laboratory is contained in an area of 20,000 square feet. The permanent installation consisting mainly of three fumes; one of two feet wide, one four feet wide and the remaining one twelve feet wide. Apart from this they have a special fume 100 feet long which is used in special wave propagation studies. Extensive work is done here for Hydro Electric Commissions and basic plans are laid regarding the foundation of new communities.

When Neyrpic Canada Limited was first approached regarding the St. Lawrence Seaway, they were unable to do the scheduled work in this area and so erected a special building of 300,000 square feet. In this building they planned and scaled two large models, one for the Lachine Rapids Section of The Seaway, between Lake St. Louis and the rapids, and one for the Montreal Harbour section from the Laprairie Basin to Longueuil. The scales are 1/125 vertical and 1/200 horizontal. The real flows on the St. awrence River vary from 180,000 to 520,000 cubic feet per second. They were reproduced at 1/250,000. The scale for the velocities was 1/11.2.

On these two scale models the various stages of the river, harbour, bridges and Seaway were reproduced

covering the period from 1860 to 1959. Tests on flows, velocities and levels were carried out at those different stages with different flows. Velocity charts were established from each test. Highly qualified men and technicians were in charge of this study and continuous research has been going on since the inception of The Seaway.

Apart from this, Neyrpic was engaged to check cofferdams for the alterations on Victoria Bridge.

The chief purpose of this firm is General Scientific Research. This includes hydro electric structures such as dams, cofferdams, diversions, surge tanks, sand and gravel traps, water intakes, spillways, bottom outlets and tail race.

Their services also extend to maritime hydraulic projects for which they have done research on structures, harbours, tetrapods and protection of coasts and harbours against erosion or silting.

With the inception of hydraulically equipped machinery, Neyrpic Canada Limited have dealt extensively in the hydraulic transportation of solids and classification of materials. In the field of irrigation and water supply, the Company has contributed greatly to the construction of canals, water intakes, penstocks and automatic flow controls. They have cooperated with cities, towns and municipalities in the erecting of sewage systems and controls.

The work being carried out by Neyrpic Canada Limited is never ending. Scale models have been built for Hydro-Quebec, the City of Montreal and various consulting engineers. The Lachine Rapids Section scale model is also used to carry out research and experiments for the Lachine power house and dams.

Under the diligent supervision of Mr. J. A. Benard, the President of Neyrpic Canada Limited, the Company has made great strides in Canada and their untiring efforts in the development of the St. Lawrence Seaway and Power Project are highly commendable.

BURNS BROS. & COMPANY LIMITED
BURNS BROS. & DENTON LIMITED

Since the end of the last war Canada has undergone a period of prosperity which cannot be matched by any other nation. Thousands of people, notably from war torn Europe have flocked to these shores in search of a new and better life. The enormous mineral wealth that lay hidden in the northland was realized and new industries sprung up almost overnight. Millions of dollars have been invested by Canadians in the development of their country over the past few years, much of it being done through the various investment houses.

Serving and advising Canadians in this field since 1932 is the Toronto firm of Burns Bros. & Company Limited.

Early in 1932, in the depths of the Great Depression, Charles F. W. Burns founded Charles Burns Company as a sole proprietorship. Later in the same year he was joined by his brother, H. Latham Burns, and the two formed Burns Bros. & Company to engage in both the stock and bond business.

By 1936 the business of the Burns brothers had grown to the point where purchase of a seat on the Toronto Stock Exchange was considered desirable to improve the services available for their growing clientele. In the same year a second company, Burns Bros. Limited, was incorporated to transact the organization's bond business.

After Latham Burns sudden death in 1936 Charles Burns carried on as sole proprietor of the business. In 1939 Wilfred H. Denton joined Mr. Burns and acquired a 50 per cent interest in Burns Bros. Limited and the name of the latter company was changed to its present, Burns Bros. & Denton Limited. This firm then assumed the organization's function in the bond business and intensified its interest in the vast field of initiating and participating in the underwriting of issues of Canadian government and corporate bodies. At the same time Burns Bros. & Company concentrated its efforts on broadening and deepening its interest in the stock brokerage business. Since that time the two organizations have continued to carry out their separate functions, while at the same time offering a complete investment service to their customers.

With the advent of World War II, the companies accepted the challenge of selling Victory bonds on behalf of the Canadian Government's war effort. At the end of the war research facilities were rapidly expanded and the two companies entered into a period of progress in conjunction with Canada's post war boom.

In 1952 a new affiliate, Burns Bros. & Denton Inc., was formed in the United States. The Company, located on New York's Wall Street, has enabled clients to deal more effectively in the United States and has broadened the ability of the organization to contribute to the Canadian securities scene.

Having grown from an organization of three people in 1932 to an organization of over 200 in 1958, the Burns Bros. companies take great pride in the diversity of their activities through which they are able to meet the varying requirements of a wide clientele. These activities range from acting as "jobbers" in the money market to taking a prominent role in western oil development, uranium financing and varying other fields as occasion demands. Company offices are located in Toronto, Hamilton and Ottawa in Ontario; Montreal, Quebec; Winnipeg, Manitoba, and in the City of New York.

An important function of the Burns Bros. organization is to know all markets, listed and unlisted, and to be able to buy or sell securities for clients at prevailing prices promptly and efficiently. Through their correspondents, Burns Bros. act on behalf of clients in markets in the United States, the United Kingdom, Europe and other security trading areas.

Through experienced bond traders Burns Bros. clients are able to sell or purchase at prevailing market prices high grade, government and provincial, municipal and corporation bonds. Connections with other bond dealers and markets enable Burns Bros. to execute transactions quickly and efficiently. In addition, an inventory of bonds is maintained at all times, affording clients a wide range of securities from which to choose.

A vast private communications network is employed by the Burns Bros. organization and is staffed by highly trained and experienced traders who keep themselves continually abreast of changing markets and conditions.

Underwriting is another specialty of Burns Bros. which initiates and underwrites security issues for governments and corporations and participates with other houses in distributing such securities. Their research and underwriting departments provide the facilities and experience to assist Canadian companies to obtain funds for expansion and other purposes.

Burns Bros. & Denton Limited is one of a limited number of jobbers dealing in the money market in Canada. This market, a relatively new phase of Canada's investment industry, now enables banks, financial institutions, corporations and individuals to borrow or loan funds for short periods of time.

Burns Bros. & Company and Burns Bros. & Denton will continue to take great such in the diversity of their activities through which they are able to meet the varying requirements of an expanding clientele.

Aerial view of major portion of Miron & Freres' plant.

MIRON & FRERES LIMITED

The year was 1928, the place Montreal. Two brothers of French-Canadian ancestry, by the name of Miron, pooled their resources, invested in a horse and buggy and started a small excavating and transportation company. Little did these two brothers realize then that 30 years later the name of Miron would be ranked among the foremost names in the building supply and excavation fields.

From this humble beginning, Miron & Freres Limited has grown steadily until today it is recognized as one of the largest organizations of its kind in the world.

In 1947 the Company was incorporated under the laws of the Province of Quebec and took over the holdings of the former companies which the Miron family had been operating for nearly twenty years.

All the operations of Miron & Freres, including those of its associated companies and subsidiaries, are centrally located at approximately the geographical centre of the Island of Montreal. Here are situated head office, plants and quarries, all in an area measuring some 20,000,000 square feet.

Miron & Freres chief business is concrete and the manufacture of concrete pipes and blocks. Crushed stone, another Miron & Freres specialty, is also used extensively by builders and contractors in and around the Montreal area. However, the Company is still well known for its excavation achievements and capabilities and the big yellow equipment, the hallmark of Miron & Freres, is almost sure to be seen wherever a construction project is taking place. At least 50 diesel powered shovels of all sizes, up to 6 cubic yards, feed over 300 modern trucks daily. In addition, two asphalt plants are going continuously around the clock, during the summer season, preparing different mixes for use in paving. During peak periods, Miron & Freres employ over 2,000 workers weekly.

The Company is especially proud of its four stationary concrete mixers, one of which is the largest in Canada. Mobile mixers, totalling 120, deliver the product throughout the surrounding areas.

Also to be found on Miron & Freres extensive property is the only manufactured sand plant and agricultural lime plant of its kind in the country. Here too, is one of the most modern concrete block plants with an actual capacity of 6,500 blocks an hour, making it also one of the largest in North America. All maintenance and repair work on the 1,000 mobile units and other equipment are carried out in the Company's spacious and ultra modern shops with the maximum of efficiency.

During the past three years, Miron & Freres have taken an active part in one of the greatest construction projects of all time... the St. Lawrence Seaway and Power Projects. Six contracts were awarded directly to the Company and its subsidiaries and an additional contract was undertaken by a joint venture group in which Miron & Freres had a substantial interest. The Company takes great pride in the fact that the first contract to be completed on the Seaway, the excavating and diking of the Cote Ste. Catherine channel, was terminated 8½ months ahead of schedule... a typical example of Miron & Freres capabilities.

The Company's concrete products were also used in tremendous quantities by other Seaway contractors. This included pre-mixed concrete, concrete pipes, crushed stone and stone dust.

With the completion of their Seaway contracts, Miron & Freres have turned their concentrated efforts to the construction of Montreal's new Metropolitan Boulevard.

These activities, briefly described above, summarize the buoyant life of a main Canadian enterprise which has all the stamina of a youthful organization and the solid know-how of a veteran company, combined under the direction of six brothers who started working relentlessly 25 years ago and who have not, as yet, found time to stop doing so.

Directors of Miron & Freres Limited are: Gerard Miron, Adrien Miron, Louis A. Lapointe, Q.C., Raymond Miron, Arthur Miron, Gilbert Miron, Vincent Miron, Jean Girard and Laurent Girard. The Officers are comprised of Gerard Miron, President and General Manager; Adrien Miron, 1st Vice-President; Raymond Miron, 2nd Vice-President; Louis A. Lapointe, Q.C., 3rd Vice-President; Laurent Girard, Secretary Treasurer.

Wire rope lifting stop logs at Iroquois Lock.

DOMINION WIRE ROPE LTD.

Since the beginning of time man has used rope to fulfill many of his needs. His crude house, his conveyance for crossing treacherous stretches of water, his weapons for hunting and protection of his family, all these and many more were bound together by man's first rope... the long vines that hung in abundance in the forests around him.

Today man uses rope for a great many more things than did his ancestors a thousand years ago. But he no longer has to make his own rope, he has machines which do the job for him, a great deal faster and much more efficiently. The first such machine was used in England in 1820 and it was about 60 years later than Dominion Wire Rope Ltd. became one of the first companies to manufacture wire rope in Canada.

One of the early wire ropes made by Dominion Wire Rope was for the Incline Railway at the Eastern end of Mount Royal in Montreal, Quebec. These particular ropes gave long and notable service.

Since its early beginnings in the old Grey Nunnery Building facing Norman Street in Montreal, the Company has relocated, enlarged and extended its premises and manufacturing facilities at Lachine, a suburb of Montreal. In this modernized plant at Lachine, Dominion Wire Rope Ltd. manufactures all sizes and types of wire ropes and strand, in addition to extruding nylon polymers, vinylites, etc. To wire rope, strand and synthetic cordage.

Dominion Wire Rope Ltd. were pioneers in Canada of synthetic cordage and a modern plant has recently been constructed for the exclusive manufacture of this type of cordage. Here highly trained personnel turn out miles of synthetic cordage to meet the ever-increasing demand of the consumer.

Few are the industries that do not make use of wire rope in one phase or another of their business and Dominion Wire Rope Limited has serviced a large proportion of them from Newfoundland, on the East Coast, to British Columbia on the West.

Dominion Wire Rope Ltd. has been associated with many of the big projects in Canada's expansion, and since the turn of the century the Company has been in the forefront of prime contractors for bridge strand and suspender ropes. Dominion supplied wire rope and strands for the International Thousand Islands Bridge. Dedicated in 1938, the Thousand Islands Bridge spans the St. Lawrence River between Collins Landing, New York, and Ivy Lea, Ontario. Built in five spans, the bridge is more than eight miles long, including five miles of connecting highway on Wellesley Island, one of the group of 1,800 picturesque islands in the St. Lawrence River.

Another bridge project which made full use of Dominion's renowned wire strand was the Isle of Orleans Bridge connecting the mainland of Quebec on the North Shore, a few miles below Quebec City, to the small island in the lower St. Lawrence River.

More recently there was the Angus L. McDonald Bridge spanning world famous Halifax Harbour in Nova Scotia. Notably the bridge is suspended from two main 13½-inch Dominion Wire Rope cables, each cable being composed of 61 strands 1 15/52 of an inch in diameter and each strand containing 51 steel wires. It is interesting to note that if all this wire were laid end to end it would span the distance from Halifax Harbour to the well known Rocky Mountains in the West.

The St. Lawrence Seaway and Power Project has naturally been a very large consumer of wire rope, and Dominion Wire Rope Ltd. is proud to have supplied immense quantities of these ropes to contractors on the Seaway. One of those was the railway lift bridge at the famed Indian Reservation at Caughnawaga on the outstkirts of Montreal. Another was the replacement of a portion of the ropes on the Welland Canal lift bridge in Ontario.

It can be said that Dominion Wire Rope Ltd. has contributed greatly to Canada's steady progress and the years of prosperity that are forecast for the country will see Dominion maintaining its place as one of the prime manufacturers of wire rope and cordage in North America.

Aerial view of Canadian Vickers plant, Montreal.

CANADIAN VICKERS LIMITED

The early wisdom of selecting a Montreal ship-building site at the foot of the Lachine Rapids has become more and more apparent as the natural development of Canada progresses toward its ultimate. In the pioneer days of 1911, the year of its birth, Canadian Vickers Ltd. stood at the gateway to the Seven Seas. Today, stationed at the entrance of the St. Lawrence Seaway and Power Projects, this company's vista extends, not only toward thousands of miles of salt water travel, but also inland towards the thousands of miles of fresh water routes. Where the ocean service ends and where lake waters finally pour from the Seaway locks, there you find Canada's extensive shipbuilding and repairing facilities complete with materials, machines and men, ready to launch new ships or to repair the disabled. There too, you find other machines and other men able to design and build the many and varied types of machinery and equipment necessary to Canada's thriving industries.

This wide-spread organization, founded by the worldwide Vickers Group, and established to build Canada's warships, has greatly developed its engineering branches and is now supplying machinery needs to a large number of diversified industries. It is only natural with 35 years of experience in the manufacturing of Hydraulic Gates and kindred equipment, that Canadian Vickers should be selected as one of the principal equipment suppliers for this International Seaway.

Of unique interest, in the overall construction of these Hydraulic Gates, was the universal application of modern welding designs and methods, especially developed to manufacture gates which are economic, structurally sound and easy to maintain. Welding was done by thoroughly qualified welders applying the most modern equipment in automatic and hand welding work.

Samples of welds and materials were constantly and vigourously tested in our Laboratories and prior to machining all weldments were stress relieved in our "car-

190

Aerial view of Canadian Vickers Limited basin, Montreal.

bottom" furnaces, the largest of which measures 18 ft. x 18 ft. x 82 ft. inside.

Thirteen pairs of important lock gates were supplied by Canadian Vickers for the St. Lawrence Seaway. Each pair of gates consisted of two leaves measuring 45 ft. in width and varying in height from 40 to 80 ft. — the height of an eight story building.

To handle a steadily increasing volume of hydro gates and other work, our Plate Shop has recently been extended to provide an extra floor area of 42,000 sq. ft. This new building has been fully equipped with heavy overhead cranes, modern automatic welders and kindred equipment, permitting final assembly, testing and checking.

Thirty-four sets of gate-operating mechanism of the strutsector gear and pinion type were also supplied to operate all gates in Canadian locks of the St. Lawrence Seaway.

The possibility of developing the great electric potential of the International Section in the St. Lawrence River has long been a cherished thought of both Cana-

dian and United States authorities. Both parties seized the opportnity of discussing this question when the Seaway construction was being planned and finalized; both agreed to avail themselves of the advantages offered in the dual and simultaneous construction of the power development and the Seaway system.

After bilateral discussions it was agreed that the Hydro-Electric Power Commission of Ontario and the United States authorities would each build half of a hydro-electric plant with an output of 1,920,000 KVA; this power house to carry 32 generators or 16 for each half. In the face of a strong international competition, Canadian Vickers Ltd. was awarded, by the Power Authority of the State of New York, an order for 32 control gates, each 50 ft. wide and 48 ft. high for installation at the Iroquois Control Dam, forming part of this project. This was the largest order ever filled by a Canadian company for gates of this type. Canadian Vickers' other contributions to this project have been the manufacturing and supply of six drum gates for the ice sluices at the power house, four of which are 75 ft. long while the other two are 50 ft. long, as well as a set of large stop logs for the control structure.

191

Previous to this undertaking the U.S. Corps of Engineers and the Hydro-Electric Power Commission of Ontario had developed an extensive program of water control at Grasse Island, a program which when completed would utilize the maximum power potential of Niagara Falls, and at the same time, preserve the natural beauty of this historical site. A structure 1500 ft. in length was erected and in it were placed 13 submersible flap type sluice gates to regulate the water flow. For this project Canadian Vickers supplied the gates, servo motor controls, embedded parts and other accessories.

In a favoured geographical position Canadian Vickers look with confidence to the future when greater use will be made of its facilities to design, construct, repair and convert all types of floating craft. Ship repairs of every kind can be carried out in our floating dry dock or in our deep water basin, emergency repairs can be undertaken also at dock sites. Specializing in conversion work and equipped to increase ship capacities to take advantage of the new Seaway draughts, we have already modified a number of bulk cargo vessels. Further upstream at the foot of the Lachine Canal is our subsidiary, Montreal Dry Dock Co., which offers other ship repairing facilities while at Quebec City we offer the services of our Lauzon plant, Geo. T. Davie & Sons Limited.

Damaged ship in dry dock at Canadian Vickers' basin.

Sluice gates under construction in Canadian Vickers' plate shop.

Lock gates being installed at St. Lambert Lock.

THE ROYAL BANK OF CANADA

The Royal Bank of Canada, whose Head Office is at 360 St. James St., Montreal, ranks first among all Canadian banks, fourth in North America and sixth in the Free World, having attained this high position in the space of 89 years. At the close of its Fiscal Year on November 30, 1957, the bank's total assets were $3,760,544,-617.

This noted Canadian institution traces its origins back to the Merchants Bank of Halifax, a single-branch local institution established in Halifax, N.S. in 1869. Interests in the sea and the markets which lay beyond the horizon came naturally to the seven Halifax merchants who founded the bank, an interest that has persisted through changing times and changing driectorates.

The growth of The Royal Bank and of the Dominion have gone hand-in-hand. From the very beginning, the bank has been a lusty child and has steadily expanded both in Canada and abroad. In the early years of the century, the bank was an integral part of the steady march west of Canadian development. In many a pioneer community, the 'Royal' was one of the first institutions to hang out its shingle and with the development of Canada's abundant natural resources and its growth as a leading industrial nation, the bank has played a vital role. In recent years, the expansion of economic activity in Canada's Northland has seen the opening of 'Royal' branches at such remote points as Frobisher Bay on Baffin Island and Port Radium, just south of the Arctic Circle.

Today, there are branches of the Royal Bank in every large centre of population in Canada and in hundreds of cities and towns from coast to coast. Each one is a "door" to business, and offers a natural avenue through which businessmen may explore sales, manufacturing, financial and production opportunities. In addition to providing all the usual banking services, each branch is a fruitful source of information on the area it serves. Local managers, fully familiar with their territories, and enjoying many useful business contacts, can be most helpful in securing "on the spot" information and providing sound counsel.

To co-ordinate and expedite enquiries, and to ensure that the bank's manifold services are made readily avail-

Head Office Building of The Royal Bank of Canada dominates the skyline of downtown Montreal. It is the heart and nerve centre of a network of more than 900 branches in Canada and abroad.

able to prospective as well as existing customers, the Royal Bank maintains a Business Development Department at Head Office in Montreal. Experienced officers, familiar with all phases of the bank's activities and connections, act as liaison between the client and the departments, branches and outside organizations concerned.

The object of the Business Development Department is to provide assistance, information and advice to businessmen and firms wishing to establish, expand or consolidate operations in Canada. Wide contacts, built up over the years throughout Canada and abroad, enable the bank to bring together businessmen and firms with mutual interests, to the benefit of both.

In the foreign trade field, the Royal Bank is a leader. Of its more than 915 branches, no less than 84 are in countries outside the Dominion. In South America, it has operated branches for over 40 years and is, in fact, the only Canadian bank with offices in the Southern continent. The Royal Bank of Canada's first branch in the Caribbean area was established in Cuba in 1899. Today, branches serve most of the islands of The West Indies Federation and the Carribean. There are important offices in London, Paris and New York and the bank has correspondent relations with leading banking institutions throughout the world. It also maintains special representaitves at strategic points in the United States and he Far East.

At Head Office the bank maintains a Credit Information Service, organized on a world-wide basis, to provide essential facts to those engaged in the import and export business. To keep themselves informed of new trends and developments, senior officers make periodic trips abroad, establishing new contacts and investigating new opportunities for trade and improved banking services.

Since World War II, the interchange of goods and services between Canada and countries where the 'Royal' is represented has expanded tremendously, and prospects for continued growth are even further enhanced with the coming into operation of the St. Lawrence Seaway. The Royal Bank of Canada will continue to play an important role in the financial aspects of this trade, serving businessmen of the countries concerned in a special and worthwhile fashion.

Partial view of Barnhart Island Power Dam, looking toward Canada, showing the construction as it was in January, 1958. Six months later, generators were turning. The dam was built by a Perini Corporation managed group of contractors.

PERINI CORPORATION

With the curtain set to go up on the final act of one of man's greatest construction achievements, in April 1959, it is only fitting that we pay tribute to one of the principal contractors, Perini Corporation of Framingham, Massachusetts, who toiled day in and day out, through all kinds of weather, for the past four years, building the deep waterway navigational facilities as well as the United States half of the Barnhart Island Power Dam.

Perini Corporation, one of the word's foremost heavy duty construction firms, participated in almost every major operation on the American half of the St. Lawrence Seaway and Power Projects in the International Section.

The Barnhart Island Power Dam, awarded to a Perini-managed Joint Venture by the Power Authority of the State of New York, spans the north channel at the lower end of Barnhart Island, with one half in the United States and the other in Canada. Measuring 3,120 feet in length, the power dam consists of a massive concrete intake structure and the powerhouse itself, which is directly downstream and integral with the intake structure. The deck of the intake is 162 feet above the low point of the draft tubes and the maximum power head is about 87 feet. Water is admitted through the intake to the powerhouse where it drives 32 turbine-generator units, 16 on each side of the International Boundary, developing 2,200,000 HP, surpassed only by Grand Coulee Dam in the United States.

The Bertrand H. Snell Lock, awarded to Grasse River Lock Constructors, a joint venture headed by the Perini Corp. by the St. Lawrence Seaway Development Corporation in 1954, is the downstream entrance to the Wiley-Dondero ship channel. Built at a cost of over $25,000,000. the Lock like its sister, the Dwight D. Eisenhower Lock, is 800 feet long, 80 feet wide and 30

feet over the sills and has a lifting or lowering capacity of 45 feet.

Perini Corporation also participated in the joint venture construction of the Long Sault Dam which forms the main control structure for the Barnhart Island Powerhouse. Through its spillways runs all excess waters not needed to keep the head of water in the power pool required for the operation of the hydro electric power dam downstream. This dam, located entirely in United States territory, is a concrete gravity structure with its axis curved upstream. It has a maximum height above foundations of 145 feet and coupled with the Barnhart Island Dam, is capable of raising the water level about 90 feet above the river bottom.

One would surmise after reading the foregoing that Perini Corporation must have had a very elaborate beginning. On the contrary, this Company had a very humble beginning, which in fact, can be traced back to a garden in Switzerland.

Bonfiglio Perini, founder of B. Perini & Sons, was born in the year 1863 in the little Italian town of Gotolengo. While still a boy, he started work as a gardener for the Rothschilds in Switzerland. It was whilst here that he learned the rudiments of stone work and road construction for, among other things, he was responsible for the walls and driveways on the extensive grounds.

It was also during this time that Bonfiglio Perini became obsessed with the idea of coming to America, and after travelling to France, where he worked for a year and a half to earn enough money for his passage, he finally arrived in New York in 1885 at the age of twenty-one.

From New York, Bonfiglio Perini went to Boston where he worked as a common laborer and later, being an ambitious man, hired a few men to move dirt and stone on a sub-contract basis. This was the first step to his success as a prime contractor.

Bonfiglio Perini went into business for himself around 1900. Most of his earliest projects were sections of highway and bridges for the Massachusetts Department of Public Works.

These were hard working days for everyone As each son came along, he started in the construction business at six years of age by carrying water to the men at ten cents an hour for a full six day week, at the same time attending school and learning other construction skills as schooling permitted.

In January of 1918, the elder Perini incorporated his business as B. Perini & Sons, Incorporated, now known as Perini Corporation. The oldest Perini boy, Fred, since retired from the firm, was then 25 years old; Joseph, now treasurer was 18, and Louis, now President was 15. For the next seven years the Company was occupied primarily with highway work. In 1917 Perini built the first Federal-Aid hot mix, then called Topeka mix, project in the State of Rhode Island, and two years later the first Federal-Aid penetration-type macadam highway in Vermont, a job superintended by Joseph Perini.

Bonfiglio Perini died in 1924 at the age of 61, and the full load fell on the shoulders of his sons Fred, Joseph, Louis and a younger boy Charles. The year 1924 was also a critical one, business-wise, for the Perini family. They had submitted a low bid of $350,000 on a road job in the vicinity of Lakeville, Massachusetts, which was the largest single project they had ever tackled. The Commonwealth of Massachusetts was also looking to greater achievements for this was the largest contract the State had advertised to that time. The Perini boys, however, were able to convince the State and a bonding company that they could perform the work, with result the job was a success and a cycle of steady growth was begun.

In the early thirties, Perini Corporation ventured extensively into larger and more varied contracts, among which was the widening and deepening of the Cape Cod Canal in Massachusetts. Here Perini pioneered with the first bottom dump Euclids for moving the large quantities of earth involved and also built the revetment with granite blocks.

During World War II, Perini participated in various types of war work which included paving, railroad installations, grading and drainage. Post war projects included construction of Boston's Logan International Airport and the Maine Turnpike, an outstanding heavy duty asphaltic concrete dual expressway extending nearly fifty miles from Portsmouth, New Hampshire to Portland, Maine.

In 1946 Perini added a Building Division to its growing organization and carried out such outstanding

projects as the construction of the New England Telephone and Telegraph Building at Haverhill, Massachusetts; the Vermont State Office Building, a handsome structure of peerless Vermont marble at Montpelier and some good sized housing projects, two amounting to over $6,000,000 each at Worcester, Massachusetts and Hartford, Connecticut. In all the Building Division has constructed over 3,500 units of housing totaling in excess of $35,000,000.

In Canada, Perini Corporation has contributed greatly to the growth of the country. For the Hydro Electric Power Commission of Ontario, Perini managed a joint venture for the construction of twin hydraulic tunnels 51 feet in rough diameter — about the size of a four-storey building — and running from above Niagara Falls' rushing water on an average of 300 feet in depth under the city of Niagara Falls, Ontario to the Sir Adam Beck — Niagara generating station #2; for the Quebec Hydro Electric Commission Perini has had a major part in the fashioning of mighty Bersimis 1 and Bersimis 2 power projects in the virgin forests of northern Quebec, both projects involving long tunnels and both underground and outside powerhouses and tailrace tunnels; for the Aluminum Company of Canada Limited, Perini Quebec, Inc. has built a tremendous underground powerhouse with seven miles of supply tunnel and appurtenant tunnels to service the powerhouse, a project in the sum of approximately $75,000,000.

Perini Limited has built some of the largest and most handsome structures in the Province of Ontario both in the cities of Toronto and Ottawa, as well as three uranium mills in the Blind River area; one of these, for Consolidated Denison Mines Limited, the largest in all the world. Both Perini Limited and a younger company, Perini Pacific Limited of Vancouver, B. C. not only bid competitively for Provincial and Federal Governments but number among their private clients some of the outstanding industrial companies in the nation. Majestic Contractor's Limited, the Perini pipeline subsidiary, has built hundreds of miles of the Trans-Canada mainline for natural gas transmission and also oil pipelines for the major oil companies of Canada, and distribution work in the more heavily populated cities.

The Perini brothers own the World Champion Milwaukee Braves and have during the past 15 years guided their development from a second division ball club to the present eminence as an annual contender for top baseball honors.

This, then, is the story of a giant contracting concern with only a partial list of achievements mentioned due to our limited space. However, were Bonfiglio Perini alive today he would be proud of his sons who carried on where he left off and built Perini Corporation into one of the world's most respected names in the construction business.

31,000 tons, deadweight ore carrier "RUTH LAKE" built by Swan, Hunter, & Wigham Richardson, Ltd., at their Wallsend Shipyard for Iron Ore Transport Company Limited of Canada.

SWAN, HUNTER, & WIGHAM RICHARDSON
Limited

With the official opening of the St. Lawrence Seaway and Power Projects in the Spring of 1959, residents along the banks of the joint Canada-U.S.A. deep waterway system will see for the first time in their lives, giant, weather beaten ships of all nationalities plying these waters daily during the navigation season.

Among these will be the huge ore carriers like the "RUTH LAKE", pictured above. This vessel, 31,000 tons deadweight, was built by Swan, Hunter, & Wigham Richardson, Limited, of Wallsend-on-Tyne, England, for Iron Ore Transport Company Limited of Canada.

A respected name in the shipbuilding industry, the firm of Swan, Hunter, & Wigham Richardson was formed in 1903 on the amalgamation of the two famous shipbuilding and engineering firms on the River Tyne, C. S. Swan & Hunter Limited, and Wigham Richardson & Company Limited. The Company took over the Tyne Pontoons and Dry Docks Company, which gave them a continuous river frontage of 4,000 feet, with the works area taking up almost 80 acres. They also acquired The Wallsend Slipway & Engineering Company.

In 1912, Swan, Hunter, & Wigham Richardson further enlarged their business through the acquisition of Barclay, Curle & Company Limited, shipbuilders, repairers and engineers on the River Clyde in Scotland.

The Company's ship repairing facilities on the Tyne include 5 dry docks, one of which measures 715 feet in length and is the largest privately owned dry dock on England's East Coast. On the River Clyde two dry docks up to 650 feet and three graving docks up to 880 feet in length are continuously in use.

To maintain its position as a leader in the shipbuilding industry... the Company has headed the world's list of annual shipbuilding tonnage output on no less than eight occasions... Swan, Hunter, & Wigham Richardson has been spending considerable sums in the reconstruction of its Works. At the Wallsend yard a large prefabricating shed, two new berths with 10-ton and 55-ton travelling cranes and a new beam shed and shell plate shop have been constructed. While at Neptune Works reconstruction works include a new deep water quay capable of handling two ships lying alongside. New features at Clydeholm Shipyard include a Joiners shop, and construction of a berth to accommodate oil tankers up to 45,000 tons deadweight.

In the field of ship propulsion, Swan, Hunter, & Wigham Richardson own three engineering works, two on the Tyne and one on the Clyde with a total annual output capacity of over 500,000 I.H.P. The latest type of machinery... steam reciprocating, turbine and diesel ... are manufactured at these works. Doxford type diesels are the principal engines manufactured, but licences are also held to build Sulzer, Werkspoor, Atlas, Polar and Stork engines in addition to free piston machinery with Pescara type gasifyers. Boilers and oil burning installations for both the marine and shore industrial fields are also manufactured by the Company's Engine Works. More recently the Company has linked up with the Nuclear Power Plant Company for the development of the design and construction of nuclear powered ships.

Some of the world's finest ships have been built by the Swan, Hunter, & Wigham Richardson Group. These include the famed liner MAURETANIA, built in 1907 and for 22 years holder of the Atlantic Blue Ribbon... the 27,155 ton DOMINION MONARCH, built in 1938 and regarded as the most powerful motorship of her day... the passenger liner BERGENSFJORD, flagship of the Norwegian Mercantile Marine, built in 1956 ... the 21,000 ton troopship NEVASA, capable of carrying 1,000 troops in addition to 500 other passengers... twenty-three cable ships including the MONARCH, which laid the Trans Atlantic telephone cable. A total of 125 vessels of nearly half a million gross tons was built for the British Admiralty during the Second World War by the Company.

Britain's largest tanker when launched in 1950, the 28,000 ton VELUTINA, came from the Company's yards as did the 38,000 ton ZAPHON in 1957, the largest tanker to be launched on England's North East Coast. The Company plans to start work on tankers of 65,000 tons deadweight in the near future.

This then is the story of a great shipbuilding company whose products will soon be seen sailing by our very doors in the inland ports of Canada and U.S.A.

TWO NEW B of M BUILDINGS — the office built last year in the new section of Iroquois, replacing the original building in the old part of the town, now inundated; and a model of the projected $10,000,000 head-office building in Montreal, to be completed in 1961. The Iroquois office is typical of several B of M branches built in the Seaway area, while the new head-office structure will be the bank's largest building in Canada, from which the B of M's world-wide operations will be directed.

BANK OF MONTREAL

The Bank of Montreal's part in the realization of the St. Lawrence Seaway goes back more than a century and a quarter to the year 1821, when the original Lachine Canal, venerable ancestor of the mighty waterway, was built. Then, as in practically all phases of the development of the Canadian nation for the past 141 years, the B of M made a notable contribution, for it was Canada's first bank which financed the construction of the canal.

In recent years, several B of M branches along the course of the Seaway have been closed, and others have been built to replace them, reflecting changing requirements. Inundated forever are the B of M offices at Wales, Aultsville and Mille Roches, and those in the old sections of Morrisburg and Iroquois, all of which formerly served a considerable population. Now, new offices have sprung up to take their places in ultra-modern shopping-centre locations.

The Morrisburg branch was the oldest of those to go, having been opened in 1872 and now re-located about a quarter-of-a-mile to the north of its former site. At Iroquois, the office dating back to 1902 was shifted about a mile north, to the new township of Iroquois. The B of M branch at Wales, established in 1903, which also served Dickenson's Landing and Farran's Point, as well as supervising operations of the Aultsville office, has closed down completely and has been replaced by a branch in the new township of Ingleside.

But perhaps it was the office with the shortest history, that at Mille Roches, which best typified the B of M's long-standing policy of providing service as and when required. Mille Roches branch had a life of less than three years and at the time of its opening in 1954 — to provide full banking service for construction workers and others in the area — it was already known that the office would be abandoned within a short time.

Early Influence

In considering the international cooperation exemplified in the joint Canadian-United States construction of the Seaway, it is appropriate to point to the substantial contribution made to Canadian-U.S. trade by the B of M since the early days of the nineteenth century.

Only a few months after the B of M was established in Montreal on November 3, 1817, Messrs. Prime, Ward and Sands were appointed agents of the bank in New York. The B of M's own agency was established in 1859 — first Canadian bank in the U.S. Today the bank conducts extensive business in the U.S. and has offices in Chicago and San Francisco, as well as in New York.

The bank as a whole has grown to the point where it comprises more than 750 offices from coast to coast in Canada and abroad, with assets of approximately $3,000,000,000, and with a staff of some 13,000 men and women.

When the B of M was established in 1817, Canada had no native currency, and trade was conducted largely by barter. Immediately it began operations, the B of M introduced its own bills — Canada's first real money — to replace the foreign currency then in use.

To the B of M also goes credit for the establishment of the Canadian branch-banking system which has proved a major factor in Canada's concurrent growth and relative economic stability.

During the last decade, too, the bank has continued in this pioneering spirit, introducing many innovations and establishing offices wherever the need has arisen. Two such branches are those at Kitimat, B.C., and at Frobisher Airport, only 200 miles south of the Arctic Circle.

Excavating for canal and lock at Iroquois, Ont.

Euclids being loaded by big power shovel.

EUCLID DIVISION G M C

Division of General Motors Corporation
Cleveland 17, Ohio

Moving Earth and Rock
to Make the Waterway

A miracle of modern earthmoving, the St. Lawrence Seaway and Power Projects would have required many years to build and would not have been economically feasible without large capacity, high speed construction equipment typified by Euclid earthmovers

Euclid Division of General Motors Corporation with headquarters in Cleveland, Ohio, salutes those who have built North America's new "main street".

In scope and in trying conditions, the Seaway proved to be a most difficult earthmoving operation for contractors on both sides of the river. Unusual extremes in weather, unanticipated earth conditions, remoteness from established sources of materials, parts and service created a real challenge to the qualities and capabilities of men and the earthmoving machinery selected by those contractors who were awarded Seaway work. The preference for job-proved Euclid equipment is indicated by an overwhelming majority of rubber-tired "Eucs" on

the various projects. At one early count, over 500 of these mammoth dirtmovers were doing their share in bringing the Seaway nearer to completion.

To adequately handle this large population of Euclid equipment, Euclid dealers serving the Seaway area on both sides of the river set up special facilities and made special arrangements to provide almost immediate service and ready availability of parts in order to keep the machines working at maximum efficiency.

Specializing exclusively in the design and manufacture of equipment for moving such materials as earth, rock, coal, ore and logs, Euclid consistently sets the pace for the industry. As a result, 9 out of 11 of all "Eucs" ever built are still in service and 60% of those sold today are repeat orders from previous owners.

Although Euclid manufactures the most complete line of earthmoving equipment in the industry, the nature of the Seaway problems resulted in wide use of only Rear-Dumps and Bottom-Dumps. Nonetheless, several scrapers, including seven high production Twin-Power units were utilized where conditions made the use of this type of machine practical. Twin-Power Scrapers are an exclusive Euclid development incorporating the use of two engines, one in the tractor and one located behind the scraper bowl, each with its own Torqmatic Drive. "Twins" provide unmatched power and performance.

Euclid earthmovers are found at work in many parts of the globe — building roads, dams and airports; leveling plant sites, hauling coal and ore, speeding quarry and stockpiling operations. Whatever the job may be, "Eucs" excel in performance, production and long service life as proved in over 25 years of field experience.

Hauling earth and stone from Iroquois Lock.

Euclids building the cofferdam to dry up Long Sault Rapids to permit building of power dam downstream. When power plant was completed, cofferdam was blown and hugh power pool formed to operate the power plant.

Aerial view of Eisenhower Lock looking downstream. View shows the lock before water was permitted to enter. Note roadway running beneath the lock.

Massena, N.Y. Intake-water from the newly formed power pool pours through the intake to provide water for the City of Massena and the Power Canal.

MORRISON-KNUDSEN COMPANY, INC.

The Spring of 1959 will see the inauguration of one of man's greatest engineering achievements... the St. Lawrence Seaway. But long before that, ships from the Seven Seas will have sailed through a massive, basin-like structure of concrete and steel near the town of Massena, New York.

The structure, part of the joint Canada-U.S.A. deep waterway, is the Dwight D. Eisenhower Lock, one in a series of giant-size steps in a new stairway of ship locks and channels enabling deep draft navigation all the way from the Atlantic Ocean to the inner Great Lakes.

The Eisenhower Lock, a tribute to America's great leader, President Dwight D. Eisenhower, was constructed by the Morrison-Knudsen Company, Inc., of Boise, Idaho, sponsor of a joint venture operation with other contractors.

The name Morrisson-Knudsen is a "Gibraltar" in the construction world. Established in 1912 by Harry Winford Morrison and Morris H. Knudsen as a firm of construction contractors to compete for the building of reclamation works, roads, railroads and miscellaneous heavy construction projects, M-K is known throughout the globe as one of the largest of the big contractors. They have expanded extensively through the organization of subsidiary and affiliated companies in Canada, Central and South America, Mexico, England, Morocco, Turkey, Iran, Iraq, Pakistan, Afghanistan, Indonesia, Korea, Philippine Islands, Australia and New Zealand.

Their contribution to the billion-dollar Seaway navigation and power project was indeed a major one. They were commissioned to build three projects of great importance. The first one was the enlargement of the Galop Island South Channel, near Ogdensburg, New

York, under a contract with the Power Authority of the State of New York. Approximately 6,500,000 cubic yards of earth and rock were excavated in the improvement of this channel. The second was the Massena Intake, a dam-like structure of concrete with adjoining earthen dikes, which serves a dual purpose in the new waterway system. The third one was the Eisenhower Lock, previously mentioned.

The Massena Intake was necessary to help wall off the vast new power pool created by the St. Lawrence Power Dam and the nearby Long Sault Dam. Also, the Intake is vital to the operation of the Aluminum Company of America plant and to the town of Massena itself as its domestic water supply will be provided through four huge pumps installed in this structure.

The Eisenhower Lock, standing within the Wiley-Dondero Canal, formerly called Long Sault Canal, is some 3½ miles upstream from its "cousin," the Bertrand H. Snell Lock. The last named Lock was built by Perini Corporation, sponsors of a five-company joint venture in which Morrison-Knudsen also participated. Both Locks were constructed under contracts awarded by the Corps of Engineers of the U. S. Army, the contracting agency for the Saint Lawrence Seaway Development Corporation of the U. S. Government.

Built to handle vessels up to 768 feet in length with a 27-foot draft, the Eisenhower Lock measures 80 feet in width. It can raise or lower a ship the 45 feet separating the downstream flow level of the canal and the upstream pool created by the dams.

Passing beneath the upstream end of the Eisenhower Lock is a concrete-lined 24-foot wide highway tunnel through which traffic can flow freely.

An additional feature of the Morrison-Knudsen built lock is the huge vertical lift gate weighing 965,000 pounds which can be raised from out of a recess in the bottom of the upstream end of the Lock for the purpose of sealing off all water in the event of an emergency.

Constructed of welded steel sections, the main operating gates at both ends of the Lock are of the mitre type that swing on giant hinges. The upstream gate reaches a height of 45 feet while the downstream "double door" measures 85 feet from top to bottom.

Forming the sides of the Lock are concrete walls as thick as 78 feet at the base and 115 feet in height. A total of 510,000 cubic yards of concrete was poured into the gigantic structure. Included in this figure was the enormous quantity of masonry required for the 50-foot high guide walls that reach out nearly a quarter of a mile from both ends of the Lock to help shepherd ships into it.

Unlike masonry dams that are practically solid masses of concrete, the Eisenhower Lock is practically half structural type concrete which involved intricate form-work and the embedding of hundreds of items such as mooring bits, hoisting gear, valves and strips of steel armor to guard against damage from ships' hulls scraping the walls. The lower walls also are honeycombed with culverts and ports that fill and empty the actual lock chamber with water.

While Morrison-Knudsen employees were toiling vigorously on the huge Eisenhower Lock, their confreres were busy constructing the Massena Intake a few miles away.

The contract for the Massena Intake was awarded Morrison-Knudsen and associates in August, 1955 by the Power Authority of the State of New York. The work was completed in December, 1957.

Construction of the Intake required a total of 194,000 cubic yards of concrete and 2,350,000 cubic yards of earth moving, including some 650,000 cubic yards of material that was compacted into the dikes flanking the structure.

The Intake blocks the old Massena Power Canal, a three-mile channel that was opened in 1903 by the Aluminum Company of America to carry water from the St. Lawrence to a power-house serving Alcoa's Massena plant with what was originally the first electricity used in the commercial production of aluminum in the United States.

The canal in which the Intake stands is a river in itself, for the waterway carries a swirling flow of 25,000 cubic feet of water per second.

Built in two separate sections... one during the 1956 work season and the other in 1957... the Intake measures 118 feet in maximum height and 3,990 feet in total length, including the earthen dikes.

One of the main features of the Massena Intake is its 145-foot long pumphouse block, which includes four big pumping units with provision for future installation of two additional units. Each pump has a 600-horsepower motor capable of delivering 10,000 gallons of water per minute.

Morrison-Knudsen was a joint venture partner of Peter Kiewit Sons' Co., who sponsored operations under contracts for two of the largest and most difficult excavation projects of the St. Lawrence Seaway and Power Development. One contract, awarded by the Corps of Engineers of the U. S. Army, involved excavation of the Wiley-Dondero (Long Sault) Canal. The other contract, awarded by the Power Authority of the State of New York, involved widening and deepening of the river channel for power-pool and navigation purposes at Point Three Points, located some 20 miles upstream, near the town of Waddington.

Excavation of the Wiley-Dondero Canal, a broad, man-made waterway that carries ships around the International Rapids section of the St. Lawrence River where it is dammed for power near Massena, was started in June, 1955. At the peak of operations during the summer of 1957, the two PK-MK jobs were working a massive array of as many as 20 big power shovels and 116 trucks and self-propelled scrapers.

Under two separate contracts awarded by the St. Lawrence Seaway Authority of Canada, Canadian subsidiaries of Morrison-Knudsen excavated approximately six miles of channel and built six miles of dikes near Laprairie, Quebec for the Lachine Section of the Seaway on the Canadian side.

Morrison-Knudsen also had joint venture participations in contracts awarded by the Power Authority of the State of New York for construction of Long Sault Dam and Barnhart Island Power Plant, other key units of the St. Lawrence Seaway and Power Development. The first named was constructed under the sponsorship of Walsh Construction Company; the second, under the sponsorship of Perini Corporation.

The movement of ships from the far corners of the world through the Wiley-Dondero Canal and into the Eisenhower Lock, marks the achievement of a great engineering and construction triumph over formidable natural difficulties. To the men of Morrison-Knudsen — the company whose name is associated with the building of Hoover Dam, San Francisco Bay Bridge, Grand Coulee Dam Pumping Plant, the Great Salt Lake Causeway, the Kemano Underground Power Plant in British Columbia, Canada, and numerous other dams, railroads and industrial facilities throughout the world — goes the satisfaction of having met successfully another great construction challenge.

Aerial view of Canadian Ingersoll-Rand plant at Sherbrooke, Que.

CANADIAN INGERSOLL-RAND COMPANY LIMITED

Air under pressure has been put to practical use since time immemorial but it was only in 1871 that compressed air became a decided factor in the world's industrial progress.

In that year, air compressors and pneumatic rock drills were developed on a commercial scale, thus solving many problems associated with the use of steam — and compressed air began to play an increasingly important part in construction, mining and subsequently in general industry throughout the world.

Since that time in Canada many marvellous undertakings in engineering construction, of which the St. Lawrence Seaway and Power Project is one of the leading examples, have become substantially more practical by the use of air compressors driving pneumatic drills and other air powered equipment. To provide these tools of progress as early as 1882 the Ingersoll-Rock Drill Company of Canada set up shop in Montreal. Seven years later in Sherbrooke, Quebec the Canadian Rand Drill Company was formed under the terms of an agreement between two enterprising Canadians, the Jenckes

Brothers, who were already producing mining machinery in that city, and the Rand Drill Company of New York. Following the amalgamation of the Ingersoll and Rand Companies in the States in 1906, the Canadian Ingersoll-Rand Company was incorporated in 1912 and ever since has been closely identified not only with construction and mining but with virtually every phase of industry in Canada and many foreign countries.

The application of compressed air has expanded considerably over the years — to the extent that Canadian Ingersoll-Rand will help not only to build the "Seaway" but will provide de-watering pumps for the permanent lock installations, machines for the factories and other industrial establishments and for the municipal expansion that will naturally follow the completion of this trade route to the continent's interior and the new availability of thousands more kilowatts of hydro electric power.

Air operated production tools are now vital to the efficiency of most manufacturing industries. Air pres-

202

Large diameter blast hole truck mounted drill working beside a crawler mounted machine on Seaway, opposite Montreal.

Drill boat on Welland Canal during deepening operations for 27' draft Seaway.

sure and its opposite force vacuum, is used extensively in the chemical and process industries.

Canadian Ingersoll-Rand has applied its plant to the production of other lines of equipment that will help all our country's industries benefit from the economic impetus expected from the Seaway. It also manufactures a complete line of pumps, pulp and paper machinery, electric and air hoists for mines, and a new machine that makes the coal miner's work considerably safer and more productive.

Through the years Canadian Ingersoll-Rand has been expanding its plant facilities and the skills of its people both in the 25 acre factory at Sherbrooke and in branch offices in every Province of the Dominion. It has done this with faith in the nation builders, the men of vision who conceive and build such projects as the St. Lawrence Seaway and Power Project — with faith in their long range objectives, based on a sensible development of our country's natural resources, and continuing attention to the building of a strong manufacturing industry with markets all over the world.

CIR dewatering pumps as installed at all Canadian Seaway locks.

CIR air compressors used during construction of the Seaway and in Canadian industry.

MLW stop logs being swung into place at Iroquois Lock.

MONTREAL LOCOMOTIVE WORKS, LIMITED

Brought to bear whenever repairs are needed at lock gates along the Canadian portion of the St. Lawrence Seaway is special equipment manufactured by one of Canada's oldest and most respected industrial concerns: Montreal Locomotive Works, Limited.

The procedure, thanks to this equipment, is a simple one. Via slots left in the deep concrete lock walls, massive steel stop logs are lowered by crane. They are stacked in sets of ten at both ends of the lock, forming a temporary but thoroughly watertight barrier. Against them laps the river while repairs are made "in the dry."

For the five Canadian locks between St. Lambert, Quebec and Iroquois, Ontario, 102 of these steel stop logs were needed. Each is 86 feet long, and weighs 32 tons. All, together with ten lifting booms, were fashioned at MLW's plant in east-end Montreal.

At first, the picture of a famous locomotive builder manufacturing equipment for a great waterway may seem a paradox. But nowadays the very name "Montreal Locomotive Works" is a little deceptive. True, the company builds locomotives — scores of them each year. Not only in Canada but in several foreign lands as well, MLW diesel-electrics every day perform the countless different hauling jobs that together spell railroading. In dozens of freight yards, as this is being read, MLW switchers are busy moving boxcars and making up trains. Elsewhere, streaking across prairie plains, through narrow mountain passes, into the great cities and the tiny hamlets of three continents, MLW road diesels are hauling long cargoes of passengers and freight.

During the past decade, more than one thousand new diesel-electric locomotives have rolled from the production line at MLW's Montreal shops, freshly painted in the colors of 24 different railroads. But for several years

now, not content with producing only locomotives, MLW has been reaching into new fields. As the owner of one of Canada's largest and best-equipped machine shops, and the employer of a team of skilled and dedicated specialists, it was geared to produce almost any conceivable type of equipment fashioned from steel. And so diversification became its keynote, and stop logs for the Seaway a quite natural development.

Today at Montreal Locomotive Works, a youthful enthusiasm for new ideas blends with the patient craftsmanship born of nearly half a century of manufacturing experience.

As a direct result, MLW has become one of Canada's leading builders of heat exchangers, pressure vessels, condensers, reboilers and towers for the petroleum refining industry. Chemical processing plants also look to it for heat exchangers, pressure vessels and towers.

For the steel industry, the company manufactures rolling mill machinery, and components both for rolling mills and blast furnaces. Machinery and equipment for the pulp and paper industry is still another MLW specialty.

Many Canadian cities and towns buy water and sewer pipe bearing the MLW brand, while for the power industry, both thermal and hydraulic, Montreal Locomotive manufactures feedwater heaters, evaporators, penstocks and welded steel pipe. Inland waterways, which have also been customers for this pipe, buy lock gates and machinery and, of course, stop logs.

All these — and the list grows longer each year — together with an expanding general business in plate fabrication and machine work' are evidence of the new look today behind one of the proudest names in Canadian manufacturing.

St. Lawrence River near Morrisburg, Ontario

THE CANADIAN BANK OF COMMERCE
The Seaway and World Trade

From its earliest years The Canadian Bank of Commerce has been active in promoting and facilitating Canada's overseas trade in all parts of the world.

The opening up of the Great Lakes to ocean-going cargo vessels will give Canada a vast new "seaboard" which will greatly facilitate the export of our products and which should benefit the entire economy.

The Canadian Bank of Commerce, which was founded in Toronto in 1867, opened its first agency outside Canada at New York City in 1872, but even before that date was doing a brisk foreign business through correspondent banks.

In 1900 a branch was established at Seattle, Wash., and in the following year, when the Bank of British Columbia joined The Commerce, the Bank gained branches at Portland, Ore., San Francisco and London, England.

Today the Bank has branches at Bridgetown, Barbados; Kingston and Port Antonio, Jamaica; Port of Spain, Trinidad; Nassau, Bahamas; a second London

branch in Berkeley Square, and resident representatives in Chicago, and Dallas, Texas. A second California branch, at Los Angeles, is now incorporated with the San Francisco branch in The Canadian Bank of Commerce (California), a wholly owned subsidiary of the Bank.

Domestic branches in Canada today number more than 775, and are located from coast to coast and as far north as Inuvik, 60 miles from the Arctic Ocean.

For any aspect of Canadian trade at home or abroad, The Canadian Bank of Commerce offers the finest of facilities and a body of experience accumulated during more than ninety years of growing with Canada.

As we enter a new era of world trade with the opening of the Seaway, The Canadian Bank of Commerce stands ready with all its facilities to assist in the further growth of Canada's commerce at home and abroad.

More than 775 branches across Canada ready to serve YOU

Long Sault Dam — looking upstream at the huge control dam after the power pool was raised to elevation 238.

WALSH CONSTRUCTION COMPANY

Since the end of hostilities in 1945, Canada has made great strides towards becoming a major power among the leading nations of the world. Her frontiers have been pushed back, exposing unlimited mineral wealth. New industries have come into being almost overnight. But what is regarded as probably her greatest achievement, one which will benefit not only her own people, but the rest of the free world as well, was her decision to build, along with her neighbor, the United States, a much needed deep waterway system leading from the Atlantic ocean to the Great Lakes. This waterway, the St. Lawrence Seaway and Power Development project, commenced in 1954, will become a reality in the Spring of 1959, but only through the relentless efforts of the world's foremost construction companies who threw their full resources behind this gigantic project.

A typical example is the Walsh Construction Company at Davenport, Iowa, sponsors of the $32,300,000 Long Sault Dam contract in the International Section, and the $5,294,000 channel excavating and dike building contract in the Laprairie Basin, in the Montreal area of the Seaway. While the former contract was awarded by the Power Authority of the State of New York, the latter was placed by the St. Lawrence Seaway Authority for the Canadian Government and was accomplished by Walsh-Canadian Construction Company Limited.

In addition, Walsh took part in four other joint venture contracts for the Seaway. These were the Barnhart Island Power House, the huge Massena Intake, the Dwight D. Eisenhower Lock, and the Bertrand H. Snell Lock.

The history of one of the world's major construction companies dates back to the year 1899, at which time the Company was incorporated in the State of Iowa. For 59 years Walsh Construction Company has been in continuous and active operation and has completed construction projects of all types valued at over $2,000,000,000.

The corporate office is located in Davenport, and the executive and administrative office is maintained in New York City. The executive management and control of all construction projects, as well as the financing and accounting control, is operated from the New York office.

A branch office of the Company is located in San Francisco, California, and other branch offices with an executive in charge, are established from time to time as may be advantageous for close supervision of work under operation.

The Walsh-Canadian Construction Company, Limited, a subsidiary of the Walsh Construction Company, was established in 1954 with headquarters in Montreal. Other projects are being actively carried on in Canada at the present time for which the administrative and financial resources of the parent company are available at all times.

Walsh's pioneer organization was made up of alert and energetic men who, by their skill and industry, set high standards of performance and workmanship which launched their enterprise into a successful career. In its nearly 60 years of existence, Walsh has progressed from the days of "mules and men" through the early stages of mechanization and into the modern and intricate construction practices of today. Experiences along the way have been many and varied.

It is appropriate to point out that Walsh has not limited its work to any specialized type. Their long list of completed and current project, represents a fair cross section of the entire construction field, including railroads, bridges, industrial and office buildings, hard rock and soft ground tunnels, pneumatic shield tunnels, earth and concrete dams, dry docks, shipyard construction and ship building, air fields, military construction with appurtenant utilities, water supply and sewer systems, and sewage disposal plants.

Long Sault Dam showing second stage of the construction. At upper right is the completed first stage of the dam.

There were the string of military baes, air fields and installations in the Caribbean and on the mainland of Dutch Guiana, British Guiana and Venezuela, which Walsh carved out of jungles in record times during the last war and which ultimately became the stepping stones for Allied victory in Europe.

There was the construction, for the United States Government, of the Grand Coulee Dam in the State of Washington. This is the largest concrete dam in the world with 10,500,000 cubic yards of concrete. This project was awarded in two sections to two joint venture companies organized for this work, with Walsh being a member of both. Walsh managed the construction of the first section of the Dam. Concrete placement records of 17,000 cubic yards per day were often made, and placing of 400,000 cubic yards per month was maintained for several months.

There was the United Nations Headquarters project in New York City. Here Walsh was one of the joint sponsors and joint managers of a special corporation awarded the general contract.

During the last war, under the presidency of T. J. Walsh, Walsh-Kaiser Company, Incorporated, of Providence, Rhode Island, turned out ocean going vessels by the score for the United States Maritime Commission.

Near the town of Roscoe, New York, Walsh Construction Company managed the joint venture contract for the construction of the East Delaware Water Supply Tunnels for the City of New York Board of Water Supply. The contract included the excavation and lining of approximately 25 miles of hard rock tunnel, 11 feet 4 inches in diameter after lining, the excavation and lining of two shafts, one 605 feet in depth, and the other 965 feet deep.

As a mark of its versatility, Walsh later constructed a bomb manufacturing plant in Boston and another in Portland, Maine, for the U. S. Army Ordinance Department. Walsh installed the machinery and then operated both plants to produce a large quantity of complete casings for 700 pound demolition bombs.

A project of a different nature was the construction of an Atomic Power Laboratory for the Atomic Energy Commission, under General Electric Company operation, at Schenectady, New York.

The 27-storey Canada House building in New York City was another Walsh accomplishment.

Current contracts include the building of air bases and facilities in Spain, a dam, power house and tunnel in Cooma, Australia, cement plants in Miami, Florida, and Lake Charles Louisiana, a modern Department Store in Jamaica, New York, a mine shaft for the M. A. Hanna Company at Iron River, Michigan, a large extension to the Bethlehem Steel Plant at Sparrows Point, Maryland, and tunnels for the Pacific Gas and Electric Company in California. The list of Walsh accomplishments could go on almost indefinitely, but unfortunately space does not allow for this. However, regardless of the nature of work encountered, Walsh Construction Company has come through in each instance with flying colours.

Also worthy of comment is the fact that Walsh, since its inception, has been continuously active, developing its staff and facilities, to handle a steadily expanding volume of work. Time and methods change, but the sound policies and tradition of accomplishments established by the founders have been jealously preserved without interruption.

The officers of Walsh Construction Company are: T. J. Walsh, Chairman of the Board; W. A. Durkin, Chairman of the Executive Committee; T. J. Walsh, jr., President. The Vice Presidents include, H. H. Dugan, J. J. Walsh, D. G. Aronberg, E. P. Walsh, C D. Riddle, J. H. Gill and J. J. Murphy. The Treasurer is F. B. Smith and the Assistant Secretary Treasurer, D. C. Cook. M. A. Kennedy acts as Secretary and T. F. Taylor is Chief Engineer of the Company. The manager of Walsh-Canadian Construction Company is K. C. Griffith.

One of the two lift span bridge superstructures, over the Beauharnois Ship Canal which were constructed by Dominion Structural Steel Limited, member of the Canada Iron Group.

CANADA IRON FOUNDRIES, LIMITED

Canada Iron Foundries, Limited and The Canada Iron Group of Companies have long been a vital link in the industrial growth of the St. Lawrence Basin.

For more than two centuries, The Canada Iron Group and its predecessors have participated in the commercial life of the city of Trois Rivières, and later, of Montreal and Quebec City.

The iron for the stoves of early Canadian settlers was made at Trois Rivières, as was the shot and shell which helped to defend the river settlements, right up until the nineteenth century.

The age of sail to the age of the giant modern transatlantic liner symbolizes the transition and growth of this continent's remarkable economy. Canada Iron Foundries, Limited, incorporated under Dominion Charter in 1915, has established a similar proud record of achievement, and is pleased to have had its member companies closely associated with the St. Lawrence Seaway and Power Projects.

The role played by The Canada Iron Group in current Seaway development is impressive in its diversity and scope. Principal units supplied were structural steel, castings, electric motors, joists and reinforcing steel, reinforced concrete, steel cylinder water pipe, non-cylinder concrete pipe, cast iron pipe and fittings, and many special installations as outlined below.

Since many of the Group companies contributed directly to Seaway, Power and adjacent municipal re-development, it is appropriate to list The Canada Iron

Group, as presently constituted, with eight manufacturing companies, and four sales agency and distribution companies:

Canada Iron Foundries, Limited
Calgary Structural Steel Ltd.
C. W. Carry Ltd.
Dominion Structural Steel Limited
Disher Steel Division of Dominion Structural
   Steel Limited
Pressure Pipe Company of Canada Limited
Tamper Limited
Western Bridge & Steel Fabricators Ltd.
Railway & Power Engineering Corporation, Limited
C. M. Lovsted & Company (Canada) Limited
Paper Machinery Limited
Paper Mill Equipment Limited

This is an all-Canadian group of companies, with 21 manufacturing plants. Although it was principally the Ontario and Quebec units of The Canada Iron Group which supplied the Seaway development, Canada Iron has coast-to-coast service and facilities.

Seaway Bridges

Dominion Structural Steel Limited, of The Canada Iron Group, was awarded contracts by the St. Lawrence Seaway Authority of Canada for the supply and construction of two Lift Span Bridge Superstructures over the 15-mile Beauharnois ship canal channel, thirty miles southwest of Montreal.

The vertical life span sections are part of the St. Louis and Valleyfield bridges which cross the Beauharnois Canal. These are 3/4 mile long bridges and carry both rail and highway traffic.

A section of each of these bridges was replaced by moveable lift spans, 220 feet long and 50 feet wide. In the event of power failure, generators manufactured by Tamper Limited will provide the power to operate these lift spans.

The lift spans are counterbalanced at each end with 700 tons of concrete which rise and fall in opposition to the spans. The operating machinery and the operator are located on the span.

Dominion Structural Steel engineered, fabricated and erected the complicated steel towers, lift and approach spans and, as General Contractor, co-ordinated the entire project. Dominion Structural Steel also designed and built the permanent and semi-permanent materials handling equipment used on the project including cranes, stiff-legged and guy derricks.

Canada Iron Foundries, Limited manufactured the mechanical apparatus for these bridges.

Other Seaway Projects

The eight-storey St. Lawrence Seaway Authority Headquarters building in Cornwall, Ontario, was undertaken by Dominion Structural Steel Limited as a unit project of reinforced concrete construction. This structure required 600,000 pounds of steel.

The switchgear building for the Barnhart Island Powerhouse, 2560 feet long, has a steel structure by Dominion Structural Steel Limited. The steel work for the Canadian portion of this project, including an administration office, amounted to 1,400,000 pounds and was fabricated at the Company's plant in Montreal.

For pouring the retaining walls of the Iroquois Locks, Dominion Structural Steel Limited fabricated a mobile form termed the "Flying Form". Each form weighed 150,000 pounds. The forms were altered as conditions required, enabling pours to be made in a matter of hours rather than weeks.

Steel bulkheads, required to hold out water when large valves are drained for maintenance, were another Dominion Structural Steel Limited project. The Company supplied and erected forty bulkheads for this purpose, weighing 700,000 pounds. The bulkheads are located at the Iroquois, St. Lambert, Cote St. Catherine, Upper Beauharnois and Lower Beauharnois locks. The unwatering pumps and their auxiliaries for all the Seaway locks are driven by Tamper Limited motors.

The Company supplied and erected four unwatering well pump bulkheads, weighing 40,000 pounds, for vertical deep well pumps used to empty locks during inspection. Regulating gate unwatering bulkheads were also produced and installed. The bulkheads are at the St. Lambert lock and Cote Ste. Catherine lock. These

bulkheads, 23 of which were installed totalling 300,000 pounds, permit maintenance work on the regulating gates.

To hold steep stop log girders in proper alignment, Dominion Structural Steel Limited fabricated 2,800,000 pounds of steel check and sill units in precision made sub-assemblies. These units were anchored in concrete to form vertical guides.

Dominion Structural Steel Limited built two railroad bridge structures as part of the railroad track relocation due to Seaway flooding. This project involved some 450,000 pounds of fabricated steel.

For the new schools in the neighbourhood of relocated towns Ingleside and Long Sault, the Company supplied 500,000 pounds of structural steel, including TAYMAR long span and short span open web joists, TAYMAR roof-deck and reinforcing steel.

Tamper Limited supplied the large vertical motors for the sewage and storm water pumps at the Montreal South Sewage Pumping Station. These motors range up to 300 H.P. at 327 R.P.M.

Reinforced Concrete Steel Cylinder Water Pipe for Seaway Towns and Industry

In conjunction with Seaway development and consequent relocation of municipal and industrial water supply systems, Pressure Pipe Company of Canada Limited supplied Hyprescon reinforced concrete steel cylinder water pipe and non-cylinder concrete pipe to many major projects. These projects included Courtaulds (Canada) Limited, Cornwall, Ontario: a water intake, 4400 linear feet of 30 in. pipe. The Town of St. Lambert, Quebec, altered water intake and sewer outfall, using 2980 linear feet of Hyprescon pipe. The Town of Laprairie, Quebec, used 1060 linear feet of 36 in. Hyprescon pipe for a water intake. The Town of Montreal South, Quebec, also used this pipe for a water intake.

A section of some of these lines was laid inland. The balance was extended into the river and was constructed with subaqueous type Hyprescon, reinforced concrete steel cylinder water pipe.

Cast Iron Pipe and Fittings for Seaway Towns Water Distribution

For the new communities of Iroquois, Morrisburg, Ingleside and Long Sault, Ontario, Canada Iron Foundries Limited supplied more than 3,000 tons of Canada Iron cast iron pipe and fittings, ranging from 4 in. to 18 in. diameter.

The Canada Iron Foundries, Limited Group of companies is proud to have played a specialized and diversified role in the development of the St. Lawrence Seaway. This all-Canadian Group of Companies salutes a great milestone in Canadian progress.

Some of the modern mechanical lifting equipment used by Cullen Stevedoring Company Limited.

CULLEN STEVEDORING COMPANY LIMITED

When a project the size of the St. Lawrence Seaway and Power Projects is undertaken, the problems that arise and have to be overcome are many and varied. Quite a number of the problems are not even related to the actual construction job, but have to do with the side effects of the enterprise.

One of the major problems which had to be overcome by port authorities along the Seaway route was the rejuvenating of docking facilities and services to handle the increased ship traffic which will materialize with the official opening of the Seaway.

Of prime concern was the stevedoring facilities which their individual ports had to offer. A number of these inland Great Lakes ports, however, are fortunate in that they can offer steamship owners and operators the very best in stevedoring services. The Port of Toronto is in this position, for here, a young, progressive stevedoring and terminal operating company has made a big and lasting impression on both the harbour authorities and local marine businesses. This firm is Cullen Stevedoring Company Limited, located in Marine Terminal II, on Toronto's waterfront.

Founded in 1955 by Henry Cullen, this company also maintains offices in Hamilton, Canada's steel centre, and in the twin cities of Fort William and Port Arthur, Ontario, at the head of Lake Superior.

In Toronto alone Cullen Stevedoring has made great strides. The Company rejuvenated the waterfront by fast and efficient deliveries to consignees and through keen supervision on behalf of their principals. No longer are delays experienced in the delivery of cargo from the dock-side. A modern fleet of fork-lift trucks and cranes speeds up the loading and discharging of cargoes. In addition, Cullen Stevedoring Company Limited employs a well organized pallet system, a highly trained staff and uses fifty per cent of the Toronto Terminal space, with more to come.

When Cullen Stevedoring Company Limited commenced operations in the Spring of 1955, they had but one contract to handle vessels at the ports of Toronto and Hamilton. Now, just three years later, the Company holds contracts with some of the world's leading steamship companies, included among which are: Canadian Pacific Steamships, Cunard Steamships, Donaldson Line, Head Line, Ellerman Line, Montship Line, and Capo Line. Still, with all these contracts, Cullen Stevedoring does not believe in standing still and are busy preparing and expanding their facilities to handle the increased tonnage which is anticipated with the official opening of the St. Lawrence Seaway in the Spring of 1959.

Cullen Stevedoring Company Limited offers a complete service to their clients through equipment and labour which are available at all times for despatch to other Great Lakes ports if necessary. At Fort William, the Company is prepared for gain loading, fitting and cargo handling. They have already fitted vessels in Toronto for grain, and have loaded at such ports as Prescott and Kingston, Ontario.

Cullen Stevedoring Company Limited are satisfied with their rate of progress in the past three years and are eagerly looking forward to further expansion of trade in the Great Lakes area following completion of the St. Lawrence Seaway.

CHICAGO TOWING COMPANY

One of Chicago Towing Company's modern twin 500 hp. diesel tugs.

As we look ahead to April, 1959, the date set for the official opening of the billion dollar St. Lawrence Seaway and Power Projects by the heads of two great nations, Her Majesty, Queen Elizabeth II and President Dwight D. Eisenhower, we can visualize the constant stream of ship traffic which will flow during the navigation season on the St. Lawrence River and the Great Lakes.

The importance of the ports situated in the Great Lakes area, now being referred to as the "Eighth Sea", has taken on a new note in the light of these developments. Harbor services and facilities have already been extended and improved upon to the point where the large deep sea vessels using the St. Lawrence Seaway system can be handled speedily and efficiently without any loss of valuable time.

Playing an important role in the handling of these steel giants of the sea lanes are the innocent looking but tough little tug boats which are a familiar sight any day of the week on the Great Lakes. These boats are by far the hardest working craft on the inland waterway, for where their big brothers, the freighters, bulk carriers and oil tankers, earn a rest everytime they arrive in port, the tow boat is continually on the move. Whether it be assisting a ship to berth or towing a long line of heavily laden barges from one port to another, makes no difference to these little fellows, it's all in a day's work.

Organized in 1945 for the purpose of serving the oil industry in their problem of completing the voyages of barges from the start of fixed bridge program to the terminals on both the Chicago Sanitary District and the Sag Channel. The terminal development has ballooned to where the tonnage moved by water accounts for a major portion of the total Illinois water movement.

The first boat purchased by the Chicago Towing Company in 1945 was a small 65 horsepower Kahlenber diesel tug. Since then the Company has enlarged its fleet and operations and, by trading and rebuilding old equipment, has emerged with a modern, streamlined-fleet of lake-river combination tug boats and river design push-pull craft.

The steady growth of Chicago Towing is reflected in the purchase in 1956 of the first of a series of modern tugs equipped with pushing knees and powered by two 500 horsepower Caterpillar diesel engines. In 1958 increasing business demands necessitated the purchase of the second of the same type of tug. This latter boat is powered by one 500 horsepower Superior diesel engine. Future plans of Chicago Towing include, among other things, the construction of a 1500 horsepower heavy duty tug boat, which will be used on long towing contracts on the Great Lakes. This will round out a "pat" hand of towing equipment consisting of the ACE, KING, QUEEN, JACK and TEN.

The future of Chicago Towing Company and its place in the overall marine picture in and around the sprawling Chicago harbor is well assured with the completion in the Spring of 1959, of the St. Lawrence Seaway and Power Projects, which, without a doubt, will result in a big up-swing in water borne commerce.

Piers for new high level extension of Honoré Mercier Bridge across Seaway channel near Montreal.

PENTAGON CONSTRUCTION CO. LTD.

Four years ago, in 1954, two neighbouring nations joined forces in a history-making event which, in years to come, will have its effect on the economic future of both these countries. The nations were Canada and the United States of America, and the event was the start of construction on the billion dollar St. Lawrence Seaway and Power Projects.

It was announced then that the St. Lawrence Seaway would be completed and ready for opening of the 1959 navigation season on the St. Lawrence River. But had it not been for the efficient handling of the actual job itself by the various contractors the curtain could not have risen on the final act. These companies and the men in their employ are the real heroes of the The St. Lawrence Seaway and Power Projects.

Pentagon Construction Co. Ltd., a Montreal firm of general contractors, was one such company which played its role well, particularly in the part concerning the alteration of the Honore Mercier Bridge.

The creation of the new St. Lawrence Seaway Channel on the south shore of the river, opposite the Island of Montreal, required the alteration of four major bridges to permit the passage of ocean-going vessels up to twenty-seven foot draught.

One of these bridges was the Honore Mercier Bridge, erected in 1934 for vehicular traffic and spanning the St. Lawrence River from the mid-western end of Montreal. In this case it was decided to demolish the existing concrete viaduct at the southern approach and to replace it with a steel structure on concrete piers from the south shore of the river northward to a point beyond the new channel. This new structure was designed to provide the 120 foot clearance needed above the water surface in the Seaway channel.

Pentagon was awarded the contract on the basis of competitive bids for the construction of fourteen of the major piers necessary for this structure. The piers, ranging from 58 feet to 157 feet in height, are twin-shaft structures with trans-

verse concrete beams at their tops to support a four-lane roadway. The longest piers were surmounted by beams 9' 6" x 15' 0" x 75' 2" containing some 400 cubic yards of concrete each. The job was started and completed in 1957.

In addition to its own direct contracts with The St. Lawrence Seaway Authority, Pentagon is a significant shareholder in two all-Canadian groups, namely Iroquois Constructors Limited and United Waterways Constructors Limited presently carrying out Seaway power and navigation developments to the value of approximately $75,000,000.

Originally formed in 1948 by five experienced Canadian construction engineers for the purpose of serving both industry and government in the "heavy" and "engineering" construction fields, Pentagon Construction have been engaged on numerous projects, all of which were of considerable size and importance to Canada. These include a 168,000 H.P. power development for the Ontario Hydro-Electric Commission; reconstruction of a Montreal pier for the National Harbours Board involving air caissons; aluminum smelters for the Aluminum Company of Canada at Isle Maligne, Quebec; "Secret" installation for Defence Construction (1951) Limited; a 250,000 H.P. power development for the Aluminum Company of Canada in northern Quebec; an ore dock at Port Arthur, Ontario, for Canadian National Railways; titanium smelters for Quebec Iron and Titanium Corporation at Sorel, Quebec; marine towers and a grain elevator in Montreal for the National Harbours Board; a 50,000 H.P. power development for The James MacLaren Company at Buckingham, Quebec and industrial plants for the Canadian Johns-Manville Company, Sperry-Gyroscope of Canada, Jenkins Brothers and many others.

Officers and Directors of Pentagon Construction Co. Ltd. are: C. Howard Gordon, President; Hugh R. Montgomery, Vice-President and General Manager; W. E. Williams, Secretary-Treasurer; F. B. Rolph and G. A. Campbell, Directors, and Contract Managers.

M/V Alexander T. Wood

H. C. DOWNER & ASSOCIATES, INC.

For decades men have dreamed of big ocean-going ships sailing into Canada's Gulf of St. Lawrence, up through the mighty St. Lawrence River and on into the thriving Great Lakes ports in the very heartland of North America. They pictured those ships . . . general cargo freighters, ore carriers and oil tankers . . . discharging cargoes which had been picked up in countries all over the world. Their enthusiasm rose as they envisioned these same ships making the return trip loaded with rich harvests from our farms, with raw materials from our mines, and with finished products from our inland factories.

As the years rolled by, these men strove mightily to make their dreams come true. The ALEXANDER T. WOOD is tangible evidence of that striving. Named after the president of the Wilson Marine Transit Company of Cleveland, Ohio, this ship, on May 1, 1958, became the first large vessel designed and built to operate with equal facility on the ocean or from the ocean to the Great Lakes and vice versa through the billion dollar joint U.S.A.-Canada St. Lawrence Seaway system. Westriver Ore Transport Ltd., owner of the ALEXANDER T. WOOD also operates the M. V. Westriver. Headquarters are in Montreal.

H. C. Downer & Associates, Incorporated, Naval Architects and Marine Engineers of Cleveland, Ohio, are proud of the part they played in the evolution of this historic vessel. Acting as owners design agent and providing complete general and resident inspection service, they cooperated with the building yard, Canadian Vickers in Montreal, Quebec, to produce a ship full of innovations and superlatives from stem to stern.

Constructed to Lloyd's Class 100 A 1 the ALEXANDER T. WOOD is longitudinally framed at double bottom and deck, and is strengthened for heavy cargo. Her cargo space is subdivided into six holds and her MacGregor steel hatch covers of the mechanical type are operated by special winches which insure fast and efficient operation.

An eight cylinder Nordberg Diesel, 6,800 maximum B.H.P., drives what at time of delivery was the largest KaMeWa controllable pitch propeller fitted to any cargo vessel. This propeller can be controlled from the wheel house as well as from the engine room. The ballast valves are operated from a central station in the engine room, further emphasizing the degree of remote control that characterizes this ship. And, carrying all of the modern aids to navigation, she is truly one of the safest ships afloat.

In addition, Westriver Ore ransports Ltd. through the design agent H. C. Downer & Associates, Inc., have spared no expense in providing spacious living quarters for the crew of the ALEXANDER T. WOOD. Cabins and staterooms are fully equipped with every modern convenience to make the ship a home away from home.

The ALEXANDER T. WOOD and her younger sister, the AVERY C. ADAMS, are glowing testimony to the men who made their St. Lawrence Seaway dreams come true. We at H. C. Downer & Associates, Inc., are also investing some of our time and effort in dreams, because we know that unless we do, we most certainly will not be ready for tomorrow, and we intend to be ready!

THE ROBERT REFORD COMPANY, LIMITED

General Steamship Agents

•

Chartering

Liner Services

•

Bulk Cargoes

Operating since 1866 in Montreal.

The development of shipping services adequate to Canadian needs has characterized the work of The Robert Reford Company as the oldest steamship agency in Canada, which is operating today under the direction of Eric Reford, who represents the third generation to control this privately owned business.

Arrangements concluded between Robert Reford and William Ross, a former business associate in Toronto who had gone to live in the United Kingdom, resulted in the steamship agency being established in Montreal in 1866 to handle the Ross Line as the first regular steamship service from London.

Robert Reford's earliest participation in overseas trade was an interest in the voyage of the 227 ton brigantine "Seagull" built at Oakville which, in 1865, took a cargo loaded in Toronto and Montreal to South Africa, returning with passengers to Boston before entering the Great Lakes trade like other vessels of her class.

Such a venture was probably not considered too unusual in those days when the records of transportation include such feats as those of the North West Company in freighting trade goods from Montreal by canoe and overland portage to the Pacific coast.

Increasing requirements, particularly in the trans-Atlantic trade, enabled the Reford firm to push ahead with the establishment of the Donaldson Line on a Glasgow service in 1877 and the expansion of the Thomson Line, which had taken over from the Ross Line, to include occasional ships from the Mediterranean and later into the passenger business.

In 1911 the Cunard Line, founded by a Halifax man, bought the Thomson Line passenger ships and thus, after many years, returned to the Canadian trade, with Refords looking after their interests until after the second World War.

Following Robert Reford's death in 1913, his son, Robert W. Reford, continued as President of the Company until 1946, when he was succeeded by his son, Eric Reford.

During the whole of the period of some 90 years, many lines, additional to those mentioned, engaged in a great variety of services, have been represented.

Montreal's geographical position has encouraged this initiative and the extent of the financial investment in the early days of shipping is indeed remarkable. An exceptional advantage which Montreal enjoys is that it is a terminal port for ships which load at its docks and sail directly to all points of the compass. This fact has become of increasing significance with the development of the country and it places in some perspective the situation of Montreal in relation to the St. Lawrence Seaway and Power Project.

The Robert Reford Company, with its own office in Toronto and agents at all eastern Canadian ports, now represents in Canada the Maersk Line, with regular sailings every month to Japan and on a round-the-world service . . . Flota Mercante Grancolombiana, S.A., which has built more ocean going ships in Canadian shipyards than any other commercial concern, and which is making an outstanding contribution to the broad basis of Canadian trade with South America with regular and frequent sailings to Colombia, Ecuador and Peru as well as Cuba and Mexico and other central American ports . . . Compania Anonima Venezolana de Navegacion . . . he Finlake Line, which operates from Finland up into the Great Lakes . . . Newfoundland Canada Steamships, an important domestic connection.

Another phase of the business is in connection with the movement of bulk cargoes both as agents attending the ships and in providing all the services of chartering brokers, both in obtaining tonnage to accommodate cargoes and to finding cargoes for ships requiring them. The increasing demands in this connection are met by an experienced ship agency department and a qualified chartering manager.

This brief history of the oldest steamship agency in Canada illustrates the contribution which a specialized business can make in the promotion of trade and the shipping services which it requires.

A Canadian National train crossing St. Lambert Lock, via modified Victoria Bridge, in Montreal area.

CANADIAN NATIONAL RAILWAYS
Salutes the Seaway

The waters of the St. Lawrence River are now part of a great Seaway, reaching from the Atlantic Ocean into the industrial heartland of North America. This river has witnessed earlier developments in the evolution of transportation in Canada. For example, its currents once coursed past a trestle that was part of the old, 16-mile Champlain and St. Lawrence Railroad, Canada's first railway. It started service in 1836.

In 1955, Seaway workers excavated timbers from the river bank near Montreal, which were once part of the trestle. Despite their 119 years, they were well preserved. Canadian National Railways took keen interest in this find, for the route of the Champlain and St. Lawrence is now part of the CNR.

Canadian National, North America's largest railway, serves all 10 provinces of Canada and 12 states in the USA. It has 32,000 miles of track and about 125,000 employees. It is the largest single employer in Canada and its largest single purchaser of industrial materials. CNR also operates its own express service and a far-flung commercial telecommunications system; owns deep-sea vessels, car ferries, nine year-round hotels, a summer resort and Trans-Canada Air Lines.

Canada would not be the nation she is today were it not for her railways. It took sturdy steel tracks to bind this country together, sprawling as it does, for nearly 4,000 miles, from ocean to ocean. Brawny track gangs and visionary engineers conquered awesome physical barriers to close wide gaps that separated cities, towns and villages. Since our pioneer days, railway building has been the keystone of nation building.

Canadian National welcomes the St. Lawrence Seaway as a partner in the development of this country. Rail and water services complement each other and, where transportation costs are low and other factors balance, the environment favors industrial expansion.

In the wake of this great waterway, there will inevitably arise an accelerated industrial growth, from which CNR will benefit. Some adjacent areas will feel the impact more than others, depending upon how far-sighted local governments are in anticipating the requirements of industry.

But the St. Lawrence River area is not alone in anticipating the industrial expansion that will rise as a result of the Seaway. All the way to the head of the Great Lakes, the potential of present port areas has increased. Other areas, which as yet have no dock facilities, now possess a more important industrial potential.

The Welland Canal area is an example. It could become more than a link between Lake Ontario and Lake Erie. With foresight, it could also become a protected waterway, capable of supporting docks at strategic points. Canadian National's exclusive lines at the Canal's rear would support such an arrangement..

Our industrial development officers consider all these factors in their constant watch over the Seaway project. But all of Canada is their field of operations, with the best interests of industry paramount in their planning. They are trained in industrial placement and work in strictest confidence.

There are CNR industrial officers across Canada, at Moncton, Quebec City, Montreal, Toronto, Winnipeg, Edmonton and Vancouver. Representatives may also be consulted at New York and Detroit in the United States, and in London, England. Thus the facilities of North America's largest railway and largest waterway are jointly applied to the creation of more wealth for the people of this country.

The Bank of Nova Scotia General Office, Toronto, Ont.

THE BANK OF NOVA SCOTIA

When, in 1832, The Bank of Nova Scotia was founded by merchants of Halifax — that thriving port whose economic life centered on the ships that plied the trade routes of the Atlantic Ocean — the Canadian shore of that ocean was already moving further to the West. Seven years earlier, in 1825, the completion of the first Lachine canal had marked the beginning of the long process by which the commerce of the Atlantic has been progressively extended into the middle of the continent.

In the century-and-a-quarter since it was founded, the Bank, too, has moved into and across the continent, and outward across the sea as well. Today the institution that began in the "banking chambers" in John Romans' building in Halifax has more than 530 branches — from coast to coast in Canada and abroad, ranging from Trinidad to London, England. Though maintaining its special interest in the Atlantic Provinces of Canada, it has been a national and international bank since well before the beginning of this century and since 1900 its managerial offices have been in Toronto.

The Bank of Nova Scotia is particularly well represented in the Caribbean area, where it was the first Canadian Bank to establish branch offices. From that first West Indies branch, opened in Kingston, Jamaica in 1889, the number of branches in the area has grown to 37 — in Jamaica, Cuba, Puerto Rico, Dominican Republic, Bahamas, Trinidad, and Barbados. Its staff in these branches numbers more than six hundred.

Early in 1958, The Bank of Nova Scotia Trust Company (Bahamas) Limited, was founded, with headquarters in Nassau. Three well-known British institutions, the Eagle Star Insurance Company Limited, Philip Hill, Higginson and Company, and Sir Robert McAlpine & Sons, joined the Bank in forming the new Company which provides a complete range of individual and corporate trust services.

As an institution that from its founding helped finance the trades of the Atlantic and that plays so integral a part in the whole Canadian economy, The Bank of Nova Scotia is naturally interested in the economic changes and new opportunities for Canada which may follow the opening of the Seaway. (Indeed, in its "Monthly Review" for July-August 1952 it published one of the first comprehensive studies of the Seaway project to be issued in this country.) Well represented in the port towns and cities of the St. Lawrence and the Great Lakes, with branches from the Gaspé to Fort William, this Bank intends to play an active role in promoting the economic expansion promised by the new transport and power facilities of the Seaway.

The power development at Shawinigan, with an installed capacity of 310,700 kilowatts, is the largest of the Company's seven hydro-electric developments on the St. Maurice river.

Shawinigan's terminal station at Trois-Rivières to which power from the Company's seven St. Maurice river plants is transmitted for distribution to homes and industries throughout Shawinigan's widespread system.

THE SHAWINIGAN WATER AND POWER COMPANY

Lying astride the great St. Lawrence Seaway, main street of North American commerce and trade, is a 31,-000 square mile territory of modern homes, farms, stores, mines, mills and factories served by the vast Shawinigan hydro-electric system.

Extending along both sides of the St. Lawrence in the Province of Quebec, from above Montreal to a point some 125 miles below Quebec City, the territory lies in the very heart of an area which has one of the greatest industrial potentials of any in North America. Three power companies comprise the Shawinigan system which supplies the territory with its life blood: the parent Shawinigan Water and Power Company, one of the largest investor owned electric utilities in the world; Quebec Power Company and Southern Canada Power Company, Limited.

Focal point of the vast Shawinigan system is at the City of Shawinigan in the Province of Quebec located on the St. Maurice River about 20 miles from the point where the St. Maurice joins the mighty St. Lawrence. Shawinigan is today a bustling city of 43,000 population, one of a large number of such centres in the Company's territory. Sixty years ago it was just a clearing in a wooded wilderness beside a rushing waterfall.

It was to this waterfall — which was given the Indian name Shawinigan — that a group of enterprising businessmen were attracted just before the turn of the century. When they formed The Shawinigan Water and Power Company in 1898 to harness the falls' energy, their visions were looked upon pretty skeptically and their venture was considered rather risky. However in the three score years since, their dreams have been realized many times over. The two generators in the original powerhouse, which were among the largest in the world at that time, had a total capacity of 7,500 kilowatts. Today Shawinigan's seven hydro-electric developments on the St. Maurice have a total capacity of more than a million and a half kilowatts. The original transmission line which carried power at a 'fantastic' 50,000 volts over an 'unheard of' distance of 85 miles from Shawinigan to Montreal has grown to a total of more than 20,000 miles of transmission and distribution lines carrying power at up to 230,000 volts.

The Shawinigan Company's growth has been coincident with that of the territory it serves as well as with that of the Province of Quebec and of Canada. And the Company has played its part in the industrial development of Quebec Province through its Industrial Development department which is devoted solely to assisting new and existing industries to establish in the Company's territory.

Great as the industrial development of the Shawinigan territory has been, there are still greater things ahead for this land of unlimited opportunity on the banks of the Seaway.

Raw materials ranging from iron ore and many non-ferrous metals to asbestos, abound within or adjacent to Shawinigan's territory. In addition, many materials such as wood pulp, paper, natural gas, crude oil delivered by pipe lines, chemicals and oil refinery products are in plentiful supply.

Transportation facilities in the territory are second to none. Four major inland ports at Montreal, Quebec City, Trois-Rivières and Sorel provide extensive facilities for all types of water-borne shipments and deliveries; rail lines fan out from Montreal to all parts of Canada and the United States; and a network of modern highways covers the area.

Manpower, too, is readily available. The Shawinigan territory, encompassing one of Canada's most populous areas has as its greatest resource, tens of thousands of highly skilled and semi-skilled men and women. A large number of excellent trade and technical schools assure an adequate and steady flow of trained and stable workers.

Of vital importance, the Shawinigan territory has an abundant capacity of developed electric power which is playing an increasingly important role in industrialization of the area. The Company's long-established policy of developing sources of electric power in advance of actual requirements assures a sufficient supply of power throughout the whole territory.

217

St. Lawrence Power Dam viewed from the American side during construction in December 1957. Upstream side of dam had been completely dewatered. After inundation, the dry land shown at left became Lake St. Lawrence.

UTAH CONSTRUCTION COMPANY

Along the great St. Lawrence Seaway massive structures in steel and concrete stand today as symbols of the big muscle and joint enterprise of the American construction industry.

Among them are the Bertrand S. Snell Lock, Massena, Intake Structure, Long Sault Dam and Barnhart Island Powerhouse—projects which involved construction contracts totalling more than $100,000,000 and the combined forces of several major United States contractors, one of which was Utah Construction Company.

It is literally true that the sun never sets on the far-flung operations of Utah Construction Company nor upon the engineering triumphs with which the firm's name has been linked in more than half a century of globe-circling construction achievement.

Current and recent activities include construction of the Karnafuli Dam in East Pakistan; erection of uranium processing mills in Wyoming and New Mexico; a bridge and steam power plant in Australia; highway, dam and canal construction in Mexico; a mine shaft and facilities in Saskatchewan; and a dredging project for airport expansion on San Francisco Bay.

Joint venture projects with other contractors include—in addition to the Seaway activities—a power tunnel on California's Feather River, Table Rock Dam in Missouri, a new facility for the United States Atomic Energy Commission near St. Louis, a chemical plant in Korea and the Serre Poncon Dam in Southern France.

But Utah Construction Company is more than a builder; it is continually branching out into new fields, putting into effective action its conviction that the construction industry offers tremendous possibilities for diversification.

For example, Utah today has become a major mining concern, operating its own mines and offering services to clients that range from initial exploration through process testing and design to production, marketing and even shipping.

It also has interests in ocean shipping, in operation of grain elevators and industrial plants, in construction and operation of commercial and residential developments—and once even controlled a million-acre ranching operation in the West.

The ranching activity stemmed from the need to provide fuel for the "hayburners"—the mules that provided the power for the company's pioneer railroad building when Utah was but an infant at the turn of the century.

From that early beginning, Utah gained the experience during the galloping growth of the West which today is the foundation of its operations on five continents.

That experience has been handed down in the company until today the second and third generations of Utah's founders are directing the world-wide enterprise which sprang from the small but spirited company which was incorporated—with a capital of only $25,000— at Ogden, Utah, in 1900.

All three members of the Utah executive committee — Board Chairman Marriner S. Eccles, President Allen D. Christensen and Executive Vice President Edmund W. Littlefield — are descendants of the firm's pioneers.

Throughout its long and progressive history Utah has successfully applied the experience of the past to the new horizons of the future . . . from the mule teams of pioneer railroading to the task of furnishing the fuel for the Atomic Age with a new uranium processing plant in Wyoming.

218

Wiley-Dondero Ship Channel is shown at left in above aerial view. Bertrand H. Snell Lock appears in the lower left corner. Power dam is just below center of photo. Picture taken prior to flooding of the area.

Railroad building was the mainstay of Utah's business for the first two decades of its existence. In 1906 the company drove Western Pacific's main line from Salt Lake City to Oroville, California, via the famed Feather River Gorge. The building of that line through some of the West's most forbidding terrain, requiring more than forty tunnels and scores of bridges, trestles, cuts, and fills, was a history-making achievement. The company's impressive performance record on that job led to a long list of other contracts and thousands of miles of other railroad construction.

As the West grew, the firm also expanded, entering other fields. Utah took on canal and irrigation work in Washington, New Mexico, and California. It gained its first road-building experience throughout California, Nevada, Colorado, and Idaho.

Recognized today as one of the world's leading dam builders, with participation in more than forty of the world's foremost hydraulic structures to its credit, Utah built its first dams—earth and rockfill structures—on its own ranch property as an adjunct to its cattle and sheep raising activities.

These relatively primitive structures were the foundation of the dam building "know-how" which was to enable Utah to spearhead construction of Hoover Dam, one of the greatest engineering projects in the history of the world. No one company was big enough to tackle Hoover Dam alone, so Utah joined the history-making Six Companies which built it, combining forces as on the Seaway with other major contractors to harness nature for the betterment of mankind.

Many of the world's other great structures and construction works also saw Utah associated in their building—Bonneville and Grand Coulee in America and Australia's Big Eildon among dams, the Alcan Highway and the San Francisco-Oakland Bay Bridge.

During the past quarter century, Utah also has been a leading contributor to the industrial construction demanded by the booming development of the American West. Major installations for the nation's foremost producers of metals, and construction for oil companies, food producers and packagers, the automobile and aircraft industries, and a host of others have kept Utah in the forefront of the industrial construction field.

The West's explosive growth has brought an almost insatiable need for housing and industrial sites, a need which Utah has stepped in to help fill by actually creating new land in areas where geography has been restricting new developments and growth.

On California's San Francisco Bay, Utah has literally lifted a new community from the bay bottom and is building a $50,000,000 industrial development on what was once a tidal marsh.

In the City of Alameda, Utah's giant hydraulic dredge —one of the world's most powerful construction tools— pumped up more than 9,000,000 cubic yards of sand from a mile and a half in the bay, reclaiming tidelands to build 400 acres of new land. This once useless land is now being turned by Utah into an ultra-modern community of homes and apartments for nearly 3000 families plus schools, parks, shopping centres and a vast public beach.

Across the bay at South San Francisco, Utah is developing sites for more than 100 industries, moving a mountain onto nearby lowlands to add nearly 250 acres of prime industrial land to the region's economy.

Utah then is continuing its early role of building the American West, even as it is building for progress across the globe. And as future generations around the world work and play on land wrested from the sea, or ride the rails, or turn on their light switches, or irrigate their crops—their activities will bear testimony to the validity of the Utah Construction Company motto:

"The permanent public value of our work is the accurate measure of our success."

A Clarke ship passing Plains of Abraham, Quebec City.

CLARKE STEAMSHIP CO. LIMITED

The Golden North — The Clarke Story

In the summer of 1900, two brothers cruised along the lonely and little known northern shores of the Gulf of St. Lawrence in their yacht. They were William and James Clarke of Toronto. The voyage, though intended for relaxation, was destined to turn them from a family of publishers to a family of shipowners. As they sailed down the St. Lawrence reaches, the vision of vast untouched forests gave birth to an exciting idea in their minds. Here was an unlimited source of paper!

The Clarke family were at that time owners and publishers of the famous Encyclopedia Britannica. One of their main publishing problems had been to find a satisfactory source of paper supply. The sight of the unlimited miles of northern forests engendered in the Clarke brothers a desire to produce their own paper with which to feed their hungry printing presses. The North Shore thus held the promise of a solution to their most urgent problem.

Upon their return home they impressed upon their two younger brothers the importance of their discovery; and so it was that in 1901 John and George Clarke in turn visited these regions. This eventually led to the erection of a paper mill and power dam on the St. Margaret's River, on Quebec's North Shore. The mill was situated nine miles inland from Seven Islands and to reach it rugged forest land had to be crossed. This was the beginning.

In 1902, the North Shore Paper Railway and Navigation Company was formed. As mill workers increased, modern houses were built, a new town was established complete with church, school, hospital and hotel. It was christened Clarke City. The settlement was connected with its tiny port of Pointe Noire on Seven

Islands Bay, by a nine-mile railway — the only one east of Murray Bay until very recently. Clarke City is still a busy newspulp centre.

In 1921 the Clarke Steamship Company Limited was formed and has grown steadily ever since, expanding its passenger and freight facilities as the needs of the Gulf increased. With two first-rate liners, Clarke developed summer cruise services to Labrador, Newfoundland, Gulf ports and the Maritimes.

During the Second World War, Clarke suspended its cruise services, its vessels being on war duties as auxiliary cruisers and transports; other ships carried war supplies and personnel.

Since the war, Baie Comeau, Seven Islands, Havre St. Pierre, and other ports, have become new hives of industry. They are today gateways to substantial empires in pulp and paper, hydro-power, iron ore, titanium, aluminum. Clarke freight ships actively aided this industrial development; they are now once again pioneering northward into Labrador and Ungava ports such as Goose Bay and Chimo.

Clarke freight ships regularly serve all Gulf of St. Lawrence ports, Newfoundland, Southern Labrador; and maintain to many of them also an all-winter service from Pointe-au-Pic, near Quebec.

The House of Clarke reflects the practical faith of a single Canadian family in the progress of this part of Canada. In a devoted and single-minded half-century of enterprise, the Clarke Steamship Company Limited has contributed substantially to the tremendous promise and growing wealth of the new "Golden North".

1876   1958

Montreal Harbour — 1878

BLAIKLOCK BROS. LIMITED

In this era of super cargo ships, steam turbines and diesel power engines, the sight of a four masted square rigger beating into Montreal's sprawling harbour, against rushing currents and adverse winds, would indeed prove a novelty. But though the days of the square rigger are gone forever they still linger on in the minds of the oldtimers who, on occasion, can still be seen around the harbour . . . a harbour which has expanded greatly over the years to keep abreast of a thing called progress.

Then, too, there are the fine old landmarks along the waterfront which have lived through these decades of progress and which will go on living long after the oldtimers have passed on. Imagine, could they talk, the tales these landmarks could tell of the once proud sailing vessels and of a harbour so different from what we know it to be today.

Back in the year 1876, Montreal was a comparatively young city and means of travel and communication were somewhat primitive by today's standards, but far-sighted men could visualize the beginning of a wonderful new era. They might have dreamed, even then, of a deep waterway system stretching the length of the mighty St. Lawrence River and right on through to the fast growing commercial ports on the inland Great Lakes. A highly fantastic dream which has now been transformed into a reality.

It was in this year, 1876, that the firm of Blaiklock Bros. Limited, one of the original "landmarks", was founded as Customs Brokers and Forwarders.

The firm was built on young ideals and sound business principles, with a spirit of adventure. Blaiklock Bros. Limited could see the ever increasing need for the services which they could offer and could also foresee, that as business and government became more complicated, their services would be of major importance to progressive business organizations. Down through the years they

have served business until today their services have become indispensable.

Since 1876 Blaiklock Bros. Limited have come a long way, continually expanding their services to keep up with the ever-changing times. However, they have maintained one link with the past. They still occupy the same premises on old Common Street which are a solid landmark on the Montreal waterfront. The walls of Blaiklock Bros. Limited building, standing today as firmly as they did 82 years ago, reflect the solidarity of sound business principles for which Blaiklock is so well respected. Their impressive list of regular clients is a fitting testimonial to the faith of the founders.

With over eighty years of highly efficient service to their clients, Blaiklock Bros. Limited continues to speed shipments by land, sea and air to the four corners of the globe. With extensive facilities for handling every kind of shipment, the Company serves the world as Customs Brokers and Consultants and employs an experienced staff to advise and assist their clients in all phases of customs procedure. Their extensive warehousing facilities include bonded service, reshipping and distribution of goods. A modern fleet of heavy duty, medium and light panel trucks stand ready and fully equipped to transport all classes of freight, large or small.

And this is not all. Blaiklock Bros. Limited have also been active in the building of the St. Lawrence Seaway through the services they have rendered to the multitude of firms responsible for the actual construction of the billion-dollar "ditch."

The Directors of this old and respected firm . . . Fred P. Hudon, President; M. H. Robinson, Vice-President; R. G. Scroggie, Secretary and Director and Claude S. Richardson, Q.C. Director . . . look forward with a great deal of anticipation in sharing with countless others the benefits that the St. Lawrence Seaway and Power Projects will provide.

THE TORONTO — DOMINION BANK

When The Bank of Toronto and The Dominion Bank amalgamated on February 1, 1955, over 183 years of banking experience came together to form one of the foremost banks in Canada. Now named The Toronto-Dominion Bank, the new bank had much to offer Canadians with its sound background of security and experience coupled with the renewed vigour that springs from the fresh viewpoint and enthusiasm of a new organization. The combining of its personnel, facilities and services made The Toronto-Dominion greater than either of its parts and it became the fourth ranking bank in the country.

It was said at the time of the amalgamation that considering "the two organizations that were brought to the 'wedding' there was never any doubt that a strong and successful new bank would emerge." The blending of two great banks is no easy undertaking and the officers and staff of both organizations brought about a smoothness of transition that was hailed as being "little short of a miracle."

Through their separate histories the banks had been friendly rivals but had pursued similar policies. When the time was ripe their amalgamation seemed a natural occurrence.

The Bank of Toronto was the elder of the partners, being 99 years old at the time of the amalgamation. It had its beginning in 1856, in a Toronto that didn't know a building over five stories and in a Canada whose Confederation was still eleven years away. It was the child of a group of flour producers whose trade had developed into a major export industry. They had found a crying need for more banking facilities and founded The Bank of Toronto which opened its doors for business in a modest little building on Church Street on July 8, 1856.

It was just 15 years later that a group of prominent business and professional men in the Toronto area formed The Dominion Bank that opened its first office at 40 King Street East just around the corner from The Bank of Toronto. Perhaps as a portent of their amalgamation almost a century later, The Bank of Toronto was chosen by the Dominion founders as the deposit place for the proceeds of the initial issue of their capital stock.

The two young banks grew and flourished in a country that was also young and growing. Every year saw expansion with branches opening in newly-populated sections of the country. As railroads and other transportation facilities developed new settlements sprung up and another branch of a bank was needed. Both banks finally had branches from coast to coast to keep pace with a maturing, booming Canada. Year after year, they expanded their services to cope with the expanding economy.

Just as a prosperous nation fast outgrowing its facilities brought about the founding of the two banks, the same conditions in Canada of the 1950's brought about their amalgamation. A rapid post-war growth in population coupled with an equally expanding gross national product made amalgamation the answer to the banks' problem of adequately meeting their country's needs.

So it was that The Bank of Toronto celebrated its 100th birthday as the new partner of The Dominion Bank. When they joined hands on February 1, 1955, they became Canada's fourth largest chartered bank with more than 450 branches from coast to coast and assets in excess of one billion dollars. The joining of the two well-known and respected organizations created an enlarged institution with combined experience and resources better able to serve the future development of the country.

Since amalgamation Canada has continued to develop at a rapid rate and The Bank has needed its newly found strength and facilities to keep pace with the county's expansion.

In the three short years since amalgamation, over 50 new branches have been opened by the Bank, many in communities where neither of the parent banks has been represented. The province of Prince Edward Island saw its first branch of the Bank open in Charlottetown in the spring of 1957. Now with over 500 branches across the country, the Bank is continually broadening its service to the Canadian public.

Today, The Toronto-Dominion Bank or "The Bank" as it is familiarly known, has over 1,500 employees from coast to coast. Besides its Head Office in Toronto it has four Divisional Offices in Montreal, Winnipeg, Edmonton and Vancouver, as well as a branch in London, England and in New York and Chicago.

In 1957 more than 7,000 people held shares in the Bank. At the 102nd Annual Meeting in December, 1957, President A. C. Ashforth told the shareholders that 1957 was again a record year with earnings, deposits and assets rising to new heights. Assets exceeded $1,382 millions, deposits $1,296 millions and profits were over $4 millions.

Canadian in character and international in scope, The Toronto-Dominion Bank is a commercial bank serving businesses large and small and a savings bank for Canadians in all walks of life. Today, "The Nicest Girls in Banking" are known to all Canadians and stand as a symbol for the friendly, courteous service that has been the keystone of The Bank's policy from its earliest beginnings, as it will continue to be in the future.

MILNE, GILMORE & GERMAN

Naval Architects and Marine Surveyors

The present internationally known firm of Milne, Gilmore & German, Naval Architects and Marine Surveyors, had its inception in 1919 when Mr. Walter Lambert opened a small office in Montreal as a consulting naval architect. For nine years Mr. Lambert carried on his practice alone, but his clientele increased to such an extent that in 1928 he was joined by Mr. Horace H. German who brought to the partnership an experience in naval architecture and marine engineering extending over fourteen years.

The reputation and proficiency of this alliance were responsible for a considerable expansion in activity and in 1936 Mr. W. Harold Milne, whose background in ship design and repair work both in England and Canada was extensive, joined the partnership. The name of the firm was changed to Lambert, German & Milne and subsequently, upon Mr. Lambert's retirement from active practice of naval architecture in Canada, to German & Milne.

Time wrought its usual changes and eventually Mr. Horace German retired from active participation in the partnership and in 1950 Mr. James Gilmore, a naval architect with a wide experience in Scotland and in Canada who had joined the firm in 1946, became a partner. In due course, Messrs. William H. German, J. Gordon German and William J. Milne, sons of the original "German & Milne" combination became partners, thus bringing into existence the present firm. These three younger partners have all had specialized training and experience in naval architecture and marine engineering, having served in British, European and Canadian shipyards, where they acquired a thorough and practical knowledge of ship design and construction techniques in addition to their university training.

Since its inception the firm has engaged in the many diversified phases of naval architecture, including ship designing, supervision of construction, conversions and repairs, development of detailed working plans, surveys, appraisals, brokerage, court testimony in connection with marine matters, and preparation of economic studies on water transportation. New trends and achievements in shipbuilding and marine engineering have been carefully studied and every effort has been made to take advantage of the most modern and efficient developments in these fields.

Until just prior the World War II the firm specialized chiefly in commercial designs, but during the war years and those immediately preceding that period they were engaged in designing, supervising and preparing working plans for the Royal Canadian Navy, the Department of Munitions & Supply and the British Ministry of War Transport. Since the cessation of hostilities a close association has been maintained with various government departments and the resumption of peacetime activities has resulted in renewed relationships with previous clients and the acquisition of new ones in various fields of industry and commerce.

The personnel of the present firm numbers upwards of fifty, including men skilled in every branch of ship designing and engineering, shipbuilding, ship repairing and ship operating, each with a varied and extensive background in his particular line.

The designs produced over the years include practically every type and class of ship — canallers, pulpwood carriers, ocean-going freighters, newsprint vessels, tankers, upper lakers, passenger-automobile and train ferries, tugs, passenger vessels, specialized types for government requirements in both war and peace, and in addition designs have been prepared covering major reconstruction and conversion projects.

C.G.S. d'Iberville.

M.V. Princess of Vancouver.

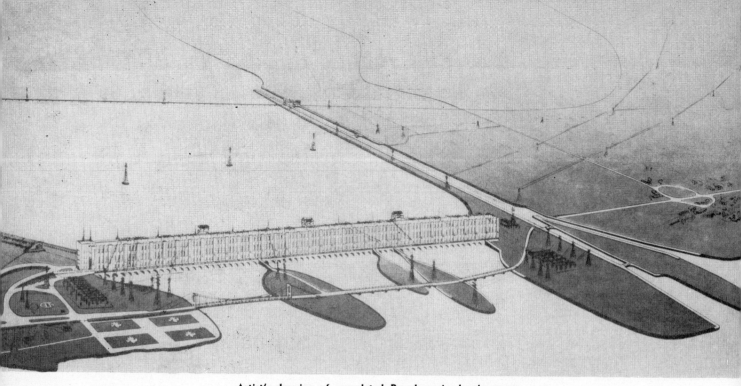

Artist's drawing of completed Beauharnois development.

HYDRO-QUEBEC'S BEAUHARNOIS CANAL
– – A Vital Part of the Seaway

Admittedly one of the most vital inland arteries of the Seaway Canal is the Soulanges section of the 14-mile Beauharnois Power Canal linking Lake St. Francis and Lake St. Louis.

That part of the Beauharnois Canal conceived for Seaway purposes is 600 feet wide. However, once excavation of the power channel has been completed, navigable water will be quite uniform over an expanse of 3,000-foot width. Two highway-railroad bridges — one located three miles below the canal intake and the other about midway in the canal — will be equipped with necessary lift spans.

This Beauharnois Canal was conceived to concentrate at one point the scattered rapids that represent the 80-foot difference in level between the two lakes. It is of proportions sufficient to carry all the water of the St. Lawrence River at a velocity low enough to permit ice formation in wintertime. This water speed, incidentally, is quite appropriate for navigation.

The proposed canal — 15 miles long and 3,300 feet wide — will require the excavation of 250,000,000 cubic yards to answer its dual purpose.

Plans towards realization of this excavation objective motivated construction of what is recognized as the biggest electric suction dredge in the world — the 'Hydro-Quebec.' Flagship of a fleet of dredges of various types, the 'Hydro-Quebec' boasts a total displacement of 2,500 long tons and has overall dimensions of 280 feet in length and 58 feet in width.

A cutter-type hydraulic dredge with a gigantic underwater rotating cutter, the 'Hydro-Quebec' works in material considered among the most difficult to cut and handle hydraulically. Excavating 'boulder clay,' a heavy, sticky type of marine clay laced with glacial boulders, it gouges some 17,000,000 cubic yards during an eight-month working season.

A large pump sucks materials through a 42-inch opening into a 36-inch pontoon-floated discharge pipe connected to a disposal area ashore — as far as three-quarters of a mile distant from the actual scene of operations. It is electrically powered by 12,000-volt current supplied from shore by submarine cable.

Apart from providing an essential link in the Seaway chain, the Beauharnois Canal will feed what eventually will be one of the largest single-site hydro-electric power houses in the world. Progressively, the installed capacity of this generating plant was 750,000 horsepower in 1934 and 1,500,000 horsepower in 1953. With completion of excavation and construction activities, it will reach a pinnacle of more than 2,250,000 horsepower and be responsible for an energy production of some 12 billion kilowatthours per year.

For purposes of comparison, this generating station will be almost the same size as the combined United States-Canada power house at Barnhart Island, with a slightly lower head but a slightly bigger flow.

With the construction of its third and last section, the Beauharnois Powerhouse will have an installed capacity of more than 2,250,000 horsepower.

The 'Hydro-Quebec' suction dredge, the largest of its kind in the world, is being used for dredging and widening the Beauharnois Canal.

M.S. Alexander T. Wood discharging her first cargo, 20,400 long tons of Labrador ore at Philadelphia, Penn., May, 1958.

WESTRIVER ORE TRANSPORT LIMITED
WILSON SHIPPING CORPORATION

As far back as we can remember ships from far off lands have been plying the Seven Seas with their holds laden with valuable trading goods. Now this is soon to change for a new sea will be added in the Spring of 1959 over the waters of which will sail some of the worlds largest freighters. The opening of the St. Lawrence Seaway and Power Project will see ships of Canada and the United States and others from many foreign nations sailing the Eight Seas of which the Great Lakes of North America will constitute the new addition.

In 1956, when it became apparent that the St. Lawrence Seaway and Power Projects would be a reality soon after the opening of navigation on the St. Lawrence River in 1959, two associate shipping companies, Westriver Ore Transports, Limited, and Wilson Shipping Corporation, Limited, both with headquarters in Montreal, Quebec, looked forward to the day when they would be able to operate ocean-going dry cargo ships into the Great Lakes.

As a result of their foresight, a new type ship, such as the M/V ALEXANDER T. WOOD (shown above), owned by Westriver Ore Transports, and her sistership, the M/V AVERY C. ADAMS, owned by Wilson Shipping Corporation, have developed from an idea in 1956 to the proud vessels they are today.

It was through the close cooperation with H. C. Downer & Associates, Incorporated, Naval Architects and Marine Engineers of Cleveland, Ohio, the owners design agent, and Canadian Vickers, Limited, the internationally known Montreal firm of shipbuilders, that these two steel giants of the waterways were developed.

Both the ALEXANDER T. WOOD and the AVERY C. ADAMS, identical in almost every respect, are of the single deck type with Poop and Forecastle, and unlike most Great Lakes Ships, the licensed and unlicensed personnel accommodation, navigation bridge and engine room are arranged at the after end of the vessels. The reason for this, planners point out, is that a clear, unobstructed deck makes cargo handling considerable easier. Their hulls are divided into Fore Peak, Deep Tank, six cargo holds, machinery space and After Peak.

The diverse conditions of service that these two vessels will encounter have led to the incorporation of many special design features. Some of these features are commonly found only on vessels plying the Great Lakes, while others are found only on ocean-going ships, and still others have been specially devised to suit operation in the billion dollar St. Lawrence Seaway.

The two 21,000 ton ore carriers are the largest dry cargo ships ever to be built in Canada and the biggest to be constructed for dual ocean and Great Lakes service following the completion of the St. Lawrence Seaway.

Designed to haul iron ore from the port of Seven Islands on Quebec's North Shore to the great ore smelting plants in United States Great Lake ports, the vessels measure 580 feet overall, are 72 feet wide and draw 30 feet of water when fully loaded.

As previously mentioned, the cargo holds of both the ALEXANDER T. WOOD and the AVERY C. ADAMS are divided into six separate holds with a total cubic grain capacity of over 850,000 cubic feet. With this cubic capacity these ships are equally at home in the transportation of any and all dry bulk cargo. Modern mechanical steel hatch covers which fit snugly over the holds insure against damage by water to the valuable cargos entrusted to these two ships.

The investment in and development of this type of ship by both Westriver Ore Transports and Wilson Shipping Corporation is concrete evidence of their conviction that with the opening of the St. Lawrence Seaway and Power Projects, the Great Lakes area will indeed become the Eighth Sea.

DOMINION BRIDGE
COMPANY LIMITED

ॐ~ॐ

Climbing jacks, sector gates, continuous deck trusses, through trusses, vertical lift spans . . . words without a meaning to the average layman, but to the men who erect bridges and other steel structures across the wide expanse of our land, these are words with a great deal of meaning.

To the men of Dominion Bridge Company Limited, in particular, they are everyday words. As members of the largest bridge building family in Canada theirs is a history which goes back 76 years, with a long list of achievements down through the years that followed.

Since the first plant was erected at Lachine, a suburb of Montreal, in 1882, Dominion Bridge has expanded with Canada, becoming almost a household word from coast to coast.

From a single plant, the Company has grown into a nation-wide organization. From a single activity, bridge building, it has become more and more diversified to meet the many and complex industrial needs of the times.

More recently Dominion Bridge undertook and completed not one, but seven major projects associated with the St. Lawrence Seaway and Power Projects. The diversity of this work, which included design, manufacture and erection, was matched by the diversity of Dominion Bridge facilities. Their part in the construction of the Seaway is indeed a prime example of the Company's many activities.

Believed to be the largest project of its kind ever undertaken, and certainly one of the most complicated on the Seaway, was the permanent raising of the southern end of Jacques Cartier Bridge.

The bridge, originally fabricated and erected by Dominion Bridge in 1929, links the Island of Montreal to the town of Longueuil on the south shore. With the Seaway channel passing beneath its southern portion, and with only a 40-foot clearance at the approach section, it was necessary to provide a ship clearance of 120 feet over the new canal.

To get the additional 80 feet, the bridge was jacked 50 feet and the deck truss span over the canal was replaced with a through truss span to gain an additional 30 feet.

Twin vertical lift spans on the Canadian Pacific Railway near Caughnawaga provide Seaway Canal clearance.

Jacking a bridge that high is a feat in itself, but maintaining traffic at the same time is a job of spectacular proportions. And that is exactly what Dominion Bridge accomplished. With virtually no interruption of the heavy four-lane traffic overhead, Dominion Bridge raised the Jacques Cartier Bridge 50 feet above its original grade.

The jacking was done by eighteen 500 and twelve 400 long ton hydraulic jacks. Each pier member was replaced by a heavy steel weldment called a climbing jack. The climbing jacks were inverted U shaped members with hydraulic jacks placed between the legs.

Four climbing jacks were set up on each pier, replacing the bearing shoes at each corner of the two adjoining truss spans. In a synchronized operation, one pier at a time, pressure was applied to the four hydraulic jacks, lifting the two spans and also the legs of the climbing jacks.

When the spans were raised 6 inches, precast concrete blocks were placed under the legs, the ram was retracted and another block placed under its head, completing the cycle. And so it went until the road grade was at its final elevation.

There are many ways to increase the height of an existing bridge . . . and in the Montreal region where numerous structures had to be elevated to provide clearance needed by the St. Lawrence Seaway, a variety of methods was employed. The Jacques Cartier Bridge was jacked up, but in the case of the Honoré Mercier bridge the long approach section was "blown up" before the new construction could proceed. And here again traffic flowed normally without interruption — this was achieved by the use of a temporary approach.

227

Shipment of 48 headgates for the Robert H. Saunders —
St. Lawrence generating station, near Cornwall, Ont.

300 ton D.B. gantry crane raising 230-ton rotor at the
Robert H. Saunders — St. Lawrence generating station.

At this location, the Seaway is a canal, cut south of the St. Lawrence River under the new land approaches to the existing bridge, to bypass the Lachine Rapids of the river just 2 miles southwest of Montreal.

Built in 1934 by Dominion Bridge, the 2,900-foot long Mercier Bridge consisted of a concrete roadway supported by 11 deck truss spans, 13 concrete piers and a 400-foot continuous tied arch span which provided clearance for river steamers "shooting" the Lachine Rapids, once a thrilling tourist attraction.

The new bridge additions, which consist of a 300 ft. span 120 ft. above the canal and four 1500 ft. approaches contain 11,000 tons of steelwork. One approach connects the existing bridge to the new structure and

three others handle south and west traffic.

To keep traffic moving over the main part of the structure, it was necessary to build a high fill bypass at the south end of the bridge which was connected by means of a timber trestle with the main bridge at the edge of the river.

The Canadian Pacific Railway Company's double track line from Montreal to the south shore crosses the Seaway channel at the famed Indian Reservation at Caughnawaga. Two independent lift bridges, one for each track, were built side by side by Dominion Bridge over the channel to give a clearance for shipping of 120 feet from the high water level. The two bridges are identical except for secondary details such as stairs and walkways.

One of four pairs of sector gates, Iroquois, Ont. Each
pair is 45 ft. high and weighs about 500 tons.

Aerial view of Seaway, Caughnawaga area, near Montreal, showing C.P.R. bridge, new twin lift spans and Honoré Mercier bridge with new south shore approaches.

Each bridge consists of a 322-foot truss lift span, at each end of which is a tower having an overall height of 140 feet 6 inches above the base of the rail. The lower portion of each tower forms a 66-foot truss span. Leading to the towers, at each end of the bridge, there is a 55-foot deck plate girder span. The overall length of the bridge is 595 feet. Each movable span weighs 1,000 tons and can be raised or lowered in 75 seconds.

Dominion Bridge also built two lift spans for the St. Lawrence Seaway Authority at Montreal's Victoria Bridge. For this complex project two lift spans, one at each end of the St. Lambert Lock, were provided so that railway and highway traffic would not be delayed by the operation of the Seaway. When either of the spans is raised to permit passage of ships, traffic can flow without interruption over the Seaway channel.

Dominion Bridge's diversified activities can readily be seen in several other large contracts which the Company was awarded on the St. Lawrence Seaway project.

For the Barnhart Island Power Project, Dominion Bridge fabricated for Ontario Hydro 48 hydraulic head gates with hoists and bedded parts, the largest order of its kind ever placed in Canada. The Company also built a 90-ton gantry crane for serving the gates. They are designed for openings 17 feet wide by 37 feet high and each can withstand a pressure of 3,000,000 pounds under a 93-foot head of water.

Besides the gates, Dominion Bridge designed, fabricated and installed a 300-ton gantry crane of unique design for the Canadian half of the Barnhart Island Power House.

This huge crane which, in effect, acts as a "travelling power house" is the largest of its type ever built in Canada. Completely enclosed, the crane illustrates a modern trend in design.

Last but not least, Dominion Bridge fabricated and installed at Iroquois, Ontario, four pairs of sector gates for the Seaway canal. These gates are to act as the operating gates of the lock at Iroquois. Each pair is 45 feet high and weighs around 500 tons. There is also one pair of guard gates of similar design for each of the two locks at Beauharnois and the single lock at Cote Ste. Catherine in the Quebec section of the Seaway.

These projects on the St. Lawrence Seaway and Power Projects represent another milestone in the long and successful record of achievements by Dominion Bridge Company Limited — a company which since its foundation in 1882 has built, as of September 1958, 3,071 bridges of many and diverse types, including most of the major bridges in Canada. A majority of the major steel buildings in the country were erected by Dominion Bridge. These include Montreal's new Queen Elizabeth Hotel, the Sun Life Building, also in Montreal and the largest office building in the British Commonwealth; the Royal Bank Building, Montreal, and Royal York Hotel and extension, Toronto; the new seven-storey Vancouver post office building, believed to be the world's largest all-welded building and containing 7,000 tons of steel and occupying an entire city block.

Some of the bridges include, the Angus L. Macdonald bridge between Halifax and Dartmouth, N.S., with a main span of 1,477 feet and a total length of 4,420 feet; Vancouver's Granville Bridge, first eight-lane highway bridge in Canada; the main span of Burlington Skyway Bridge on the Queen Elizabeth Way, between Niagara Falls and Toronto; the four-lane Midtown bridge in Winnipeg, Manitoba; the longest aluminum highway bridge in the world with a span of 504 feet erected over the Saguenay River, Arvida, Quebec. Indeed an enviable record which speaks for itself and one of which Dominion Bridge can well be proud.

Climbing jacks in operation at Jacques Cartier Bridge, Montreal.

Jacques Cartier Bridge showing completed modification which will provide a ship clearance of 120 ft. over the Seaway canal.

Aerial view of Cornwall, Ont., "The Seaway City".

CITY OF CORNWALL

"The Seaway City" gears for new industry

No city is more intimately associated with the St. Lawrence Seaway — or in a position to offer more attractive economic advantages because of it — than Cornwall, Ontario, otherwise known as "The Seaway City".

Cornwall comes by its newly-acquired title honestly. For as the headquarters of the St. Lawrence Seaway Authority and the site of the Canadian section of the massive new St. Lawrence Power Development, it is the Canadian nerve centre of both the waterway and power phases of the gigantic Seaway project.

Of primary importance is the strategic location of "The Seaway City" in relation to mass markets. Cornwall lies in the middle of the three great market areas of Canada: Montreal, Canada's metropolis, only 70 miles to the east; Toronto, the country's second largest city, 265 miles to the west; and Ottawa, Canada's capital, 75 miles to the north, with Cornwall providing the closest and natural port of entry. Together, these three market areas embrace a population of more than 10,000,000 people — nearly two-thirds of the total population of Canada.

Modern and expansive harbour facilities are being developed which will give Cornwall the status of a World Port. Cornwall harbour will be developed according to a master plan to meet the needs of new industry. Eventually, it will have a handling capacity of 4 million tons per year.

The harbour will have 11,500 feet of wharfage on the mainland and Pilon Island across from it, providing berthage for 15 ocean-going vessels at one time. The island will have off-loading and storage facilities for bulk material, and it will also serve as a fuel storage centre. A Causeway with a lift bridge will connect the island with the mainland.

A railway marshalling yard will be established in the harbour area for fast, economical loading and unloading.

Oustanding transportation facilities are Cornwall's greatest single attraction to industry.

Ocean-going and lake vessels, running into the heart of the North American continent along the St. Lawrence Seaway route or across the Atlantic to Great Britain and Europe, will use the great new Port of Cornwall when completed. Provision will be made for the quick, economical turnround of ships here.

Canada's two great transcontinental railway systems, Canadian National and Canadian Pacific, serve Cornwall direct for freight, express and passenger traffic.

Cornwall is served by the Main Montreal-Toronto thruway, Highway No. 2, and it is anticipated that a new Superhighway, No. 401, will also serve the city in the near future. Public carrier trucks provide regular service to Montreal, Toronto and other points.

An international airport is located at Massena, N. Y., only 12 miles away, and measures are being taken to establish a large airport on the outskirts of Cornwall. As soon as it is completed it will be put on regular T.C.A. scheduled services.

Cornwall is a Canadian Port of Entry from the United States. Work has started on construction of two new four-lane elevated bridges that will connect with the thruway to New York City.

Situated on the St. Lawrence river and at the site of the immense new Robert Saunders power development, Cornwall has an abundance of fresh water and hydro-electric power for new industries.

Added to the existing electrical power supply, which is plentiful and economical, energy from this great new source which has an annual Canadian output expected to average 6,300,000,000 kilowatt hours, makes Cornwall one of the most attractive centres of industrial power in the Western Hemisphere.

In addition, natural gas will be piped into the Cornwall area in the very near future. Water for industrial processing and human consumption alike is fresh and plentiful.

Adjacent to the Cornwall harbour area, to enable maximum efficient use of the outstanding transportation facilities, choice tracts of land have been set aside for the location of new industries.

Available for immediate development are 300 acres of service and land running up from the harbour area, while additional connecting tracts of 900 acres have been reserved for further expansion, to be serviced when needed. Other large stretches of land will also be made available in neighbouring Charlottenburg Township which adjoins Cornwall on the east.

Cornwall is in a particularly favourable position regarding the availability of manpower for new industries.

In fact, it is one of the few cities in the world with a "built-in" reserve of stable manpower. This situation has been made possible because several thousand workers — all from within a radius of 30 miles from Cornwall — gradually became available as construction work on the St. Lawrence power development neared completion.

In addition, Cornwall is able to draw from a population of over 100,000 within a close radius for skilled, semi-skilled and unskilled male and female workers.

One of the main reasons why labour turnover has been low in the Cornwall area over the years has been the prevalence of exceptionally fine fishing, hunting and other outdoor recreational facilities nearby.

Also a great appeal to residents of the area is the immense new St. Lawrence Parkway soon to be developed a short distance from the City of Cornwall. This project, which will provide one of the finest playgrounds and tourist attractions in North America, will include an artificial lake 35 miles long, swimming and boating facilities, a golf course and a yacht basin.

Cornwall is no stranger to industrial success. Some of Canada's largest companies are located in this city, including Courtaulds (Canada) Limited, (viscose), Howard Smith Paper Mills Ltd., (who recently announced a $12,500,000 expansion program here), Canadian Cottons Ltd., and Canadian Industries Limited (caustic soda).

But with the coming of the waterway and power project, "The Seaway' City's" planners and administrators look upon the present state of industrial development as only a modest beginning. They are confident that industrialists looking for a new Canadian location will echo the sentiments of Noel B. McLean, president of the Edo Corporation, New York, when his company decided recently to locate its Canadian operation, Edo (Canada) Limited, in Cornwall:

"This selection was made after an extensive study of the market for (its) products as related to the attributes of various areas in Canada which were proposed and available. The Cornwall area, strategically located as it is on the St. Lawrence, has other outstanding advantages in respect to its easy access to Montreal and Ottawa, the availability of high grade personnel, a good community atmosphere and a local government interested in the problems of businesses seeking to locate in this area.

Seaway Authority Administration Building, Cornwall.

231

Dipper Dredge "Monarch" equipped with a 6 cu. yd. Joliette-Amsco bucket.

New Type 6 yard Dipper 3 piece renewable lip with Bail and Bail Equalizer

JOLIETTE STEEL DIVISION — MANITOBA STEEL FOUNDRY DIVISION

DOMINION BRAKE SHOE COMPANY LTD.

On November 17, 1954, construction work on the St. Lawrence Seaway was begun with a single dynamite blast. This marked the beginning of excavation work on the Seaway Channel. A distance of 120 miles, over 75 million cubic yards, of canal excavation was required to open the channel from the Montreal Harbour to the Head of Lake Ontario.

As the first of the $200,000,000 in contracts was awarded, contractors and power equipment manufacturers called on Joliette Steel Division to supply their renewable-lip design dippers and dipper parts for their shovels and earth moving equipment. Dipper capacities ranged from 1 yard to 6 yards.

One of the biggest problems encountered was moving away the excavated earth and spreading it. For this tremendous operation, contractors equipped their powerful tractors, bulldozers and scrapers with Joliette-cast Manganese steel dozer blades, tractor pads and end bits. The Manganese parts outlasted other metals through the heavy rock and gravel-filled localities.

Deepening the bottoms of the canals and lakes called for removal of over 25 million cubic yards of sand-gravel and some heavy rock. Again, Manganese steel was required for the two-piece 5-yard dipper which was fitted to the huge Monarch dredge.

Concrete work for both the St. Lawrence Seaway and Power Projects, totalling over 3 million cubic yards, required a steady supply of aggregate rock that was close at hand. To insure supply, and uniform crushing, Joliette Steel equipped the crushing plants with Manganese Steel jaw plates, bowl liners, and mantles for Cone Crushers. The abrasive structure of the aggregate rock called for long wearing Joliette Manganese steel cast parts.

Joliette Steel was established at Joliette, P.Q. in 1917, for the production of war materials and carbon steel castings for the railroads.

In 1924, Mr. P. H. Desrosiers, now Executive Vice-President of the present Company, was appointed Managing Director of Joliette Steel Ltd.

The Company made agreements with manufacturers of crushers, ball and rod mills, feeders, and other machinery in the mining and construction industries. This enabled users of Manganese Steel castings to secure the highest quality Manganese Steel replacement parts at price savings.

In 1946, the name "Amsco" — universally known for the high quality standard of its products — was added to Joliette, when American Manganese Steel Division of American Brake Shoe Co. took control of the company.

During 1957, the assets of Manitoba Steel Foundries Ltd., in Selkirk, Manitoba, were acquired. This is now operated as the Manitoba Steel Foundry Division.

A multi-million dollar expansion programme at Joliette, Que. is presently underway. It is designed to increase present production 10% to a maximum capacity of 12,000 tons annually. Apart from building expansion, there is new equipment installations planned, including sandslingers, a rotomold, shakeouts, roto-feed and rol-a-draw machines, a shot blast unit, a tower core oven and a speedmullor. Plans also include equipment to produce a newly designed easy-to-change magnetic dipper tooth point.

Joliette Steel Division, Manitoba Steel Foundry Division, Dominion Brake Shoe Co. Ltd., Head Office, 1405 Peel Street, Montreal; Sales Offices, Saint John, N.B., Toronto, Ont., Kirkland Lake, Ont., Sudbury, Ont., Winnipeg, Manitoba, and Vancouver, B.C. Foundries at Joliette, Que., and Selkirk, Manitoba.

232

R. C. L. Dipper Dredge the "Andrew B" operating in the Welland Canal preparing 27' channel.

RUSSELL CONSTRUCTION LIMITED

The story of Russell Construction Limited is the story of the last forty years of dock and harbour development along the Canadian shores of the Great Lakes from Georgian Bay to Kingston, Ontario. During that time the red and black of Russell's tugs, dredges and floating derricks have become a familiar sight to two generations.

A fitting climax to this long and prominent association with Canadian marine construction came with Russell Construction Limited's participation in the building of the St. Lawrence Seaway and Power Projects.

This consisted of the deepening of a four mile section of the Welland Ship Canal from the town of Thorold to Allanburg village. The Welland Canal links lakes Ontario and Erie and is one of the most vital links in the chain of waterways which make up the St. Lawrence Seaway.

The contract awarded by the Canadian St. Lawrence Seaway Authority to Russell Construction Limited required the removal by suction-dredge of some 250,000 cubic yards of "soft" material, and the drilling, blasting and dredging of almost 400,000 cubic yards of limestone rock.

Work of this magnitude demands the use of the most modern and efficient equipment operated and controlled by men of wide knowledge and experience. With their long years of operation in the field of marine construction, Russell Construction Limited have been able to provide both.

In 1954 Russell Construction Limited became a subsidiary of Balfour, Beatty & Co. (Canada) Limited and so joined the Balfour Beatty Group of the United Kingdom which has world-wide interests in Engineering and Construction ranging from docks and dams to nuclear power stations.

With the opening of the St. Lawrence Seaway, Canada will be drawn into even closer association with the rest of the world and will become more acutely concerned with industrial developments in other countries particularly insofar as these might affect international trade and commerce.

Russell Construction Limited considers its association with the Balfour, Beatty Co. Ltd. a valuable asset in enabling it to bring a wider and more comprehensive viewpoint to Canadian Construction problems.

It is not only in the field of marine construction that Russell Construction Limited are contributing to Canada's industrial growth. A progressive and expanding department is maintained to handle civil engineering and building projects such as Sewage-treatment and Water Filtration Plants, Bridges and commercial and industrial structures of all kinds. In addition the Company specializes in piled foundations.

Russell Construction Limited brings a wealth of experience and knowledge, plus modern efficient equipment, to any construction project large or small and at the same time gives that close personal attention to detail which results in a job "well done"!

233

BP Tanker Company's 35,000 ton oil tanker "British Architect" seen during her North Sea trials.

BP CANADA LIMITED
Subsidiary of The British Petroleum Company Ltd.

Destined to provide deepwater navigation facilities from the Atlantic to the industrial heart of North America, the billion-dollar St. Lawrence Seaway and Power Projects will see ships of many denominations traversing its giant man-made lock structures and canals.

Standing ready to service these ships in their fuel needs is one of the largest petroleum companies in the world. The British Petroleum Company Ltd. has located in Canada and — through its wholly owned subsidiary, BP Canada Ltd. — is in the process of constructing the most modern oil refinery in the country.

Due to come on stream in mid-1960, the refinery will produce, among other products, fuel oil for the ships which will travel the new waterway.

Bunkering Big Business

Bunkering services form an important branch of the oil industry. More than 92 percent of the world's merchant shipping is fitted for oil propulsion and there

are approximately 250 ports in world shipping trade routes at which ships take bunker oils. In all, it is estimated that more than 65 million tons of marine fuel is supplied yearly to ocean vessels.

Facilities for this trade are constantly being improved and extended. For example, in Aden — the largest bunkering port in the eastern hemisphere — the British Petroleum Company is presently doubling its pumping rate to nearly 6,000 gallons a minute to meet the needs of large passenger liners.

It was in 1861, just two years after the first oil well had been drilled in Pennsylvania, that an ocean cargo of oil crossed the Atlantic. This first "tanker" was the 244-ton brig "ELIZABETH WATTS".

Today, oil has become the world's most valuable seaborne cargo. One out of every five ships sailing on the high seas today is an oil tanker. On an average day, 17 million tons of petroleum are carried across the waters of the world, either as crude oil from oilfields or as finished products from refineries.

Modern Armada

The BP Tanker Company, shipping organization of The British Petroleum Company operates the largest fleet sailing under one flag in the world. Its offices in London are the controlling point of a vast and intricate system which governs the movements of its 150 ships and also of a similar number of vessels on charter which together carry oil between some 500 ports scattered throughout the world.

Six 28,000-ton and fourteen 32,000-ton tankers were commissioned by British Petroleum between 1950 and 1958. An additional 31 vessels, including 22 tankers ranging in size from 35,000 to 50,000 tons are due for delivery between 1958 and 1960. And in June 1957, new orders were announced for 26 tankers, including 7 ships of 65,000 tons and 11 of 50,000 tons.

BP Installation at Trieste, one of eight ports in Italy where bunkers are supplied by BP INTERNATIONAL OIL BUNKERING service.

BP INTERNATIONAL OIL BUNKERING — FRANCE
BP bunkering S.S. "Chambord" at Dunkirk.

Search for Oil Global

British Petroleum's principal sources of crude oil are in the Middle East. Through its prospecting subsidiary, BP Exploration Company, it also has oil production or exploration interests in many other parts of the world. In Canada, BP has a 50 percent interest in Triad Oil Company which is actively engaged in oil exploration in Western Canada. Triad has substantial interests in six million acres in Alberta, British Columbia, Saskatchewan, Manitoba and the Northwest Territories.

World-Wide Operation

The BP Group operates refineries in Great Britain, Australia, Aden, France, Germany, Belgium, Italy and the Middle East. In association with chemical producers, it has growing interests in the petroleum chemical field in the United Kingdom, France and Germany. Its marketing network, extending over most of the eastern hemisphere, now includes Canada. In this country, BP has concentrated its initial efforts on building a chain of service stations in Quebec and Ontario. Just two years after BP's first Canadian service station was opened, this rapidly expanding chain totalled 500 outlets.

Townsend Company Limited trucks delivering seastores to the M/V Glenpark.

TOWNSEND COMPANY LIMITED

There is a saying amongst sailors the world over which goes, "A happy ship is a ship that feeds well." This saying is a well known fact, but in some ports it is not often easy to acquire quality stores. In the Port of Montreal, however, this is no problem as steamship operators and agents familiar with the port's facilities and services will tell you.

Since its inception in 1917, Townsend Company Limited, ship suppliers, has been serving the marine industry in this Eastern Canadian port efficiently and economically. In 1957 alone, the Company supplied some 1000 ships in Montreal with such stores as meats, dry stores, fruit and vegetables, and all manner of hardware pertaining to Deck, Cabin and Engine Room Departments.

With so many foreign ships calling at Montreal these days, Townsend Company has made it a point of employing a staff able to converse fluently in almost any language. Being able to speak such languages as German, French, Italian, Spanish, Greek, English and all Scandinavian, makes it possible for Townsend representatives to get better acquainted with the specialized food items required by each of these nations.

In their Hardware Department, Townsend Company has found it necessary to import large quantities of goods from the major shipbuilding nations of the world, due to the specialized aspects of the requirements in the marine services. Items such as cargo handling gear, wire ropes and blocks have to meet the standard specifications of the world market because of the safety factors involved.

Regarding the Provision Department, most new ships today have sufficient refrigeration storage space, which enables them to carry anywhere from 6 to 9 months stores, and as a result, these ships are able to purchase stores in almost any area, where a saving can be effected. In Canada, most tinned fruits, vegetables and flour are of a better quality and more favourable price-wise, but as far as meats are concerned, there are certain areas in the world where meats are available at one third to one half the price of Canadian meats. This disadvantage has made it necessary for Townsend Company to import their own meats from far off New Zealand. In order to create a demand for this item and keep abreast of foreign prices, Townsend has had to sell it at a much lower price compared to the similar quality meat available in Canada.

To meet the great demand for their services, Townsend recently increased their operations through the forming of a separate company to handle all Italian shipping business, namely Joseph Bianchi and Son Limited. In the Maritime provinces the Townsend Company (Maritime) Limited, in addition to being the "feeder" for the Company's winter operations, is also one of the largest suppliers of tubular steel scaffolding to the construction industry.

As the dawn of a new era for Canada is about to break with the opening of the billion dollar St. Lawrence Seaway and Power Projects, Townsend Company Limited looks forward to an era of increased business which is sure to materialize from the greater volume of ship traffic on the new waterway system.

SS. "Paterson" at the N. M. Paterson & Sons Limited terminal elevator at Fort William, Ont.

N. M. PATERSON & SONS LIMITED

Of all the Canadian shipping companies whose ships will operate along the St. Lawrence Seaway route when it is officially inaugurated in April 1959, the firm of N. M. Paterson and Sons Limited is probably one of the largest and oldest. This year, 1958, Paterson and Sons celebrate their Fifieth Anniversary, for it was in 1908 that Senator N. M. Paterson opened his grain office at Fort William, Ontario, and embarked on a career which down through the years has gained for him the reputation of being one of the most illustrious of Canadian Shipping magnates.

With its head office still located in Fort William, N. M. Paterson and Sons Limited also maintain offices in Winnipeg, Manitoba, Montreal, Quebec and Cleveland, Ohio. At the present time, the Steamship Division of N. M. Paterson and Sons Limited consists of thirty-six steamers and three barges, ranging in cargo carrying capacity from 2,500 to 15,000 gross tons. In addition the Company owns and operates, in its Grain Division, 105 country elevators throughout Western Canada with an immense terminal elevator at Fort William, situated at the head of Lake Superior.

N. M. Paterson and Sons latest addition to their fine fleet of Great Lakes vessels, the SENATOR OF CANADA, was delivered by Collingwood Shipyards late in 1957. This vessel, considered the flagship of the Company, measures 605 feet in overall length with a deadweight tonnage of 15,000 gross tons.

In addition to operating its own ships, N. M. Paterson and Sons Limited also offer vessel agency services through the Fort William, Montreal and Winnipeg offices. Grain chartering facilities are available through Winnipeg Charterers Limited, a subsidiary of the Company in Winnipeg.

Western Engineering Service Limited, another subsidiary of N. M. Paterson and Sons, operates a large, up-to-date ship repair plant at Fort William. This organization is fully equipped and expertly staffed to efficiently carry out all types of repairs on steamships, with the exception of drydocking.

During World War II, the entire Canaller portion of the Paterson fleet with the exception of one vessel, played an active part in Canada's war effort. These ships were a familiar sight in the Caribbean waters and were engaged mainly in the transportation of bauxite from the Aluminum Company of Canada's plant in Mackenzie, British Guiana to St. Thomas, in the Virgin Islands and Trinidad. Of the eighteen vessels engaged in this vital service, seven were lost by enemy action, with heavy loss of life, two were lost by Marine disasters, and six were requisitioned by the United States War Shipping Administration, so that at the end of hostilities only three returned to the flag of N. M. Paterson and Sons. Since that time, however, all these vessels have been replaced and the Paterson Canal fleet now numbers twenty-one.

Officers and Directors of N. M. Paterson and Sons Limited are: Senator Norman M. Paterson, President; John N. Paterson, Vice President and General Manager; Donald S. Paterson, Vice-President; H. B. Sinfield, Secretary-Treasurer; C. G. Hacquoil, Manager, Steamship Division; I. C. McEwen, Traffic Manager, J. T. Norquay, Manager, Winnipeg Charters Limited. B. J. Knight is Manager of the Grain Division.

This bascule bridge at Iroquois lock is raised and lowered with speed and precision by Westinghouse Bridge-O-Matic controls.

CANADIAN WESTINGHOUSE COMPANY LIMITED

Hamilton, Canada

On the combined waterway and power projects of the St. Lawrence Seaway, Canadian Westinghouse has been the major supplier of electrical equipment.

Westinghouse participation in Seaway development dates back to the building of the third Welland Canal. Westinghouse installed all the controls for the canal's eleven bridges.

Early operating experience proved that winter conditions including wind, snow and ice, had a damaging effect on the bridges when they were raised or lowered. The critical points were at the nearly full open and nearly closed positions where the speed of the bridge movement had to be reduced suddenly by mechanical means.

Studies by Westinghouse engineers convinced them that a modification of Westinghouse LOAD-O-MATIC

Hoist Control, developed for mine operations, would provide the smooth, precise operation needed. In the summer of 1955 Westinghouse applied these new improved controls to one of the canal's rolling lift bridges. Existing motors were still used but the modified control gave much smoother, faster operation over the entire action of opening and closing. The winter hazards were overcome with increased safety and efficiency.

In December of 1955, the new Westinghouse BRIDGE-O-MATIC bridge control was demonstrated for bridge building officials and representatives of the Seaway Authority.

These tests were a complete success. So much so that one year later, Westinghouse BRIDGE-O-MATIC Controls were selected for seven movable bridges to be built over the St. Lawrence on the Seaway.

In addition, 67 sets of Westinghouse controls were ordered for lock, gate and fender control operation along the Canadian ship channel.

With a most complete background in design and application engineering over half a century, Westinghouse was able to meet the rigid specifications laid down by Seaway engineers and consultants. They supplied circuit breakers and current regulators as well as the actual operating motors and controls.

POWER PROJECTS

Canadian Westinghouse has also shared in the engineering and building of electrical apparatus for the two huge new power developments on the St. Lawrence.

Power from Ontario Hydro's Robert H. Saunders Generating Station near Cornwall is generated by Westinghouse equipment. Eight huge 60,000 KVA vertical waterwheel machines were engineered, built and installed by Canadian Westinghouse. These giant generators

weigh more than 600 tons each. The power they produce would serve all the requirements of a city the size of Toronto.

Westinghouse also engineered and manufactured all the transformers for the Saunders Station. Numbering 13 in all, these mammoth Transformers stand 30 feet high and weigh 103½ tons each.

At Beauharnois, Quebec Hydro's vast 2¼ million horse-power generating station 25 miles west of Montreal, Westinghouse supplied five of the first 26 generators installed there several years ago. Now, ten more Westinghouse generators, each of 65,000 KVA capacity, will be operating at Beauharnois by 1960, bringing the station to full capacity. Westinghouse transformers were also installed to step up Beauharnois' generated power from 13,500 to approximately 120,000 volts for transmission.

At Ontario Hydro's Cornwall switching station, which is fed from the vast St. Lawrence power development, Westinghouse met the challenge of high power

This giant generator shaft weighs 58 tons. Eight Westinghouse generators were built for Ontario Hydro's Robert H. Saunders power station.

switching demands with a new Canadian designed, air-blast breaker called the JETAIRE, the first installation in Canada, on the St. Lawrence.

These JETAIRE power circuit breakers first used on the St. Lawrence power project are now being ordered by Electric Utilities across Canada.

WESTINGHOUSE LIGTHING ON THE SEAWAY

Another important Westinghouse contribution to the Seaway is lighting. Westinghouse mercury luminaires, mounted on tall, gracefully tapered steel poles, provide Seaway locks and their approach walks with the finest in modern illumination.

From the beginning of work on the St. Lawrence Seaway and its power development, Westinghouse people have spent thousands upon thousands of man-hours in the planning, engineering, design and production of electrical equipment for this vast project. It is a source of great pride to these 12,000 Westinghouse citizens of Canada that they have shared in one of the greatest engineering accomplishments in the history of this country.

Westinghouse transformer for the Robert H. Saunders power station stands 30 feet high.

Westinghouse Mercury luminaires light Seaways locks and approach walls.

Scale model showing proposed development of Hamilton Harbour. Future construction shown in lighter shading.

HAMILTON — MAJOR SEAWAY PORT

Canada's steel city, the heart of the Canadian industry, lies at the extreme western end of Lake Ontario, and has the finest natural harbour on the Great Lakes.

The Port of Hamilton is Canada's third busiest — only Montreal and Vancouver rate higher in tonnage handled — and each successive year reflects even greater tonnage, number of vessels, and number of shipping lines taking advantage of the facilities provided.

Now, with the advent of the St. Lawrence Seaway, Hamilton's quarter-million inhabitants, together with its Harbour Commission, can look ahead to even brighter prospects in the future.

The three-man Harbour Commission has been planning ahead, preparing to meet the challenge of the opening of the Great Lake's Ports to the world's shipping lines.

Much more top mooring space, more wharfage, more warehousing, and more rail and road facilities for transhipments were on the drawing boards early in the 1950's. Today, they are being translated into reality via bulldozers, cranes, pile-drivers, and the muscles of men.

The three levels of government have displayed a physical and financial interest in the future of the Port of Hamilton. The Federal Government has long since given the "go ahead" to wharf construction and dredging preliminary to a vast programme of land reclamation which will, when completed, realize an additional 1,000 acres of space for marine and industrial use.

The Department of Public Works has also authorized the construction of a new vertical-lift bridge for railway, vehicular, and pedestrian traffic across the Burlington channel entrance to the Port. This new $5,000,-000 bridge will replace the present bascule highway bridge and the railway swing bridge, thus making possible the removal of the centre pier which now divides the canal into two channels. This will greatly facilitate entrance of the largest vessels using the Seaway.

Already in place across the entrance is the magnificent Skyway Bridge, arching to provide a clearance above highwater level of 120 feet, which is the minimum height fixed for Seaway crossings. Built by the Department of Highways of Ontario at a cost of $17,000,000 it is designed to carry four lanes of high-speed traffic flowing between Toronto, Niagara Falls, and Buffalo, becoming an integral part of the famous, and well-travelled Queen Elizabeth Way — Canada's first high-speed modern expressway.

At the municipal level, the City of Hamilton's council has already indicated approval of an elaborate programme of highway interchanges at the north-east and north-west ends of the City. These will link major city thoroughfares with provincial highways and expressways.

It should be emphasized that Hamilton lies at the heart of what is called the Golden Horseshoe — an area stretching from beyond Toronto around to the eastern end of the Niagara Peninsula, in which is centred Canada's wealthiest industries, real estate, and road and rail networks. Three major railway lines lead to the Port's docks and a network of well-paved, fast-travelled highways, add up to quick transhipments, and fast turnarounds for shipping lines.

The Port of Hamilton welcomes the St. Lawrence Seaway advent, and stands ready to deal efficiently with what it confidently anticipates will be a tremendous increase in marine business.

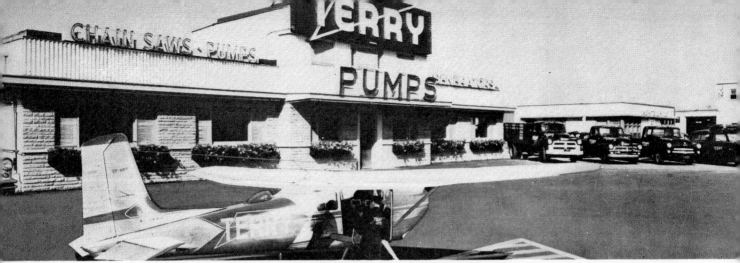

Terry plant on the outskirts of Montreal.

TERRY MACHINERY COMPANY LIMITED

In 1938, W. Harrison Terry, a native of Philadelphia, started a small pump selling concern on a lonely stretch of highway on the outskirts of Montreal, and it was in May of that same year that Bill Terry sold his first Homelite pump. From that day on he never looked back.

Today Terry Machinery, with fully staffed branches in Vancouver and Prince George, British Columbia; Edmonton, Alberta; Port Arthur, Toronto and Ottawa, Ontario; Quebec City; Moncton, New Brunswick and Cornerbrook, Newfoundland, is one of the most important and newsworthy companies in the country. It not only buys and sells but also manufactures fire pumps, generators, chain saws and other electrical control systems. While it serves the general public, Terry Machinery Company specializes in serving industry.

Built in 1940, the manufacturing plant in Montreal has tripled in size and at present occupies some 20,000 square feet of floor space, 10,100 square feet of office space and 10,700 square feet of shop.

Terry Machinery has built an enviable record through its service to industry. In Montreal the company maintains a 24-hour service with seven pump specialists on immediate call, fully equipped for on the spot repairs. Major repairs, of course, are carried out by the highly trained machine shop personnel. Terry makes absolutely certain that all pumps are tested before dispatching to the jobsite. Even new units are given a thorough going over before leaving the plant.

To handle the constant flow of business quickly and efficiently in and around the Montreal area, Terry Machinery Company has a fleet of trucks, demonstration cars and two airplanes. These planes enable the executive and sales personnel to keep in closer touch with the branch offices, dealer distributors and customers. It also comes in handy for emergency shipments, particularly on delivery of chain saws into the far northern reaches of the country.

While the pump and generator business gave Bill

Terry the chance to build the foundation of his organization, the arrival of the Homelite Chain Saw in 1950 opened up greater markets and he was able to materially enlarge his selling organization. Today, Terry Machinery boasts one of the biggest and best organized sales staff selling chain saws, pumps and generators in Canada. It is an established fact that Homelite Chain Saws outsell all other makes in Canada.

What does the future hold for Terry Machinery and Homelite Products in Canada. The 20th Century has been termed as Canada's Century. The tremendous developments of its natural resources and the emigration program, will result in greater demand for high quality products as manufactured by Terry and Homelite. This, coupled with the team spirit built in the Company by its founder and President, Bill Terry, points up to a bright selling future for both Terry Machinery and Homelite.

Directors of Terry Machinery Company include William H. Terry, President; Roland Cadieux, Director of Finances; Al Gilfillan, Sales Director; and Cliff Makinson, Production Director.

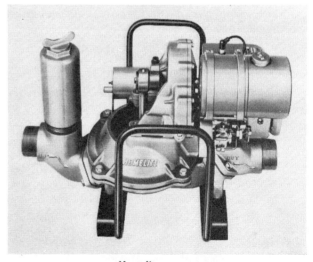

Homelite pump.

NORTHERN ELECTRIC COMPANY, LIMITED

The two elements which later combined to form Northern Electric Company Limited, as it exists **today**, were born out of the invention of the telephone. The electrical industry was in its infancy in 1882, the year in which the newly formed Bell Telephone Company of Canada opened a one-room electrical shop in Montreal to make and repair telephone sets for its system. Known to the industry as the Manufacturing Department of The Bell Telephone Company, the shop employed ten men; but its limited facilities were easily able to cope with the tasks assigned to it.

Rapid multiplication of those tasks accompanied the phenomenal acceptance in Canada of "Mr. Bell's remarkable invention" and, in 1895, the department found it expedient to become a separate entity under the name Northern Electric and Manufacturing Company Limited.

In the same year, the newly created need for wire and cable for the telephone industry encouraged an enterprising Montreal Scotsman, Alexander Barrie, to open a small factory to manufacture bare and insulated wires and cables. Demand soon outstripped Barrie's limited production capacity, and four years later he sold his plant to a Montreal syndicate, which formed a new company, The Wire and Cable Company, and it later became the Imperial Wire and Cable Company Ltd.

Both companies prospered and became national in their scope as the telephone industry expanded throughout Canada. By 1914, the interests of the two companies were alike to such an extent that they amalgamated under the name, Northern Electric Company, Ltd., and a large new plant was erected in Montreal to afford the new company adequate manufacturing facilities.

The growth of the company has kept pace with Canada's industrialization and today, with about 17,000 employees, three large manufacturing plants, and with distributing houses and sales offices in the country's largest cities, Northern Electric is recognized as one of Canada's great industrial enterprises.

Factories. — The three factories of the company are situated in Montreal, Que.; Lachine, Que.; and Belleville, Ont. Together they comprise a total of 2,385,000 square feet of manufacturing floor space, house many millions of dollars worth of modern production machinery, and give employment to about 14,000 employees.

Largest link in Northern Electric's manufacturing chain is the eight-storey plant in Montreal. Occupying a complete city block, it is one of the biggest industrial buildings in the city and, until comparatively recently, housed the entire production facilities of the company. There are located the engineering departments and facilities for the manufacture of telephone apparatus, including telephone sets, switchboards, and central office equipment. Some executive offices of the company are located in this building.

The manufacture of Northern Electric wires and cables is carried out in the factory at Lachine, Que. One of the most modern wire and cable plants on the continent, the Lachine plant was opened in 1948 as part of the company's post-war multi-million dollar expansion programme, and extended on two subsequent occasions. Almost all types of telephone and power cables are produced there.

The electronics operations of the company are located at Belleville, Ont., in a new factory which is Northern Electric's first plant to be located outside the province of Quebec. A wide variety of electronic products are manufactured there for the radio broadcasting and reception, the traffic signal and fire alarm, sound, motion picture and other electronics fields.

Sales. — Since its establishment, Northern Electric has gradually developed an elaborate and complete sales organization to distribute a great range and volume of electrical products to all parts of the country. Large sales and engineering staffs are maintained to provide service and engineering advice while skilled and experienced personnel are available to assist customers in all phases of the electrical industry.

In addition to the wire and cable, telephone apparatus, and electronics equipment of its own manufacture, the company distributes on a wholesale basis through its sales outlets the products of a large number of other Canadian, U.K., and U.S. manufactures, and is therefore able to supply almost anything electrical required for industrial use. Customers include industrial, commercial, utility, mines, transportation general, provincial and municipal customers of all types.

Distribution. — General: Montreal, Quebec City, Chicoutimi, Sherbrooke, Three Rivers and Val d'Or, Que.; Halifax, N.S.; Moncton, N.B.; Saint John, N.B.; St. John's, Nfld.; Ottawa, Toronto, Kingston, Hamilton, Windsor, St. Catharines, Kitchener, London, Sudbury, Kirkland Lake, Timmins and Fort William, Ont.; Winnipeg, Man.; Regina and Saskatoon, Sask.; Edmonton and Calgary, Alta.; Vancouver, Victoria, Vernon and New Westminster, B.C.

Sales Offices. — Sydney, N.S.; Montreal, Que.; Toronto and Sarnia, Ont.; Brandon, Man.; Trail and Prince George, B.C.

Telephone Distributing Houses. — Montreal, Que.; Toronto, Ont.; Saint John, N.B.

Administration. — President, R. Dickson Harkness, D.S.O., M.C., B.Sc.

Address. — 1600 Dorchester St. W., Montreal, Que.

PANHANDLE EASTERN PIPE LINE COMPANY

Among the many benefits enjoyed by the Great Lakes area, which the St. Lawrence Seaway now establishes as the continent's newest coastline and gateway to world trade, is a dependable supply of clean, efficient fuel — natural gas.

As the first long-distance pipe line to bring natural gas into the area, Panhandle Eastern Pipe Line Company has been closely identified with the development or the region since 1936.

Today, with natural gas derived from the Panhandle system serving consuming areas on four of the five Great Lakes, and on both sides of the border, no other natural gas pipe line is so clearly linked with the Seaway's future.

Through 6500 miles of pipe line, stretching from Texas and the Gulf of Mexico to Lake Erie and the Seaway Gate, Panhandle and its subsidiary, Trunkline Gas Company, deliver over a billion cubic feet of gas each day to utility and industrial customers. In the Great Lakes region, the users of Panhandle gas include homes and industries in Michigan areas tributary to Lakes Michigan, Huron, and Erie; in Indiana and Ohio areas tributary to Lake Erie; and in Ontario areas tributary to Lakes Erie and Ontario.

Specifically, the company's pipe line system extends a total of 1300 miles from its sources of supply in Texas, Oklahoma and Kansas to its termini in Michigan. Trunk-

line's pipe line facilities extend a distance of 1200 miles from the Rio Grande Valley in Texas to a point in central Illinois near Tuscola where it supplies gas to the main pipe line system of the Company. These facilities together comprise a total of 6500 miles of pipe line. The Company's main line system consists of three parallel large diameter pipe lines and 18 compressor stations with a total of 290,000 installed horsepower. Trunkline's facilities consist of a single large diameter pipe line and 13 compressor stations with a total of 95,000 installed horsepower. The maximum-day delivery capacity of the combined systems is approximately 1.3 billion cubic feet.

The Panhandle story began in 1930, when Missouri-Kansas Pipe Line Company had amassed sufficient natural gas reserves in the Texas Panhandle area to justify construction of a pipe line to distant markets. Difficulties were encountered in financing the construction of the new line and obtaining markets.

It was at this time that William G. Maguire, the present head of the Company, became associated with Missouri-Kansas and Panhandle. Despite Maguire's efforts control of the new enterprise was obtained by the Columbia Gas and Electric holding company system, a large distributor of natural gas in Ohio, West Virginia, and Pennsylvania. This was a departure from the original concept of the new pipe line as a wholly independent enterprise.

Thirteen years later — in 1943 — after a struggle against tremendous odds and powerful adversaries, Panhandle emerged once more as an "independent" when control of the company was restored to its original Missouri-Kansas backers headed by Maguire. Panhandle's survival and success as an independent enterprise is a conspicuous triumph of vision and leadership.

Panhandle has continued to move forward in more recent years as is evidenced by company figures for 1957 covering use of its gas in the Great Lakes area, and the expected use of gas in this same market in the years ahead.

In Ohio (principally the Toledo-Cleveland area) Panhandle supplied 84 billion cubic feet of gas in 1957. Michigan last year consumed 143 billion cubic feet from Panhandle lines. During 1957, Panhandle delivered 11 billion cubic feet of natural gas to its Canadian customer, Union Gas Company of Canada, Ltd., which serves the Windsor-Hamilton area of Ontario. This was 60 per cent of the total as the utility distributed that year. Deliveries to Michigan are expected to further in-

crease in late 1959 when new Trunkline Gas Company facilities, now being planned to transport Gulf Coast gas, are scheduled to be in operation.

Vast quantities of Panhandle gas are stored underground during the summer months to meet year-round requirements of industries and homes. Natural gas from the Gulf Coast, the Texas Panhandle, and southwest Kansas is brought to the Great Lakes region, the summer surplus being piped to storage reservoirs in Ohio and Michigan. Consumers Power Company, (the utility distributing Panhandle gas in southern and central Michigan), and Panhandle, through a jointly owned subsidiary, Michigan Gas Storage Company, operate vast storage fields in that state. Panhandle Eastern gas is also stored underground in Ohio by two of Panhandle's larger customers.

The St. Lawrence Seaway promises much for the people of the two great nations that it serves. With its tremendous reserves of natural gas, Panhandle Eastern expects to participate in and benefit from the Seaway area's industrial growth.

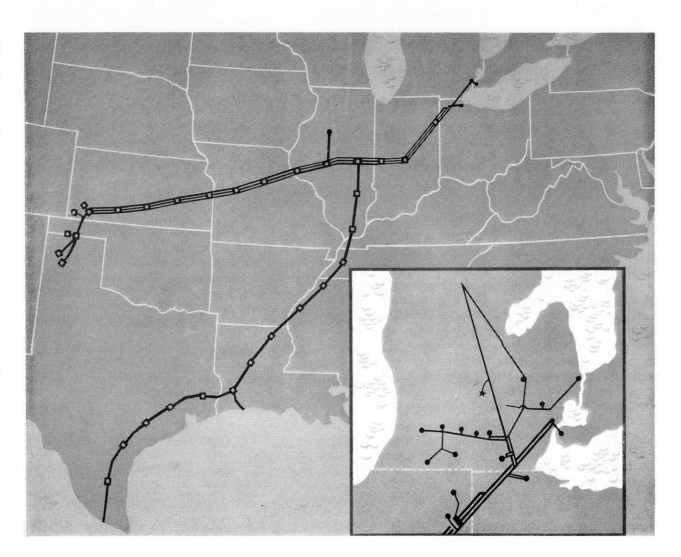

Factory Assembly of Stator, Upper-Bracket, Cover and Ventilating Air Housing.

CANADIAN GENERAL ELECTRIC . . .

COMPANY LIMITED

Canada's oldest and largest electrical manufacturing Company, Canadian General Electric, was privileged to supply a large share of the electrical apparatus needed in the St. Lawrence Power Project. The diverse nature of this equipment indicates this modern and progressive Company's varied operations. Included were eight hydro-electric generators; seven 230,000 volt Air Blast Circuit Breakers; three 230 KV potential transformers; eight generator neutral cubicles; a relay switchboard and numerous relays and instruments; 230 KV Power Line Carrier Current Potential Devices and Line Traps and Carrier Current Transmitter — Receiver Equipment and also the Variable Speed drive, for the 300 ton Gantry Crane used at the Power House.

Generators

Interest is focused largely on the Barnhart Island Power House where thirty-two hydro-electric generators utilize the enormous flow of the St. Lawrence River. Twenty-four of these huge machines bear the familiar General Electric monogram. Of these, eight (on the

Canadian side of the Power House) were designed and manufactured by Canadian General Electric at Peterborough, Ontario.

Although these eight generators totalling 480,000 KVA represent a substantial order, yet over twenty-five times that amount (over 12,000,000 KVA) in generators have been produced by this Company.

Each generator is literally a hand-built machine. It has to be because no two hydro-electric power projects are identical. Each project requires its own specifically designed generators in order that the maximum amount of power will be drawn from the head and volume of water available. Also, continuous improvement in design takes place and is incorporated into each new machine. For these reasons, mass production of large Generators is not feasible. Each is built to the exact requirements of the project for which it is intended.

The Barnhart Island Dam provides an approximate head of 81 feet. This is considered to be a relatively

One of the seven G-E Air Blast Circuit Breakers at Cornwall.

A 26-foot Diameter Generator Rotor Spider Weldment.

its participation in the St. Lawrence Power Project . . .

low head, but the tremendous flow of water coupled with this head produces vast quantities of power. Under these conditions large low-speed generators are required. The overall weight of each of the eight G-E generators is approximately 660 tons. Each rotor alone weighs approximately 261 tons and revolves at 94.7 R.P.M. Each generator produces 60,000 KVA at 13,800 volts.

Generators of this size and complexity pose fairly difficult installation problems and these are ably handled by the Company's own experienced erection staff.

To eliminate field adjustments and facilitate installation, a trial assembly of the major parts of each generator, such as the assembeld stator, the rotor rim and some field poles, upper bracket, covers, and ventilating air housing, was made at the factory. To meet shipping limitations, the components are then dis-assembled and final assembly is made on site.

On disassembly and packing at the factory, the generators were shipped individually to the site at suit-

able intervals. The heaviest part shipped was the lower bracket weighing approximately 88,000 lbs. and the lightest weighing about 5 lbs. Each machine required a 35 car freight train to transport it. Approximately a year and a half will elapse between completion of the first and last generator.

Air Blast Breakers

Power from the Barnhart Island Station is fed into the Southern Ontario System of the Hydro Electric Power Commission of Ontario. The introduction of this large block of power obviously increased the fault-capacity of the system and vastly increased rates of rise of recovery voltage that can now occur.

For use on this 230 KV system Canadian General Electric was privileged to supply a total of 35 Air Blast Circuit Breakers of a new design with interrupting capacities of 15,000 and 20,000 MVA. Seven of these breakers are located at Cornwall to control power fed into the system from the St. Lawrence Power Project.

Fire Department of Reed, Shaw & McNaught is a busy hub of activity creating protection for Canada's economy.

REED, SHAW & McNAUGHT

With the near completion of the St. Lawrence Seaway and Power Projects we tend to look back over the short history of Canada and contemplate the numerous achievements of this young nation. It is true that there are many outside interests established in Canada, but let us not overlook our all-Canadian firms. We have a particular one in mind, that of Reed, Shaw & McNaught, with offices in Toronto, Montreal and Edmonton.

The origin of this firm can be traced back to the year 1872 when the late Samuel B. Shaw decided to make insurance his career. Some two years later, in 1874, the late Joseph B. Reed, made a similar decision. Both represented entirely different companies. From this very humble beginning of two separate one-man insurance agencies has grown one of Canada's largest and most respected firms of insurance agents.

By 1875 Samuel Shaw was well established as the first agent of the Mercantile Insurance Company. That appointment has continued uninterrupted to the present day, a period of 83 years. In similar fashion, Joseph B. Reed was appointed agent of the Liverpool & London & Globe Insurance Company, which connection has continued unbroken for 81 years.

The late Charles B. McNaught, for 28 years a principal partner in the firm of Joseph B. Reed & Sons, commenced his insurance career in 1895 representing the Northern Assurance Company. Mr. McNaught established his own agency business in 1901.

Then followed a series of amalgamations commencing in 1903 when Mr. McNaught and Shaw & Son joined together to form the partnership of Shaw & McNaught. Shortly after, in 1905, Mr. Joseph B. Reed died and the business of J. B. Reed & Sons was carried on by his sons, to be amalgamated one year later with Shaw & McNaught under the style of Joseph B. Reed & Sons, Shaw & McNaught.

The changing of this cumbersome name to its present title came about in 1908. A firm legend goes along with the change. Seemingly a customer writing out a cheque to pay a premium was unable to write the entire name of the payee on the face of the cheque and was compelled to continue on the reverse. Now Reed, Shaw & McNaught is the registered title known to all Canadians.

Today this all-Canadian agency represents fifty-five of the leading Canadian, British and American insurance companies and transacts business throughout Canada. Their clientele includes many of the best known educational institutions, industries and merchants in the country, among them pulp and paper companies, automobile manufacturers, departmental stores, mines, building contractors and other representative industries of all classes.

To handle such a large volume of business an efficient staff of 145 in Toronto and 30 in Montreal and 4 in Edmonton is maintained, with the head of each department a specialist in his particular class of insurance. Catering to its clientele the Agency provides a complete engineering service and a plan drawing department of five draughtsmen.

Following the taking over of the clients' accounts, the firm's representatives make periodic visits to the insured properties in order to be constantly familiar with existing conditions. As a result, recommendations are made for safeguarding the property if new hazards are introduced; policy wordings are kept up-to-date, and coverages revised if found necessary. Written reports following these periodic visits are sent to the client.

One of the most valuable services that this firm renders to its clients is the complete assistance when a loss occurs. Their experience in this respect is extensive and results in losses being expeditiously and equitably adjusted.

The efficiency of the organization is well known. The firm's new offices in the "Knight" building on Toronto's bustling Adelaide Street, are a reflection of the intelligent planning which characterizes every operation of the firm.

IMPERIAL BANK OF CANADA

It All Began In The Nineteenth Century

From modest beginnings in 1875 Imperial Bank of Canada has grown to a stature today where it enjoys a name as one of the world's great banking institutions, offering an efficient banking service to shipbuilders, shippers, industry and business enterprises not only along the Seaway from Halifax on the Eastern Seaboard to Fort William at the Western extremity, but also serving Canadians through a trans-Canada chain of branches. Supported by agents and banking correspondents throughout the world, Imperial Bank of Canada is ready to offer banking service of the highest order to any firm doing business in Canada or in any other part of the world.

The St. Lawrence Waterway with its ship channel and series of canals comprises the world's greatest inland navigation system covering a distance from the Atlantic Ocean to the western end of Lake Superior of more than 2,200 miles.

The development of this waterway throughout the years has had an important effect on the Canadian

Imperial Bank of Canada, Oshawa, Ont.

The two photographs shown on this page illustrate the Belleville Branch (photographed at night) and the Oshawa Branch of Imperial Bank of Canada.
Both these cities are part of the great industrial development along the banks of the St. Lawrence River and Lake Ontario, and these two relatively new branches of Imperial Bank help to bring additional banking service to these expanding and developing centres.

economy, for not only does it provide an economical means of transportation but also supplies cheap hydro electric power to manufacturing and industrial centres which lie along its banks.

It has been said that the beginning of this great shipping artery commenced with the old St. Lawrence canals and the construction of the Welland Canal system which links Lake Ontario with Lake Erie. Both these canal systems had their beginnings during the nineteenth century.

Imperial Bank of Canada has more than a perfunctory interest in the Welland Canal, because it was the same Merritt family who had the vision which prompted the linking of the Great Lakes with what is now known as the Seaway, thus bringing into being the Welland Canal, and who also founded the Niagara District Bank which later became a member of Imperial Bank of Canada. It was T. R. Merritt who was the first Vice-President of Imperial Bank of Canada after its formation in 1875.

The original Welland Canal opened in 1829 extending from Port Dalhousie on Lake Ontario to the town of Port Robinson, where it joined the Niagara River, a distance of some 27 miles with a fall of 325 feet on the Niagara River. In 1887 this Canal was widened and deepened so that its Locks had the same dimensions as those of the St. Lawrence Canals. In 1913 a new Canal was begun, known as the Welland Ship Canal which carries the shipping of today. It has seven lift locks with a depth of 30 feet of water over the sills, and one of these, the Humberstone Lock, is the longest lock in the world.

Imperial Bank of Canada, Belleville, Ont.

Aerial view of Valleyfield.

CITY OF VALLEYFIELD
Province of Quebec

The original settlement of what was later to become the City of Valleyfield, was set up as a point from which the wood cut from the neighboring forests could be shipped. Water abounded on all sides and provided an easy and cheap mode of transportation. The community grew and in 1874 it was incorporated as the City of Salaberry-De-Valleyfield or as it is generally known, Valleyfield. It is located 37 miles southwest of Montreal.

Location of Seaway

The year 1959 should be a big event in the life of Valleyfield. The opening of the mighty St. Lawrence Seaway will place Valleyfield astride one of the world's most important shipping lanes, since the southern extremities of the City border on the Beauharnois Ship Canal. This canal, twenty-seven feet deep and over 3,000 feet wide, is one of the main links in the Seaway system and can accommodate large ocean freighters without any further dredging. In order to take advantage of this, the City of Valleyfield has set aside certain parcels of land adjacent to the Beauharnois Canal for the construction of wharves capable of handling large ocean-going ships. With shipping facilities of this nature, Valleyfield will be in a position to bring in raw materials from all over the world, process them and then ship the finished products directly to almost any country in the world.

Rail and Road Facilities

Valleyfield is also very strategically located both to ship and receive goods via railroad or motor truck transportation. A spur line connects Valleyfield with the main line of the Canadian National Railways Transcontinental system. The New York Central line provides direct connections to all points in the United States as well as Montreal. The Msgr. Langlois Bridge, linking Valleyfield on the south side of the river with the No. 2 Highway on the north shore, gives Valleyfield easy access to the main highways leading to Montreal, Ottawa, Toronto and for that matter, to almost anywhere in Canada.

Hydro-Electric Power

In locating a new business, one of the most important factors to be considered is the availability of electric power. Here again Valleyfield is a most fortunate location. Located on the westerly end of the Beauharnois Canal, Valleyfield is within site of the huge Beauharnois hydro-electric power plant which derives its motive power from the water pouring out of the easterly end of the canal into the Lake St. Louis section of the St. Lawrence River. One of the largest hydro-electric power plants in the world, the Beauharnois plant has a capacity of 2,200,000 horse-power and is capable of providing all the necessary electrical power needed for the industrial expansion of the area for years to come.

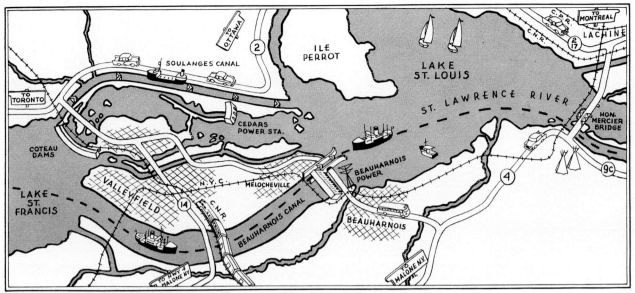

Map showing Valleyfield and path of Seaway.

Manpower

Availability of manpower is a vital factor to take into consideration when considering the location of a new industry or the expansion of one already in operation. Valleyfield, with a population of over 26,000, has a labor reservoir of over 9,000 persons, two-thirds of whom are male. A large part of this available manpower is highly skilled and bilingual.

Air Transportation

Within a half hour drive from Valleyfield, is Dorval Airport, one of the world's large international air terminals. Planes from all over the world make Dorval Airport their Canadian base. This affords businessmen very convenient travel facilities to and from points in the United States as well as overseas. Among the well-known airlines using Dorval as their Canadian base are Trans-Canada Air Lines, Air France, K.L.M., B.O.A.C., Eastern Airlines and many other local or privately chartered lines.

Abundant Water Supply

Many industries require large quantities of water in their manufacturing processes and it should be pointed out that this creates no problem for industries located in Valleyfield. With its position on the St. Lawrence River, unlimited quantities of good, clear water are available at all times.

Excellent Living Conditions

The living conditions at Valleyfield are very desirable and do attract a high type of labor. Whole sections of the city are being developed with new, modern type homes of varied styles of architecture. The commercial part of the city boasts a wide variety of stores stocked with modern, attractive merchandise. Educational needs of the community are taken care of by adequate, well-staffed schools where children may be educated in either French or English. Without going outside of Valleyfield, students may complete their education up to the level of university entrance and then it is only an hour's ride to Montreal and its excellent universities where scholars may complete their studies in any of the professions, arts or sciences. As a result of the educational facilities that are available, industry can depend on a supply of well educated, skilled workers. A well trained police and fire department add to the safety of the community.

Among the industries that have already established themselves in Valleyfield are:

Canadian Arsenals Limited
Canadian Bronze Powder Works Limited
Canadian Converters Co. Ltd.
Canadian Schenley Company Ltd.
Davison Chemical Company Ltd.
Duplan Dyeing Co. Ltd.
Merck & Co. Ltd.
McDonald & Robb Limited
The Montreal Cottons Ltd.
National Silicates Limited
The Nichols Chemical Company Ltd.

Companies that are interested in learning more about the advantages of locating in the City of Valleyfield should write to: The Industrial Planning Board, City Hall, Salaberry-de-Valleyfield, Quebec, Canada. You will receive a warm welcome and the City of Valleyfield will be pleased to provide you with any information you may require.

Four vessels of the Davie Transportation fleet at their winter quarters prior to resuming carrying newsprint from Quebec mills to New York via the Richelieu-Lake Champlain route.

GUY TOMBS LIMITED (1921)
MONTREAL

Davie Transportation Limited (1936)   Guy Tombs Marine Services Ltd. (1946)

"Guy Tombs Limited" emerged from the Canadian pulp and paper industry, after some 25 years of previous experience of its founder in the pioneer railway and steamship services of that stirring period in the Province of Quebec.

Chief duties then were the moving of newsprint and later fine papers and pulps to destinations in Canada, the United States and overseas as cheaply, expeditiously and safely as possible, as well as the incoming raw materials to the mills.

The wide trade and transport experience of the Company led to its participation in such important matters as improvements to the Port of Montreal, Richelieu Canals, the Maritime Freight Rates Act, Canada West Indies Reciprocal Agreement, Canadian-Australian Treaty and Winter Navigation.

Two outstanding missions denote its competence and versatility. 1: Public investigation of international freight rates on newsprint paper (1928). 2: Co-ordination and shipment of UNRRA supplies from Canada (1945). Thirteen Canadian paper companies were represented. The benefits of the 1930 decision must have been worth several millions of dollars to the industry.

The mining developments and vigorous promotion of other fields of transport, notably "Travel" were followed in 1936 by the revival of the Richelieu River route to New York through a subsidiary, Davie Transportation Limited, whose seven 230 ton capacity vessels carry newsprint southbound, returning with raw materials or package freight. Incidentally each master of these efficient little boats, which scrape through the antique locks of the Chambly Canal, expects to complete his 400th round trip during the 1958 season, having carried more than a million tons between them.

Sixteen of the parent staff served World War II in various capacities, two of whom did not return.

The second, and greatest never-to-be-forgotten task, was the handling of world relief supplies, which began during 1945. A simple telephone call from Washington offered the shipping agency in Canada for the great United Nations Relief and Rehabilitation Administration (UNRRA). The magnitude and variety of the cargoes from flour to fertilizer, pickled herring to horsemeat, trucks to horses, penicillin to rinderpest, totalled well over one million tons. These went to 16 devastated countries, from 12 Canadian and 3 U.S. ports, in the same period as the Netherlands Purchasing Commission's vast orders, two major undertakings, requiring utmost efficiency and co-operation.

The Company has continued to act for UNICEF and other affiliated bodies of the United Nations.

None of the unexpected assignments resulted from solicitation; whether hauling M.T.B.'s up and down the Richelieu-New York waterway, the great worldwide distributions, occasional pilgrimages to Rome or Lourdes, or groups of engineers to distant fields.

Export forwarding of paper and other commodities remains high; European, Canadian and U.S. interests require transport advice and overseas travel continues unabated. The activities of the Company have become more and more comprehensive, resembling in that respect, British or Continental firms.

View of McColl-Frontenac's refinery and huge storage facilities at Montreal East.

McCOLL-FRONTENAC OIL COMPANY LIMITED

The giant St. Lawrence Seaway and the accompanying hydro-electric projects will go into full operation in the Spring of 1959. A 50 year dream of Americans and Canadians alike will come true.

Before this modern miracle of engineering could be completed, millions of cubic yards of rock, clay and mud had to be moved and millions of cubic yards of concrete had to be mixed, transported and poured. To accomplish this feat, hundreds of pieces of heavy construction equipment had to be put into efficient operation. Not one cubic yard of earth could have been moved, not a foot of dike built, not a cubic yard of concrete poured, had it not been for the driving force derived from gasoline and other petroleum fuels. At the same time lubricants were required to keep the moving parts of these great machines free from the damaging effects of friction and enable them to complete their share in the over-all development.

The Company is justly proud of the important part it played in the construction of the Seaway Projects. One of the most important factors to be faced by contractors was the operation and maintenance of the huge excavating machines, earth moving dumpers, tractors, trucks and other equipment.

All equipment, large and small, had to be kept operating without interruption and with an absolute minimum of "repair time" as one machine was often dependent upon another.

Because of the excellent reputation that Texaco fuels and lubricants have enjoyed throughout Canada and the U.S.A., Texaco was the choice of many contractors to meet the exacting demands encountered in the operation and maintenance of their equipment and for peak performance under extreme working conditions. The result was that more Texaco fuels and lubricants were used in the construction of the Seaway Projects than any other brand.

McColl-Frontenac Lubrication Engineers were at all times available to study the contractors' problems with regard to fuels and lubricants and to make practical recommendations based on their vast experience. The team-work between the contractors' engineers and those of the McColl-Frontenac organization had much to do in making it possible for this great engineering task to be completed on schedule.

One of Canada's Major Suppliers of Petroleum Products

McColl-Frontenac Oil Company Limited came into corporate being in 1927 as a result of the amalgamation of McColl Brothers Limited (commenced in 1873 as McColl and Anderson) and Frontenac Oil Refineries Limited. Today, McColl-Frontenac Oil Company Limited is one of Canada's major suppliers of petroleum products, employing thousands of Canadians. With its multiple operations in marketing, exploration, refining, sea, road and rail transport, storage plants, marine terminals, and stock interest in pipe lines, McColl-Frontenac spans the nation.

It is the policy of the company to keep abreast of the rapid industrial growth of Canada. Its technical and research staff is constantly seeking to improve its products or to develop new ones to coincide with the advances made by the manufacturers of all types of mechanical equipment. You are assured of top quality performance whenever you buy in Canada under the famous Texaco sign with the large red star and green "T".

SURVEYER, NENNIGER & CHENEVERT
Consulting Engineers

In any project so vast as that undertaken by the St. Lawrence Seaway Authority in providing the industrial Great Lakes centres with a new deep waterway system, it is inevitable that there will be many side effects. The main purpose of the Authority was to build a canal linking the St. Lawrence River below Montreal with the same river at Iroquois, Ontario, 111 miles away and 225 feet higher, while at the same time the New York State and Ontario Hydro authorities undertook to harness the tremendous power of the river. In the course of the work many secondary problems arose.

The firm of Surveyer, Nenniger and Chenevert Consulting Engineers of the City of Montreal, was engaged by the St. Lawrence Seaway Authority to investigate certain of these problems in the Montreal area to produce a satisfactory solution.

It must be remembered that the construction of the St. Lawrence Seaway and Power Projects cut across other existing lines of communication ... bridges, railways and power lines. All these had to be altered to suit the needs of the new canal.

Equally important, though not so apparent, are the changes which were required in the lines of communication with the St. Lawrence River used to satisfy the needs of the inhabitants along the shore for water supply, drainage and the discharge of sewers. In the area between Longueuil, on the south shore of the river below Montreal's Jacques Cartier Bridge, and Caughnawaga, site of the ancient Mohawk Indian Reservation, at the foot of Lake St. Louis, there is a population of over 60,000 people which is expected to increase to 250,000 within the next forty years.

At least a dozen communities touch the shores of the river and more are located in the drainage basin which discharges into the river. The construction of the Seaway between Longueuil and Lake St. Louis cut off all direct access to the river throughout the whole area. It was up to Surveyer, Nenniger and Chenevert to propose a plan which would provide the same access to the water for municipal services as existed before the construction of the Seaway, and of sufficient capacity to take care of the expected growth in population.

The works undertaken to achieve this result totalled $7,600,000 in value. The design, drawings and specifications were prepared by Surveyer, Nenniger and Chenevert and were built either as separate contracts, or as part of one of the major contracts for Seaway work. Construction was carried out under the supervision of St. Lawrence Seaway Authority personnel.

In general, the works consisted of enlarging and expanding water intakes under the canal to connect with the river. In all, four operating intakes have been extended in this way, and provision for four more for future use by building lines under the canal. One of these "future" intakes is already in use.

Similarly, existing sewer outfalls were extended under the canal to the river. Actually, only two operating outlets were provided passing under the canal and connected to the river, one serving the Town of Laprairie, on the south shore, and the other serving all the communities along the canal from the Jacques Cartier Bridge to one mile above Preville. To do this, a collector sewer three miles long and from 8 to 12 feet in diameter was built along the old shore line to collect all existing outlets. In addition three connections were provided under the canal for future use. Here again one of these "future" outlets is already in service.

Pumping stations have been provided at both the operating connections, to pump the flow under the canal and into the river. The larger of these stations has a capacity of 187,500 gallons per minute.

While the value of this work is dwarfed by the total cost of the St. Lawrence Seaway and Power Projects, it is an essential and important piece of engineering in itself, and Surveyer, Nenniger and Chenevert are proud to have been entrusted with it.

Champion Savings Corporation Limited

If every man produced for himself all the needs he wanted, there would be no need for money, credit, banks or investment companies. No man does this, however, and thus we have developed specialization to a high degree. While this has increased our production power, it has also made man more dependent upon the co-operation of other men and upon the smooth functioning of an increasingly complicated mechanism of production, transportation and exchange. All economic activity has one common denominator, money and credit. Loans and investments are dynamic factors contained within the objectives of any monetary policy which will assure a flow of money enabling the consumer to buy the produce of industry and the investor to maintain and expand existing plants in order to meet the needs of the population.

The healthy and impressive growth of investment companies in Canada during the past quarter century indicates public confidence and a widespread acceptance in this type of investment. Champion Savings Corporation Limited was organized in 1932 by its continuing President, L. R. Champion. During the difficult years that followed the 1929 market decline, the Company specialized in the issuance and distribution of Face Amount Installment Savings Certificates. Certificates guaranteed by the Company as to return of principal and interest, are further guaranteed by a unique Trust Agreement whereby reserves, provided on an actuarial basis examined annually and approved by an independent actuary, are accumulated with Prudential Trust Company Limited, a long established Canadian trust company, for the protection of certificate holders.

Since the end of World War II conditions have been changing in Canada. Steady immigration and a relatively higher birth-rate than other nations are reflected in a rapidly increasing population. The airplane has opened up the more isolated northern regions, the Trans-Canada Highway is scheduled for an early completion and the development of the St. Lawrence waterways will provide both power and transportation between the interior and the sea. Her economic development during the post war period, based on an abundance of natural resources, growing population and a favorable political climate, has attracted the capital needed for industrial development.

To keep in step with and to take advantage of this strong growth trend of the Canadian economy, the organization of Champion Savings Corporation Limited has steadily expanded and now has available a wide range of investment services. These include the distribution of mutual fund shares of Champion Mutual Fund of Canada Limited. Personal Investment Plans of Champion and Company Limited and a Retirement Savings Plan eligible for registration under Section 79B of the Income Tax Act enacted by the Canadian Parliament early in 1957.

Many investors are too engrossed in their own activities to afford the time required for adequate analysis of individual securities. The mutual fund company has the time, money, personnel and personal contacts needed to watch an investment once it is made. Often information is obtained that is not available to the individual investor until a later date. Decisions can be made on timely changes which only the exceptional individual investor can duplicate. Mutual fund companies can follow and take advantage of new developments in industrial techniques and technology far more effectively than the individual investor.

The administration of the aforementioned Trust Deed, the Personal Investment Plans, and the Registered Retirement Savings Plans rests with an associated trust company, Prudential Trust Company Limited. The association of this 1909 incorporated trust company with the other Champion interests took place in 1940 and rounds out the many services performed by the group through the inclusion of trustee administration, stock transfers, real estate sales and management, mortgage loans and insurance brokerage.

The Canadian economy is becoming increasingly complex. Along with population increase we have increased our production capacity, our skills and technical know how. Problems have been solved through electronics, but new ones have also been created. In this state of constant change, many industries have been hurt, others have greatly benefitted. It has become more and more difficult to keep abreast of the many developments. This is one of many reasons why more and more investors are turning to take professional assistance made available to all by the investment companies.

Services to the public have been further enhanced through the installation of punched card equipment. The Company's relationship with clients has thus been improved through such a program which includes automatic premium notices, faster processing of deposits and quarterly statements of all transactions. Internally the Company has mechanized daily listings of cash receipts, dividend calculations, mortgage loans and calculations of actuarial reserves. In addition, there is now available numerous types of sales reports and statistical data made available to the Company as a by-product of this mechanization. The Company is confident that it is, and will continue to be, one of the leaders in the field of improved services and greater efficiency through the use of modern machine accounting.

CANDIAC
DEVELOPMENT CORP.

Map showing location of town of Candiac, across the river from Montreal.

With the birth of the St. Lawrence Seaway and Power Projects, numerous new land developments have literally sprung up overnight along the shores of the mighty river. These developments, which at one time were mere dreams, became a reality through the efforts of farsighted men who visualized the tremendous potential of towns situated along the Seaway route and with easy access to the deep waterway.

One such development is the Town of Candiac, Quebec, situated on a 3,000 acre tract of land and located right on the St. Lawrence Seaway, on the South Shore of the St. Lawrence River, directly opposite the metropolis of Montreal.

The original idea to create this community was conceived by a group of Montreal citizens, who first started promoting a land assembly in the Spring of 1953. The site was chosen as it offered tremendous reasons for maximum appreciation. It was the largest undeveloped land area closest to Montreal and in addition to the Seaway, it afforded the best transportation facilities possible.

The land assembly was completed in June 1956 without interfering with or disrupting any of the few residents in the area.

The financing of the entire project, which amounted to millions of dollars, was secured from Canadian, American and European interests.

Before application for a Municipal Charter could be made, a name had to be chosen for the Town. The name Candiac was decided upon for its originality and because it had the historical significance of being the name of the original residence in France of the famous general, the Marquis de Montcalm, The coat-of-arms designed for the Town includes the basic Montcalm format.

One unusual factor which makes Candiac unique as compared to all other major land developments is that a Bill, No. 194, was passed by the Quebec Legislature on January 24th, 1957, incorporating the entire area as a Town while it was still entirely farmland.

The Bill was specially prepared with certain unusual features in order to expedite rapid but orderly growth. For example, it was ruled that the first general elections in the Municipality would not need to be held before February 1962, and further, that at the discretion of the Minister of Municipal Affairs, such elections could be postponed an additional two years. Rights of franchise for 25 years were granted to persons, companies and corporations as privilege to own and maintain transportation facilities within the Town, hydro-electric power, gas, the water filtration plant and supply system and sewage services. The latter ruling made it possible for private investors to proceed with such services without the immediate problem of municipal financing.

It is anticipated that the Candiac Development Corporation will spend approximately thirty million dollars for services including sidewalks, roads and parks. A large portion of the industrial zone is now serviced and other areas which will include a wide range of housing values are also serviced. Several major industrial sales have already been completed and future prospects for the rapid growth of the industrial zone are excellent. It is expected that eventually over 100 plants of the light manufacturing and warehousing type will be located in Candiac. Industries having excessive emission of smoke or odors are not acceptable.

The completed residential zones will have between 12,000 and 14,000 housing units ranging from low rental apartments to luxurious single family dwellings. Neighborhood shopping centers are being created in addition to the main town center and shopping section which will, when completed, embody approximately 150 retail outlets, plus the various municipal and office buildings. It is expected that Candiac's population will reach 60,000 by 1970 with between 6,000 and 10,000 employees in the industrial zone alone.

Modern planning includes rear lot hydro and telephone lines and footpaths at the rear of the houses so that children may walk to and from school without having to cross major traffic arteries.

Three main highways cross the townsite and two railway lines service the municipality regularly. A new four-lane highway is also planned to cross the Quebec Hydro dam which will be built just west of Candiac.

It can truthfully be said that Candiac is Canada's most progressive city on the Seaway.

Officers of Candiac Development Corporation are: Jean Leman, President and Mayor of Candiac; D. Stewart Patterson, Vice-President, Pierre Ostiguy, Secretary Treasurer. Directors include, Marc A. Dhavernas, Marcel Faribault, Walter L. Forster, P. M. Fox, Louis P. Gelinas, John D. Gibson, Jean Leman, Pierre Ostiguy, Alfred Paradis, D. Stewart Patterson, Neil F. Phillips and Jean Raymond.

View of J. & R. Weir's plant.

J. & R. WEIR LIMITED

As work on the St. Lawrence Seaway and Power Project goes into its final stages, the full realization of what this billion-dollar deep waterway system will mean becomes apparent. Not only will it mean increased trade with other countries, but it means prosperity for Canadian business and industry.

Ready 24 hours per day with its services to all shipping J. & R. Weir Limited is one of the oldest marine engineering and ship repairing firms in Canada. Known to shipowners over most of the world, this firm has served the marine industry for over 80 years and from the same location in Montreal, Quebec. From a modest beginning, this organization together with its wholly-owned subsidiary, Welding Engineers Limited, has plant and facilities covering more than a city block and is located at Nazareth, Brennan, Duke and Prince Streets, situated near the dock and convenient to all those it serves.

J. & R. Weir's contribution to the St. Lawrence Seaway has been mainly repair and maintenance work on dredges and tugs working between Quebec and Ontario.

This company, founded in 1875, in addition to marine engineering is also engaged in boiler making, pressure vessels, tank building, fabrication of steel work of all kinds, electrical and mechanical work, coppersmithing, welding (both electrical and oxy-acetylene) forging cast iron, steel, bronze, aluminum and copper castings, pattern making and all general machine shop work.

Welding Engineers Limited of Montreal, a wholly-owned subsidiary of J. & R. Weir Limited, has a fleet of portable welding machines as well as air compressors with operators and equipment for welding, riveting, burning, chipping and drilling steel, rock or concrete. Their services are in constant demand by contractors throughout the province. This organization occupies a fine plant located within two blocks of the parent company.

Directors and Officers of J. & R. Weir Limited are:—William Thow, President; Norman W. Benson, B'Eng., Vice-President and Technical Engineer; John W. Robinson, Vice-President and Secretary; Thomas Thomson, Treasurer; Henry H. Vint, General Manager.

Raoul Fiset is Manager of Welding Engineers Ltd.

257

Downstream view of the St. Lambert Lock during the construction stages. The section of the C.N.R. Victoria Bridge shown above was later replaced by a new lift span. The St. Lambert Lock and the adjoining canal were built by McNamara-Pigott-Peacock, a joint venture.

McNAMARA CONSTRUCTION CO. LIMITED

With the opening of the power phase of the St. Lawrence Seaway and Power Projects accomplished on July 1, 1958, even more attention is being focussed on the new deep waterway itself, . . . the great inland water transportation route which will be opened up to enable ocean-going vessels to reach the industrial heart of Canada and the United States of America.

Canadian and American contractors alike are working virtually around the clock to ensure the opening of this vast marine transportation system in April 1959 and among these the units of McNamara Construction Company Limited of Toronto, Ontario, are playing a leading role.

The contribution of the McNamara Construction Company to the St. Lawrence Seaway has been particularly diversified, consisting not only of lock and bridge construction, but also of millions of yards of marine dredging and road construction directly connected with the creation of this mammoth inland waterway.

The large projects on which this company was engaged were the canal leading to the St. Lambert Lock, the St. Lambert Lock and Approaches, all opposite the City of Montreal; the new International High-Level Bridge between Cornwall Island in Ontario and Roose-

veltown, New York; dredging projects at several locations in Lake St. Louis and Lake St. Francis; submarine drilling, blasting and dredging projects at Cornwall Island and in the Welland Canal; relocation of No. 2 highway which runs between Montreal and Toronto and the building of a scenic highway route in the Cornwall area.

McNamara Construction joined with the Pigott Construction Company and Peacock & McQuigge Limited in a joint venture known as McNamara-Pigott-Peacock to build both the canal leading to the St. Lambert Lock and the Lock itself. The canal excavation began at a point just downstream from the Jacques Cartier Bridge on the south side of the St. Lawrence and extended for 7,500 feet up-river to the Victoria Bridge. An integral part of this excavation work, which was the first contract let by the St. Lawrence Seaway Authority of Canada, was the building of a permanent dyke on the river side of the excavation. This permanent dyke of impervious material rose 60 feet above the canal bottom.

The McNamara-Pigott-Peacock crews excavated a total of 4,300,000 cubic yards of material to complete this canal eight months ahead of schedule. It was on this project that the first blast was touched off in the entire

The above piers were erected by McNamara Construction Co. Limited, To support the new high-level suspension bridge connecting Cornwall Island, Ont. and Rooseveltown, N.Y.

complex of construction jobs needed to make the Seaway a reality.

The contract for the St. Lambert Lock, the first lock which shipping entering the St. Lawrence Seaway will use, was the largest contract awarded by the Canadian Seaway Authority in terms of total volume of concrete. Located underneath, and on either side of, the Victoria Bridge across the river from Montreal, this lock and its approaches contains over 455,000 cubic yards of concrete. It measures 6,285 feet from entrance to exit and the lock structure itself from gate to gate is 900 feet in length.

The huge amount of concrete making up its massive form was poured in record volume of up to 4,000 cubic yards per day and 77,700 yards in a single month. The joint venture crews used every concrete-pouring method in the book, including a conveyor belt system with travelling stacker, conveyors mounted on a low-bed float supplied by dumpcrete trucks, a boom mounted on a Euclid chassis, and crane-and-bucket arrangements. The locks completed by these methods are 80 feet wide and will accommodate ships with a draught of 30 feet and lift them 16 feet.

At Cornwall Island and Rooseveltown, New York, the McNamara Construction Company carried out the task of building the sub-structure for the new International High-Level Bridge, a suspension bridge some 5,900 feet in length, including approaches, which connects Canada with the United States. This bridge replaces the old bridge 1,200 feet downstream, a structure too low to allow the larger ships which will be using the Seaway to pass underneath. The new bridge has a clearance of 120 feet between the deck and the river.

In building the sub-structure for this new connecting link between Canada and the United States, McNamara Construction erected 20 land piers ranging from 57 to 68 feet in height, two mammoth river piers on each side of the St. Lawrence, and large abutments and anchor blocks. A total of 18,700 cubic yards of concrete was poured to complete these land structures.

The main river piers were formed by driving 58-foot steel pilings weighing a ton each into the river bottom after the glacial till of the riverbed had been excavated in preparation. These were driven to form circular steel cells 30 feet in diameter. The cells were then filled to the top with intrusion prepakt concrete to make a massive, solid base for the main supporting columns of the bridge steelwork.

In its position as one of the leading dredging firms in Canada, the McNamara Construction Co. Limited has carried out many dredging contracts all along the Seaway route to deepen it to the required depth of 27 feet. Altogether, the dredges of this company's Marine Division have dug over 3,650,000 cubic yards of Class

The 5-yard dipper dredge "Howard M" of the Marine Division of the McNamara Construction Co. Limited is shown at right working with derrick dredge "Skyhook", another McNamara vessel, digging up rock blasted from the bottom of Welland Canal at Port Colborne, Ont.

"B" material and drilled, blasted and dredged an additional 1,070,000 cubic yards of submarine rock in carrying out these contracts. Dredging of Class "B" material has been concentrated mostly at various locations in Lake St. Louis, Lake St. Francis, Cornwall Island and the Welland Canal.

In the latter two locations it has been necessary to remove several feet of rock from the bottom of the St. Lawrence and the canal in order to bring them to the Seaway depth of 27 feet. On these projects McNamara Construction has put its fleet of 6 dipper dredges, 4 derrick dredges, 3 hydraulic dredges, 2 hopper dredges, 11 tugs and 18 dump scows.

Along the Port Colborne, Ontario, section of the Welland Canal, McNamara Construction removed 850,-000 cubic yards of submarine rock and Class "B" material over a distance of 8,700 feet of the waterway. In the North Channel of the St. Lawrence at Cornwall Island this Company's drill boats and dredges drilled off, blasted and dredged 215,000 cubic yards of rock, and dredged an additional 300,000 cubic yards of Class "B" material.

In addition to these dredging projects directly connected with the St. Lawrence Seaway, McNamara has also drilled, blasted and dredged, hundreds of thousands of additional yards of rock and other material to deepen the harbours at Toronto, Port Arthur, Whitby and Oshawa in addition to many other Great Lake ports so that they can accommodate the larger vessels which will be using the Seaway route. At Toronto's inner harbour and Western Gap the Marine Division of this company has drilled, blasted and dredged a total of 690,000 cubic yards of rock and dredged an additional 2,100,000 cubic yards of sand, mud and silt, scow measurement.

The new lake created above Cornwall by the St. Lawrence Seaway meant that a lengthy section of No. 2 Highway, the main highway between Toronto and Montreal had to be relocated. McNamara Construction carried out virtually all of the work of building this new section of highway between Moulinette, Ontario and Iroquois, Ontario. On this 25-mile stretch of new highway the Company moved over a million yards of earth during 1956 alone. The highway was opened for use in 1957.

While the St. Lawrence Seaway was created for power and ease of transportation, consideration has also been given to beauty. The Ontario St. Lawrence Development Commission has created beautiful parks in the Cornwall area for the thousands of tourists who will be visiting it each year to enjoy its scenic splendour. In this locality the McNamara Construction Company was chosen to build the 7½-mile Long Sault Parkway, a scenic highway route which is one of the main tourist

The 6-yard dipper dredge "William B. Dilly" of the Marine Division of the McNamara Construction Co. Limited, is shown at right on dredging work in Lake St. Louis, a few miles upstream from Montreal.

attractions in the area. The Parkway branches south from No. 2 Highway near the new town of Long Sault, winds through the new lake created by the flooding and travels north again to the new town of Ingleside. It joins nine islands created by the flooding and affords a picturesque view of the Ontario and New York countryside and the beautiful waters of the Seaway in between.

When the large earth cofferdam on the St. Lawrence Seaway project near Cornwall was blasted out on July 1, 1958, to flood the area west of the Barnhart Island Power Dam and thus create the head pond for this international power development, the flooding also put the Long Sault Parkway and a shoreline improvement project of McNamara into use. The shoreline improvement project consists of extensive cut-and-fill work along the edges of the area flooded by the Dominion Day blast. This work has created a definite shoreline and beautiful sandy bathing beaches rather than unsightly shallow areas which would have become weedy swamps. Another phase of this job was the removal of 2,000 feet of side road and several thousand feet of old Canadian National mainline roadbed.

Aside from the Seaway work, McNamara Construction Company has been interested in many other giant projects. Gnawing away with 25-yard bites the big DW-20 self-propelled scrapers of the Grading Division of Mc-

namara are speedily and surely making a big dent in the 4,000,000 yard total of earth to be moved at Asbestos, Quebec, by the end of 1959. Up to the end of this year, McNamara Construction had hauled away about half of the 150-foot layer of silty earth overburden to be stripped from the East side of the Jeffrey open pit mine so that the Canadian Johns-Manville Company can increase the size of its vast open pit mining operation. This project was started on May 1, 1958.

Other projects previously undertaken by McNamara Construction from Coast to Coast include, in Quebec, a 7¼-mile section of the Montreal-Laurentian Autoroute, the six-lane super highway which will be Canada's first toll road; re-building 18-miles of No. 11 Highway west of Kapuskasing, Ontario. This stretch was originally built by McNamara in the late 1930's; a 20-mile stretch of road between Yellowknife and Fort Rae in Canada's North West Territories; numerous dredging projects; tunneling jobs in Toronto and Montreal; a hydro electric power dam at Nelson River, Manitoba and the construction of new runways and parking aprons for the huge International Airport at Gander, Newfoundland.

From the foregoing it can be concluded that McNamara Construction Company is a giant among Canadian builders, and as such shall continue to play an important role in the shaping of this country's future.

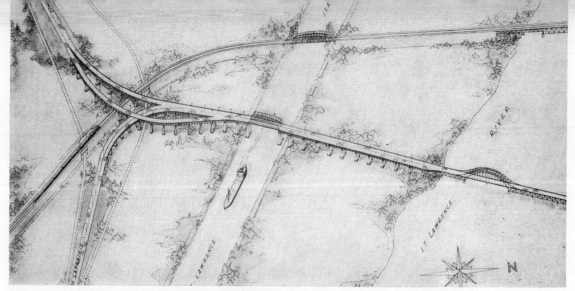

Honore Mercier Bridge Extension — C.P.R. Bridge at top.

LALONDE & VALOIS

For the past five years, engineering firms in Canada have been busily engaged in the design and building of one of the greatest construction projects of all time . . . The St. Lawrence Seaway and Power Developments.

Such a firm is Lalonde & Valois, Consulting Engineers of Montreal. Founded by Jean-Paul Lalonde and Romeo Valois, the company has been active as consulting engineers in all phases of civil engineering work.

They were commissioned by the St. Lawrence Seaway Authority of Canada to design and supervise the construction of the Honore Mercier Bridge extension in the Lachine Section of the Seaway.

The Honore Mercier Bridge, erected in 1934, is a highway bridge which spans the St. Lawrence River from the mid-western end of the Island of Montreal, to a point on the south shore near the famed Indian Reservation at Caughnawaga.

The extension was deemed necessary to allow sufficient headroom for ships traversing the Seaway canal at this particular section. The prospect of a moveable bridge across the Seaway Canal was definitely undesirable due to the already heavily congested roadway traffic at this point. The raising of a portion of the existing steel bridge together with the concrete viaduct of the South approach was contemplated and found impractical.

The only alternative was to demolish the existing concrete approach and replace it with a new high-level structure capable of meeting future traffic needs.

Prior to the demolition of this approach and while the excavation of the Seaway channel progressed, it was necessary to construct a temporary timber trestle and a rock-filled embankment on which the traffic could be diverted.

The temporary bridge was put into service in April 1957 and the demolition of the 25 deck spans and the 24 sets of twin pillars of the concrete viaduct was carried out without a hitch.

Worthy of mention are the following major engineering projects designed by Lalonde & Valois' Public Works Department:

The four lane vehicular tunnel under the present Lachine Canal at Atwater Ave. in the City of Montreal.

Eleven structures for the Canadian National Railways — new belt line in the northern section of the City of Montreal.

Structures at all railroad crossings for the six lane divided controlled access expressway presently under construction for the Montreal-Laurentian Autoroute Board.

This expressway will relieve traffic congestion on the eighteen mile section of Highway No. 11 between Ste. Rose and St. Jerome. Incidentally, Lalonde & Valois designed and supervised construction, in 1937, of this three lane highway including all bridges and the three railroad viaducts. After 21 years of heavy service, this highway No. 11 is in very good condition.

The other engineering departments are:

Structures — concrete, pre-stressed concrete and steel constructions.

Municipal Works — waterworks — filtration plants — sewage — pumping stations and collectors.

Soil Mechanics — including foundations and underpinning.

Supervision and Control of Works

Example of Lalonde & Valois' work can be seen in seven provinces and in the Northwest Territories. It is a compact and efficient engineering team under the personal control of the two associates. They are proud to present heads of their departments, all professional engineers:

Messrs. J. Croteau — A. Denis — J. P. Dionne — B. Lamarre — M. Neithard — G. Réne de Cotret — A. Roberge and J. C. Valiquette.

The above are some of the men who are helping to shape Canada's future in world trade through the joint Canada-U.S.A. St. Lawrence Seaway.

Aerial view of St. Lawrence Power Project, Cornwall, showing Dike built by Atlas Construction Co Limited.

ATLAS CONSTRUCTION CO LIMITED

Atlas Construction Co Limited was founded in the year 1911 and its growth has been consistent with that of Canada's expanding economy. The Company is primarily experienced in Heavy Construction, or Engineering Works, but over the years it has successfully completed many Industrial and Commercial Building contracts.

The St. Lawrence Seaway and Power Development has been one of the largest and most important feats of engineering and construction that has taken place in our time. It has presented a great challenge to the engineers who were charged with the design and to the contractors who were responsible for its construction.

Atlas Construction Co Limited has been engaged in several Seaway projects during the past four years and has brought all of their contracts to a successful conclusion within the scheduled time allowed.

The first major contract was undertaken in the summer of 1955 when the Hydro-Electric Power Commission of Ontario awarded a contract for the construction of approximately three miles of dyke upstream of the main power site at Cornwall, Ontario. This job was completed in the autumn of 1957. The work involved the moving of approximately 5,000,000 cubic yards of glacial till and other materials.

In the spring of 1957, the Hydro-Electric Power Commission of Ontario awarded the Company a contract to enlarge the Channel at Point Three Points near Iroquois, Ontario. This contract consisted of the removal of approximately 2,000,000 cubic yards of materials to be excavated both in the dry and under-water. This contract was completed at the end of October, 1958.

In the year 1956. Atlas formed a joint venture Company with Winston Bros. Company of Minneapolis, Minnesota, U.S.A. This Company is known as Atlas-Winston Limited, and was successful in obtaining two large excavation contracts in the Montreal area. Atlas Construction Co Limited being the managing contractor.

The first of these contracts was the Stage I Excava-

tion for both the Upper and Lower Beauharnois Locks, along with the excavation for the relocation of Quebec Provincial Highway No. 3. The contract consisted mainly of the excavation of approximately 1,000,000 cubic yards of extremely hard and abrasive sand-stone. In addition there was a large cofferdam to be built in order to allow the construction of the Lower Lock to be carried out in the dry. All of this work was completed in a little over six months and allowed the contractors for the lock construction to proceed on schedule.

The second contract was for the excavation of approximately 3500 lineal feet of Seaway Channel at Caughnawaga, Quebec. Included in this contract was the construction of the abutments for the two new lift bridges for the Canadian Pacific Railway spanning the Seaway Canal. This job involved the excavation of approximately 2,000,000 cubic yards of earth and rock and the placing of 30,000 cubic yards of reinforced concrete.

Atlas was awarded a contract by the Dominion Bridge Company for the extension of the concrete piers of the Jacques Cartier Bridge when Dominion Bridge were carrying out the immense task of raising the bridge over the Seaway Channel. Prior to this work Atlas had been awarded a contract to enlarge the existing piers of the Jacques Cartier Bridge to permit the raising operation to take place.

The Company has also carried out work for National Harbours Board by constructing the concrete piers for that section of the Nuns Island Bridge which will span the Seaway Channel.

The Canadian National Railways awarded a contract to Atlas to build the river piers to carry the Division Bridge, which will bring rail traffic over the Seaway Canal when the main lift bridges are raised.

Atlas Construction Co Limited is proud to have taken part in this gigantic engineering project, a project that will have such a beneficial effect on the economy of Canada.

Downstream view of Cote St. Catherine Lock showing one of the huge gantry cranes brought from France.

CANAMONT & CANIT

Construction Limited

Excavation of five million cubic yards of earth, glacial till and shale and pouring of 400,000 cubic yards of concrete through the use of equipment unique in America were among the highlights of construction of the Cote St. Catherine Lock of the St. Lawrence Seaway.

The Cote St. Catherine Lock, with a 30-foot lift covering most of the difference in elevation between Lake St. Louis and the Laprairie Basin near Montreal, was built as a joint project by two companies with headquarters in Montreal — Canamont Construction Limited and Canit Construction Limited.

"Canamont" was incorporated in 1954 by four leading Montreal construction and engineering firms: Deschamps & Belanger Limited, Dufresne Engineering Company Limited, A. Janin & Company Limited and The Key Construction Limited. "Canit" was incorporated in 1952.

The Cote St. Catherine Lock contract was under the management of The Key Construction Limited.

The construction of the lock was part of a contract awarded in 1955. The lock walls are 80 feet high and,

as in the other St. Lawrence Seaway locks, the depth over sills is 30 feet, with an 80-foot width and a 768-foot usable length.

The contract was awarded on the basis of a $7,107,-480 tender, but work was carried out amounting to more than twice that figure because of additions, alterations and extraordinary difficulties — including, during the 1955-56 winter season, a double flooding of the entire site by the St. Lawrence River as the result of unexpected ice barriers.

In addition to the construction of the lock itself, the contract called for the excavation of 10,000 feet of channel together with a turning basin, and for the construction of dykes, approach walls and regulating works.

Later, the construction of a concrete spillway was added, designed in conjunction with the Hydro-Quebec Lachine Power Project.

Excavation was carried out mainly by means of two 4-cubic yard shovels serviced by a fleet of 35-ton, 22-ton and 15-ton trucks.

Work goes ahead on the south wall of the lock. Note the great width of the base of the lock wall. May, 1957.

One of the features of construction of the Cote St. Catherine Lock was the steel travelling form shown above.

However, the most interesting phase of the construction of the Cote St. Catherine Lock was the manner in which concrete was poured. From the contractor's own concrete plant on the site, concrete was hauled by 6-cubic yard dump trucks fitted with a special body during the concrete season. From these vehicles concrete was dumped into 3-cubic yard buckets and poured into place by means of four tall, slim gantry cranes, manufactured in France and believed to be the first of their kind in North America.

The tower of each crane is 100 feet high (and could be increased at will); the horizontal boom is 100 feet long. Mounted on a 15-foot square base, the crane travels on tracks, with the operator conveniently located in a cabin in the tower under the boom.

Each crane weighs only 100 tons, half steel, half concrete counterweights; but it is capable of lifting seven tons at a 50-foot radius and three and one-half tons at 100-foot radius. An agerage pour of 60 cubic yards an hour has been attained.

Another striking feature on the Canamont-Canit site was the steel travelling form designed by the contractor's engineers for the concreting of lock and entrance walls.

Forty feet high and 40 feet wide, this 100-ton steel structure was electrically self-propelling and self-con-

creting. Concrete was distributed automatically along the form with such speed and precision that the structure moved along to build a new monolith every 24 hours. Its capacity was 810 cubic yards a day.

Mass construction on Cote St. Catherine Lock, which bypasses the treacherous Lachine Rapids, was completed in the spring of 1958. Despite unexpected obstacles, including flood, Canamont-Canit completed the project as requested in the original schedule. Careful planning and superior equipment maintenance were important factors in success.

Canamont Construction Limited and Canit Construction Limited are proud to have contributed their part to the further growth and industrial development of Canada.

Chairman of the board of Canamont Construction Limited is the Honorable Wilfrid Gagnon. Mr. Albert Deschamps is president; and Mr. Paul Dufresne, vice-president. Other officers are Mr. Gaston Jouven, of A. Janin & Company Limited, secretary, and Mr. P. H. Mora, of The Key Construction Limited, treasurer. Mr. Mora served as project manager for the Cote St. Catherine Lock contract.

President of Canit Construction Limited is Mr. Jules Archambault; Messrs. Jean Raymond and Salvatore Randaccio are vice-presidents, and Mr. Claude Marchand, secretary-treasurer.

An excellent aerial view of the City and Port of Montreal, looking from the waterfront toward Mount Royal.

PORT OF MONTREAL
The World's Largest Inland Seaport

Montreal, the metropolis of Canada and the world's largest inland seaport, had its future predestined thousands of years ago, not by man but by nature. Geographically, the Montreal area is the crossroads of navigation going East, West, North or South. The mighty St. Lawrence River provided a deep waterway from the sea directly to Montreal and beyond Montreal, going in a westerly direction, the St. Lawrence River continued on to the entrance to the Great Lakes although in many places, navigation was impeded by fast flowing rapids. Directly to the west of Montreal, the Ottawa River flows down through the fertile Ottawa Valley to join the St. Lawrence from the north and a little to the east of Montreal, the Richelieu River linked New York City with the St. Lawrence via Lake Champlain and the Hudson River.

After the coming of the early settlers and for the many years thereafter, ocean going ships could go no further than Montreal because of the rapids existing to the west and their cargos had to be transshipped in smaller vessels. As the country grew, the Port of Montreal was constantly increasing its importance as the focal point of Canada's international trade. Transcontinental railways, highways for motor trucks, and air routes converge on Montreal.

With the opening of the St. Lawrence Seaway in the Spring of 1959, the Port of Montreal will continue to serve as transfer point for cargos and, in addition, will be able to service the previously landlocked huge Great Lakes inland fleet which up to the time of the opening of the Seaway could not navigate downstream much beyond the entrance to the St. Lawrence from Lake Ontario.

The merchants and shipping men who had initiated the construction of a port and harbour at Montreal in the early Nineteenth Century also created an administrative organization to manage the port and develop its commercial possibilities. The first such organization was Trinity House, later supplanted by the Harbour Trust, and in 1850, the Montreal Harbour Commission was founded.

Collier CRYSTAL GEM unloading coal at a wharf in Montreal Harbour.

Cunard Line's CARINTHIA passes under Jacques Cartier Bridge as it enters Montreal Harbour.

The federal power of supervision over load lines and grain regulations through the office of the Port Warden devolved upon the Montreal Board of Trade, founded in 1822 as the Committee of Trade. Both the Montreal Board of Trade and the Chamber of Commerce have been consistently active in promoting the development and efficiency of the Port.

Between 1830 and 1907, six different experiments were made in harbour administration, all attempting to leave the management in the hands of the merchants and their various organizations, including the city government, with appointees of the Federal government often participating.

In 1936, as a result of a report by Sir Alexander Gibb, who had been commissioned by the Canadian Government to make an appraisal of Canadian harbours and advance recommendations as to their future organization and management, the Federal government took over administration of eight Canadian harbours, including Montreal, which were to be known as National Harbours, administered by a National Harbours Board through local Port Managers.

Federal services available at the Port of Montreal outside the jurisdiction of the National Harbours Board include Customs and Immigration, Quarantine and Health, and the examination of imported livestock, plants, fresh and processed foods.

At present the Port of Montreal is usually open from the first of April to the middle of December. Winter navigation of the St. Lawrence River below Quebec City has already been proved practicable, but there is still some doubt as to extending winter voyages to Montreal, largely because Lake St. Peter is a wide and relatively shallow widening of the river with a sluggish current where icebreaking activities are easily countered by adverse winds. On the other hand, Montreal physicists, who have been studying the problem for many years, state that it has always been possible to keep the river open through the winter. When the demand for an ice-free navigation of the St. Lawrence below Montreal becomes sufficiently strong, no doubt the necessary means will be forthcoming.

The St. Lawrence Ship Channel extends from a point approximately 38 miles below Quebec City to Montreal, a total distance of 180 miles, of which approximately 100 miles are dredged. Below Quebec City the limiting channel depth is 30 feet below low tide, but some 14 feet more when tides are favourable. From Quebec City to Montreal, approximately 140 nautical miles, the channel is maintained at a minimum depth of 35 feet below low water and a maximum width of 550 feet. More recently, curves have been widened to 1,500 feet and additional anchorage and turning basins have been provided.

The St. Lawrence Ship Channel from Montreal to the sea is under the jurisdiction of the Federal Department of Transport, which ensures the provision of modern and efficient aids to navigation and the services of a fleet of ice-breaking vessels to facilitate ship movement during the opening and closing periods of navigation.

The Port and Harbour of Montreal extends from approximately 3600 feet above the Victoria Bridge, the approaches to which mark the upper limits of the harbour basin and the lower end of the old Lachine Canal, and Bout de l'Ile, the lower end of Montreal Island where the two north rivers draining the Ottawa River, after uniting into one, join the St. Lawrence. The St. Mary's Current divides the port area into the Upper and Lower Harbour.

Outside the actual limits of the Port of Montreal, and along the lower reaches of the eight-and-a-half mile Lachine Canal that empties into the Harbour basin, there are coal docks capable of storing 355,000 tons. One of these is 256 feet in length and has a discharge rate of 190 tons and storage space for 305,000 tons. The other is 300 feet long, with a discharge rate of 100 tons per hour and storage space for 50,000 tons.

There are now four grain elevators in the Port of Montreal proper with a total storage capacity of 15,182,-000 bushels. Two additional elevators planned for the Lower Harbour will add another 6,900,000 bushel capacity. A privately owned elevator just outside the port limits provides storage for 750,000 bushels, and there is elevator space in the Lachine Canal area with a total capacity of 3,550,000 bushels, mostly for milling.

The present receiving capacity of the four port elevators is 1,250,000 bushels per thirteen-hour day, and the outward shipping capacity for the same period is between 1,250,000 and 1,500,000 bushels. In one year, 217 million bushels of grain were received, and 211 million bushels shipped . . . equalling the cargoes of seven hundred ten-thousand-ton ships.

There are 30 grain berths in the Port, only 8 of which are open. Six berths are equipped with marine legs — ten in all — which are used in unloading. The grain is elevated from the hold in bucket conveyors, passed to garners, weighed, and stored.

The Port has five railway-car dumpers, each having a capacity of six railway cars, and capable of discharging 72,000 bushels an hour.

Conveyor galleries make it possible for a ship to load partially with grain and partially with other cargo without the necessity of moving from its berth. Grain can be delivered to twenty ocean vessels at the same time.

The speed and efficiency achieved in the handling of grain, which has been made possible by the development of these facilities, will be of added importance when the large lakers are able to descend the new St. Lawrence Seaway to Montreal, discharging their cargo directly into the holds of the deep sea giants.

There are eleven miles of berthing space in the Harbour of Montreal providing 121 berths, of which 87 are open. Minimum depth alongside ranges from 25 to 35 feet and only 600 linear feet of this mileage has less.

Special anchorage or mooring space approximately one mile long and a thousand feet wide is available within the Port limits.

There are 4,975 linear feet of open piers with an overall rate of discharge of 3,050 tons per hour and storage space for 1,820,000 tons. Coal, mineral ores, steel, scrap iron, lumber, and other such products can be adequately handled on these open piers, of which there are five.

The National Harbours Board owns and operates a 62-mile terminal railway at the Port of Montreal which is equipped with eight diesel electric locomotives of 660 horsepower.

The Port railway is connected with the two great transcontinental railway systems of Canada, which handle an estimated 15,000 freight cars in the Montreal area alone. All principal railway lines from the Pacific Coast, the Western prairies, and the northern mining areas of Ontario come together at Montreal. From Montreal the railway lines fan out along the St. Lawrence, eastward into the Maritime Provinces, and southward into the United States. Montreal is the hub and center of the entire vast national railway network. This is the measure of greatness of any primary port.

In addition, Montreal is also the headquarters of the International Civil Aviation Organization and International Air Transport Association, which should make it the "air capital" of the world.

Trucking lines have their own terminals and warehouses in the Montreal area providing short and long-distance hauling to and from harbour installations and warehouses.

As a matter of general practice, freight handling and stevedoring services are provided by private companies utilizing their own trucks, fork lifts, mobile cranes, and other material-handling equipment, but the Port of Montreal also operates much of this heavy-lift machinery. It has a floating crane with a rated capacity of 75 tons, capable of lifting up to 90 tons with restricted outreach. It has a diesel caterpillar crane of 30 tons capacity and six locomotive cranes with capacities varying from 10 to 30 tons. A privately-owned shearlegs of 125 tons capacity is available.

The transfer of package freight from wharf face to transit shed is handled almost exclusively by ships' gear.

Sixteen firms with modern equipment and trained staffs provide efficient stevedoring service at the Port of Montreal. Stevedoring work is performed on Sundays and recognized holidays at double pay. For 22 years there has been no strike or work stoppage by stevedores at the Port of Montreal.

Several private firms operate docks in the Harbour of Montreal which possess coal and oil bunkering facilities available during the day or night. Privately-owned bunkering craft are prepared to pump fuel oil aboard while the ship is loading or discharging cargo at its berth.

Tugs are required for harbour work, notably to ease large ocean liners alongside their piers. A private firm operating a fleet of nineteen harbour, canal, and ocean-going tugs of 650 to 1000 horsepower provide these services at the Port of Montreal. This fleet is being augmented to meet the opening of the St. Lawrence Seaway.

Fire hydrants are located throughout the harbour area, and the Port is equipped with two tugs furnished with fire-fighting equipment.

The National Harbours Board maintains a special police force of 52 men who have operative authority over port matters within a 25-mile radius of the Harbour.

The activities of a port must be supported by shipyards capable of producing and repairing ships. Montreal shipbuilding yards have constructed many types of vessels and employ approximately 2,300 workers directly and another 1,000 indirectly and produce goods having a gross selling value of from 66 to 87 million dollars. In the City of Montreal engineering works, machine shops, foundries and electrical plants produce the necessary components and equipment for ship construction and repair.

The Port of Montreal as it appeared in 1875.

Montreal also offers a complete range of specialized marine services, including naval architects and surveyors, marine equipment, ship brokers, ship suppliers, custom house brokers, freight forwarding agents, etc.

Storage facilities at the Port of Montreal are sufficient to meet all present needs, and are being constantly increased to meet future requirements. At present there are 34 transit sheds, having a floor area of 2,565,000 square feet. The Federal government recognizes nine classifications of warehouses. In some, manufacturing or processing is permitted, but most are bonded warehouses, of which there are 54. An eight-storey refrigerated warehouse having a capacity of 3,000,000 cubic feet, 30,000 cubic feet of which are equipped for quick-freeze, 1,200,000 cubic feet for refrigeration at a minimum of zero, and 600,000 cubic feet for the conservation of fruits and vegetables. The remaining capacity provides storage for a diversity of commodities.

Petroleum products rank second only to grain in volume and importance to the Port of Montreal. Seven special berths are assigned to this trade in order to ensure a quick turnaround for tankers bringing in crude oil to the refineries, and additional berthing accomodation is under construction.

Approximately 400,000 tons of raw sugar are imported into Montreal annually. Half of this volume is in bulk. The two Montreal sugar refineries have a combined daily melting capacity of 1800 short tons, which is more than half of Canada's total cane sugar production.

Of special interest to Port users and shipping men is the six international banks which have their headquarters in the City of Montreal. There are 150 ocean steamship lines represented by 36 agents. Eighteen coastal, and 38 Great Lakes steamship companies have offices in Montreal. Forty foreign government bureaus and consular offices are located in the City.

On February 28, 1958, the Montreal Port Council was officially inaugurated to study, develop and promote the Port in many different ways including the volume of shipping and the movement of cargos.

The effect of the Seaway on the Port of Montreal has also been a matter of considerable speculation. The dominating factor in the situation is, however, that Montreal has always been the primary point of transshipment between the Great Lakes and the sea, originally no doubt because of its strategic situation at the head of navigation, but a century's preeminence in the efficient operation of superior equipment cannot fail to attract the new trade of the giant lakers now able to reach Montreal and the ocean shipping they will find there, which, because of their peculiar construction fitted only for calm waters, cannot sail the high seas. This situation can only result in an increased demand upon the facilities and services of the Port of Montreal, which have been expanded and modernized to cope with the increased traffic to be brought to it through the new deep waterway. With this in view the City and Harbour of Montreal may confidently advance into a secure future.

Montreal's bustling inner harbour, looking downstream.

BARNES INVESTIGATION BUREAU LTD.

Complete Waterfront Protection Service

Barnes Investigation Bureau Headquarters in Montreal.

With the opening of the 1959 navigation season on the St. Lawrence River, ships from many far off lands will traverse the new St. Lawrence Seaway loaded with goods and merchandise vital to the Canadian economy. On their outward bound trip they will carry in their holds the produce of this great nation which will be used in trade or sold outright in other parts of the world. The word "security" then takes on an even greater meaning, for with increased trade comes increased traffic along our waterway system necessitating the need for an alert security force. However, shippers, and receivers as well as shipowners, in the ports of Montreal, Toronto and Hamilton, Ontario, know that the goods they handle are being afforded the maximum protection from one of the foremost security organizations in North America.

The name, "Barnes Investigation Bureau Ltd.", in the space of ten short years, has become a name second to none in the field of protection and investigation in Canada. Founded in 1948 by former Director of the Montreal Police Department, Charles Barnes, J. P., the Bureau has expanded to include Toronto and Hamilton due to the demand for its services. In addition, a special police force is maintained in the area of Seven Islands, Quebec, and with progress still on the march other branch offices elsewhere in Canada are contemplated.

The protection of valuable cargoes has long been the cause for much concern among shipowners and warehousemen alike. The ports of Montreal, Quebec, and Toronto, Ontario, are no different in this respect to any other port in the world. A constant vigil must be kept at all times by trained security officers to ensure that the goods in shipment are not tampered with.

The ability of Barnes Investigation Bureau to minimize the loss through pilferage and breakage to all cargoes placed in their care over the years is a well known and highly respected fact. The art, for it can truly be called an art, of adequately protecting cargoes is a specialty in which Barnes personnel excell.

When a ship is discharging cargo, for instance, in any of the ports where Barnes services are utilized, a security guard or watchman is stationed in the ships hold where he is better able to determine the extent of pilferage or breakage that might have occured either at sea or in a foreign port. Any sign of damaged goods is immediately brought to the attention of the ships officer on duty, who in turn has the merchandise brought out of the hold separately.

While the cargo sling or pallette is being raised from the hold, another Barnes guard is positioned nearby where he can keep a close watch on the whole operation until the cargo is safely placed on the wharf. This security measure insures that cargo does not fall from the sling or pallette nor get tampered with on its way to the dockside.

The safeguarding of the cargo does not, however, end there. Another Barnes guard is strategically placed where he can watch the cargo from the time it lands on the wharf until it is placed in the shed. At this point yet another uniformed guard is assigned the task of keeping the goods under constant surveillance until it is finally picked up by the consignee. Overseeing the entire operation is a Barnes supervisor who keeps in close contact with his headquarters through the use of his radio equipped patrol automobile.

Barnes Investigation Bureau does not limit its services to the safety of cargoes. There is also the ship itself which needs protection. In this case a uniformed guard is stationed at the ships gangway for the purpose of preventing unauthorized persons from boarding the vessel, and also sees to it that persons leaving the ships do not take off goods or other merchandise which has not been duly cleared. This guard also doubles as a guide in aiding visitors to find the ships officers, or directing them to specific areas aboard the vessel.

During the night the Barnes Bureau details an extra guard to patrol the ships deck's, checking locks, hatches, mooring lines, watching for fire and in general making sure all is secure. He is also available to assist the gangway guard in the event of any trouble that might occur.

A large majority of steamship companies make full use of Barnes services and include, Cunard Steamship Company, Canadian Pacific Steamships, County Lines, Canada Steamships Lines, Furness Withy & Company, Federal Commerce & Navigation, March Shipping Company, Montreal Shipping, McLean Kennedy, North American Marine, The Robert Reford Company.

Broadly speaking, Barnes Investigation Bureau offers a variety of services in two principal categories — investigation, protection and security.

The Bureau handles all types of commercial, industrial and personal investigation, excepting divorce cases. For this work, the Company is equipped with the most modern facilities available . . . lie detectors, Speak-O-Phone, candid and movie cameras, wire recorders and miniature recorders, fingerprint equipment, ultra-violet lamps and battery operated lamps to detect invisible powders and a forgery kit. Every modern secret service method known to exports in America and Europe is employed by Barnes, with result there does not exist an investigation problem which can not be handled efficiently and quickly by the highly trained personnel of the Barnes Bureau.

In addition to its waterfront protection services, Barnes offers complete protection to commercial and industrial establishments alike. Only high calibre men are employed in this specialized work who in turn are under constant supervision of patrol supervisors. These supervisors work around the clock, insuring that clients instructions are carried out and straightening out difficulties that arise from time to time.

All Barnes guards and watchmen report to headquarters by telephone every hour during the night while on duty, so that, in the event a call is missed, the nearest patrol can be dispatched to the scene in a matter of minutes. This practice insures prompt assistance in the event of trouble.

Uniformed Barnes guards have been a familiar sight on the St. Lawrence Seaway where they have played an important role in the tight security of the billion dollar deep waterway system. In the years of prosperity which will result from the opening of the St. Lawrence Seaway and Power Project, these men can be depended on to maintain their strict vigilance over Canadian industry and merchandise, and by so doing, also maintain the name of Barnes Investigation Bureau as a leader in the field of private police work.

In charge of traffic control on Seaway.

Protecting cargo in freight shed.

P. L. PRATLEY, CONSULTING ENGINEER

With a construction venture the size of the St. Lawrence Seaway and Power Project the average layman focusses his attention and heaps his praise on the huge machines which do the actual work. He does not, for a moment, stop to think of that small group of men behind the scenes who, in reality, were entrusted with and held responsible for the building of the entire development. This small group of individuals are specialists in their field, they are the consulting engineers. Their opinions and decisions are held in high esteem by construction men the world over for it is from their drawing boards that the plans for the actual construction develops.

Such a man is P. L. Pratley, D.Eng., M. Inst. C.E., Professional Engineer of Montreal, Quebec.

Retained by the St. Lawrence Seaway Authority for work on three of their major projects, P. L. Pratley has been associated with the industrial development of Canada since the turn of the century.

His commission by the St. Lawrence Seaway Authority included the history-making raising of the southern approach of the Jacques Cartier, a bridge which he himself designed in 1926, to provide clearance for ship traffic using the deep waterway system and for which he devised a scheme with virtually no interruption to the flow of traffic during the operation. He was also Foundation Consultant for the International Bridge, spanning the South Channel of the St. Lawrence River at Cornwall, Ontario, and was Consulting Engineer for a new high level bridge crossing the North Channel of the St. Lawrence River also at Cornwall.

The most dramatic of the three projects was the raising of Montreal's Jacques Cartier Bridge. Designer of the original bridge structure in 1926, Dr. Pratley was commissioned to redesign the modification to the bridge. The raising or "jacking" of the southern portion of the bridge which links the Island of Montreal to the town of Longueuil on the south shore, is believed to be the largest project of its kind ever undertaken.

Employing a series of 400 to 500 long ton hydraulic jacks, the Jacques Cartier Bridge was jacked 50 feet and the deck truss span over the canal was replaced with a through truss span to gain an additional 30 feet, providing a minimum vertical clearance of 120 feet. The entire operation was carried out with virtually no interruption of the heavy four-lane traffic overhead.

P. L. Pratley first became a "name" in the Canadian Construction field when he was appointed Chief Designer for the Quebec Bridge Board in 1909, a post which he held until 1910. In 1910, he was Designing Engineer for the St. Lawrence Bridge Company. From 1912 to 1920 Mr. Pratley held the position of Assistant Designing Engineer and later Designing Engineer for Dominion Bridge Company Limited. He resigned this post to become Engineer of Bridges for the Grank Trunk Railway Arbitration from 1920 to 1921. From 1921 to 1940, Mr. Pratley was Consulting Engineer in partnership with Lt. Col. C. N. Monsarrat.

In addition to his participation on both the original Jacques Cartier Bridge, in 1926, and its more recent modification, P. L. Pratley has acted as Consulting Engineer in the design and construction of such major Canadian Bridge structures as the 4,420-foot long Angus L. Macdonald bridge between Halifax and Dartmouth, Nova Scotia; the Burlington Skyway High level bridge, near Hamilton, Ontario, which has a 459-foot central span, providing 120-foot clearance above high water level; the Lions' Gate Bridge, Vancouver, B.C.; Canadian portion of the Thousand Island Bridge; the Isle of Orleans Bridge linking this lower St. Lawrence River island with the mainland on the north shore. Mr. Pratley also designed the reconstruction of the Second Narrows Bridge, Vancouver, B.C., in addition to various other smaller bridges across the country.

P. L. Pratley's knowledge of design and construction of bridge structures was not confined to the Canadian scene. He acted as Canadian Engineer on the Blue Water Bridge, linking Sarnia, Ontario, with Port Huron, Michigan; the Ambassador Bridge, between Windsor, Ontario and Detroit, Michigan, and the Ogdensburg International Bridge at Ogdensburg, New York. He was also Consulting Engineer for the new Champlain Bridge linking Montreal and the south shore via Nun's Island, a small island in the St. Lawrence River.

P. L. Pratley was considered one of Canada's foremost consulting engineers, a reputation gained through long years of participation and association with the Country's growth. His untimely death in August 1958 meant a great loss to the engineering profession and to the country as a whole.

His son, H. H. L. Pratley, B.Eng., MEIC., has succeeded his father in carrying on the business.

Head Office, St. Arnaud & Bergevin Limited, Montreal.

ST. ARNAUD & BERGEVIN LIMITED

Customs Brokers — International Freight Forwarders — Warehousemen
118 St. Peter St., Montreal

Canada, like most other countries, depends a great deal on international trade for without this liberty to buy and sell freely, she could not hope to survive. Over the years, the increase in her import and export business has played a major role in the nation's economy.

Authorities on International Trade have expressed their honest belief that Canada's future is assured with the inauguration of the St. Lawrence Seaway and Power Projects. Her national economy will reach new heights with the increase in trade with other countries which the new deep waterway system will bring.

Offering invaluable service in this field is the firm of St. Arnaud & Bergevin Limited, Customs Brokers, International Freight Fodwarders, Warehousemen and Cartage Contractors.

Located in the heart of Montreal, Quebec's bustling waterfront section, St. Arnaud & Bergevin Limited, has been serving Canadian importers and exporters for 34 years, since 1924.

Known throughout the world for its efficiency in handling all types of cargoes, St. Arnaud & Bergevin Ltd. does not limit its activities to the Montreal harbour. The Company undertakes the clearing of merchandise imported in Canada at any Canadian Customs Port. In addition, St. Arnaud & Bergevin Limited will forward merchandise from any port in North America to all parts of the world. St. Arnaud & Bergevin Ltd. agents and correspondents are located all over the world to handle shipments from point of origin to final destination.

Although not directly associated with the building of the mighty St. Lawrence Seaway, St. Arnaud & Bergevin Limited can still boast an indirect participation in the billion-dollar project. A great proportion of the Compqany's clients supplied the machinery which was necessary for the construction of the Seaway and St. Arnaud & Bergevin was responsible for clearing the goods through customs.

One of St. Arnaud & Bergevin Limited's contribution has been the clearance of most of the material imported by The Iron Ore Co. of Canada in the building of the 357 miles railroad from Seven Islands to Knob Lake in Northern Quebec, as well as the material for mining operations and building of the various townsites.

Its long and enviable record for efficient service to clients is made possible through St. Arnaud & Bergevin Limited's highly trained personnel. Department heads and their assistants have been in the employ of the Company for twenty-five years and more. In addition, a special staff is retained to handle shipments that require particular attention du to urgency or other extraordinary formalities.

Located, as they are, at the entrance to the St. Lawrence Seaway, in Montreal, St. Arnaud & Bergevin Limited foresee a great future ahead and are making plans to expand their operations accordingly.

Officers and Directors of St. Arnaud & Bergevin Limited are : President, Mrs. Alice Lymburner St. Arnaud; Vice-President, A. R. Bergevin; Director, Bertrand St. Arnaud.

Above are the directors of Chas. T. Main Inc., parent company of Uhl, Hall & Rich.
Left to Right: G. R. Rich, R. T. Colburn, R. W. Logan, W. F. Uhl,
W. M. Hall, F. M. Gunby, M. Jacobs.

UHL, HALL & RICH

On June 7, 1954 when the final legal obstacle to the hydro-electric power development on the St. Lawrence River was overcome, a Boston, Massachusetts, engineering consulting firm went to work laying the groundwork for one of the world's largest and most spectacular power projects.

The Power Authority of the State of New York engaged the firm of Uhl, Hall and Rich, consulting engineers, of Boston, Mass., to design and supervise all phases of the power project in the International Section. Uhl, Hall and Rich is a partnership directly affiliated with the parent company, Chas. T. Main, Inc., also of Boston, Mass., who are probably the world's largest firm of consulting engineers specializing in the field of hydro-electric power. The reason for the formation of the subsidiary company was a requirement of New York State's education law and its provision prohibiting engineering work in the area of public practice by corporations.

The Uhl, Hall and Rich partnership has a separate payroll that has numbered near 300 between field and office. The office work done in Boston is physically separated in an annex apart from Main's 80 Federal Street headquarters. But in actuality the corporation and its affiliated partnership have a common management and a common pool of engineering manpower.

The nation's biggest, busiest consulting engineering firm, Chas. T. Main, Inc., is an integrated engineering and construction management organization comprising a complete staff of engineers, architects, project managers, procurement personnel, construction supervisors and supporting services personnel.

The engineering partnership that began as Dean and Main in 1893 became Chas. T. Main, Engineer, in 1907. It was incorporated under its present name in 1926.

The era-spanning existence of Chas. T. Main included

pre-World War 1 days as mill engineers. During World War 1, Mr. Main turned down a lucrative Boston Army Base assignment, lest it appear his presidency of the American Society of Mechanical Engineers at the time had brought the contract.

The Twenties were largely industrial development years in the United States and abroad. The Thirties saw much work with TVA and other federal agencies in hydro. The Forties had World War II and the spectacular RDX munitions plant while the Fifties have been the truly big hydro years as well as being big in industrial work — a Charlotte, N.C., branch office was opened to follow the New England textile industries south.

Since 1893, Chas. T. Main, Inc., has designed more than eighty hydro-electric plants with a total capacity of over seven million horsepower. These plants are located throughout the United States and in several foreign countries including Turkey, Colombia, South America and the Belgian Congo.

In addition, Chas. T. Main, Inc., has acted as engineering consultant on many hydro-electric power plants and storage and flood control dams designed by other engineers. The company has also prepared numerous reports with estimates of cost relating to the physical and economic feasibility of projects, developed and undeveloped water rights, damages due to diversion for domestic purposes, and valuations of existing properties. In many instances, Chas. T. Main, Inc., personnel have provided expert testimony in connection with depreciation, water rights, value, condemnation, rates and other cases.

The Board of Directors of Chas. T. Main, Inc., are: William F. Uhl, Chairman; Wilfred M. Hall, President; Robert T. Colburn, Vice President; Richard W. Logan, Treasurer; Directors, Milton Jacobs, George R. Rich and Frank M. Gunby.

BEDARD GIRARD LIMITED

Construction Division

The St. Lawrence Seaway Project was undertaken in part to provide rapid water transport between the Great Lakes and Montreal. Along its route, run some of the busiest railroads and highways connecting important cities in Canada, as well as with the United States. It was therefore, necessary that both the land and water traffic be free to flow without interfering with one another. This serious problem was solved by the design and construction of several electrically operated movable bridges. BEDARD GIRARD LIMITED have considerable electrical installation experience in light and heavy industries, in distribution lines, substations and other special projects and have the valuable experience of their switchboard and switchgear manufacturing and motor sales and service divisions. They were highly qualified to do this exacting work and have had the privilege of doing the complete installation and the wiring of all electrical motive and control equipment. As the traffic requirements vary considerably between each location, several designs of movable bridges had to be built. At Victoria Bridge, for instance, it was necessary to replace one section of the existing bridge by a lift span. As described elsewhere, this bridge is located at the downstream end of the St. Lambert Lock. A second lift span was built at the upstream end of the lock, so that there is always one bridge opened to the railroad and highway traffic. This arrangement makes Victoria Bridge one of the few "Y" bridges in the world, and it requires very careful co-ordination between the operations of the bridges, the lock, and highway and railroad traffic signalization. This co-ordination has been achieved through the use of a very complex electrical control network. Similar problems had to be solved for the twin span railroad lift bridge at Caughnawaga and also for the lift spans of the St. Louis and Valleyfield bridges. Electrical Power for the operation of the bridges is normally obtained from the public utilities at 12000 volt. Substations have been built to transform this energy from 12,000 volt to 550 volt. In case of electrical power failure, emergency diesel driven alternators have been provided which can operate the lift bridges, either eleltrically by supplying electric power to the motors or by mechanical means only, whenever required.

The choice of the material to be used in the wiring of a bridge must be done with the utmost care and the installation of this material must be carried out in the

St. Lambert Bridge tower showing the moveable cable.

proper manner in order to resist the large amount of vibration always present, and also the action of corrosive and weathering agents. The vibration problem is most severe in the long vertical cable runs. The long flexible cables joining the moving span to the end towers must be selected and installed with care to withstand the continuous bending to which they are subjected. The machinery room above the bridge is necessarily of limited size, and in order to accomodate the large number of cables required, they are installed in formed steel sheet cableways and are thus adequately protected. Once the electrical installation was completed, considerable testing was carried out to ascertain that the operation of each part of the electrical equipment was according to specification, and also to allow the necessary final adjustments to be made.

A large amount of electric power was required in the construction of The St. Lawrence Seaway Project, and BEDARD GIRARD LIMITED, did much of the installation of the temporary substations, distribution lines and lighting circuits. As several operations and considerable amount of work were done during the night, an extensive temporary lighting system was built. Power was required also for a complete concrete mixing plant, for shops, compressors, etc. However, the larger part of the installed 1000 H.P. was required for the operation of the pump motors needed for the dewatering of the different sections of the project in order to make possible the large amount of dry excavation necessary. Temporary electric power was required for the operation of the motorized hydraulic jacks used in the spectacular raising of the southern end of the Jacques Cartier Bridge, and also to feed the temporary water work system built for Longueuil and Ville Jacques-Cartier.

Prescott, Ont. where, prior to the opening of the Seaway in 1959, the deep draft, heavily laden lakers had to transfer their grain cargoes to the 14' draft canallers for the downstream trip to Montreal or overseas.

THE SEAWAY AND THE GRAIN TRADE

From Producer to Consumer

Artificial channels between the Great Lakes and the sea were first undertaken more than a century and a quarter ago. As far back as the year 1800 a canal to assist navigation was constructed at the Canadian Sault, a replica of which is now preserved as a relic of the past.

The feasibility and necessity of improvement to the St. Lawrence Waterway to make it navigable for ocean-going vessels from the Upper Lakes to the sea has been the subject of commissions and treaties for decades.

In fact, ever since the St. Lawrence River was discovered in 1535 by Jacques Cartier, men have dreamed of digging the necessary channels and building locks so that large ships may sail from the Atlantic to Lake Superior. Volumes have been written and millions of words spoken in description of the benefits which were estimated could accrue from the completion of what was described in the 1920's as the "Mediterranean of the North", an ocean in the midst of the Continent, which would provide sea

Sketch of trading scene on floor of the Winnipeg Grain Exchange.

ports within a half thousand miles of the grain fields of the prairies.

Most of the improvements developed over the years were for the purpose of accommodating domestic lake traffic. The size of canals and locks had usually been related to specially designed lake boats rather than to sea-going ships. However, the history of 19th century lake channel development was occasionally marked by agitation in favor of a true deep-draft seaway, but serious consideration on both sides of the international boundary did not begin to develop until the early 1900's. Hearings and commissions were held, treaties negotiated and reports issued, defeats and delays surmounted, culminating in the present project.

From the outset of serious organized promotion there has been a two-way approach to the proposal, the maximum efficiency in both navigation and power.

The power factor has been and is relatively of much greater interest to the provinces and states through which the St. Lawrence River flows, than is the matter of navigation. Central Canada's industrial growth, its manufac-

turing expansion can be expected to materially increase as the power potential of the project is attained.

But the people of the agricultural West have never hoped for any such benefit. Nor has anyone held out the promise of rewards other than reductions in transportation costs for bulk cargoes — inward and outgoing. In fact, from the inception of the market place, the Winnipeg Grain Exchange at Winnipeg in 1887, there has been a continuing and active interest in the seaway project, among not only members of the Exchange engaged in the shipping and export grain trade but among operators of country elevators who could envisage savings in transportation cost which could accrue to the benefit of their customers — the grain growers on the Canadian prairies.

Members of the grain trade have been foremost in the struggle for construction of this inland waterway which would make Fort William and Port Arthur ocean ports, and shall continue to press their views until the 27-foot draft in the Eastern section will be uniform in all connecting channels. Until this has become a fact, the full benefits cannot be achieved.

1887-1959

Seventy Two Years of Service to Producers and Consumers

THE WINNIPEG
GRAIN EXCHANGE
WINNIPEG   CANADA

Entrance to The Winnipeg Grain Exchange.

United Grain Growers terminal elevator at Port Arthur, Ont.

UNITED GRAIN GROWERS LIMITED

United Grain Growers Limited is one of the Canadian companies which has watched with a great deal of interest the successful development of the St. Lawrence Seaway. As a farmer-owned company, any development promising lower transportation costs for farm products is of great importance not only to the farmer but to the corresponding institution which serves him. In addition, grain is expected to flow more rapidly and in greater quantity through the Company's facilities at Port Arthur.

United Grain Growers Limited is one of the largest grain elevator companies in Western Canada, operating 675 country elevators and with terminal elevators at Port Arthur and Vancouver. It is also the oldest farmer-owned co-operative company in that area and one of the oldest and largest of such companies in Canada.

HISTORY: Originally incorporated in 1906 as the Grain Growers Grain Company, the Company was a direct outgrowth of the farmers' movement in the early years of the century. It represented the first effort of that movement to improve the position of the western farmer, under the difficult and trying conditions of pioneer life on the prairies, by directly entering the commercial field of marketing and handling grain. It is engaged both in marketing its members' products and in the distribution of such necessary farm supplies as coal, feeds, agricultural chemicals, fertilizers, binder and baler twine and other like commodities. In this field it was a pioneer, as it had been in co-operative grain handling, and it also pioneered the co-operative marketing of livestock in Western Canada. Beginning with a limited membership and limited capital resources, the Company expanded to keep pace with the development of agriculture on the prairies until its shareholding body now includes over 50,000 farmers. It has a large investment in physical equipment, and financial resources consistent with handling a considerable percentage of grain crops of Western Canada.

The Company began as a commission agency, handling carloads of grain on consignment at a time when it was expected that the operation of terminal and country elevators would become a function of the governments of Canada and the provinces. That idea was abandoned shortly thereafter and the Company commenced the operation of elevators. The new co-operative farmers' companies were established for operation of elevators in Saskatchewan and Alberta, and in 1917 the Grain Growers Grain Company amalgamated with the latter, the Alberta Farmers' Co-operative Elevator Company Limited, and the present name was assumed. Expansion in membership and in physical assets in all western provinces has continued steadily since that time on the wider basis then established.

COUNTRY ELEVATOR SYSTEM: The Company owns and operates some 675 country elevators at local shipping points in Manitoba, Saskatchewan and Alberta, and in that portion of the Peace River district which lies within British Columbia.

A typical country elevator is equipped to receive and weigh grain in truckload quantities as delivered by farmers, and to ship it in carload quantities to terminal elevators. The country elevator has bins for the separate handling of different kinds and grades of grain with a storage capacity from 25,000 to 80,000 bushels, while additional storage capacity from 25,000 to 150,000 bushels may be provided in adjacent annexes. During recent years the need for large storage capacity at country points has increased. This is explained by the fact that under modern conditions of mechanized farming, harvest operations proceed much more rapidly than formerly and grain is delivered at country points more rapidly than the railways are able to move it forward. Also, large carryovers of western grains during years of heavy production have made necessary additional storage facilities.

In respect to wheat, oats and barley, all handled by the Canadian Wheat Board, the Company acts as agent for the Board in accepting grain at country elevators and making initial payments to farmers. Other grains, mostly flax and rye, which farmers sell individually, are mainly bought and paid for at the Company's country elevators and subsequently sold in carload or in cargo quantities. Farmers can also forward such grain in carload quantities to terminal elevators to be sold there on their behalf by the Company acting as a commission agent.

TERMINAL ELEVATORS: Just as the country elevator receives grain in truckload quantities and assembles it for carload shipment, the terminal elevators receive grain in carload quantities and assemble and ship it in cargo quantities, by sea from Vancouver or by lake vessel from the head of the lakes to eastern Atlantic ports. The terminal elevator is typically a massive concrete structure with large concrete bins 100 feet or more tall, each holding some 30,000 bushels of grain. Their function includes the rapid unloading of boxcars, the cleaning, accumulation and storing of cargo quantities of grain and the subsequent rapid loading of such grain into vessels. The terminal of United Grain Growers Limited at Port Arthur has a capacity of 6,500,000 bushels, whereas, its terminal at Vancouver, B.C., which is under lease from the National Harbours Board of Canada, has a capacity of 2,700,000 bushels. With its terminals situated as they are, the Company is well equipped to handle grain received in the country by either the eastern or western route.

At Port Arthur and Fort William, twin ports on Lake Superior, at the head of navigation for the St. Lawrence Seaway, there are 24 different terminal elevators with a total capacity of some 90,000,000 bushels where western grain is accumulated for shipment by water to Atlantic ports. With their large capacities, these terminals accumulate huge quantities of grain during the winter months for quick shipment in the Spring when navigation opens.

Terminal elevators on the west coast are constructed on the same general principle except that for shipment grain is conveyed by belts through loading galleries over the docks on either side of which ocean going vessels may be placed for concurrent loading. Here, loading occurs all year and storage capacity, although large, is somewhat smaller in relation to working capacity than is required at the head of the lakes.

ADDITIONAL SERVICES: While handling grain is the primary business of United Grain Growers Limited, many additional services are rendered to farmers through different departments or subsidiary companies. Several million dollars worth of farm supplies, among which the most important items are coal, feeds, agricultural chemicals, fertilizers, binder and baler twine, are furnished to farmers each year. Distribution is effected mainly through the Company's elevators but also through a considerable number of other agencies. At Edmonton, Alberta, the Company manufactures a line of livestock and poultry feeds under the brand name "Money Maker".

The farm supplies business is carried on as a department of the parent Company, but certain other operations are conducted through several wholly-owned subsidiaries.

United Grain Growers Securities Company Limited conducts a general insurance agency serving farmers through Company elevator agents and local representatives in most types of insurance except life.

PRINTING & PUBLISHING: The Company publishes and distributes a national farm magazine "The Country Guide", a monthly magazine having a circulation of 300,000 copies. The character of this magazine is largely educational and through the years it has influenced and stimulated farm-thinking not only on farm practice but also on public policy relating to agriculture. Another monthly is "Canadian Cattlemen", devoted to the beef cattle industry. This publishing enterprise together with a large commercial printing business is carried on by a subsidiary company, "The Public Press Limited".

CONSTITUTION AND FINANCIAL STRUCTURE: Like the co-operatives of Great Britain, the Company is organized on a share capital basis. Its charter is found in a special Act of the Parliament of Canada, which has been amended on a number of occasions. There are two classes of shares. Class "B" membership shares, which can be issued only to farmer-customers, have a par value of $5.00 each, and no individual may hold more than twenty-five of such shares. Each member has one vote only, exercised in one of the 321 shareholder Locals to which he is attached, and each Local elects a delegate to the Annual Meeting. The Annual Meeting is constituted of some 321 delegates representing the shareholders' Locals. Such meetings last two whole days and the travelling and living expenses of delegates are paid.

Class "A" Non-Cumulative five per cent redeemable preferred shares have a par value of $20.00 each. They are non-voting and while originally issued only to farmers in Western Canada, they may be transferred freely with a limit of holding up to 250 shares.

Paid up capital is $4,804,445.00 and total shareholders' equity, including reserves is $10,495,585.00. The 1957 balance sheet showed current assets, including grain inventories, of $45,143,616.00 and working capital of $7,327,218.00. Fixed assets, including elevator properties with original cost of $27,397,505.00 and after accumulated depreciation of $12,846,707.00 were carried at $14,550,798.00.

ADMINISTRATION:
Head Office — Winnipeg, Manitoba.
President & General Manager — J. E. Brownlee, Q.C.
First Vice-President — R. C. Brown.
Second Vice-President — J. Harvey Lane.

BANKERS: The Royal Bank of Canada, Imperial Bank of Canada, Canadian Bank of Commerce and the Bank of Montreal.

View of the lower lock at Beauharnois as it neared completion. Note the Montreal-Valleyfield highway cutting across under the upper entrance to the lock. Cofferdam will be removed when lock is ready, opening directly into Lake St. Louis and the St. Lawrence River.

CANIT CONSTRUCTION LIMITED

Constructing ships locks big enough to handle ocean freighters is no mean job at any time, but when it becomes necessary to blast nearly three million cubic yards of solid rock in order to lay down two of these giant concrete structures, then the job really becomes immense.

Such was the task facing Canit Construction Limited in the Soulanges Section of the St. Lawrence Seaway when it was awarded a $15 million contract by the St. Lawrence Seaway Authority for the construction of the downstream lock of the Beauharnois twin locks.

The Seaway was not the only reason why the founders of this company were attracted to Canada. They were attracted by the rapid industrial expansion that was taking place there and as a result, realized that much new heavy construction business was becoming available.

The combination was Salvatore Randaccio, Industrialist from Bologna, Giovanni Ghella, a heavy engineering contractor from Rome, and Jules Archambault, a Professional Engineer from Montreal, who incorporated the Company in the Province of Quebec in 1952. With the awarding of the downstream Beauharnois lock contract in 1956, the Societa Edison of Milan joined the original group and a policy of permanence was instituted.

Representing one of the toughest projects on the St. Lawrence Seaway, the twin locks at Beauharnois cost close to $30 million.

Together with its twin, the upstream or Upper Lock as it is called, the concrete monoliths can raise or lower a ship a total of 84 feet. The contract for the downstream or Lower Beauharnois Lock awarded to Canit, included the actual construction of the lock, excavation of 120,000 cubic yards of common excavation and 1,600,000 cubic yards of rock excavation. It also included the construction of a four-lane highway tunnel at the upper end of the

Lower Beauharnois Lock to ensure uninterrupted traffic on the highway to and from Valleyfield, Quebec.

On paper, the Lower Lock at Beauharnois looked fairly routine. But that's where it ended. The real difficulties commenced only when the overburden of clay was stripped away and the rock laid bare.

Fleets of churn drills and wagon drills were brought in by Canit Construction, but the Company's engineers soon found that here was no easy job. Shovel teeth wore out, sometimes in less than eight hours. Grader blades lasted generally about a day. Tractor pads sometimes had to be replaced after only a few weeks. Worst of all was the slow pace at which drills were able to penetrate the rock. If Canit drillers averaged four feet an hour they thought they were doing well. And they were, for earlier construction jobs around Beauharnois had averaged only two.

However, with extra large supplies of spare bits specially stocked, complete sharpening facilities maintained, and extensive machine shop and garage facilities set up to replace worn out parts and keep the machines going, Canit Construction Limited completed the project on time and by so doing became, within the short space of two years, a name to be reckoned with in the general industrial construction field.

Canit Construction Limited now looks ahead to the future with all intentions of soliciting heavy engineering work throughout Canada, as the invaluable experience gained on the St. Lawrence Seaway job has produced personnel well qualified to carry out any type of engineering and construction work. Through the use of fine, modern equipment and fully integrated staff of engineers and building construction experts, Canit Construction Limited is able to offer a complete service for the continued development of Canada.

Head office and main plant.   Rolling mill and power cable plant.

Pirelli Cables, Conduits Limited

Within the last 50 years Canada has developed from adolescence into manhod. Today it occupies an enviable position in the family of adult nations. In many fields it leads larger and older nations, particularly in the discovery and development of natural resources.

It is within this period that Cables, Conduits and Fittings Limited, manufacturers of electric wires and cables, was born, nurtured and expanded.

The acquisition of Cables, Conduits and Fittings Limited by Société Internationale Pirelli S.A. came about in 1953. Complete reorganization of the production facilities were gradually brought about, culminating with the opening of the first building on a large industrial site acquired in St. Johns, Quebec, about 30 miles south of Montreal, in the spring of 1956.

Today under the name of Pirelli Cables, Conduits Limited, their products are nationally known, distributed and used by recognized electrical distributors, utilities, Federal and Provincial Departments, railways and mines.

The name Pirelli, well known in virtually all parts of the world, was founded in 1872 by Senator Ingegnere B. G. Pirelli, and was one of the first industries of its kind to be created in Italy. In 1880 Pirelli widened its production to include electric insulated cables ... of every type. One year later the initial manufacture of military field telegraph wires was started and followed in 1890 by that of electric power cables insulated with impregnated paper, and in 1899 by "Patterson" type insulated telephone cables.

The first industrial activity outside Italy was created in Spain in 1902. Since that time, in addition to Italy and Spain, the International Pirelli Group has opened plants and acquired interests in England, France, Belgium, Brazil, Argentina, Canada and Mexico.

In 1924 Pirelli built one of the first cables capable of carrying a tension, hitherto considered unfeasible, of 130,000 volts. This special cable is called a "Fluid-oil cable" or "Emanueli cable" after its inventor, a researcher of world-wide renown who gave Pirelli the distinction of being among the first to make it possible. Today this type of cable, the technical design of which was based for the first time on truly scientific principles, is still unsurpassed, so much so that cables up to 320 KV, some of which are in use in Canada, have been designed and built by Pirelli.

Pirelli Cables, Conduits Limited manufacturing plants and executive offices are situated in St. Johns, Quebec with sales offices and representatives located in St. John's, Newfoundland; New Glasgow, Nova Scotia; Montreal, Quebec; Toronto, Ontario; Winnipeg, Manitoba; Regina, Saskatchewan; Calgary and Edmonton, Alberta and Vancouver, British Columbia.

As industry in Canada expands so does Pirelli. In the past few years Pirelli Cables, Conduits Limited spent two million dollars on a new power cable plant and more recently in 1956, opened a two and a half million dollar copper rolling mill and wire drawing plant. The area required for this latter expansion is housed in a completely new and separate building adjoining the modern power cable plant.

With the addition of the new mill with its modern equipment, many units of which are unique in the industry, the Pirelli operations in Canada have become completely autonomous.

Pirelli Cables, Conduits Limited were one of the prime suppliers of wires and cables to the million dollar St. Lawrence Seaway and Power Projects. Included in the miles of wires and cables used in the building of the Seaway were PVC Insulated and PVC Jacketed Cables; Rubber Insulated Lead Covered Control Cables with Neoprene Jacket and Paper Insulated Lead covered Cables 25 KV undergrounded with Polyethylene Jacket overall; Butyl Insulated Neoprene Jacketed Cables.

While best known in Canada for electric cables of all kinds for every application, the Pirelli name is respected throughout the world for tires for all types of vehicles, and the production of sundry rubber and plastic articles.

Officers and directors of the Pirelli Cables, Conduits Limited are: C. S. Richardson, Q.C., Chairman of the Board; J. A. deLalanne, C.A., President; Dr. V. Rostagno, Dr. L. Rossari, J. A. deLalanne, V. N. Longtin and Miss R. M. Martell, Directors. The General Manager is Ottorino Sarcoli, and Miss Martell is Secretary.

CANADIAN PACIFIC RAILWAY COMPANY

Conceived in 1880 to weld the Confederation of Canada by joining together its farflung provinces, the Canadian Pacific Railway Company is now the world's greatest transportation system.

More than just a railway, Canadian Pacific owns, operates and manages a large fleet of ocean, coastal and inland water vessels; an airline; a large group of hotels across Canada; a world-wide express service and a huge communications network.

In anticipation of the opening of the St. Lawrence Seaway, Canadian Pacific has been operating under charter arrangement small ships between European and Great Lakes ports since 1957. In the first year of this operation, two ships were under charter and this year four are in operation.

In his address to shareholders at the 1958 annual meeting of the Canadian Pacific Railway Company, N. R. Crump, president, said completion of the Seaway may greatly affect the earning capacity of the seven transatlantic cargo vessels now operated.

"Consideration is being given to the desirability of replacing them within a few years with ships of modern design, fully adaptable to both ocean and Great Lakes operations. It is estimated that the replacement of all seven of the cargo vessels now in service would cost $28 million," he said.

At first, as the railway drove westward over the prairies and through the tortuous passes of the Rockies, dire forecasts of impending disaster were made by many, for the road had no goods or passengers to transport through the sparsely settled regions it served. Undaunted, the nation builders made plans for creating traffic.

In 1887, a fleet of three ships was chartered to bring tea and silk from the Orient to Canada's west coast to provide eastbound freight for the new transcontinental railway.

These three ships were the forerunners of the great "White Empress" fleet of the Canadian Pacific. The hotels and tea houses established in the Canadian wilderness to entice early travellers have since grown into a chain of year-round hotels and palatial resorts. Addition to the Royal York Hotel in Toronto was constructed.

The Canadian Pacific brought settlers from the United Kingdom and Europe to settle the untenanted plains, and irrigation schemes supervised by the company made veritable gardens out of some arid and once unproductive regions.

Telegraph services, first used for train dispatching, were made available to settlers of the prairies and in fact to all of Canada. Today these same communication lines, since vastly augmented and improved, are used for radio broadcasts, telephone communications and television networks.

In Canada, Canadian Pacific comprises more than 17,000 miles of railway and owns or controls another 5,000 miles of track in the United States.

Extensive dieselization of passenger and freight operations has been made throughout the system, including yard and terminal operations. The company plans complete dieselization by 1961.

The Canadian Pacific's crack passenger train, "The Canadian", an all-stainless steel streamliner, spans the nation in 70 hours, providing luxury service.

Canadian Pacific has experienced an increasing demand for its piggyback services by which highway trailers are carried from city to city on flat cars.

In Western Canada, Canadian Pacific Transport Company has been operating an integrated piggyback service since 1954. In 1958, Canadian Pacific acquired a controlling interest in Smithsons Holdings Limited, owners of Smith Transport Limited, largest trucking company in Canada, whose highway transport operations and affiliations extend in eastern Canada from Nova Scotia to Manitoba.

Canadian Pacific's British Columbia Coast Steamship service serves all important ports along the Pacific coast from Seattle, Victoria, Vancouver and Alaska.

Canadian Pacific also operates cargo and passenger ships on the Canadian Great Lakes and on the Bay of Fundy between Saint John, New Brunswick, and Digby, Nova Scotia.

Canadian Pacific Airlines was formed in 1942 and now operates 6,915 miles of domestic air routes forming a north-south network in Canada, and more than 35,000 miles of international routes connecting five continents.

World-wide transportation and financial service is offered by the Canadian Pacific Express Company, which operates over land and sea for more than 33,000 miles. Its organization includes almost 9,000 offices and correspondents in Canada and abroad.

In January, 1957 the company announced the formation of Canadian Pacific Oil and Gas Limited with power to engage in all phases of the discovery, development, operation and sale of oil, gas and other mineral resources and their products on its 11.3 million acres of mineral lands in the Prairie Provinces.

Air view of Chicago Harbor looking toward the southwest. The entrance to the Chicago River may be seen in the center foreground. Chicago's "Loop" district in the background. Underneath the drive at the mouth of the river, indicated by arrow, Wacker Warehouse Co. Inc., operates 100,000 square feet of space with 650 feet of dock with 21-foot draft. Aerial photograph by Chicago Aerial Industries Inc.

CHICAGO STEVEDORING CO., INC.

Associated closely with Chicago Stevedoring Co., Inc., with headquarters at 400 West Madison Street in Chicago, is Wacker Warehouse Co., Inc. Upon the latter's premises, Chicago Stevedoring performs services for water-borne freight.

Wacker Warehouse Co., Inc., features 100,000 square feet of single story space served by the Illinois Central Railroad with 15 car capacity. There are ample truck docks and a 650-foot dock for water-borne freight. The entire operations are completely mechanized.

The company specializes in newsprint, sugar and general packaged merchandise, and also provides storage in transit and pool car distribution.

Of particular importance is the central downtown location of Wacker Warehouse at 430 East Wacker Drive. The company is licensed and bonded in the State of Illinois and its premises are protected by ADT Aero Alarm.

Another feature, of Chicago Stevedoring Co., Inc., are the excellent stevedoring facilities, including a 5-ton crane with a 40-foot boom on the dock side.

President of Chicago Stevedoring Co., Inc., is Mr. H. G. Marsh. The President of Wacker Warehouse Co., Inc. is Mr. Anton P. Nelson.

M.V. "North Voyageur" of Gulf Ports Steamship Co. Ltd.

GEO. T. DAVIE & SONS, LTD.

Although only a young nation compared to some, Canada for many years, has been known far and wide for her prowess in the shipbuilding field. Ships of all types... tankers, freighters, grain carriers... have all been turned out in Canadian yards on both the east and west coasts over the years.

One of the best known of the Canadian shipbuilders is the firm of Geo. T. Davie & Sons, Ltd., of Lauzon, Quebec.

Situated on the lower reaches of the mighty St. Lawrence River, directly opposite the ancient and historical city of Quebec, Geo. T. Davie & Sons, Ltd., can trace their connection with Lauzon Shipbuilding back some one hundred and thirty-one years, to the time of the first British warship ever built in Canada. This was in 1827 when the 18-gun brig "Kingfisher" was built at Lauzon.

Geo. T. Davie & Sons, Ltd., was first incorporated under the Companies Act in 1941. However, since 1951, the Company has been a subsidiary of Canadian Vickers Limited which is part of the huge Vickers Limited of England group, that Company having acquired the controlling interest in the Canadian organization.

Many of the Canadian deep-sea merchant ships which braved the U-boat patrolled sea lanes during World War II came off the ways of Geo. T. Davie & Sons Ltd. The majority of these vessels were the sturdy 4,700-ton deadweight "Park" type ships. In addition numerous craft for the Royal Canadian Navy were turned out at the Company's yards in Lauzon. These included the "workhorses" of the Atlantic convoys, the tough little Corvettes, and also Frigates and Minesweepers.

Since the end of the war in 1945, shipbuilding in Canada has fallen off considerably. However, Geo. T. Davie & Sons, Ltd., has managed to keep busy building numerous types of small coasters and more recently fullfilling a contract for the construction of a modern submarine chaser for the Royal Canadian Navy.

In the line of merchant vessels built at Geo. T.

Royal Canadian Mounted Police "Wood".

Davie & Sons, Ltd. yards since the end of the last war, was the huge 12,825 deadweight dry cargo carrier S. S. Sunrip, launched in 1954 and reputed to the largest cargo vessel ever built in a Canadian shipyard. Also, in 1954 the largest oil tanker to be produced in Canada was launched at Geo. T. Davie & Sons, Ltd. This was the Andro Fortune, a 28,070-ton deadweight tanker.

Geo. T. Davie & Sons, Ltd., facilities for building and repairing ships are probably the most extensive in Eastern Canada. Two Government-owned graving docks are located at Lauzon with capacities for handling some of the largest ships afloat. The "Champlain" measures 1,150 feet in length with a breadth at the entrance of the dock of 120 feet, while the "Lorne", a smaller graving dock, employs a length of 600 feet, with a 62,-foot breadth at the entrance. In addition, a Marine Railway, with a lifting capacity of 2,000 tons is continually in service. Four building berths suitable for constructing ships up to 350 feet in length are located in the yards of Geo. T. Davie & Sons, Ltd., at Lauzon.

Complete facilities for all types of ship repairs can be found at Geo. T. Davie & Sons, Ltd., and the effi-ciency and precision with which this work is carried out by Davie engineers is well known to ship owners and operators the world over.

Through its wholly-owned subsidiary Riverside Steel Works, Ltd., general engineering contractors, all types of machinery and equipment are produced for Canadian industry. These include, tanks, towers, pressure vessels, drums, water tube steam boilers, fire tube steam boilers and heating boilers for everyday domestic use.

Geo. T. Davie & Sons, Ltd., look forward with anticipation to the opening of the St. Lawrence Seaway and Power Projects which is most certain to bring increased demands for the Company's services through the tremendous flow of ship traffic using the mighty deep waterway system.

Officers and Directors of Geo. T. Davie & Sons, Ltd., are: Wilbrod Bherer, Q.C., Chairman of the Board; Lewis J. B. Forbes, Vice President; J. Arthur Paquet, Secretary; Maurice Paquet, Treasurer and General Manager; Directors, J. Edwin Richardson, Jean Raymond, Q.C., R. K. Thoman, J. Mossop, and J. A. S. Peck.

COFFERDAM (left), upstream from the giant new international powerhouse at Cornwall, Ontario, was blasted on July 1st 1958. Through the breach (right) flowed pent up waters creating a new lake in accordance with the plan devised by Ontario Hydro engineers.

CANADIAN INDUSTRIES LIMITED

One hot summer day in 1957, a 900 foot section of the Honoré Mercier Bridge shuddered briefly, and then collapsed. Puffs of dust rose as the pillars crumbled. Within seconds the entire section, a viaduct leading to the main span, was reduced to rubble. The blast that felled the 18 spans of the Mercier Bridge, was a unique application of what is known as split-second blasting. The pillars supporting the spans actually disintegrated, and there was almost no scattering of material. Great lengths of reinforced concrete, which for nearly a quarter of a century had supported traffic between Montreal Island and the south shore of the St. Lawrence River, lay shattered, and the way had been opened for construction of a new and higher approach necessary for clearance above ships passing through the St. Lawrence Seaway.

By all odds the most spectacular, the demolition was also one of the largest of its kind performed for many years in the Montreal area. And it was carried out, as were so many others, along both the St. Lawrence Seaway and the Power Project, with C-I-L Explosives.

Throughout the construction period, in fact, C-I-L supplied the explosives used along the Canadian side. Between summer of 1954 and fall of 1958 the Company shipped over 20,000,000 pounds, to wherever work was underway along the great waterway. Three different types of explosives depending on the job to be done, were used. For general rock excavation "Forcite" was employed, while "Dynamex" was used for blasting hard and glacial till. "Nitrone", a blasting agent which does not deteriorate under water, was used for channel excavation and submarine blasting.

Just as important as the physical quantities, moreover, was the technical advice that went with them. From Montreal to Welland, Technical Service Representatives from C-I-L's Explosives Division were constantly on the job, working closely with contractors, with the Seaway Authority and with Ontario Hydro. In some cases they developed blasting techniques that had never before been used. Time and again, in others, they prescribed remedies for overcoming difficult problems of construction.

Only a few miles east of Mercier Bridge at Cote Ste Catherine, for example, lies a section of Seaway canal with a 4000-foot docking wall of rock; smooth and straight, it is a truly amazing testimony to the ingenuity and skill shown by the engineers charged with hewing it.

At first, when construction crews began working here, the results were discouraging. Standard blasting techniques were fracturing the rock to leave a jagged, uneven face.

A solution, however, was developed by C-I-L Explosives engineers working closely with the contractor and Seaway Authority. Using a combination of "line" drilling and "cushion" blasting, the broken rock was, in effect, peeled off the face to eliminate back-break, and leave a smooth wall.

In deepening operations in the Welland Canal, C-I-L developed an entirely new underwater blasting technique, one that may also prove of immense value in such industries as mining.

Always, in blasting, the force of the explosive gases follows the line of least resistance. When a charge is set off underwater, this line is toward the surface, and the action from each blast hole tends to produce a cone-shaped crater.

On the Welland, 11 of its 28 miles were to be deepened from 25 feet to 27 feet, canal authorities were, for this reason, concerned about possible damage to canal walls and installations. They ruled that no blasts be set off closer than 14 feet to the walls.

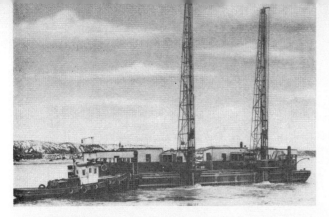

WELLAND CANAL — Deepening operations here involved underwater blasting. The "air cushion" technique, developed by C-I-L, minimized hydraulic shock and seismic vibrations and made it possible to carry out submarine blasting operations very close to the canal walls without damaging them.

MONTREAL — Demolition of the southern end of the Honoré Mercier Bridge was necessary to arrange for construction of a new approach which would provide the required vertical clearance for the Seaway channel. A split-second blast completely disintegrated pillars and gave excellent fragmentation.

Application of this rule, however, left a sloping "berm" along either side of the canal, about four feet deep and an obstacle to both docking and passage of ships. To avoid scraping the berm, ship masters would have to steer a course at least 15 feet away from the walls.

Resolving that it must somehow be possible to overcome this problem, C-I-L's Explosives Division developed "Air Cushion" blasting. In surface blasting, a line of weakness is produced by a row of close line-drilled holes. In submarine work a row of holes is normally of little use, because the holes are filled with water and water is almost as incompressible as rock. C-I-L decided that if the holes could be kept open and waterfree the force of the blast would be directed toward them, and the rock would break away clean at this man-made line of weakness.

Construction crews first drilled a line of six-inch holes on sixteen-inch centres. Into each of these was placed an empty, hermetically-sealed can, fashioned from ordinary eavestroughing and capped at either end to provide a compressible column of air six feet long. When the blast was fired it broke precisely to this "air-cushioned" line of holes. So successful was the experiment that the contractor was later allowed to blast flush along

the foundation line of the retaining wall, avoiding any berm whatsoever,

Of the hundreds of assignments carried out with C-I-L Explosives on the Seaway, one of the largest and certainly the most important came in the summer of 1958. For three and a half-months, technicians had been busy loading thirty tons of "Nitrone" — chosen because it does not deteriorate under water — in the great cofferdam upstream from the Ontario Hydro power-house near Cornwall. Blast holes had been connected into five thousand individual groups, which would detonate in sequence a few thousandths of a second apart.

On the first of July, two great holes were ripped in the cofferdam and through them surged the pent-up waters to fill the headpound of the powerhouse, downstream.

Explosives played a major role in the construction of the St. Lawrence Seaway and Power Projects and C-I-L was proud to have been called upon to supply this commodity.

C-I-L Explosives and Technical Service Representatives are proud to have served on the St. Lawrence Seaway and Power Project, one of the greatest undertakings in our country's history and one which will contribute much to Canada's growth and development.

COTE STE. CATHERINE — A combination of "line drilling" and "cushion blasting", developed by C-I-L Explosives engineers, was the answer to creating a smooth, straight, 4,000-foot dock wall. Standard blasting methods would have resulted in excessive overbreak due to the type of rock formation in this area.

BEAUHARNOIS — Three million cubic yards of hard quartzite, an exceptionally abrasive rock, had to be blasted in the forebay of the Lower Beauharnois Locks. Due to proximity of the operating power plant and other structures, great precautions had to be taken during all blasting operations.

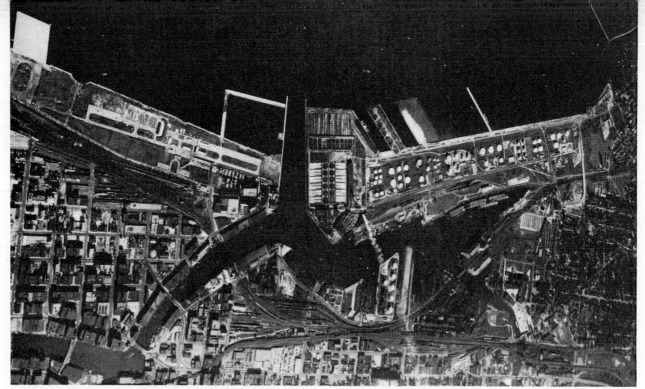

Aerial view of Milwaukee's outer harbor area showing modern port facilities for lake and ocean shipping. Large Seaway construction projects include new passenger pier shown at extreme right of picture; bulkheads to enclose new land fill just north of harbor entrance; and new $6 million general cargo pier, Municipal South Pier No. 2, the central one of the three piers appearing on the lakeside of the South Harbor Tract. Note breakwater system protecting outer harbor docks and river entrance to inner harbor.

PORT OF MILWAUKEE, WISCONSIN

Milwaukee Builds For Its Role As a Major Seaway Gateway

At this particular moment in history, three observations might be made about the Port of Milwaukee. Having fought for the seaway for forty years, it feels a sense of fulfillment as the seaway nears completion. Secondly, it has a high degree of readiness for the seaway, with a port of large capacity, and with modern facilities for lake, ocean and river traffic. Thirdly, it is a port where public and private enterprise coexist on the most friendly terms, with understanding and appreciation of the objectives and purposes of each.

The St. Lawrence Seaway will not come as a sudden shock to Milwaukee, but like a friend whose coming has long been anticipated. Milwaukee has been preparing for the advent of this friend for the past four decades. The need for deep water berths, modern piers, and heavy-lift cranes to accommodate seaway shipping presents no problem at Milwaukee, because it has been engaged in building and providing these things in confident anticipation of the seaway. The first deep-draft ships moving through the seaway toward Lake Michigan will find outer harbor slips 30 ft. deep; some of the most modern cargo terminals in the world; one of the world's finest heavy-lift cranes; and a port which prides itself on modern facilities, prompt dispatch and the high esprit-de-corps which prevails along the entire waterfront. The longshoremen who serve present lake and ocean ship-

ping at the Port of Milwaukee await the big ocean ships with determination that Milwaukee will maintain its good reputation for friendly and efficient handling of ships and cargo of all categories.

The City of Milwaukee has since 1920 continuously developed a modern outer harbor which has won worldwide recognition. A forlorn sandbar, on which stood the squatters' shacks of fishermen, was recognized as the key to Milwaukee's harbor future. The rough and irregular sandbar of 1918 has by 1958 been transformed into a symmetrical peninsula lined by the most modern port facilities; served by good railroad and highway access; and bustling with industry.

In 1929 the first ships called at Milwaukee's municipal outer harbor docks. Thirty years later a busy parade of ocean ships, lake vessels and inland waterway barges moves constantly to and from these modern wharves. Thousands of ships and millions of tons of cargo are handled each year at these accessible terminals. No bridges block these channels, and ships move freely in and out without the aid of tugs.

Milwaukee's reputation as a port of diversified shipping is exemplified by the teeming commerce which moves through the municipal harbor. Ocean general

The flags of many nations flutter over ocean ships lining Milwaukee's outer harbor municipal wharves.

cargo of infinite variety; steel, pig iron and scrap materials; salt and building materials; petroleum; machinery of every description; trucks and automobiles; granite, marble and limestone; car ferry traffic and other cargoes move in busy procession across the public wharves. Railroad cars and trucks by the thousands shuttle to and from the docks, to make interchange between land and water carriers. Modern salt water vessels, the largest Great Lakes bulk freighters, Lake Michigan car ferries, fleets of tankers, passenger and automobile ships, inland waterway barges, and even little fish tugs, busily ply on the slips and channels leading to the Milwaukee municipal docks.

A variety of industrial establishments are also firmly anchored in the municipal harbor area, generating commerce for public wharves, and assuring substantial revenues to the port both from land rents and from cargo movements for these industries.

Backing up Milwaukee's modern outer harbor development is a great industrial harbor lying along three river channels. The banks of these rivers are lined with terminals and industries, and through them moves a busy commerce, mostly in industrial raw materials. Coal, grain, cement, scrap metals, sand and stone, and general cargo move on these river channels in the range of six million tons per year. Another three million tons of high value commerce moving through the municipal harbor brings Milwaukee up to the nine million ton rank. Given several years of Seaway stimulation, and of good business conditions, and Milwaukee confidently expects to cross the ten million ton mark in commerce and by 1965 to be a twelve million ton port.

In some Great Lakes ports there are misgivings and misunderstandings as to the role of public and private enterprise in the building of a port. Not so in Milwaukee. The public port concentrates on the development of new business, and the whole community shares the economic stimulus of this policy. River channels and the industrial harbor continue undisturbed in their traditional role of moving the harbor's bulk traffic. A friendly and cooperative spirit prevails throughout the port, and the public development has stimulated land values, waterborne commerce, and the industrial attraction of the Milwaukee area.

Not resting on its laurels, the Milwaukee waterfront is buzzing with the largest marine construction program in the entire history of the city, as Milwaukee builds for the Seaway. Rapidly taking form for 1959 and 1960 completion are one of the world's most modern general cargo piers, a new $6 million facility for deep draft ocean shipping; a new passenger pier to serve both lake and ocean passenger vessels; and a 20-acre land fill, enclosed with modern dock structures for future development.

Landward of these three great new waterfront structures can be seen an impressive new access highway and viaduct to smooth the flow of trucks and automobiles in and out the port area; together with a new marginal highway linking all of the outer harbor piers. The traditional task of rail and water interchange is not overlooked, and large expansion of the municipal harbor railroad system is under way. Large new cargo sheds; new cranes, and new industrial installations, further characterize Milwaukee's dynamic outer harbor development.

This is one port that knows what it expects from the St. Lawrence Seaway, and confidently meets it as an old friend bringing new challenges.

One of the company's new, modernly equipped sheds.

THREE RIVERS SHIPPING COMPANY LIMITED

Serving two major St. Lawrence River ports, Three Rivers and Quebec City, are the Three Rivers Shipping Company Limited and its subsidiary, Quebec Terminals Limited.

Established in 1943, Three Rivers Shipping Company Limited specializes in stevedoring and steamship agency work. Other business operations are warehousing, trucking and contracting. A family company, the firm was formed by Mr. Lucien Paquin, president and general manager. Mr. Paquin's experience in stevedoring and steamship agency work spans nearly 40 years.

Quebec Terminals Limited, with headquarters at 40 Dalhousie Street in Quebec City, was established in 1951 under the general managership of Mr. Roger Paquin. This company also is active in warehousing, trucking, stevedoring and as steamship agents.

Three Rivers Shipping Company Limited, with headquarters in Three Rivers, owns and operates a fleet of trucks in connection with the operations of the various phases of its own business. With head offices in its own office building, the company has two large warehouses — of 50 by 120 feet — and also leases a government shed of 100 by 550 feet alongside ship to serve its stevedoring business and steamship agencies.

The two companies are fully equipped with pallets (8,000), modern lift trucks and cranes for efficient operation and shipping service.

For future operations, a new company has been organized recently for the purpose of building and equipping a modern ocean terminal on the deep water wharf at Levis, Quebec. This terminal will serve both coastal and overseas trade.

One phase of the company's operations — movement of pulpwood.

J. C. MALONE & COMPANY LIMITED

Three Rivers, Que.

Through three generations and sixty-two years the J. C. Malone stevedoring organization has served the port of Three Rivers, to the point, in fact, where it is almost as much an institution as the port itself. Indeed the business was founded a few years after the first wharves were built. J. C. Malone, the founder and grandfather of the present chief executive of the company, foresaw that the port must one day become a great factor in the economic development of the St. Maurice Valley, although that was not to come in his day.

PROGRESS — He died prematurely in 1901, and in 1907 his son, Sarsfield, assumed the direction of the business. The First World War and the movement of enormous tonnage of war materials presented him with a test and a task, both of which he performed efficiently. It provided the experience for the vastly greater tonnages of World War II, when during one navigation season the company handled 63,787,090 FBM of lumber. The operations called for the discharging of 2,500 cars, the sorting of the lumber according to species, grades, and specifications, and its reloading into vessels for shipment to Allied ports.

The Canadian Government used the company's warehouse facilities for the storage of heavy tonnages of cotton, sugar, tea and coffee.

The peacetime operations of the company are also on an important scale. For many years it acted as local freight agent for the Canadian Pacific Railway and was responsible for the loadings and unloadings and deliveries. The stevedoring contracts for the handling of newsprint and the associated cargoes of pulpwood, sulphur, and china clay have for years been one of the Malone company's major activities.

Grain cargoes from the 2,000,000 bushel elevator at Three Rivers are another important item. For the rest, although stevedoring and warehousing are the basic operations, the handling of commodities, and whatever else offers a business opportunity, is in the same category.

Mr. Sarsfield Malone died in 1942 and his wife became the owner and president of the company. Mr. Desmond Malone, the grandson of the founder, was then appointed managing director. His efforts have been directed to the modernization of handling equipment, which has resulted in time and overhead saving that has induced shippers of many commodities to utilize the considerable facilities of this growing port of Three Rivers.

The Company takes great satisfaction in being the representative of all the leading steamship companies whose vessels call here to load cargoes for the ports of the world.

ADDRESS — Three Rivers, P. Q.

The Bruning Copyflex Model 35 reproduction machine, sold by the Charles Bruning Company (Canada) Ltd. Canadian Westinghouse used a machine like this for speedily producing black-on-white prints of drawings required for construction of its new Bridge-O-Matic control system. The Bridge-O-Matic control system will operate and control all but one of the entire chain of bridges, gates, and fenders along the St. Lawrence Seaway. The Copyflex machine reproduces drawings up to 42 inches wide by any length at a cost of only about two cents per square foot.

THE CHARLES BRUNING COMPANY (CANADA) LTD.

Today's mammoth engineering projects require thousands of what engineers call "prints", and the St. Lawrence Seaway Project — one of the greatest engineering feats of all time — is certainly no exception. From its very conception, engineering prints played an important part in the development of the Seaway. And throughout its existence, engineering prints will play an important part in the Seaway's maintenance and operation.

What are engineering prints? Often seen by the layman, but not always fully understood as to where they come from, engineering prints are simply reproductions of original drawings created by engineers and draftsmen at the drawing board.

Before any piece of machinery or even a simple object can be engineered and produced, it must be conceived in the mind, and then it must be transferred to paper in the form of an easily understood drawing.

A simple object such as an ash tray might require only one or a few drawings, while a complex object — such as a generator for the St. Lawrence Seaway Project — might require hundreds of different drawings!

Most drawings today represent valuable investments — with a single drawing often requiring hundreds of hours of work by an engineer or draftsman. It's no wonder, then, that when St. Lawrence Seaway engineers and workers must refer to an engineering design, layout, or assembly, they use prints made from the drawings instead of the original drawings themselves. The loss or misplacement of one drawing in the field could delay or seriously tie up a multitude of operations if exact reproductions were not available.

Consider, for example, the eight huge generators, 13 transformers, and numerous bridge, gate, and fender controls produced by Canadian Westinghouse for the St. Lawrence Seaway Project. As an indication of their collective immensity and complexity, these units — if stacked together on a scale — would weigh a total of 13,120,000 pounds, and the wire used in their construction — if laid out in a single strand — would cover almost 800 miles. Into each of these units went many components — one depending upon another for successful operation of the entire unit. And before each individual component could be built and assembled with the others, drawings had to be made and reproduced for reference by the men constructing the units. Without engineering

prints of each drawing, the complex units could never reach the operative stage.

One instance of the essential role that engineering prints played in the Seaway project is the Bridge-O-Matic controls produced by the Industrial Controls Division of Canadian Westinghouse Company Limited. These controls — which will operate and control all but one of the entire chain of bridges, gates, and fenders along the Seaway — are a modification of the company's Load-O-Matic crane control system. The new Bridge-O-Matic controls were especially designed to provide smooth, fast opening and closing of each bridge without danger of structural stress on bridge members.

A total of 2,500 prints of 180 drawings were required for production of the Bridge-O-Matic modifications. The prints, representing more than 14,000 square feet of total area, were referred to constantly by the eight Canadian Westinghouse engineers and 20 shop personnel directly concerned with constructing the con-

Complex projects such as this giant Canadian Westinghouse transformer often require hundreds and sometimes thousands of engineering prints. The transformer is for the St. Lawrence Seaway power project.

Toronto headquarters and paper sensitizing plant of the Charles Bruning Company (Canada) Ltd.

trols — although hundreds of other workers were also connected with the project.

All these prints, produced at a cost of only about two cents per square foot, were made by a single operator using one of the most advanced, economical engineering reproduction machines available. Called the Bruning Copyflex Model 35, it is one of several Bruning Copyflex machines owned and operated by Canadian Westinghouse.

One of the advantages of these machines is that they produce positive (black-on-white) reproductions directly from an engineering drawing. These reproductions are not to be confused with the blueprint reproductions (white line on blue background) which were more common in days past. Using Copyflex whiteprints, Canadian Westinghouse engineers thus enjoyed the benefit of reading prints which were exact facsimiles of the original drawings.

Like the Bridge-O-Matic controls constructed by Canadian Westinghouse for the Seaway, the reproduction process utilized by the Copyflex Model 35 is a true example of modern engineering progress. To make a print on a Copyflex machine, the operator simply lays the original drawing on a sheet of Copyflex sensitized paper and inserts them into the machine. An ultraviolet light in the machine penetrates the white or unmarked areas of the drawing and causes a latent image of the drawn areas to appear on the sensitized paper. The latent image is transformed into a permanent, black-line facsimile of the drawing when the exposed sensitized paper is fed into the developer section of the machine. The finished print is delivered seconds later, ready for immediate use.

As well as being fast, economical, and easy to operate, the Bruning Copyflex machines used by Canadian Westinghouse require no special lighting conditions, and they are clean, quiet, and odorless. Thus they can be placed almost anywhere without need for special installation.

Canadian Westinghouse purchased its Copyflex machines from the Charles Bruning Company (Canada) Ltd., one of the younger Canadian companies. Organized in 1955, the Bruning Canadian company has headquarters in Toronto and four branch offices and six sales offices in the Dominion. Sensitized materials for use in Copyflex machines in Canada are coated in a modern, 10,000 square foot plant located in Toronto.

In addition to Copyflex machines and materials, Bruning also is a leading Canadian source for engineering and drafting supplies and furniture and for surveying instruments and equipment.

The Charles Bruning Company, Inc., in the United States has four plants and 36 branches and sales offices in that country, with headquarters located in Mount Prospect, Illinois.

The engineering prints made for Canadian Westinghouse by its Bruning Copyflex machines, and the service provided Canadian Westinghouse by Bruning representatives are another example of how teamwork among the many companies involved in the St. Lawrence Seaway Project has made the Seaway a "dream come true".

How Engineering Prints Are Made in a Bruning Copyflex Machine

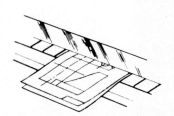

The original drawing is placed on a sheet of Copyflex sensitized paper and the two are fed into the machine.

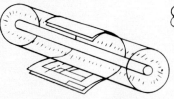

Ultraviolet light in the machine penetrates the drawing and causes a latent image of the drawing to be produced on the sensitized paper.

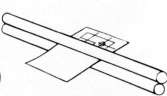

Developer rollers in the machine convert the latent image on the sensitized paper to a permanent, black-line facsimile of the original drawing.

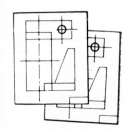

Finished print is delivered seconds later — dry, flat, and ready for immediate use.

The huge hydro-electric power dam, stretching over 3,300 feet between Canada and the United States, on which Marine Office of America played a major insurance role.

MARINE OFFICE OF AMERICA

Insurance Plays A Vital Role!

It staggers the imagination to think of the countless ingredients that go into the building of a highway to the seven seas — the St. Lawrence Seaway Project. Knowledge and planning of architects and engineers, bulldozers, dredges, raw materials, mammoth machinery, equipment, scientific instruments and armies of skilled and unskilled labor all played their part in bringing to completion this miracle of the century.

The one underlying ingredient, vital and important in this and all great undertakings for economic progress is insurance protection. Before a dredge operates, a pile is driven, a bridge or wharf is built, man's investments in property must be protected. So must the risks and costly liability he may face should an accident happen or other trouble strike.

The Marine Office of America, specialists in marine insurance is proud of the role it played in providing many and intricate types of protection so necessary to the completion of the Seaway. It is equally proud of the role it will continue to play in providing insurance protection for the piers, terminals, bridges, tugs, barges, river and ocean ships and the mountains of cargoes they will carry to the far-flung corners of the world.

A few of the many forms of policies required for this project and its continuing operation are: Ocean and Lake Cargo; Cargo on Docks; Commercial Hull; Protection and Indemnity; Piers and Wharves; Ship Repairer's Legal Liability; Stevedore's Legal Liability; Terminal Operators Legal Liability; Bridges and Dams; Marine Casualty; Transportation; Contractor's Equipment.

To provide proper protection each of these policies must be skillfully patterned to the specific risks by marine insurance experts . . . and behind each policy there must be the safeguard of unquestioned financial strength. This is the foundation upon which man's visions and dreams are converted into the reality of progress.

To make available this type of insurance protection the Marine Office of America was established in 1919 as the marine department of the following outstanding and dependable American Capital Stock Insurance Companies: The American Insurance Company; The Continental Insurance Company; Fidelity-Phenix Fire Insurance Company; Firemen's Insurance Company; Glens Falls Insurance Company; The Hanover Insurance Company; Niagara Fire Insurance Company.

Each risk underwritten by the Marine Office in any of these member companies is reinsured automatically by all of the others to the extent of their agreed to participation.

Though this substantial capacity combined with integrity and world-wide facilities are vitally important to all insureds, equally so is the alertness of the Marine Office to new challenges . . . ever striving for better ways to better protection so that when there are new frontiers to cross it again will play a major role in making those crossings possible.

New Chevrolet Division plant under construction for General Motors Corporation. In upper left is the high level bridge to Cornwall Island.

Reynolds Metal Company plant under construction. Snell Lock and Robert Moses Power Station in upper background.

TOWN OF MASSENA

The Town of Massena was created by an act of the New York State Legislature, on March 2nd, 1802, and was named after Andre Massena, a famous Marshall of France in Napoleon's Army at that time.

Massena originally covered about two-thirds of St. Lawrence County's 2701 square miles area, but later this was reduced to 31,376 acres or approximately 49 plus square miles by the creation of additional towns by the State Legislature. Today the incorporated Village of Massena occupies approximately 2523 acres, or nearly 1/8 of the total area of the Town. According to a Special Federal Census of 1957 the total population of the Town was 19,382 persons.

From its incorporation, Massena was no different from any other small hamlet of the time. Farming and land clearing was the principle occupation until 1822, when the first hotel accommodations were built for use of persons coming here to use the mineral spring waters which had gained a reputation for curative qualities for various complaints. The rest of the century private capital developed and promoted these springs by the erection of other hotels, bath houses and pavilions, and many hundreds of persons, some of them invalids, were accommodated here each year. The waters were also bottled and shipped from Massena to many ports of the country for years.

Thus Massena was made famous as a health resort and some who came here for the medicinal properties of its springs, remained here as permanent residents, and the Town grew much faster than the surrounding settlements. However, shortly after the turn of the century, the health resort project was abandoned and the buildings were either torn down or later destroyed by fire.

In 1896 the St. Lawrence Power Company of Massena was formed to dig and maintain a canal from the St. Lawrence River to the Grasse River, a distance of approximately two and a half miles, for the purpose of generating and transmitting electrical power. This paved the way for the industrial expansion of Massena. The Aluminum Company of America established an aluminum reduction plant here and for many years has been the largest employer of labor in this region, with the attendant growth of the Town of Massena and the area.

In 1954 the Power Authority of the State of New York, in cooperation with the Hydro-Electric Power Commission of Ontario, began the construction of the St. Lawrence River Power Project at Massena and Cornwall, Ontario. Later the St. Lawrence Seaway Development Corporation also started construction on the St. Lawrence River ship canal and locks located in the Town of Massena. These projects were finished and put into operation in 1959, at a cost of nearly One Billion Dollars.

By reason of these developments, the Reynolds Metal Company and the Chevrolet Division of the General Motors Corporation have obtained sites and are now building an aluminum reduction plant and an aluminum castings plant, respectively, both located in the Town of Massena. It is expected that they will be completed and in full operation before the end of 1959.

The total employment needed by these and other industries to come assures the Town of Massena substantial growth in future years. Additional school facilities, stores, and a large shopping center has been recently built and are now in operation.

The Town of Massena owns and operates the 100-bed Massena Memorial Hospital, The Massena Public Library, the Town Hall auditorium and office building, and the Town of Massena 600 acres airport, all of which are operated for the benefit of all the residents of the Town. These facilities will be expanded when and if the need arises.

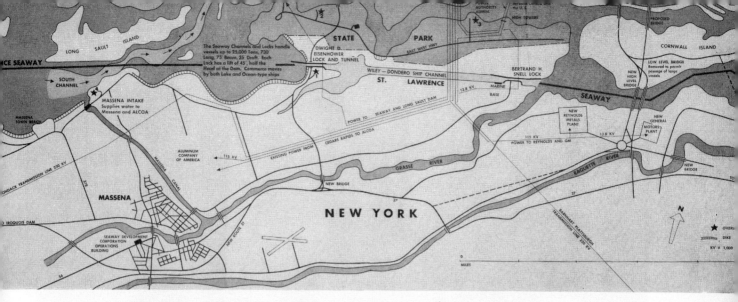

THE VILLAGE OF MASSENA

The Village of Massena is located in the northern part of New York State; one hundred and seventy-five miles north of the City of Syracuse and seven miles southwest from its Canadian neighbor — the City of Cornwall, Ontario. The Village has an area of approximately 25 square miles and its present population is 15,981. Two rivers flow through its boundaries, the Grasse and the Racquette Rivers, and empty into the St. Lawrence River seven miles north.

The Village, which was incorporated in 1886 with a population of 1,006, received its name from the Town of Massena, which was named in honor of Marshall Massena, a war hero in the army of Napoleon 1. The early settlers were Frenchmen from Montreal, Quebec, who came into this area around 1730 to cut timber and float it down the Grasse River to the St. Lawrence River and then, via the St. Lawrence, to Montreal. During the period of 1798-1810, permanent settlers, who had received Revolutionary War land grants, came from Vermont and began farming in the area. Shortly after the Civil War, fame was gained from the operation of the then-famous mineral springs as a health resort and people came from all over the country to benefit from the therapeutic effects of the sulphur water baths.

A power development was started here in 1897 by the digging of a canal from the St. Lawrence River to the Grasse River. The power, derived from this canal, was sold to the Aluminum Company of America who began operations here on the 27th day of August, 1903. The coming of the aluminum industry was the beginning of a long, progressive period of expansion for the community which has continued to the present time. This industry has brought prosperity, not only to the Village of Massena, but to the entire north country. Workmen commute to the giant aluminum plant from within an area of fifty miles.

The recent development of the St. Lawrence River, opposite Massena, for power and navigation purposes has brought added industries to the Village including the Reynolds Metals Company and the Chevrolet Division of General Motors. With these added sources of employ-

ment, and the recreational features of the St. Lawrence River, Massena is bound to grow.

Massena has ten churches representing the different denominations. The present capacity of the educational system is over 5,000 pupils and consists of a Senior and Junior High School, eight grade schools and two parochial schools. The community is served by two commercial banks, a 60-man volunteer Fire Department, two railroads, a 100-bed hospital, a modern airport, a 30-man Police Force, a newspaper published twice a week, a 15,000 volume public library, two radio stations, one of 1340 kilocycles, 250 watts and a new station of 1050 kilocycles, 1,000 watts, and an active Chamber of Commerce.

St. Lawrence River water is sand-filtered and pumped by the Aluminum Company into the Village-owned water distribution system. Under construction, at the present time, is a new $1,700,000.00 Sewage Treatment Plant and Interceptor Sewer System which, when completed in 1959, will take care of a population of 22,000. The Village Department of Public Works carries on a continuous street improvement program which will, in a few years, give every Village street a hard-top wearing surface.

A new shopping center, the largest north of Syracuse, was completed in the Village this year. This, added to the established stores in the downtown area, makes Massena the shopping center of Northern New York and neighboring Canada.

Recreational services, sponsored by the School, Town and Village, include playing fields, bathing beaches, etc. Little League and Babe Ruth baseball leagues are active as well as adult softball leagues, a semi-pro football team, a Driving Association with an excellent track, Bowling Associations, etc. A new 18-hole golf course is under construction on the shores of Lake Saint Lawrence to replace the old course of nine holes which was flooded out by the construction of the Seaway.

Massena is a good place in which to live, work and play.

Canadian Marconi Company Head Office and Plant, Town of Mount Royal, Que.

CANADIAN MARCONI COMPANY

Even before the night of the Titanic tragedy, in 1912, when Maritime nations of the world held the first International Conference for Safety of Life at Sea, Marconi had been a familiar name to shipping people the world over.

Canadian Marconi Company was the first to enter this new field in North America when it received its Dominion of Canada Charter in 1904.

The Maritime Department of the Commercial Products Division maintains the tradition of the Company for leadership in marine communications. This division operates marine service depots in all principal coastal and inland ports.

Engineering provides continuing development of advanced marine communications and navigational equipments. A prime example of this can be found in the Company's development of 65 watt ten channel and 25 watt eight channel H. F. Radiotelephone complying fully with the latest Department of Transport Radio Electronics specifications. To this range of communications equipment, a 30 watt 12 channel V.H.F. Radiotelephone has been added to serve the increasing demands of marine communications in the higher frequency bands.

The Company established its reputation in the Marine field in Canada by specializing in communications and navigational aids for Great Lakes and Coastal vessels.

Canada's inland waterway, the forerunner to the modern billion-dollar St. Lawrence Seaway, and Canadian Marconi are no strangers to each other. The Company has been operating St. Lawrence River, Gulf of St. Lawrence and Great Lakes coast stations for many years. They have been the prime supplier of electronic equipment to vessels plying the system since electronics was first used. In addition to their Radiotelephone, Direction Finders and Radar units utilized by Canadian shipowners throughout the Great Lakes, Canadian Marconi has also been providing the shipping companies with highly trained wireless operators for a great many years.

One of Canadian Marconi's earliest achievements was the execution of a Government contract for the erection of coastal radio stations on Canada's eastern seaboard, the Gulf and St. Lawrence River and in the Great Lakes. These stations formed the first trans-Atlantic radio link between Europe and the New World and also assisted in the protection of life at sea and as navigational aids.

In 1919 Canadian Marconi installed valve transmitters and receivers on board ships operating on long waves. The spark was still being used on medium frequencies. Three years later, in 1922, Canadian Marconi installed on Canadian ships the first Direction Finder unit. From 1925 to 1927, Canadian Marconi developed a new transmitter, type 100 W3, W4, and W5A, which provided radiotelegraph facilities. Point to point stations were established and many vessels fitted with the equipment.

From 1926 to 1927, Canadian Marconi engineers designed and fitted, on ocean going vessels, 500 Watt CW-ICW long wave transmitters, and the following year through to 1929, they developed automatic Radio Beacon equipment which was supplied to the Canadian Government for use as navigational aids.

By 1939, although many coastal stations and ships had already replaced their spark transmitters with more up-to-date equipment using tubes, the end of the year saw the compulsory elimination of spark on board ship except for emergency purposes and limited to 50 Watts output.

From 1940 to 1945 Canadian Marconi made a valuable contribution to Canada's war effort through the design and manufacture of large quantities of electronic equipment which was supplied to the Armed Forces. Included were 250 complete equipments for Canadian merchant vessels which delivered millions of tons of vital cargo in the face of the most intense U-Boat activity.

With the cessation of hostilities in 1945, Canadian Marconi once again turned their attention to the building of improved electronic equipment for peace time consumption. The development of the first commercial Marine Radar in Canada was carried out by Canadian Marconi in 1948 in cooperation with the National Research Council. Units of this Radar equipment, type LN 16, were supplied to the Royal Canadian Navy, the Department of Transport, for use on Government vessels, and also installed on many merchant vessels.

However, Canadian Marconi's search for improved Radar units did not stop there. Three years later, in 1951, Marconi engineers developed a new high power Radar for marine use. This new type is known as the LN 27. Shortly after, Marconi went to work to meet the growing demands of the numerous small boat owners who were clamoring for more electronic devices to make the job of navigating easier. While the conventional Radar units as utilized on the larger cargo and naval vessels were too bulky for the small boat, the new unit had to be just as effective. The result was, in 1954, an entirely new small Radar unit designed especially for use on smaller craft. This type, the LN 35, is very popular among pleasure boat and commercial small-boat owners in Canada today.

New Radar development by the Company includes designs using dual antenna systems, shorter pulse length (.06 microseconds) and wider IF and video bandwidths on short ranges. This short range (10 to 15 miles) performance has been achieved without compromising long range capabilities.

In the field of aviation, Canadian Marconi has developed an automatic direction finder, type CMA-301, specially designed to meet the latest requirements of air-lines operating on the North American Continent. It incorporates new techniques enabling the production of a unit which is extremely sensitive, gives very good performance and conforms to the small size and low weight needs of airlines. The equipment is suitable for smaller types of aircraft as well as large transport planes.

In collaboration with the Canadian Government Defence Research Board, Canadian Marconi has designed and is producing a dobbler navigator for measuring the drift angle and true ground speed of aircraft. In conjunction with a computer it can guide an airplane between specified points without reference to ground stations.

Canadian Marconi also operates a special Services Division which was formed early in 1953 to consolidate the various installation, maintenance and systems engineering activities of the Company. It has since developed into an organization capable of undertaking any type of communication, radar, construction, technical installation or field maintenance projects in any location.

Most of Special Services activities have been confined to Government Defence projects in the almost inaccessible arctic and sub-arctic regions of Canada's northern frontier. The scope of its operation embraces such activities as the operation of "package unit" C.W. and radio teletype communication systems for construction projects, the complete operation and maintenance of a portion of a radio defence line with its complex equipment, and the attendant logistic support to its many stations.

With the opening of the St. Lawrence Seaway and Power Projects . . . the new deepsea route to the industrial heart of North America . . . Canadian Marconi can feel proud in the knowledge that their part in the years of prosperity that lay ahead will be an important one. Hardly a ship will pass through the new deep waterway system which will not employ Marconi communication and navigational equipment.

The majority of Canada's Great Lakes vessels are fitted with both communications and navigational aids by Canadian Marconi.

Canadian Marconi also played an active part in the actual construction of the St. Lawrence Seaway and Power Projects through the use of their modern equipment by dredging and construction companies engaged on the project. Major Canadian companies such as McNamara Construction Company, Marine Industries Limited and Canadian Dredge and Dock, to mention but a few, were all prime users of Canadian Marconi electronic equipment to assist in controlling operations being carried on simultaneously over wide areas.

Canadian Marconi, with its skills and resources, stands ready to supply the radio needs of a fast growing nation.

Sun Life Building, Montreal.

SUN LIFE ASSURANCE COMPANY OF CANADA

The Sun Life Assurance Company of Canada, largest Canadian life insurance company, protects the holders of two million policies with more than $7 3/4 billion of life insurance. The Company's assets, which exceed $2 billion, are carefully invested in government bonds and mortgages and in high-grade corporate securities. Thus, in safeguarding their families and their own future, Sun Life policyholders indirectly help the nation by developing natural resources, building homes and schools, financing public works and industrial development.

The Sun Life was founded in 1865 by Mathew Hamilton Gault and commenced active business in 1871. The company was founded in Montreal, the fortunes of which, perhaps more than the fortunes of any other city in Canada, have always been closely linked with the St. Lawrence River. Until 100 years ago, the river was the only route into the interior of the country, and the commerce of Montreal grew and thrived upon its traffic. As a company in a city that was both river town and overseas port, the Sun Life from the beginning had a lively interest in business affairs beyond Montreal, and within 10 years it had expanded its operations across Canada and opened its first branch office outside the country.

This office – in the West Indies – was opened in 1880, and others soon followed in the Far and Near East, in Africa and South America, and finally in Great Britain and the United States. Today the Sun Life transacts business in 25 countries, three different languages and 15 currencies.

Life insurance contracts of 80 years ago had many more restrictions and limitations than they have today, because day-to-day existence was more precarious and travel was downright dangerous. The Sun Life played an important part in liberalizing these contracts as conditions improved, and was a forerunner in introducing new policy benefits that have since been adopted by nearly every life insurance company in the world.

In 1880 the Sun Life became the first life insurance company in the world to issue "unconditional" policies, making no restriction as to a policyholder's travels or occupation. It was the first life company in North America to include nonforfeiture provisions in policies, and the first in North America to use the lien arrangement for the insurance of sub-standard lives. It was also the first Canadian life insurance company to issue group insurance.

Today the Sun Life is one of the world's great life insurance companies, and for many years past has sold more life insurance each year than any other Canadian company. About a quarter of all group life insurance in force in Canada is with the Sun Life.

Growth of the Sun Life of Canada

Year	Life Insurance In Force	Assets
1878	$3 million	$349,000
1908	$119 million	$29 million
1938	$2,905 million	$875 million
1948	$4,089 million	$1,490 million
TODAY*	$7,749 million	$2,115 million

*Annual Meeting held February, 1958.

FURNESS, WITHY & COMPANY, LIMITED

Furness, Withy & Company, Limited was incorporated in West Hartlepool, England in 1891 and at that time its founder, Christopher Furness, already had offices at Boston, Baltimore and Chicago in the United States which organization was quickly expanded to include New York, Philadelphia, Norfolk, and later Los Angeles and San Francisco.

The first Canadian office was opened at Halifax, N.S. in 1895 to handle the passenger and freight services that had been acquired serving Liverpool, Newfoundland, Nova Scotia and Boston, which is now known as the Furness Warren Line. A branch office was established at St. John's, Nfld. in 1911 to add strength to this service and have representation in the Furness name at all ports of call.

During the succeeding years the Furness interests on the American Continent expanded rapidly and include a freight and passenger service between the United Kingdom and the West Coast of North America, (California to British Columbia) a freight and passenger service between New York, Maritime provinces and Newfoundland, the Furness Warren Line referred to above, and last but not least their well known passenger service between New York and Bermuda with what are almost the only luxury ships designed solely for deep sea pleasure cruising. A branch office was opened in Vancouver in 1924.

Following the opening of the Manchester (England) Ship Canal, leading industrialists in Manchester were anxious to establish regular steamship services between Manchester and Eastern Canada, using Montreal during the summer and the Maritime ports during the winter. The Furness interests were approached with the result that Manchester Liners Limited were incorporated in 1898, financed almost equally by the Manchester interests and Furness. This happy alliance still continues. To handle this service Furness immediately opened its own Montreal office and later one at Saint John, N.B. to give complete coverage at the Maritime ports. The venture commenced in a modest way with four small ships and during the sixty years of the Company's existence the fleet has included 49 vessels and to-day consists of 14 modern ships with three more building for delivery in the spring of 1959.

Manchester Liners were the first British flag company to inaugurate a service into the Great Lakes which took place in 1952 with two vessels especially built to navigate the shallow draft canals. Year by year this service has been increased until in the 1958 season five vessels are being employed and two more larger ships will be in this service when the Seaway opens.

In order to efficiently handle this new Manchester Great Lakes Service Furness, in 1952, acquired the business of F. C. Thompson Company, Toronto, who had for many years been their Ontario agents and opened a Toronto office under their own name. Since then a further branch has been opened in Milwaukee to supplement the activities of their Chicago office.

Furness in their own name also started a London Great Lakes Service in 1957 with chartered tonnage as they had no ships of their own small enough to navigate the shallow canals but they will employ their own tonnage in this Service commencing with the opening of the Seaway.

Furness, Withy & Company Limited are amongst the largest British steamship companies and their fleet with those of their subsidiary companies now comprise 73 vessels, totalling some 747,200 tons gross register. Their trading area is almost worldwide.

The activities of Furness in Eastern Canada and the Great Lakes area are not confined to their own operations in that they act as freight agents for four other old established companies all of whom operate freight services in and out of the Great Lakes in addition to serving the St. Lawrence and Maritime ports:

The British City Line of Steamships Limited under the management of Charles Hill and Sons, of Bristol, England which came under the ownership of the Hill family in 1845 in succession to the firm of Hillhouse and Company which dated back to the early 1700's who were, according to old records, the earliest firm of shipbuilders and shipowners in Bristol. Commencing with small ships that could navigate the shallow tortuous and tidal river Avon leading from the sea to Bristol, their fleet now comprises large ocean ships, using Avonmouth as their home part and serving the trade between the Bristol Channel, United States North Atlantic ports, Eastern Canada and in 1958 the Great Lakes with ships but a little larger than those that in the earlier years ran to Bristol itself. With the opening of the Seaway larger tonnage will be employed in the Lakes trade.

Cairn Line of Steamships Limited (managed by Cairns, Noble & Company Limited which company is affiliated with the Furness Group) operating liner cargo and passenger vessels between the Northeast coast of the United Kingdom, the St. Lawrence and Maritime ports. This service will be extended to the Great Lakes at an appropriate time.

The French Line (Cie Gle Transatlantique) the largest steamship company operating under the French flag, best known for its luxurious express service between France and New York but also operating liner freight services in the transatlantic trades, including the Great Lakes.

The Swedish American Line of Gothenburg are also represented by Furness at Toronto, Chicago and Milwaukee in connection with their Great Lakes and Canadian services to the Continent, Scandinavia and the Caribbean. Furness are also their general freight agents in New York for their transatlantic freight services.

1 — Erecting north upper gate leaf at St. Lambert Lock.

2 — First lower gate of completed St. Lambert Lock.

8 — Three of six Provincial cranes installed in a new transformer plant.

PROVINCIAL ENGINEERING LTD.

Niagara Falls, Canada

ST. LAWRENCE SEAWAY, long a dream of far-sighted men, has become a reality to benefit all citizens of this country. This great engineering program, like many others across Canada, has utilized the services and products of one or more of the three Divisions comprising PROVINCIAL ENGINEERING LTD.

The CONSTRUCTION DIVISION of Provincial Engineering has been engaged indirectly in the Seaway Project since January of 1951, when industrial plants had to be moved from areas to be flooded, then re-erected and put into operating condition at new locations. Provincial Engineering's services were extensively employed in the dismantling and re-erection of many of these plants.

The world's largest lock gates were also installed by our Construction Division during the past year in the locks at Cote St. Catharine, St. Lambert and Beauharnois. Photo No. 1 shows erection of the north upper gate leaves of a St. Lambert Lock Gate by Provincial Engineering forces, with two of the four sections in place at this stage of the work. Photo No. 2 is a view of the lower gate of the completed lock gates at St. Lambert, looking upstream.

The TRANSMISSION TOWER DIVISION of Provincial Engineering Ltd. designed and manufactured the steel towers to carry the transmission lines for distribution of electrical energy from powerhouses to the cities and industries where the power will be used. Photo No. 3 is a worm's-eye view of one of the 120 K.V. double circuit angle crossing towers, 224 feet in height and weighing approximately fifty tons. Maximum span between these towers is 1,000 feet and they carry conductor wire of the 715,500 CN A.C.R.S. type.

A year ago, Provincial's TRANSMISSION TOWER DIVISION completed its portion of the Trans-Canada Microwave System, covering the design, fabrication and erection of the microwave towers from Toronto to the Manitoba-Saskatchewan border. Photo No. 4 shows the largest of these towers, a 350-foot structure weighing 122 tons, while Photo No. 5 illustrates a typical Provincial suspension-type of tower for 300 K.V. Transmission Lines.

The CRANE and HOIST DIVISION of Provincial Engineering is engaged in the design and manufacture of Canada's largest and most modern overhead travelling cranes and dockside cranes. In fact, Provincial's Crane and Hoist Division overhead materials handling equipment ranges from 1/4-ton chain hoists to 450-ton capacity cranes. A typical Provincial overhead travelling crane installation is shown in Photo No. 8. Photo No. 6 shows two Provincial level luffing dockside cranes in operation on the east coast of Canada. This type of modern, high-speed material handling equipment will assist in handling cargoes entering and leaving Canada via the St. Lawrence Seaway. An installation of another Provincial electric travelling jib crane is shown in Photo No. 7.

———

In the construction of ready-to-operate plants for industry, in the design, fabrication and erection of power transmission towers and in the manufacture and installation of cranes and hoists, it has been the privilege of Provincial Engineering to contribute greatly to the industrial strength of Canada.

PROVINCIAL ENGINEERING LTD.

NIAGARA FALLS, CANADA
A Unit of Houdaille

**Industrial Construction — Transmission Towers
Cranes and Hoists**

MONTREAL — TORONTO — CHICOUTIMI

6 — Provincial Level Luffing Dock Cranes at an East Coast port.

7 — Provincial Electric Travelling Level Luffing Jib Crane.

120 K.V., 224-foot angle crossing tower by Provincial.

5 — Typical 300 K.V. double circuit power transmission tower.

4 — 350-foot Provincial Microwave Tower for Trans-Canada System.

CRAWLEY & McCRAKEN COMPANY LIMITED

Boarding and Commissary Caterers

Crawley & McCracken Company Limited organized in 1912, has pioneered a service to governments and industry, that greatly speeded and supported the vast engineering tasks performed in the development and expansion of Canada's natural resources in the past half century.

First problem to be solved in building a hydro electric plant, working a mine, or inaugurating a lumbering operation in the primeval forest, is obviously the housing, feeding and general care of the hundreds or thousands of men to be employed.

Before "Canada's Biggest Cook" entered the picture, this was a haphazard procedure, replete with headaches for management, whose attention was continually diverted from vital construction and operating procedures because of their preoccupation with keeping their men contented.

Crawley & McCracken Company Limited move in, before, or with, the client's advance party. They establish and furnish completely, kitchen, dining room, sleeping quarters and recreation facilities; store foods selected for quality and variety; find water; install heating and sanitation requirements. Not forgotten is a complete canteen where men can obtain any necessity from a tube of tooth paste, to a complete working outfit. They provide thoroughly trained, experienced, on-the-spot camp management and complete staff.

From the first day of their arrival, employees are provided hot and appetizingly planned meals, comfortable sleeping quarters and recreation facilities for their spare time.

In the course of 46 years, Crawley & McCracken Company Limited has developed a Canada-wide service. Their clients include construction companies, mines, railways, military establishments, staff houses, canteens and industrial cafeterias. Head Office is in Montreal and regional offices are maintained in Toronto, North Bay, Sudbury, Capreol, Cochrane, Winnipeg, Edmonton and Vancouver.

Key to the Company's amazing growth has been its success in carrying out its contracts; to feed and care for men away from home – in all localities – against the pressure of time and the hazards of distance, weather and wild terrain – and its ability to continue to function effectively and uninterruptedly, because of the

CANADA'S BIGGEST COOK

calibre of its men, – carefully chosen to meet the special demands of this critical work.

Through the years, the Company has become known as "Canada's Biggest Cook" and their trademark is recognized everywhere.

It has been the Company's privilege to be intimately associated with Federal and Provincial governments, railways and leading corporations in the development of Canada's natural resources and the expansion of her industries. The diversified nature of these operations over the entire Dominion is the measure of the Company's versatility and capacity, successfully to meet the basically important requirements entrusted to them.

Its multi-million dollar turnover, places them at the top in this unique field and is realistic evidence of the esteem and confidence their performance has earned.

The executive officers are, W. F. Harris, President; J. K. Cullen, Vice-President and General Manager; E. H. Richardson, Secretary-Treasurer; G. P. Crichton, Assistant General Manager and W. C. Brown, General Superintendent. Each of these executives has been with the company for a minimum of twenty-five years.

EMPIRE STEVEDORING COMPANY LIMITED

The increased flow of steamship traffic resulting from the building of the St. Lawrence Seaway and Power Projects will, in turn, create stepped-up activities in the St. Lawrence River and Great Lakes ports. Stevedoring firms are one of the many concerns which have enlarged their operations to efficiently handle the increased number of cargoes which will pour in and out of Canadian and American ports.

Empire Stevedoring's first contract was secured in October, 1931, and called for the stevedoring of eleven vessels of the Tree Line Navigation Company. These vessels, of from 1,500 to 2,500 tons, traded between Montreal and Canadian and American Great Lakes ports.

Empire Stevedoring, under the guidance of Samuel Chodos, grew and expanded with the times. Mr. Chodos, who grew up on Montreal's waterfront area, was continually giving thought to ways and means of speeding up the loading or discharging of ships' cargoes. During the middle Thirties, he established a procedure whereby from three to four days was saved in the discharging of export flour consigned to as many as twelve steamship companies from the holds of Great Lakes vessels. The flour was discharged into trucks at one open dock and delivered to the various steamship companies' sheds within a period of two days. Previously it was uncertain whether the consignee could get an overside delivery on time or not, and also the Lakes vessel could not always get a berth at one of the consignee's terminal sheds. This resulted in the Great Lakes carrier spending anywhere from four to six days discharging her cargo. Mr. Chodos' plan saw the Lakes vessel turning around on the return trip in approximately half the time, and the cost of the trucking was more than offset by the saving of valuable ship's time.

Another device for speeding up and increasing cargo handling was conceived by Sam Chodos in 1935. This concerned the loading of scrap which, at the time, was being shipped to Japan. The scrap had been loaded from piles or from railway cars alongside the ship. The charters had great difficulty loading ten tons per gang hour and keeping ships on schedule. Mr. Chodos, at that time a comparative newcomer to the stevedoring business, conceived the system of using trucks with already loaded skiffs from the scrap yard, brought alongside the ship. With this system in operation the loading was speeded up to as much as thirty-five tons per gang hour and loading costs cut by two-thirds.

As time passed, Empire Stevedoring Company continued to grow and expand its scope and volume. In 1940, shortly after the beginning of World War II, the company was appointed a sub-contractor to the Department of Munitions and Supply for degaussing ships. The Company supplied Northern Electric Company, the prin-

Mr. S. Chodos explains to officials of the Port of New York, how grain is loaded aboard a tanker for shipment to Europe. This is believed to be the first time that grain has been loaded in a tanker in Canada.

cipal contractor, with as many as 200 men per day to perform this very important work on as many as six ships daily. Empire Stevedoring carried out this work for the next five years and received a citation from the Department of Munitions and Supply as being the most efficient and reliable of the sub-contractors.

In addition to contracts held with numerous Canadian and American shipping lines, Empire Stevedoring holds over 200 contracts with shipowners throughout Europe. The Company's volume of business had developed to the point where it now owns in the vicinity of $1,000,000 worth of equipment consisting of motorized lift trucks, tractors, mobile cranes, automatic grain trimming machines, magnets and generators.

In addition to its operations and its own terminal in Montreal, Empire Stevedoring has branch offices in the ports of Sorel, Three Rivers and Quebec, Que., St. John, N.B., Halifax, N.S., and Churchill, Manitoba. Branch offices are also located in all major Canadian Great Lakes ports. More recently the Company handled eight vessels in Chicago, Detroit and Duluth.

Anticipating heavy traffic resulting from the birth of the St. Lawrence Seaway in years to come, Empire Stevedoring Company has laid plans for further expansion in the Canadian Great Lakes area.

SINCENNES-McNAUGHTON LINE LTD.

In 1849 Captain J. Felix Sincennes and Mr. Wm. McNaughton entered into a partnership in a towboat enterprise on the St. Lawrence, Ottawa and Richelieu Rivers. This became known as the SINCENNES-McNAUGHTON LINE, and the resulting towing and salvage organization is the oldest Company of its kind on the Great Lakes and St. Lawrence River.

At that time Montreal was by no means the important port it is today — the channel from Quebec to Montreal was shallow, and the sailing vessels found it necessary to be assisted through narrow buoyed channels.

Timber traffic, originating on the Great Lakes and Ottawa River, was handled in huge rafts, steered by men with "sweeps" through the River currents. These required assistance from tugs in the quiet waters of certain sections of the River. Tugs were also required for barges with sawn lumber from the Ottawa River to Lake Champlain points via the St. Lawrence and Richelieu Rivers and Chambly Canal. "Pinplats" carrying hay and other farm products, also brick, stone and other commodities required tug service from numerous small ports on the St. Lawrence and Richelieu Rivers.

Until the 1880's all tugs were of the side paddle wheel type. The single engine in these tugs made it impossible to use the side wheels separately and in handling a heavy vessel the tugs had a tendency to heel over. To overcome this a box on wheels filled with chain was used and run from one side of the tug to the other as required.

During the 1880's a number of screw tugs were commissioned but the side wheelers remained favourites for a long time both for ship handling and raft towing.

Sailing vessels were no longer using the St. Lawrence River at this time, and whereas previously Sincennes-McNaughton tugs handled these vessels all the way from Quebec to Montreal, their duties were now largely confined to berthing steamers at Montreal, and handling barges from points from Lachine to Quebec to Chambly.

Attention at this time was therefore directed to the coal barging trade between Oswego and Fair Haven, N.Y. on Lake Ontario to Montreal. The Sincennes-McNaughton Line purchased a number of old Great Lakes sailing vessels, dismasted them, converting them into tow barges for this purpose.

This trade functioned until about 1930, when the advent of fuel oil greatly diminished the old Lake Ontario hard coal trade which had given employment to Canadian vessels for so many years. A considerable trade in soft coal still exists, but this is now carried in canal sized steamers.

Attention was also given in the 1920's to the Port Colborne to Montreal grain trade. Prior to the opening of the new Welland Canal in 1930 Sincennes-McNaughton tugs and barges handled considerable grain on this route, their places being taken in 1930 by a fleet of new steel barges which were later converted into motorships.

Today the Company's tugs engage in berthing vessels in Montreal Harbour, and maintain tugs and salvage equipment at Montreal and Sorel in the province of Quebec and Kingston in Ontario.

The steamtugs which have given such good service for a number of years are gradually being converted to diesel propulsion, and new tugs are being added, and with the opening of the St. Lawrence to large vessels of both ocean and lake types the Company will be in a position to provide towing service where required.

First Canadian-built steamship being assisted up the St. Mary's current in Montreal harbor.

Tugs assisting the "Empress of England" outward bound.

Port of Montreal as it was 85 years ago.

Modern photo of Montreal Harbour.

MONTREAL SHIPPING COMPANY LIMITED

MONTREAL SHIPPING COMPANY LIMITED was founded in 1925 by London shipping interests and full control of the Company passed into Canadian hands prior to the second great war. Since then the Company has remained wholly Canadian and its activities have progressed alike with Canadian trade and development.

The Company conducts the business of liner and tramp steamship agents, chartering brokers and vessel operators. Branch offices are maintained at Toronto, Halifax, Saint John, Botwood, Newfoundland, and at Churchill, Manitoba, during the limited navigation season of the latter port. For the handling of its own business, the Company maintains a subsidiary company, Canadian Chartering (New York) Limited, with offices in New York City.

In its role of tramp vessel agents, the Company has over the years acquired the representation of an enviable group of foreign steamship owners for whom it acts as agent when their vessels are in Eastern Canadian waters. The year 1931 marked the opening of the "Bay Route" which saw Canadian grain moving through the Port of Churchill in Hudson Bay. To meet the requirements of its Owner friends, the Company pioneered as vessel agents in this first northern port and which agency it has always continued. The Company takes great pride in its tramp agency work and Owners throughout the world have learned to depend on the careful attention given to their interests by Montreal Shipping Company Limited.

Subsequent to its foundation in 1925, the Company became liner agents for the Lloyd Mediterraneo service between Eastern Canada and the Mediterranean area with the Italian trade being, and remaining today, the predominant factor. The Company, with the exception of the war years, has always maintained its position in the Mediterranean trade and today represents Montship Lines Limited and Capo Line — G.E.N.S. in the Canada-Mediterranean service which has been expanded to include the Great Lakes as far west as Chicago. In 1957 the Company introduced the Brodin Line into the Canadian South

American trade. Long established from U.S.A. ports, the Brodin Line's fast modern Swedish vessels soon established a reputation for efficient and dependable service with Canadian shippers to Argentina, Brazil and Uruguay. The Company is also the Canadian representative of the Mitsui Line of Japan and the Hansa Line of Bremen. The pioneer line between the United Kingdom and Churchill, the Dalgliesh Line, is also represented by Montreal Shipping Company Limited.

In 1955 the Company founded Candwood Shipping Company Limited in conjunction with Wm. France, Fenwick & Company Limited of London whose modern British flag single deck bulk cargo vessels found fast acceptance in Canadian coastal trades. The popular "F.F." funnel markings soon became a familiar sight in Canadian ports where newsprint, coal, gypsum and other basic commodities are handled.

Montreal Shipping Company Limited has always enjoyed particularly close relations with the Canadian newsprint industry and operates a fleet of chartered vessels for the movement of newsprint and woodpulp to the publishers and users of these vital Canadian products.

The Company maintains an active Chartering Department within its over-all shipping services, and this branch of the organization plays an essential role in the representation of Canadian cargo interests in the international shipping field.

Montreal Shipping Company Limited was first managed by Mr. A. Leslie Lawes who was soon joined by his brother, Mr. C. Clifford Lawes. The Company owes much to the initiative and the enterprise of the Lawes brothers. Their interest in it terminated with the death of Mr. Clifford Lawes early in 1955, at which time the present officers of the Company, all associated with it for periods in excess of ten years, and well known to the Company's customers, acquired control. This comparatively young and aggressive management is now guiding the Company's affairs along the already established lines of integrity, service and progress.

This is the St. Lambert Lock with the Victoria Bridge crossing it. The electrical control apparatus for this lock was installed by Metropole Electric Inc.

Lock control distribution network, part of the St. Lambert portion of the Seaway contract was awarded to Metropole Electric Inc. which include installation of series mercury vapor lighting systems for the lock, roads, underpass and bridges; a substation for distributing current from 2 interlocked alternate 25000V lines through a 600 KVA transformer; control stations for *all lock operations at either end of the lock, with interlocking and sequence-of-operations control; 25KV cable installation for powering the Cote St. Catherine Lock and a telephone intercommunication system. All connecting wiring is laid in underground conduits. A contract for building 7 high voltage substations feeding the operational equipment on the lock and 2 lift bridges was also awarded Metropole Electric Inc.*

METROPOLE ELECTRIC INC.

Founded in 1933 by L. E. Dansereau, G. B. St-Pierre and L. Tremblay, Metropole Electric Reg'd began as a three-man operation that grew rapidly even during the depression years.

In 1938 the company was incorporated under its present name by the founders. L. E. Dansereau became president, handling sales and customer relations. G.B. St-Pierre was named secretary-treasurer and office manager while L. Tremblay took charge of supervising actual installation work.

One of the most important contracts handled during the following three years was for the electrical system of St. Joseph's Hospital in Lachine. The second world war found the company prepared to aid in the national war effort and Metropole Electric handled many installations for the armed forces, such as the airport installations at Bagotville and Mont Joli.

In a step to further improve service to its customers, Robert Riopelle, a professional electrical engineer, was asked to join the company in 1947 and shortly thereafter took charge of administration of engineering and installation.

The period following the war brought many challenging contracts, among them: The Youville Hospital in Noranda, The Quebec Liquor Commission Warehouse in Montreal, St. Joseph's Sanitarium in Montreal, The Ecole des Arts et Metiers in St. Henri and Maisonneuve.

A further re-organization occurred in 1953 when the shareholder-founders decided to increase the board of directors to seven members: L. E. Dansereau, President; G. B. St-Pierre, Secretary-treasurer; L. Tremblay, Vice-President; J. R. Dansereau, Vice President; R. Riopelle, B.A.Sc., P.Eng. Vice President; M. Parizeau, P.Eng. Director; L. Dufresne, P.Eng. Director.

Today, Metropole Electric Inc., with head office at 1260 Jean Talon Street East in Montreal and branches in Quebec City and Ottawa, has an organization capable of handling any size or kind of electrical installation.

The company is especially proud of the following installations which have placed it among the largest electrical contractors in Canada. HOSPITALS: Hotel Dieu, Montreal; Maisonneuve, Montreal; Ottawa General Hospital; Buckingham Hospital, Buckingham; St. Joseph, Sudbury; Ste. Justine, Montreal. UNIVERSITIES: Laboratory, University of Montreal; Chemistry and Administration Buildings, Ottawa University; Institute of Microbiology, University of Montreal. COMMERCIAL: Dupuis Freres Ltd., Montreal; Blue Bonnets Raceway. SCHOOLS: Ecole Centrale Arts et Métiers, Montreal; Ecole des Arts et Metiers, St. Henri, Montreal; Ecole des Arts et Metiers, Maisonneuve, Montreal; Institut des Arts Graphiques, Montreal; Boscoville Rehabilitation Centre, Riviere des Prairies. INDUSTRY: Noe Bourassa & Co. Ltd.; Service Centre, Hydro-Quebec; Garage, Hydro-Quebec. PUBLIC SERVICE: Jeanne d'Arc Substation (Hydro-Quebec); Radar Installations on Mid-Canada and Pine Tree line Distribution System, City of Joliette; Street Lighting System, City of Anjou; St. Lambert Lock (St. Lawrence Seaway); Substations (St. Lawrence Seaway).

GAYPORT SHIPPING LIMITED

Of the many cargoes that will be shipped through the St. Lawrence Seaway few have as much bearing on the average Canadian's daily life as oil. We depend on oil for almost all our needs . . . for running the machines which are necessities to every day living . . . for heating our homes and the places where we work . . . for operating our vast transportation systems. These are but a few uses for oil.

Although Canada is herself a big producer of oil, pumped up from the numerous fields in the Province of Alberta, she still imports a great deal of the "Black Gold" from the Middle East and South America. Usually shipped in crude form, the oil is brought to our shores in the mighty ocean tankers where it is refined and later transported to other parts of the country for consumption.

Charged with the responsibility of transhipping oil from the refineries in Montreal, Quebec, to the industrial centres of the Great Lakes, are the small Lake tankers of anywhere from 2,000 to 5,000 tons deadweight.

One of the prime operators of tankers engaged in the Great Lakes trade is Gayport Shipping Limited of Toronto, Ontario.

Incorporated in the spring of 1946 as a private company under a Dominion Charter, Gayport Shipping Limited commenced its operations with the acquisition of five tanker vessels which were under charter to the British American Oil Company Limited. The services being rendered at the time were the transportation of crude petroleum and all its refined products.

With the increasing demand for oil, which was fast taking over from coal in the industrial world, Gayport Shipping Limited expanded and modernized its fleet of oil carriers. In 1950, the Company acquired a new vessel and immediately put it into service. This was repeated in 1951, again in 1955 and once more in 1956. Also in the latter year, Gayport Shipping Limited sold two of their original vessels, one of which was too small to pay for itself in the highly competitive trade, and the other was completely obsolete.

At the present time, Gayport Shipping Limited owns and operates a total of seven tanker vessels, ranging in size from 2,800 tons to 4,300 tons deadweight. Of these, two are diesel-powered and the remaining five, steam driven.

Gayport Shipping has limited its interests to the transportation and distribution of comparatively small parcels of liquid cargoes. Today, the Company caters primarily to the Canadian Petroleum industry and is currently employed by five of the major Canadian oil refining companies and two of the Country's major jobbers of petroleum products.

The vessels transport very little crude petroleum but each concentrates principally in the distribution of petroleum products. In addition to this, however, such liquid cargoes as tars, creosotes, chemicals, molasses, vegetable oils and even fish oils, are carried.

Originally, the sphere of operation was concentrated in the vast Great Lakes area. This has now spread to the east coast of Canada, Labrador, Hudson Bay, the Arctic, east coast of the United States of America and as far away as the Caribbean Islands, Cuba, South America and Europe.

Although, as stated previously Gayport Shipping Limited limits its operation to comparatively small tankers, it also operates additional tonnage to that which it owns.

Of the total personnel enrolment, there are in the vicinity of three hundred employees with Gayport Shipping. Of these, eighty percent have a service record in excess of five years, and sixty percent of those originally employed in 1946 are still actively engaged. The Company is proud of this record and of the cordial labour relations which exist at all times.

Gayport Shipping Limited has great faith in the future and expansion of the trades in which it is currently interested and plans are already underway to further develop and increase its tanker services to all parts of the world.

Ogilvie's Montreal mill, the largest of six mills across the country.

THE OGILVIE FLOUR MILL CO. LIMITED

The bulky volumes of recorded debate, and the mountain of unrecorded argument, which together enveloped the St. Lawrence Seaway for half a century, sometimes veiled the true birthdate of hopes for deep waterway from the lakehead to the sea.

And yet if one reached back far enough, it would be hard to detect a more logical starting point than the year 1874.

Early that spring a young Canadian left Montreal, to begin his first business trip to the west. His name was John Ogilvie. For nearly 75 years, his family had been millers. Lately they had been buying grain, and milling it, as far afield as Western Ontario. But beyond the Great Lakes, deep in the American mid-west, hard wheat was now for the first time being harvested on a large scale. The Ogilvies had decided to test it.

Journeying into the Dakota territory that year, John Ogilvie bought 800 bushels of hard spring wheat. It was the first western wheat shipped to Eastern Canada. The flour it produced was magnificient, and ever afterwards the Ogilvies made it their business to spur by every possible means the farming of hard wheat on Canada's virgin prairie plains.

For many years, largely because of the severe climate, the Canadian west yielded only a trickle of grain. But the Ogilvies' faith in the destiny of this sleeping land remained unshaken, and in 1881, against the advice of shocked financial friends, they built a mill at Winnipeg, in Manitoba. From it, four years later, went the first export of western flour in Canada's history. It was a small shipment, but it went to Great Britain, whose list of suppliers at that time did not include Canada. Back, almost by return mail, came an order for half a million dollars worth of Manitoba wheat and flour.

With that, the forces which would later emerge into a persistent demand for deep-draft shipping from the head of Lake Superior to the Gulf of St. Lawrence were set in motion. And by the early twentieth century, as special varieties of wheat adapted to the Canadian climate were developed and the trickle of export flour and grain became a flood, those forces took tangible form. The first international discussions began.

Early and intimately, the future of the Ogilvie companies was thus bonded to that of the west and of the waterway which linked the west with distant continents. Down the years that followed, through successive periods of boom, depression, war and peace, this link has grown steadily stronger.

The firm which boldly brought western grain east for milling was called A. W. Ogilvie & Company Limited, and its first pioneer venture beyond the lakes was followed by a succession of others. Western Canada's first grain elevator, built in 1881 at Gretna, Manitoba, was also the first of the Ogilvie chain. Soon there were more. At the same time, Ogilvie was expanding in the east, adding new milling and elevator capacity at Montreal. By shortly after the turn of the century, its wheat-flour empire included four mills and seventy country elevators.

Just as the early years of the twentieth century bred a revolution in Canada's prairie economy, they brought a sharp round of expansion to what was newly-christened The Ogilvie Flour Mills Co. Limited. Soon, new mills were being built in Fort William, Ontario and Medicine Hat, Alberta. Three out of every ten barrels of Ogilvie Flour were going abroad. The Ogilvie trademark was becoming a familiar sight to stevedores in ports the world over. South Africa, West Africa, Uruguay, Paraguay, Sweden, Denmark, Norway, Japan — all became new customers. And King George the Fifth of England bestowed his Royal Warrant on the flour he had previously honored as Prince of Wales.

The years since those early days of the century have wrought many changes in the Ogilvie milling business, changes partly the natural result of a steadily rising North American standard of living and partly the response to trade restrictions abroad. Ever since the first world war, to encourage local industry, many nations have tightened their rules on imports. For this reason, Canada's exports of flour have never matched the sharp growth in her foreign sales of wheat.

But from the magic of the chemists have come whole families of new and profitable products that would have astonished the early Ogilvies. Bran and shorts, long ignored as by-products of wheat, today form the foundation of a major Ogilvie business in animal feeds. Wheat starch and gluten now come from Ogilvie factories. From others flow a steady stream of cereals and of bright packages filled with one of the most essential ingredients of modern living: the ready cake-mix.

When Alexander Ogilvie, founder of the milling dynasty which bears his name, first began business in 1801, he could produce 40 tons of flour a day at his tiny grist mill in Jacques Cartier, on the banks of the St. Lawrence. Alexander used a single pair of fine French millstones, his most precious possession when he emigrated from Scotland.

Today, Ogilvie milling complex includes 11 mills and factories, with a daily output of 50,000 bags of flour, cereals and feeds. Eight terminal elevators, and 125 country elevators, support these mills, and warehouses are located in 25 cities and towns across Canada.

Alexander Ogilvie milled three grades of flour. His successors market 12 different wheat flours, and produce others for special purposes. They process five different breakfast cereals and 10 Ready Mixes for cakes, biscuits, rolls, muffins, pie-crusts and ginger-bread.

Other products include Tonik Wheat Germ, Pot and Pearl Barley, Wheat Starch, Gluten and related lines, 18 chops and coarse grain animal feeds, two complete ranges of balanced rations for poultry, cattle, hogs, rabbits, dogs, foxes, and mink.

The Ogilvie Winnipeg mill.

The VALERIA, one of the vessels specially built to operate into the Great Lakes on the opening of the Seaway.

KERR STEAMSHIPS LIMITED

Trade, for generations a major source of income for Canada, has shown signs of further development since the decision of both the Canadian and United States Governments to construct the billion-dollar St. Lawrence Seaway and Power Projects. Already steamship companies operating vessels between the Great Lakes and Overseas ports are stepping up their activities to handle the increased business resulting from the new deep waterway system leading to the industrial heart of North America.

One such company is Kerr Steamships Limited of Montreal. Formed in 1947, as a fully owned subsidiary of Kerr Steamship Company, Inc., of New York, which organisation comprises fifteen offices in the United States and includes Great Lakes port offices at Detroit, Michigan, Chicago, Illinois, and Cleveland, Ohio, Kerr Steamships Limited operates branch offices at Toronto, Ontario, Saint John, New Brunswick, and Halifax, Nova Scotia. In addition, the Company owns its own modern head office building, the Clegg Building, located in the heart of Montreal's steamship section.

Kerr Steamships chief business is that of General Agent for liner services embracing the four corners of the globe.

The services represented include: Christensen Canadian African Lines, with ships plying a regular route between Canada and South, East and West Africa; Columbus line, regular service between Canada, Brazil, Uruguay and Argentina; Canada Jamaica Line, linking this country with the largest island in the new West Indies Federation group; Leif Hoegh & Company, from India and other Far East ports; and the Great Lakes Joint Service of Hamburg Chicago Line (A. Kirsten, Sartori & Berger), Hamburg America Line, North German Lloyd, and Ahrenkiel & Bene, to and from Continental ports, Bordeaux/Hamburg range.

In addition to acting as General Agents for the foregoing liner services, Kerr Steamships Limited handles tramp steamer agency consignments, oil tanker agency work, and represents a number of major shipowners as Owner's Agent.

A subsidiary of Kerr Steamships Limited is Dominion Chartering Company Limited, engaged solely in dry cargo and tanker chartering.

Kerr Steamships main office in Montreal as well as its branch offices in the Great Lakes and on Canada's Eastern Seaboard, are fully experienced in the handling of all types of liner services and tramp operations.

With the official opening of the St. Lawrence Seaway scheduled for 1959, Kerr Steamships Limited have prepared in advance to increase and extend their connection with Great Lakes Services.

Officers and directors of Kerr Steamships Limited are: Chairman, A. E. Clegg; President, A. S. Dillon; Vice-President and Managing Director, D. C. Connor; Vice-President and Director, Cortland D. Linder; and Secretary-Treasurer, H. I. H. Dietz.

RCA VICTOR COMPANY, LTD.

Marine Electronics and the St. Lawrence Seaway

Change — a byword to Canadians, who are used to rapid development — acquired a new meaning with the start of the Seaway project. Vast changes in our nation's economy resulted: new port facilities, new ship designs, different shipping methods and modified operations of allied industries. Not the least affected was the Marine Electronic field.

For Seaway contractors, RCA Victor planned and installed, on land and sea, novel communications systems. Each station of a system covered both the VHF and HF radiotelephone bands and provided private channels for the contractor plus the usual marine channels. A shore station controlled several dredge, tug and barge teams to form a network. Yet, any tug or dredge of one network could be moved and linked into other of the same contractor's networks along the Seaway. Despite the complexities involved, all units installed met future regulations for marine communications.

Under these new rules, nearly all vessels using the Great Lakes system must have approved radiotelephones. Few foreign ships entering the Lakes had such equipment and, since they were usually only evaluating future Great Lakes trade routes, it was not economically sound for them to purchase suitable units. To aid these floating ambassadors, RCA Victor provided them with radiotelephones for use while in the Lakes. Sets were installed and removed at Montreal as the ships passed in each direction. The cost was little but the good-will created was great.

During this stage, RCA Victor's plans for the future were being carried out. New equipment for new ships was designed, new products acquired, new service ports created and additional service engineers trained.

Because of this planning, RCA Victor is now the leader in equipping such ships as the "ALEXANDER T. WOOD". She and her sister ship are examples of new designs for the Seaway — ships which carry huge bulk cargoes between the Lakes and overseas. But new ship design meant new Marine Electronic design.

It meant unique radio-telephones with remotes on the bridge for Seaway operation, remotes in the radio-room for ocean use, twenty channels for multi-port use, high power for long range. Designing a radio with all these features was an achievement.

It meant improved radar with extreme short range (15 yards or less), narrow beam for river use, wide beam and high power for ocean use. A commercial radar with all these was never seen before.

It meant depth sounding systems, not units. Systems to measure depths both fore and aft, to record on one unit in the chart room and indicate simultaneously on another on the bridge, to be accurate at greater depths and in shallow water. No commercial ship ever had such a system.

RCA Victor's development program was equal to these tasks. Today, RCA Victor can fulfill every marine electronic requirement of any commercial vessel of any size. Radar and gyro, loran and depth sounder, auto-pilot and wireless telegraph, all these and more have been re-designed or acquired since the signing of the Seaway pact in 1954. No other firm in the world offers a more modern or more complete line of marine electronic equipment.

But why such a complete product line?

The Seaway was built to speed water transportation, and stops along it for electronic repairs would be few. Therefore, why not fit the ship completely with equipment from one supplier so one service engineer could effect any and all repairs while it was moving? The answer was obvious.

To service this wide range of products, RCA Victor established a long chain of depots strategically along the Seaway. Starting in 1954, RCA Victor created ten Marine service depots between Seven Islands and Fort William — one every 200 miles. Augmented by seven RCA depots in the United States, this is the most complete service network on the Seaway. Ports in this network are at:—

CANADA: Seven Islands, P.Q.; Quebec, P.Q.; Montreal, P.Q.; Prescott, Ont.; Kingston, Ont.; Toronto, Ont.; St. Catharines, Ont.; Windsor, Ont.; Sarnia, Ont.; Fort William, Ont.

UNITED STATES: Buffalo, N.Y.; Chicago, Ill.; Cincinnati, Ohio; Cleveland, Ohio; Conneaut, Ohio; Detroit, Mich.; Superior, Wisc.

Obviously, RCA Victor's equipment and services for ships have changed and improved since the advent of the Seaway. With continuous development and expansion, RCA Victor maintains its position as Canada's leading Marine Electronic supplier.

Photograph shows the variety of activity underway at one time. Pictured in background, tied up at outfitting berth along the Welland Ship Canal, is the S.S. Frank A. Sherman, modern bulk carrier built by Port Weller for Upper Lakes and St. Lawrence Transportation Company Limited. In left foreground is the steel work on the beginning of a sister ship for the Sherman, while at right in the graving dock is the John O. McKellar, undergoing repairs.

PORT WELLER DRY DOCKS LIMITED

Canadian shipowners today have realized that if they are to meet the demands of modern competition, their fleets must include vessels which are completely modern and equipped with the latest mechanical and labour-saving devices.

Port Weller Dry Docks Limited, one of Canada's leaders in the shipbuilding industry, has fully realized the needs of this country's shipping companies by equipping its docks in Port Weller with the latest equipment, machinery and facilities to turn out the modern tonnage needed for use on Canada's new St. Lawrence Seaway, the Great Lakes and the Seaboard.

In 1958 (when this volume was published) a shipbuilding achievement covering all of these basic requirements was the S. S. Frank A. Sherman, new flagship of the Upper Lakes and St. Lawrence Transportation Company Limited of Toronto. Christened and commissioned at an impressive ceremony on May 31, 1958, the Sherman, a 681-foot bulk carrier, is the third largest

Canadian freighter on the Great Lakes and the St. Lawrence River. As the latest addition to this major Canadian shipping firm, the vessel will carry grain, ore and coal. Its six cargo holds can accommodate some 800,000 bushels of wheat or 22,000 tons of ore. It is equipped with the very latest mechanical and navigational equipment.

Port Weller Dry Docks Limited during the last two years has carried out a 1½ million dollar modernization and expansion program. In order that the Company could undertake construction of the largest vessels laid down by the Seaway Authority for use in the new waterway, Port Weller Dry Docks Limited lengthened its building basin from 685 feet to 730 feet.

The Company's graving dock was also lengthened from 600 feet to 750 feet and with the existing 80-foot gates and 26 feet of water over the blocks it is now in a position to drydock for repairs any vessel capable of using the Seaway. In order to increase facilities for new construction and conversions and repairs, afloat,

The S.S. Frank A. Sherman, pictured above, was christened at Port Weller Dry Docks Limited on May 31, 1958. The 681 foot bulk carrier became the flagship of the Upper Lakes and St. Lawrence Transportation Company Limited, Toronto. It was the fourth large vessel of its types built at Port Weller Dry Docks Limited since the firm was founded in 1946.

a new fitting out berth 1,200 feet long has been constructed. This new fitting out berth will shortly be equipped with a new gantry type travelling crane of approximately 60 ton capacity. The completion of this fitting out berth will make available the Company's building berth four to five months earlier to proceed with the laying of another keel, since all fitting out previously had to be completed while the vessel was in the building basin.

Port Weller Dry Docks Limited combines superior marine skills, marine facilities and equipment and ideal location for the convenience of ships of all sizes using the Great Lakes. Besides the modern dry docks and fitting out berth, cranes are available for lifts up to 125 tons. For the procurement of materials and equipment, Port Weller Dry Docks are well serviced by railroads to their own siding, water transportation or truck transport service.

The shipyard is located just above Lock One on the Welland Ship Canal and about three miles from the city of St. Catharines. Port Weller is the Northern (Lake Ontario) terminus of the Welland Ship Canal.

The history of Port Weller Dry Docks is relatively short but is marked by a steady record of diversified and successful activity. The firm was founded in 1946 by the late Charles Ansell who directed its progress from its inception until his death in 1957. John F. Vaughan, who served in the Royal Canadian Navy in World War II as Lieutenant succeeded him as General Manager.

Port Weller Dry Docks has constructed ships both large and small. They include the John E. F. Misener, the John O. McKellar and the Scott Misener which are part of the fleet of Colonial Steamships Limited in Port Colborne. Canal type vessels completed to date include the Griffon and Tecumseh, both built for Beaconsfield Steamships in Montreal. In addition to the above, the Company has built a number of dredges, barges and tugs as well as carrying out numerous major ship conversions and reconstructions.

As Canada progresses and the St. Lawrence Seaway becomes a reality, Port Weller Dry Docks Limited is prepared to provide the marine needs of an increasingly more efficient merchant shipping for the expanding trade of North America and the World.

315

John N. Brocklesby Transportation Limited heavy duty haulage truck delivering huge stop logs at Iroquois Lock. Two Brocklesby cranes are busy lifting the equipment from the truck.

JOHN N. BROCKLESBY TRANSPORT LIMITED

Like many other of today's large companies, John N. Brocklesby Transport Limited had a very modest beginning. The business was started in 1904 by Mr. G. Monette as a carter, with one horse and cart. Through diligent effort, the business continued to grow under Mr. Monette's efficient management and additional equipment was added from time to time. In 1934, Mr. John N. Brocklesby joined the company as an employee and for the next ten years assisted Mr. Monette in conducting the business. In 1944, Mr. Monette retired from the business and his interests were purchased by Mr. Brocklesby who changed the name of the company to John N. Brocklesby Transport Limited.

At that time, the company had between 25 and 30 units of equipment, including trucks, shovels and similar equipment, for servicing the construction trades and for use in the haulage business. At that time, the company had no cranes. In 1949, the company added several cranes to their list of equipment and added the crane rental service to the already rapidly expanding setup.

The business continued to expand and performed considerable services during the construction stages of the St. Lawrence Seaway through the use of their heavy duty haulage equipment together with the rental service

of numerous cranes for hoisting purposes. By 1958, the company had 225 units of equipment including haulage, cranes, power shovels, hoists, etc. and had become one of the largest companies in Canada in the transportation and hoisting fields.

If anything has to be moved, either on the flat or up and down, John N. Brocklesby Transport is prepared to properly engineer the job.

The following is a list of some of the Seaway contractors and suppliers who were satisfactorily served by John N. Brocklesby Transport Limited.

McNamara, Pigott & Peacock Limited; United Waterways Limited; Dominion Bridge Company Limited; Canamont-Canit Construction Limited; Walsh (Canadian) Limited; Miron-Mannebec Construction Co. Limited; J. D. Stirling Limited; Iroquois Constructors Limited; Canadian Vickers Limited; Montreal Locomotive Works Limited; Maritime Steel Foundries Limited; Provincial Engineering Company Limited; Canadian Bridge & Tanks Company Limited.

John N. Brocklesby Transport Limited is located at 5378 Notre Dame Street East, Montreal.

316

Single story fully mechanized warehouse.

WAKEM & McLAUGHLIN, INC.

Completion of the St. Lawrence Seaway will mark a major forward step in the area of distribution. For producers and shippers, marketing and distribution factors will take on a new importance.

Within the total distribution picture is the all-important consideration of storage. Fully aware of this fact is the warehousing firm of Wakem and McLaughlin, Inc., of Chicago, Ill.

For more than seventy years, since 1886, Wakem and McLaughlin has provided warehousing methods giving complete control over all distribution cost factors—resulting in substantial distribution savings for its long list of satisfied accounts.

For producers and shippers warehousing in Chicago, Wakem and McLaughlin offers the Midwest's most modern and complete warehousing distribution service. Food products, packaged or in bulk . . . containers, metal or glass . . . electronic parts and equipment . . . paper products . raw materials, finished goods — whatever the scope of warehousing needs, Wakem and McLaughlin provides a full range of services.

With 400,000 square feet of modern warehousing, Wakem and McLaughlin's two modern warehouses are conveniently located in the heart of Chicago's industrial and commercial district — easily accessible to rail, truck, water and air. Wakem and McLaughlin's customer-designed facilities include fully-mechanized freight handling, enclosed truck docks, inside rail sidings, off-street truck drives and unlimited floor load.

Onother feature is 18 to 23-foot pile heights. All facilities are of brick and concrete construction, heated throughout and sprinkler supervisory and A. D. T. protected.

Wakem and McLaughlin's warehousing facilities stress lower distribution costs, with increased economies made possible through greatly increased efficiency. For example, Wakem and McLaughlin's off-street truck drive — as wide as a six-lane highway — leads to the dock. Trucks can back in and pull out, never hindered by street traffic, resulting in faster service. Also, because the truck dock is enclosed, weather is never a factor. A total of 24 trucks can be accommodated simultaneously, with mechanized equipment loading and unloading in the quickest, most careful way.

The depressed inside railroad siding accommodates 25 cars a day. Mechanized equipment rolls right in, picks up the load and places it in storage in one operation.

Wakem and McLaughlin's high efficiency warehousing methods traditionally have been geared to the changing and expanding needs of industry. The only Internal Revenue bonded warehouse in Chicago, Wakem and McLaughlin is a U.S. Custom Bonded Warehouse. Its warehouse receipts are honored by all financial institutions throughout the nation.

Through the time and labor saving techniques of automation in incomparably modern plant facilities, the warehousing services of Wakem and McLaughlin turn storage costs into distribution savings.

For more than seventy years, Wakem and McLaughlin has served America's leading firms with efficient, low-cost warehousing. Today, as the St. Lawrence Seaway opens a new era in distribution, Wakem and McLaughlin's expanded facilities offer an unequalled opportunity for efficient interim storage and distribution in and through the important Chicago area.

Wakem and McLaughlin, Inc., are members of American Warehousemen's Association, Illinois Association of Merchandise Warehousemen, Illinois Chamber of Commerce and Chicago Association of Commerce and Industry.

317

M.S. "Prinses Irene"

FJELL—ORANJE LINES

When the St. Lawrence Seaway opens its mighty lock gates to officially welcome the ships of many nations in 1959, one of the principal users of this billion-dollar deep waterway will be two of the oldest shipping companies to trade between Europe and Great Lakes ports.

For over a quarter of a century, Fjell-Oranje Lines have operated a regular service from the United Kingdom, the Continent and Scandinavia to St. Lawrence and Great Lakes ports.

One of the firms had its beginning in 1915, under the name of Olsen & Ugelstad, and started with lighter or barge traffic in the North Sea. In March of that year, the first steamship was purchased and by the end of 1915, the firm was managing a fleet of seven vessels totalling 9,600 tons deadweight.

During the first World War, Olsen & Ugelstad sailed their ships in the service of the allied powers, and by the end of hostilities in 1918, the fleet had grown to eleven vessels with a total deadweight tonnage of 17,810.

In the years that followed the Company steadily increased its tonnage until, by September 1939, a total of 79,825 tons deadweight comprising fifteen vessels was under the Olsen & Ugelstad house flag. These included tankers, bulk carriers and liners.

One of the pioneers of direct trade between Great Lakes and St. Lawrence ports and Europe, Olsen & Ugelstad established the Fjell Line in 1935, with six vessels plying the inland sea of North America with their cargoes from across the Atlantic.

Up until 1938, there were no competitive lines engaged in this trade. However, that same year the Oranje Line, out of Rotterdam, appeared on the scene. These two lines, Fjell and Oranje, were the only shipping companies to maintain a direct scheduled liner service link between the Great Lakes ports and Europe prior to World War II.

In 1956 the two companies decided to merge their operations under the name of Fjell-Oranje Lines. At present Fjell-Oranje Lines operate a fleet of 21 vessels, linking Scandinavian, United Kingdom, Western European ports and St. Lawrence River ports with Canadian and United States Great Lakes ports.

With the decision of both Canada and the United States to build the St. Lawrence Seaway and Power Projects, keen competition has resulted among the world's top shipowners. Numerous lines have established themselves in the Great Lakes-Europe run, but the two pioneer lines, Fjell and Oranje, are still in the forefront and intend to stay there.

The Fjell-Oranje Lines are confident that with the opening of the opening of the St. Lawrence Seaway an increase in trade from and to Canada will result. A number of larger ships, especially designed for the new deep waterway are either ready or under construction, and will come into the service of Fjell-Oranje Lines within the next two years.

Included in the new ships which have been built and added to the service, is a fast, modern passenger-cargo liner, the M.S. "Prinses Irene", of 9,000 tons deadweight which was specially designed to navigate the St. Lawrence Seaway. The Fjell-Oranje Lines have three new ships under construction which are expected to go into service by 1961.

The service of Fjell-Oranje Lines between St. Lawrence and Great Lakes ports are as follows: Hamburg/Bordeaux range, twice weekly; Continent/U.K. Service — weekly between London, Glasgow, Antwerp and Rotterdam. During the Winter months, a fortnightly service is maintained between United Kingdom and Continental ports and Halifax, N.S. and St. John, N.B. The Fjell Line Scandinavian Service includes a thrice-weekly service between Norway, Denmark, United Kingdom and St. Lawrence and Great Lakes ports.

Fjell-Oranje Lines are represented in Montreal by Canadian Overseas Shipping Ltd. In New York, Chicago and Cleveland, by Great Lakes Overseas, Inc. In Detroit and Toledo, by Overseas Shipping Agency, Inc. In Hamilton and Toronto, by Great Lakes Overseas (Canada) Ltd., and in Milwaukee, by General Steamship Agencies, Inc.

ROLLINS BURDICK HUNTER CO.
Complete Marine Insurance Facility Offers On-The-Spot Service To St. Lawrence Shippers

The M. S. Col. Robert R. McCormick of the Quebec and Ontario Transportation Co., a subsidiary of the Tribune Company, is shown here participating in a ceremony celebrating completion of one phase of construction of the St. Lawrence Seaway. The Chicago Tribune is one of the great companies served by Rollins Burdick Hunter Co. in the area of marine insurance.

With the opening of the St. Lawrence Seaway, many major shippers will find it desirable to realign their marine insurance buying. The vastly expanded St. Lawrence facilities will shift much marine insurance buying, placement and servicing from coastal ports to headquarters in major ports of the Great Lakes.

With this shift in control, many shippers are finding the insurance service and counsel they need in the strategically located offices of Rollins Burdick Hunter Co., one of the major insurance brokers in the country.

The firm of Rollins Burdick Hunter has been actively engaged in marine insurance both overseas and on the Great Lakes for more than 50 years. Both geographically and physically, this famous brokerage house is ideally equipped with the facilities and qualifications to handle any marine insurance problem. With the recent acquisition of the New York marine specialist firm of Barry and Powell, the RBH Marine Insurance Division has been expanded to make it one of the most thoroughly equipped in the country.

From a geographical point of view, the Rollins Burdick Hunter Co. offices are ideally located for St. Lawrence shippers. Fully staffed facilities are located in the Great Lakes ports of Chicago, Detroit and Montreal, supported by an international organization with offices in major cities in the United States, Canada, Brazil and Argentina as well as associate offices in most major cities of the world.

Another important facility available to Rollins Burdick Hunter marine clients is the RBH Research and Planning Group. This group is constantly engaged in the development of new forms of marine insurance as well as over-all insurance packages involving marine insurance. Through this group, Rollins Burdick Hunter is ready to build a marine insurance program from the ground up or assist in designing and servicing self insurance programs.

All the combined facilities of Rollins Burdick Hunter are ready and available for St. Lawrence shippers . . . completely equipped as average adjusters . . . capable of handling any phase of hull or cargo insurance . . . ready to effect coverage in any area where protection is needed, marine or general. Shippers with any insurance problems are invited to call RBH for counsel without obligation.

THE OFFICE SPECIALTY MANUFACTURING COMPANY LIMITED

Newmarket, Ontario

Modular Office Suite.

As we look with pride at Canada's major role in the construction of the St. Lawrence Seaway and Power Project our thoughts immediately turn to the people who dug the channels, built the bridges and poured the concrete... the rightful glory for this achievement should indeed be theirs. But if we were to stop and think for a moment of all the equipment, from a desk to a steamshovel, employed in this project, we would soon realize that much of the glory must go to the people in the background... the suppliers.

Such a company was The Office Specialty Manufacturing Company Limited of Newmarket, Ontario, who supplied much of the office equipment for the St. Lawrence Seaway Authority. Office Specialty has the distinction of being the leading manufacturer of office equipment in Canada and have maintained this leadership during the past 70 years by anticipating the requirements and buying habits of the Canadian consumer.

Office Specialty's history dates back to the days when the Shannon Arch, a humble object used for filing papers was first invented around 1880. Protection of patent rights in Canada necessitated the manufacture of the arch in this country with the result a selling organization was established in Toronto and Montreal and manufacture of the arch was begun in Toronto. However, a factory under one control was thought to be more desirable and when a building was located in Newmarket which was just suited to the Company's needs, the entire manufacturing facilities were moved to this pleasant little town in 1898.

At first snow shovels and whip sockets were included in the lines manufactured along with school desks, but as business progressed the extraneous items were discarded and only office equipment concentrated upon.

Office Specialty was incorporated in 1895 and received its Dominion Charter in 1922. From the original building in Newmarket, now completely surrounded by large extensions, has sprung a thriving industry with manufacturing floor area of over 300,000 square feet, a modern three-storey Head Office building and a chain of wholly-owned and operated branch stores from coast to coast. From the original "handfull" of employees, Office Specialty now employs over 800.

The Company consists of three separate divisions, the Metal Division, Wood Division and Paper Division, where over 3,000 items are manufactured. The Metal Plant, the largest section, mass produces desks, chairs, filing cabinets and other office equipment in many different forms and styles. The Wood Plant manufactures de luxe suites, desks and chairs while the Paper Plant produces over 2,500,000 file folders a month in addition to other component paper parts used in filing.

Expansion of Office Specialty, as in past years, is a continuing progress. In October, 1956, a new plant, the Gordon L. Manning Plant, named in honour of the Company's President and General Manager, and more commonly referred to as Plant Number Four, was opened at Holland Landing, Ontario. This plant produces desks, chairs, filing cabinets and other metal products in the most modern and efficient manner.

Growth in Office Specialty's nation-wide sales organization has been rapid. Since World War II, new stores have been built in Ottawa, Ontario, Vancouver, British Columbia, Calgary and Edmonton, Alberta and a warehouse of 10,000 square feet in Montreal. The Company is unique in that it retails only through its own stores across the country. In this way a strict control of quality and service can be maintained from initial manufacture to customer delivery. If one were to make a survey of every office in Canada it would be difficult to find one without some item carrying the "Office Specialty" label.

As Canada progresses so does Office Specialty, which, under the expert guidance of Mr. G. L. Manning, stands ready to supply the office needs of a fast-growing nation.

Headquarters of Armstrong Bros. Company Limited, Contractors, Brampton, Ont.

ARMSTRONG BROS. COMPANY LIMITED

Today as Canada expands so does her roads and highways. New avenues of travel are being built almost daily across this wide land. Playing an important role in this connection is the firm of Armstrong Bros. Company Limited, general contractors of Brampton, Ontario.

Formed as a partnership over thirty years ago by J. Elgin Armstrong and G. Edwin Armstrong, at Brampton, the Company started in the crushing and excavation field.

During the thirty years of operation, Armstrong Bros. Company Limited has so greatly expanded that it is now operating three different companies, all in the construction field. These other two companies are the Peel Construction Company Limited and Montcalm Construction, Incorporated.

Armstrong Bros. Company Limited, together with its affiliated companies, Peel Construction Company Limited and Montcalm Construction, Inc., is one of the largest road building concerns in the Dominion. The companies interests comprise many quarry operations as well as the grading, paving and general contracting business.

The companies have completed many projects in Nova Scotia, Newfoundland, Quebec and Ontario for the various Provincial and Federal Departments.

Some of the operations carried out by these companies have been highway construction which includes grading and paving, rock and gravel crushing, permanent quarry operations and gravel pit operations carried out in many parts of Ontario, and airport construction and grading and paving operations for many Government and Municipal authorities.

Present contracts held by Armstrong Bros. Company Limited and Peel Construction Company Limited would place them among the foremost road building contractors in the Province of Ontario.

Combining a career in construction and the breeding and raising of thoroughbred and standardbred horses is an unusual combination, but J. Elgin Armstrong, President of Armstrong Bros. Company Limited and its affiliated companies finds that both can be very profitable. Mr. Armstrong has had horses racing under his colors in Great Britain, the United States and Canada. Mr. Armstrong and his brother, C. Edwin Armstrong, were among the first owners, other than American owners, to win the Hambletonian classic. Their mare, Helicopter, won this race in 1953 at Goshen, New York.

Officers of Armstrong Bros. Company Limited, Peel Construction Company Limited and Montcalm Construction, Inc., are: J. Elgin Armstrong, President; C. Edwin Armstrong, Vice-President, and H. Charles Armstrong, Secretary-Treasurer.

Iroquois Lock showing upstream Control House and Operations Building, both constructed by J. Lamontagne Ltd.

J. LAMONTAGNE LTD.

All of the companies that were engaged in the construction and equipping of the St. Lawrence Seaway and Power Projects were not giants of the construction trades. Some of the companies were comparatively young and actually were almost on the threshold of their careers. One such company was J. Lamontagne Ltd. of Montreal. This company, which was formed in 1956, was young in years but had a great deal of construction experience behind it.

Mr. J. O. Lamontagne who, together with his son, controls the company had considerable experience as an architect and had been associated with the construction, mostly in Eastern Canada, of such types of buildings as schools, hospitals, presbyteries, government buildings, courthouses, theatres, banks, and other such public types of structures.

J. Lamontagne Ltd. was awarded the contract on the Seaway for the construction of the two Control Houses at Iroquois Lock, together with the necessary Operations Building, Pump House and Staff Building. These structures house the control mechanism for the efficient operation of the lock itself. It is interesting to note that in these Control Houses is the radio equipment for controlling the movements of ships approaching the lock in either direction for a distance of twenty miles.

J. Lamontagne Ltd. is proud of the fact that they completed their contract well within the schedule permitted and in a competent manner. They are now prepared to undertake such construction contracts as come within the scope of their operations.

View of upstream Control House at Iroquois Lock with gates about to open.

MENDELSSOHN BROTHERS (CANADA) LIMITED

Serving manufacturers, importers and exporters for more than a half century is the firm of Mendelssohn Brothers (Canada) Limited, with its headquarters at 361 Youville Square in Montreal.

Custom house brokers, customs consultants and international trade forwarders, Mendelssohn Brothers (Canada) Limited serves many prominent Canadian and American companies, including banks, and maintains agents in principal ports of the world, particularly in the United Kingdom and continental Europe.

With its services based upon the concept of efficiency through competent counsel, Mendelssohn Brothers (Canada) Limited's specialty services include the following areas of activity:

Custom House Brokers. The present complex customs procedure requires a great sense of responsibility, both to the importer and to the Department of National Revenue. The principals of our firm, and our staff, are skilled and experienced. They are excellently qualified to serve the importing and exporting public.

Customs Consultants. The principals and staff are fully versed in customs regulations and the Customs Act, and are in a position to advise and serve both importers and exporters.

Drawbacks and Refunds. Mendelssohn Brothers (Canada) Limited maintains an experienced department to advise importers and exporters on the proper procedure for filing and securing drawback of duty on goods exported, and on special classes of material imported and to be further processed or manufactured in Canada.

Cartage. A special affiliated cartage department renders prompt service when deliveries are required.

Storage and Warehousing. Mendelssohn Brothers (Canada) Limited maintains affiliations and friendly relations with several first-class warehouses whose rates are moderate and whose insurance charges are among the lowest in North America. The firm also acts as distributor of import shipments for importers who do not maintain such facilities in Montreal and other Canadian ports.

Freight Forwarders. A fully qualified staff in the Export Department can advise clients concerning export and import traffic. Mendelssohn Brothers also can book shipping space with shipping companies, prepare the many documents required by the importing country and, if requested, secure whatever insurance is needed.

Air Freight. Mendelssohn Brothers (Canada) Limited is a member of the International Air Transport Association and serves in an agent capacity for all air lines for air freight shipments, both domestic and foreign, the world over.

The firm maintains branch offices and affiliations at the border points of Blackpool and Lacolle, in Quebec; at the Dorval air terminal; at the intermediate terminal on Cote de Liesse Road in Montreal; and at Phillipsburg, Stanhope and Rock Island, Quebec. These branches and affiliations ensure prompt customs clearance of import shipments. Similar arrangements exist at all ports of Canada for customs clearance.

The firm of Mendelssohn Brothers (Canada) Limited was founded by Messrs. Nathan and Samuel A. Mendelssohn. Upon the latter's passing, Mr. Sam M. Meldelssohn became president and Mr. Nathan Mendelssohn, executive general manager. All members of the board of directors have been with the firm since its inception.

The firm's directors and members are Messrs. Sam M. Mendelssohn, Mortimer Levine, Ben Finkelstein, Julius Frank, Peter Martinelli, Sydney M. Mendelssohn, Joseph Mendelssohn, and Andre Germain.

With the St. Lawrence Seaway's impact upon Canadian imports and exports expected to be great, Mendelssohn Brothers (Canada) Limited stands ready to serve, in increasing measure, in Canada's development.

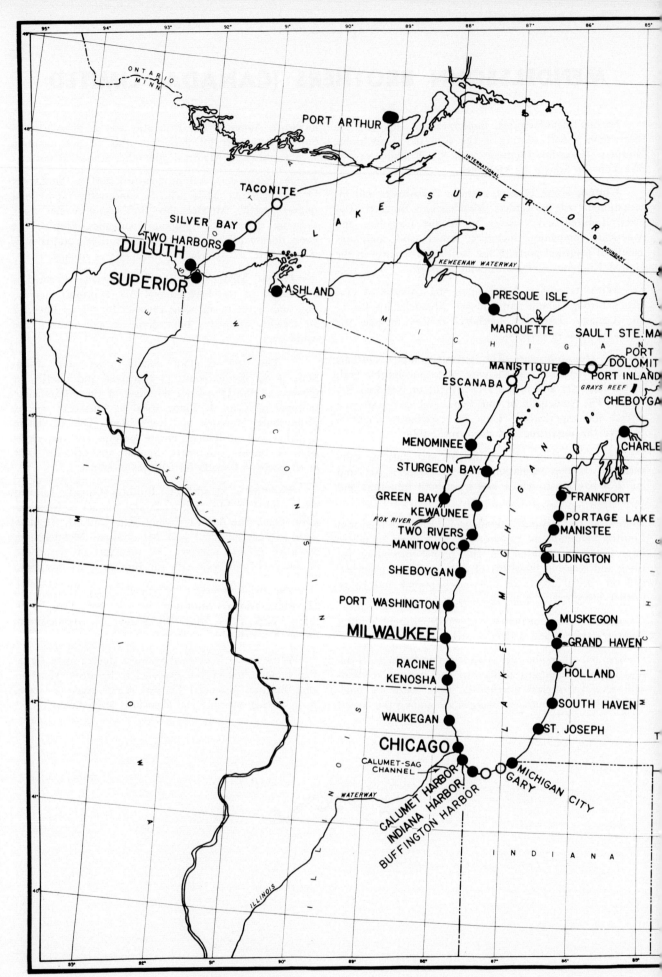

PORT ARTHUR

TACONITE

SILVER BAY

TWO HARBORS

DULUTH

SUPERIOR

ASHLAND

LAKE SUPERIOR

KEWEENAW WATERWAY

PRESQUE ISLE

MARQUETTE

SAULT STE. MA

PORT DOLOMIT

MANISTIQUE

PORT INLAND

ESCANABA

GRAYS REEF

CHEBOYGA

MENOMINEE

CHARLE

STURGEON BAY

GREEN BAY

FRANKFORT

KEWAUNEE

PORTAGE LAKE

FOX RIVER

TWO RIVERS

MANISTEE

MANITOWOC

LUDINGTON

SHEBOYGAN

PORT WASHINGTON

MUSKEGON

MILWAUKEE

GRAND HAVEN

RACINE

HOLLAND

KENOSHA

WAUKEGAN

SOUTH HAVEN

ST. JOSEPH

CHICAGO

CALUMET-SAG
CHANNEL

CALUMET HARBOR

INDIANA HARBOR

BUFFINGTON HARBOR

MICHIGAN CITY

GARY

WATERWAY

INDIANA

Army-U.S. Lake Survey, Detroit-Litho. 1956-3000 (Revised Jan. 1957-6000)

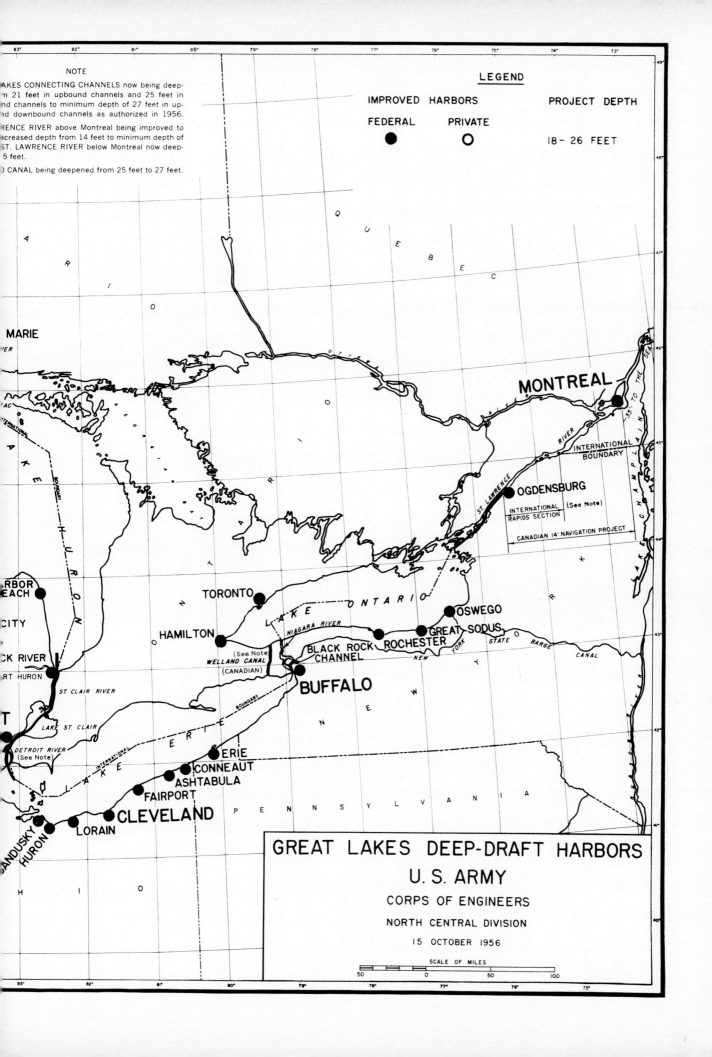

GREAT LAKES DEEP-DRAFT HARBORS
U. S. ARMY
CORPS OF ENGINEERS
NORTH CENTRAL DIVISION
15 OCTOBER 1956

CONTEMPORARY EXECUTIVES SECTION

**Executives directly or indirectly associated with
the St. Lawrence Seaway and Power Projects**

CONTEMPORARY EXECUTIVES

Executives directly or indirectly associated with the St. Lawrence Seaway and Power Projects

The Right Honourable John G. Diefenbaker,
Prime Minister of Canada.

The Right Honourable John George Diefenbaker, P.C., Q.C., M.P. . . . was born on September 18, 1895, in Grey County of Ontario, the son of William Thomas Diefenbaker and Mary Florence Bannerman. His mother is a granddaughter of George Bannerman, one of the Selkirk Settlers of the Red River (Winnipeg) area. At the age of eight, he accompanied his family to Saskatchewan, and graduated from the University of Saskatchewan in 1915 with a Bachelor of Arts degree. He won his Master of Arts degree from the same University the following year, and his Bachelor of Laws degree in 1919. In May, 1958, he was awarded an Honorary D.C.L. by his Alma Mater. He also holds Honorary LL.D.'s from McMaster University, Dartmouth College, McGill University and St. Mary's University (Halifax) and an Honorary D.C.L. from Acadia University. During World War I, Mr. Diefenbaker went overseas in the Canadian Army (1916-1917). In 1919, Mr. Diefenbaker was called to the Bar of Saskatchewan. He is also a member of the Bar of Alberta and the Bar of British Columbia, and in 1929 was created a King's Counsel. Mr. Diefenbaker was one of the Vice-Presidents of the Canadian Bar Association from 1939 to 1942. He received an honorary life membership in the Association in 1957. Mr. Diefenbaker has been a member of the House of Commons since 1940, having been elected three times as the Member for Lake Centre, Saskatchewan, and three times as the Member for Prince Albert, Saskatchewan. He was the Leader of the Conservative Party in Saskatchewan from 1937 to 1940, and in December, 1956, he was chosen to lead the Progressive Party in the federal field. He was Leader of Her Majesty's Opposition during the Fifth Session of Canada's 22nd Parliament in the spring of 1957. In the General Election of June 10, 1957, the Conservative Party won the largest group of seats in the 23rd Parliament, and Mr. Diefenbaker was called on to form a government. It was sworn into office on June 21, 1957. Mr. Diefenbaker is Canada's thirteenth Prime Minister since Confederation (1867). His government was re-elected on March 31, 1958. Mr. Diefenbaker attended the Commonwealth Prime Ministers' Conference in London in June, 1957, and in September the Queen appointed him to Her Most Honourable Privy Council. He was sworn into the Council in the presence of the Queen in London in December, 1957. In recent years he has attended various Commonwealth and NATO Parliamentary Meetings and in 1943 was Chairman of the Wartime Ottawa Conference of Parliamentarians from the British Commonwealth and Empire, meeting with Members of the United States Senate and House of Representatives. He also attended the United Nations Organization meeting in San Francisco in 1945 and was a Member of the Canadian Delegation to the Seventh Session of the United Nations General Assembly in New York in 1952. He addressed the General Assembly in New York as Prime Minister in September, 1957. In October, Mr. Diefenbaker was Minister in Attendance on Her Majesty, Queen Elizabeth II, during her visit to North America, when she opened the First Session of the Twenty-third Parliament in Ottawa, and visited Washington, D. C. Mr. Diefenbaker was married December 8, 1953, to Olive E. (Freeman) Palmer, daughter of the late Reverend Dr. and Mrs. C. B. Freeman.

★　　★　　★　　★

The Honourable Sinclair Weeks,
Secretary of Commerce, United States Government.

Sinclair Weeks . . . was inducted into office as Secretary, U. S. Department of Commerce, by the Chief Justice of the United States at a White House ceremony, January 21, 1953, following appointment by President Eisenhower. Born June 15, 1893, in West Newton, Massachusetts, son of former Secretary of War John Wingate and Martha A. (Sinclair) Weeks. Graduated from Newton High School, 1910; Harvard University, A.B., 1914. Holds honorary Doctor of Laws (LL.D) degrees from Northeastern University (1948), Tufts College (1953), Lincoln Memorial University (1954), Temple University, Harvard University, and Seaton Hall University (1956). In 1915, married Beatrice Dowse, who died in 1945. They had three sons, three daughters. In 1948, married Jane Tompkins Rankin of Nashville, Tennessee, mother of a son and daughter. They now have twenty-four grandchildren. Military Service: Began active service when Massachusetts National Guard units were activated for duty on the Mexican border, 1916. As Lieutenant in World War I, was promoted to Captain in command of "B" Battery, 101st Field Artillery Regiment, 26th (Yankee) Division, AEF. Participated in AEF actions, France, from February, 1918, through the Armistice. (This same Battery was commanded by his son, Captain John Weeks, in WW II). Business Career: Clerk, junior officer, Assistant Cashier, First National Bank of Boston, 1914-23. Became Associated with Reed & Barton Corporation, Taunton, Mass. silversmiths, as vice president in 1923; became president in 1925 and, later, chairman of the board. When Mr. Weeks severed all his official business connections on assuming his present position in 1953, he was also chairman of the board, United-Carr Fastener Corporation, Cambridge, Mass.; director of Gillette Safety Razor Company, Pacific Mills, Pullman Company, and First National Bank of Boston, where his business career began. Public Offices: Alderman, Newton, Mass., 1923-30; Mayor of Newton (three terms) 1930-35. Appointed U. S. Senator from Massachusetts to serve in place of Senator Henry Cabot Lodge, Jr. (resigned to enter military service) Feb., 1944-Dec., 1944. Appointed U. S. Secretary of Commerce by President Eisenhower, Jan. 20, 1953. Political Offices: Chairman, Massachusetts Republican State Committee, 1936-38; and Chairman of its Finance Committee, 1938-40. Member, Republican National Committee, 1940-53. Treasurer, Republican National Committee, 1941-44, and Finance Committee Chairman, 1949-53. Civil Activities: Member of the Corporation, Northeastern University, Boston, Mass.; Board of Directors, Wentworth Institute, Boston; Trustee, New England Deaconess Hospital, Boston; Board of Overseers, Boys Clubs of Boston; Trustee, Fessenden School, West Newton, Mass. Former member, Board of Overseers, Harvard University; former member, Board of Directors, and Honorary Vice-President-for-life, National Association of Manufacturers. Elected NAM "Man of the Year," 1954.

★　　★　　★　　★

The Honourable George Hees,
Minister of Transport, Canadian Government.

Hon. George Hees . . . was born June 17, 1910 in Toronto, Ontario and was educated at Trinity College School and the University of Toronto. He is a graduate of the Royal Military College, Kingston, Ontario, and spent a year at Cambridge University, England. He was married to Mabel Dunlop of Pembroke, Ontario, on June 30, 1934 and they have three daughters — Catherine, Martha and Roslyn. Mr. Hees served overseas in World War II as a Brigade Major with the 5th Infantry Brigade and was wounded on Walcheren Island Causeway, Holland. His political career began when he contested Spadina riding in 1945 and was defeated. He was first elected to the House of Commons at a by-election in the Toronto Broadview riding, May 15, 1950 and was re-elected in the general election of August 10, 1953. He was president of the Progressive Conservative Association 1954-56. Mr. Hees has always been keenly interested in sports. He played football for the University of Toronto and later for the Argonauts and was a member of the Dominion Championship Team of 1938. While attending Cambridge University, he won the British Inter-collegiate Boxing Championship. He has been associated with the Toronto City League Sports and is a ski enthusiast. Mr. Hees is a member of the following clubs: Toronto Golf, Toronto Badminton and Racquet, University, and is a Director of Woodgreen Community Centre.

★ ★ ★ ★

Bennett John Roberts,

President,
The St. Lawrence Seaway Authority.

Bennett John Roberts, B.A., C.B.E., ... born in Twillingate, Newfoundland, October 2, 1892. He graduated with a B.A. degree from the University of Toronto in 1916 and was employed by several mercantile firms and also financial and dayly newspapers in Toronto, Ont. In 1917 he entered the Department of Finance and shortly thereafter was appointed private secretary to the Minister of Finance, then Sir Thomas White. He has been in the public service of Canada for over 40 years during which time he has been closely associated with the requirements of shipping and with a number of public enquiries. In 1920 he acted as secretary of a Customs Tariff enquiry, and as financial adviser to the Royal Commission on Railways and Transportation in 1931, and secretary of the Royal Commission on Banking and Currency in 1933. In addition, he has served as a member of the Canadian Farm Loan Board, as Vice-Chairman of the Canadian Merchant Seaman Compensation Board, and as a financial adviser to the British Commonwealth Air Training Plan during World War II. He was named a Commander of the British Empire at the end of the Second World War. He has held the post of Chairman of the National Harbours Board since 1955 and had been a member of the Board since 1936, prior to which he held the position of Assistant Deputy Minister of Finance. On February 1, 1958, he was appointed President of the St. Lawrence Seaway Authority, succeeding Charles Gavsue, Q.C., C.B.E.

★ ★ ★ ★

Lewis G. Castle,

Administrator,
Saint Lawrence Seaway Development Corporation.

Lewis G. Castle ... born at Portage, Wisconsin, August 12, 1889. He was educated at Milwaukee Grade and High Schools and graduated from the University of Wisconsin, class of 1913, with letters in Science and Business Administration Courses. From 1913 to 1917 he was employed as Factory Superintendent of the Carnation Milk Company. He became Secretary of the Duluth Creamery Company in 1917 and in 1918, joined the Field Artillery Candidate Officers Training School at Camp Taylor, Louisville, Kentucky. He organized the Riverside State Bank in Duluth in 1919 and was Assistant Cashier of the Northern Minnesota National Bank in 1920. He became President of that Bank in 1947 and held the position until 1954. He is a Director of the Duluth Terminal and Cold Storage Company; Chairman of the Board of the Duluth Superior Transit Company; Secretary of the Industrial Construction Corporation engaged in building houses, navy barges and grain bins. He has held executive positions in banking for over thirty-five years and has been identified with mining, construction, shipbuilding, manufacturing, engineering, etc. accounts. He is a Past President of the Duluth Chamber of Commerce, Past President of the Kitchi Gammi

Club, Past President of the Northland Country Club and Past Chairman of the Board of the Minneapolis-St. Paul Metropolitan Airports Commission, from 1914 to 1945. He was appointed Administrator for the Saint Lawrence Seaway Development Corporation by President Dwight D. Eisenhower on June 23, 1954 and had his appointment confirmed by the Senate on July 1, 1954. Married Emelyn McDougall, of Duluth in 1915 and has been a widower since 1939. He has three children, one son and two daughters.

★ ★ ★ ★

James S. Duncan, C.M.G., LL.D.,

Chairman,
The Hydro-Electric Power Commission of Ontario.

James Stuart Duncan ... Honorary Air Commodore, C.M.G., LL.D., Chevalier of The French Legion of Honor. Chairman, The Hydro-Electric Power Commission of Ontario, 620 University Avenue, Toronto, Ont.; Governor, University of Toronto, Toronto Western Hospital; Chairman, Board of Governors of St. Andrews' College, Aurora, Ont., Dollar Sterling Trade Council, Australian-Canadian Association; Director, Atomic Energy of Canada Ltd., Odeon Theatres (Canada) Ltd.; Member of the Board Industrial Foundation on Education; Vice-Chairman, Royal Conservatory of Music, Toronto. Former Chairman and President, Massey-Harris-Ferguson Ltd., manufacturers of farm implements, Toronto. Born Paris, France, 1893, of Scottish parentage. Son of late James Stuart Duncan and Christian C. (Milne) Duncan. Educated: College Rollin, Paris, France. Entered employ of Massey-Harris Co. Ltd., 1909, in Berlin, Germany; came to Canadian headquarters of firm 1911. Returned to France at outbreak of World War I; enlisted with U. K. Forces and rose to be Captain and Adjutant of 180th Brigade of 16th Irish Divisional Artillery. Sent abroad by Massey-Harris after the war and by 1931 had become European General Manager. Served with this firm in many countries, including Canada, and in 1949 was named Chairman of Board and President. Retired in June, 1956, as Chairman and President of Massey-Harris-Ferguson and its subsiadiary companies. During World War II was appointed Acting Deputy Minister for Air, Department of National Defence, Ottawa, in 1940 and headed organization of the British Commonwealth Air Training Plan. In addition to directing important war work at Massey-Harris, he contributed to the war effort in many other ways; was Chairman, Combined Agricultural and Food Committee of UNRRA, Washington, 1941-42; Member, National Research Council, Ottawa; Honorary President, Fighting French, Toronto Section; Chairman, United Welfare Chest, Toronto; and Chairman, Toronto Board of Trade. In recognition of war services was made Companion of The Most Distinguished Order of St. Michael and St. George (C.M.G.), and Chevalier of The French Legion of Honour. Also awarded The King Haakon VII Cross of Norway, The Croix de Lorraine, and was gazetted Honorary Air Commodore of the R.C.A.F. Organized the Dollar Sterling Trade Council in 1949 at request of British and Canadian Governments, and became its Chairman. In 1956 was chosen by the U. S. National Sales Executive organization as "Canadian Businessman of the Year". In September, 1956, acted as Chairman of the National Conference on Engineering, Scientific and Technical Manpower at St. Andrews-by-the-Sea, N. B., and afterwards appointed Chairman of the National Advisory Committee on the Advancement of Education. Appointed Chairman, The Hydro-Electric Power Commission of Ontario November 1, 1956, by Premier Leslie M. Frost, at which time he resigned from the Board of many Canadian companies, including the Argus Corp. Ltd., Canada Cement Co. Ltd., Canadian Bank of Commerce, International Nickel Co. of Canada Ltd., and Page-Hersey Tubes Ltd. In April 1957 was elected Chairman of The London House Association of Canada. In September, 1957, he received the honorary degree of Doctor of Laws from Dartmouth College, Hanover, New Hampshire. In November, 1957 he was named Deputy Chairman of the Canadian Trade Delegation to Great Britain. Recognized as an internationalist, he speaks Spanish, French and German fluently and has a wide reputation as a patron of education and the arts. Presbyterian. Clubs: Toronto; York; Canadian; Empire; Rideau (Ottawa); Granite; Boisclair Fish and Game (Quebec);

Mount Royal (Montreal). Married: Victoria Martinez Alonso of Cordoba, Spain, 1936; has one son, James Stuart, and two daughters, Rose Maria and Maruja. Residence: 49 Highland Avenue, Toronto, Ontario.

*   *   *   *

Robert Moses,

Chairman,

The Power Authority of the State of New York.

In public service for more than 40 years. Served as Secretary of State under Governor Alfred E. Smith. Described often as the man who has changed the face of New York City, and in April 1958 issue of the Atlantic Monthly, Books and Men section, this was written of him:

"No New Yorker has a longer or more distinguished record of public service than Robert Moses . . ."

In addition to serving as Chairman of the Power Authority, Mr. Moses also actively fills these posts: Park Commissioner of the City of New York; Construction Coordinator for the City of New York; Chairman, Mayor's Committee on Slum Clearance; Chairman, Triborough Bridge and Tunnel Authority; President, Long Island State Park Commission; Chairman, State Council of Parks; Chairman, Jones Beach State Parkway Authority; Chairman, Bethpage Park Authority; Member, New York City Planning Commission. Mr. Moses has directed the design and construction of parkways, express-ways, bridges, tunnels and parks. He has served as adviser to many cities, states and nations and has received decorations for his public service from all over the world. He has a Bachelor of Arts, Yale; Master of Arts with honors in jurisprudence from Oxford which he attended as a Rhodes Scholar and a Doctor of Philosophy in Political Science from Columbia where he studied as a graduate student. Has received honorary degrees from more than a score of universities and colleges and lectured at leading universities. He is a contributor to magazines and newspapers on government, parks, public works, housing and recreation, reviews books, loves fishing and swimming (has played collegiate water polo). He has served the Federal Government as an advisor, surveying congested war production areas for the Army and Navy Munitions Board during war years. Also surveyed the occupation of Germany in 1947 and reported findings to the War Department.

*   *   *   *

M. W. Oettershagen

Deputy Administrator,

Saint Lawrence Seaway Development Corporation.

M. W. Oettershagen . . . born in Chicago, Illinois, Dec. 23, 1891. He was educated at Public Grammar School and Lane Technical High School, Chicago. Engineering education includes, Armour Institute of Technology, Chicago. Economics and Speech, Northwestern University, Chicago. From 1909 to 1914 served as head of party on various industrial construction jobs at Gary, Indiana, South Chicago and Indian Harbour, Indiana. Following this he joined the engineering department of the City of Chicago and was later appointed Port Manager in January 1954. Served as Consulting Engineer, Chicago Regional Port District from January 1950 to September 1954. For many years he represented the Bureau of Rivers and Harbors and the City of Chicago on port development matters locally and before national port and harbor associations and was for many years the engineering advisor to the Committee on Harbors, Wharves and Bridges on the Chicago City Council. He was the president of the American Association of Port Authorities in 1930; First President of the Propeller Club, Port of Chicago, 1933; Chairman, Committee on Fire Prevention, The American Association of Port Authorities; Member of the Committee on Harbors & Waterways, Chicago Association of Commerce and Industry; Co-author, 1933, Report on Waterway Development, Barge Traffic & Bridge Clearance, Chicago, and "Where Two Great Waterways Meet", published by the Chicago Regional Port District, February 1953. Appointed

Deputy Administrator, St. Lawrence Seaway Development Corporation, August 7, 1954. Married Amy L. Lane on May 14, 1917.

*   *   *   *

E. Reece Harrill,

Comptroller-Treasurer,

Saint Lawrence Seaway Development Corporation.

E. Reece Harrill . . . born Bostic, North Carolina, Jan. 7, 1906. He was educated at High School in North Carolina, George Washington University, Southeastern University, and Strayer College of Accountancy, Washington, D.C. Bachelor of Commercial Science in Accounting and Business Administration. He holds professional license as a Certified Public Accountant. From 1925 to 1933 he held various accounting and clerical positions and from 1933 to 1936 he did public accounting work with various firms in Washington and New York City. From 1936 to 1939 he was with the Social Security Board as Constructive Accountant and Auditor. From 1939 to 1942 he was with the Bureau of the Budget in the capacity of Budget Examiner, Fiscal Analyst and Budget Analyst. He served in the U.S. Army from 1942 to 1946, entering as Captain and being discharged as Lieutenant Colonel. Rejoined the Bureau of the Budget as Fiscal Analyst and Budget Examiner for the budgets of Government corporations upon his discharge from the Army until 1948. From 1948 to 1954 he held positions as Systems Accountant and Associate Director of the Accounting Systems Division with the General Accounting Office. In October 1954 he was appointed Comptroller-Treasurer of the Saint Lawrence Seaway Development Corporation and Chairman of the United States Tolls Committee for the Seaway Corporation. Member: American Institute of Accountants, D.C. Institute of Certified Public Accountants, Federal Government Accountants Association, American Society for Public Administration, Chairman of Committee on Governmental Accounting for the D.C. Institute of C.P.A.'s. Author: "Accounting for Construction Activities in the Federal Government", "Responsibilities and Activity Accounting in the Federal Government". Married Dorothy Sampson. Two children, daughter and son.

*   *   *   *

Lester W. Angell,

Director, Office of Engineering Design, Planning and Programs Saint Lawrence Seaway Development Corporation.

Lester W. Angell . . . born in Jefferson County, New York, July 4, 1906. Educated at Jefferson County Grade Schools; Watertown, New York High School; Clarkson College of Technology, Class of 1937 (cum laude) B.S. in Civil Engineering. Licensed as professional engineer in New York State in 1935. From 1927 to 1929, Civil Engineer with the New York State Department of Public Works. From 1930 to 1932 and in 1934 he served as designer with the Safe Harbor Water Power Corporation, Baltimore, Maryland. 1934-1940, design supervisor on heavy equipment with Tennessee Valley Authority, Knoxville. 1940-1942, Assistant to Chief of Dams Design, later Acting Chief, Corps of Engineers, U.S. Army, Massena District on preparation of the "1942 Report, St. Lawrence River Project." From 1942 to 1943 he was supervisor, Fortification Design Section, U.S. Army Corps of Engineers, New York District. From 1943 to 1946, on active duty with the U.S. Navy, and held such posts as Construction Company Commander, Engineer Officer for Naval Military Government and Base Development Liaison Officer for Tinian and the Western Carolines. 1946-1954, Engineer Specialist on Navigation, flood control and power structures with the U.S. Army in Washington, D.C. From October 1954 to January 1955 he was Design Engineer for the St. Lawrence Seaway Development Corporation in Washington after which he was appointed Chief Design Engineer and Assistant to the Deputy Administrator at Buffalo, New York. Listed in "Who's Who in Engineering". Member: American Society of Civil Engineers; Society of American Military Engineers,

American Welding Society, Building Codes Committee; ASCE, Committee on Design, Construction and Operation of Navigation and Flood Control Locks and Dams. Married Florence V. Hartge, Baltimore, April 17, 1933. Children: Son, Preston William, born 1936 and daughter, Marcia Elizabeth, born 1939.

★   ★   ★   ★

Lucius M. Hale,

Director, Office of Marine and Engineering Operations,
Saint Lawrence Seaway Development Corporation.

Lucius M. Hale . . . born Blackfoot, Idaho, March 6, 1913. He was educated in Grade School at Roseworth and Twin Falls, Idaho and at the Logan, Utah High School; UTAG College, Logan, Utah — 1937 BS CE Northwestern, Chicago, Navy Service School, Purdue, Lafayette, Indiana, Navy Service School Public Works School, Norfolk, Virginia, Navy Service School. Joined Department of Agriculture in Colorado, New Mexico and Utah in 1936, 1937 to 1939. From 1939 to 1941 he was with the U.S. Army Construction Quartermaster Corpse (construction of Air Bases), and from 1941 to 1942 with the Civil Aeronautics Administration. From November 1942 to 1949 he served with the U.S. Navy, attaining the rank of Lieut. Commander. From 1949 to 1954 he served as engineer with the Atomic Energy Commission, in Idaho. He was appointed Resident Engineer of the Saint Lawrence Seaway Development Corporation in October 1954, at the Massena Field Office, Construction of Navigation Facilities. In 1948 he was awarded the Navy Meritorious Civilian Award. He is married and has two daughters.

★   ★   ★   ★

Edward R. Place,

Director of Information,
Saint Lawrence Seaway Development Corporation.

Edward R. Place . . . born in Fall River, Mass. He graduated from Colby Academy, New London, New Hampshire, in 1920, and from Brown University, Providence, Rhode Island, in 1924. Joined the Providence Journal as a news reporter in 1924 and, in 1926, became Director of Publicity at Northeastern University in Boston. Later worked 5 years on the Boston Evening Transcript prior to joining N. W. Ayer and Son, Inc., Advertising Agency as New England Publicity Director. While with Ayer, he was in charge of the State of Maine's recreational and agricultural promotion campaigns. From 1936 to 1942, he operated the public relations firm of Edward R. Place Associates in Boston. He came to Washington in 1942 as an Information specialist with the War Production Board and later was associated with the Radio Corporation of America and National Association of Manufacturers in New York City. Resumed public relations work in Washington in 1946, and since 1951 has specialized in trade association representation with his previous firm. Appointed Director of Information of the St. Lawrence Seaway Development Corporation on May 26, 1955. Charter President of the Sertoma Club, Washington, D.C., and President-elect of the Phi Beta Kappa Association of the District of Columbia. Member: National Press Club, American Public Relations Association, Outdoor Writers Association of America, Washington Trade Association Executives, Washington Board of Trade, Brown Club of Washington, and Phi Gamma Delta fraternity. Married and has two daughters. Residence: Washington, D.C.

★   ★   ★   ★

John R. Akin,

Information Officer,
The St. Lawrence Seaway Authority.

John R. Akin . . . born at Montreal in 1916 and attended Balmy Beach School, Toronto, Town of Mount Royal High School, Montreal High School and McGill University, from which he graduated in 1938 with a degree of Bachelor of Arts. He joined the staff of the Montreal Gazette shortly thereafter and filled various editorial positions, particularly in the coverage of marine and business news. During World War II he served as an officer in the Royal Canadian Navy returning to the Gazette at the end of the war. He was Assistant Financial Editor of the Gazette when he joined the Department of Public Relations of the Canadian Pacific Railway in 1946. The same year he was transferred to New York as Assistant Public Relations Officer for the Canadian Pacific Railway in the United States, and was there until his return to Canada. While in the United States he became well known to financial, transportation and travel writers and editors in New York, Chicago, Philadelphia, Washington and other cities. Helping to tell the story of Canada, her transportation and her rapid development, he wrote numerous articles for newspapers and magazines, appeared on radio and television programs in New York and delivered addresses on Canadian transportation to various organizations. On February, 1955, he was appointed Information Officer for the St. Lawrence Seaway Authority. Clubs: Ottawa Press Club, and the Naval Officers' Club of Montreal. He is married to the former Jean Greig, of Moncton, N.B. and has a son, David, and a daughter, Madeleine.

★   ★   ★   ★

Jean-Claude Lessard,

Vice-President,
The St. Lawrence Seaway Authority.

Jean-Claude Lessard . . . born in Granby, Que. in 1904. He was educated at St. Mary's College, Montreal. Graduated from the University of Montreal in 1924 with his B.A. He attended the School of Commerce at McGill before proceeding to Harvard under a Province of Quebec Scholarship. He received his M.B.A. degree from Harvard in 1928, specializing in transportation, after which he spent some time in Western Canada and Chicago doing research on the movement of wheat and less-than-carload shipments. In 1929 he was attached to the Bureau of Economics of the Canadian National Railways at Montreal. In 1939 he joined the Board of Transport Commissioners as Transportation Economist. During the war years he was on loan to the Department of Munitions and Supply with Transit Control in Montreal and subsequently was responsible for organizing the Economics Branch of the Air Transport Board. In 1947 he was appointed Director of Transportation Economics of the Board of Transport Commissioners. In 1948 he was appointed Deputy Minister of the Department of Transport. In 1950 he was also appointed Chairman of the Canadian Maritime Commission. In 1954, retiring from Civil Service, he became attached to Standard Railway Equipment Manufacturing Company of Canada in the capacity of Vice-President. He also served recently as Transportation Consultant to the Royal Commission on Canada's Economic Prospects. On July 1st, 1957 he was appointed Vice-President of the St. Lawrence Seaway Authority. Married Miss Simone Meunier in 1933. One child, a daughter.

★   ★   ★   ★

A. G. Murphy, P. Eng.,

Chief Engineer,
The St. Lawrence Seaway Authority.

A. Gordon Murphy . . . born in Montreal in 1899. He was educated at Westmount Academy, Westmount High School and graduated from McGill University in 1922 with a degree of B.Sc. Following his graduation, Mr. Murphy was successively employed by the Canadian Bridge Company and by the Department of Railways and Canals as structural engineer. While with the latter, he served on the staffs of the Welland Ship Canal, the Hudson Bay Terminals (Churchill Development) and then the projected St. Lawrence Waterway Development. He joined the National Harbours Board upon its formation in 1936. He spent the following four years in

Montreal. During this time he supervised the construction of extensive improvements to the wharves and other facilities. He was then attached to Ottawa on the headquarters staff. He spent seven years in Ottawa, several of which he held the position as Assistant Chief Engineer. During this time he directed studies and the preparation of plans for the development of national harbours from Halifax to Vancouver. He was appointed Port Manager at Montreal on April 1, 1947. On August 1, 1954, he was appointed Chief Engineer for the St. Lawrence Seaway Authority. He is married and has one son.

★　★　★　★

C. W. West,

Member,
The St. Lawrence Seaway Authority.

C. W. West . . . born in Seymour Township, near Campbellford, Ont., in 1890. He graduated with honours in engineering from the University of Toronto in 1915. He served overseas, during World War I, with the Canadian Infantry and the Canadian Engineers. Upon his return to Canada, in 1919, he became senior assistant engineer in the construction of the Welland Ship Canal. In 1925 he was appointed division engineer. In 1934 he became the first superintending engineer of the 27-mile-long waterway between Lake Ontario and Lake Erie. He organized the operating and maintenance staff of the canal. In 1947 he was appointed Director of Canal Services, in charge of operation, maintenance and construction of all canals operated by the Department of Transport, and on January 1, 1954, he was made Senior Deputy Minister of Transport. On July 1, 1954, Mr. West

was appointed a Member of The St. Lawrence Seaway Authority. He is a Commissioner of the Canadian Maritime Commission. He has been associated, over the years, with numerous studies of the St. Lawrence River, and with much of the planning that was necessary for the combined St. Lawrence Seaway and Power Project. Member: Engineering Institute of Canada and Association of Porfessional Engineers of the Province of Ontario.

★　★　★　★

P. E. R. Malcolm,

Secretary and Director of Administration,
The St. Lawrence Seaway Authority.

P. E. R. Malcolm . . . born in England in 1918. He was educated at Neville Holt Preparatory School, England, Innsbruck College, Austria, and Massachussetts Institute of Technology. At the outbreak of World War II in 1939 he joined the R.C.A.F. and served in Canada and overseas. He retired from the R.C.A.F. in the spring of 1946 with the rank of Squadron Leader and was appointed Assistant Secretary of the Department of Reconstruction and Supply. Later that year he was appointed Director General of Administration. At the end of 1947 he was appointed to the Department of National Rvenue, Taxation Division, as Assistant Director of Administration and then Director of Administration. In 1953 he was appointed Director of Planning and Development. On August 1, 1954, he was appointed Director of Administration of the St. Lawrence Seaway Authority. Mr. Malcolm is married to the former Margot Hamel, of Ottawa. They have four children. Clubs: Rivermead Golf Club. He is also a Director of the "Cercle Universitaire d'Ottawa".

The Honorable Wilber M. Brucker
Secretary of the Army
United States Government

Wilber M. Brucker, . . . former Governor of Michigan, was sworn into office as Secretary of the Army July 21, 1955, following his nomination by President Eisenhower on June 22 and confirmation by the Senate on July 11. He had served as General Counsel of the Department of Defense from April 23, 1954, until he assumed his new office. Secretary Brucker has a background of Army experience extending back to enlistment in the Michigan National Guard in 1915 and service on the Mexican Border as a member of the 33d Infantry, Michigan National Guard, in 1916 and 1917. Following the entry of the United States into World War I, he attended the First Officers' Training Camp at Fort Sheridan, Illinois, and was commissioned a Second Lieutenant of Infantry. He served in France with the 166th Infantry, 42d (Rainbow) Division, in all the Division's engagements including Chateau Thierry, St. Mihiel, and the Meuse-Argonne. Cited by General Headquarters, AEF, for bravery under fire, he was awarded the Silver Star. He was discharged as a First Lieutenant June 5, 1919. Born June 23, 1894, in Saginaw, Michigan, the

son of Ferdinand and Roberta (Hawn) Brucker, he was graduated from the University of Michigan in 1916 with an LL.B. degree. He was Assistant Prosecuting Attorney for Saginaw County, Michigan, from 1919 to 1923; Prosecuting Attorney from 1923 to 1927, and Assistant Attorney General of Michigan until he became Attorney General February 18, 1928. On November 5, 1930, he was elected Governor of the State of Michigan and served until 1933. Thereafter to the date of his appointment as General Counsel of the Department of Defense he was a practicing lawyer with the law firm of Clark, Klein, Brucker, and Waples of Detroit, Michigan. He is a member of the Michigan State, Federal, and American Bar Associations; the American Legion, and Veterans of Foreign Wars. He is a Past National President of the Rainbow Division Veterans. Secretary Brucker is married to the former Clara Hantel. They have one child Wilber M., Jr., and two grandchildren. The family home is 56 Vendome Road, Grosse Pointe Farms, Michigan.

Beverley K. Boulton . . .born Ottawa, Ont., October 27, 1903. He was educated at High School of Quebec; Bishop's College School, Lennoxville, Que., McGill University from which he obtained his B.Sc. in Electrical Engineering in 1925. Positions held: Student Engineer on construction of Isle of Maligne Power Station, Isle of Maligne, Que., 1923-25; Junior Engineer Duke-Price Power Co. Ltd., Arvida, Que., 1925-27; Electrical Engineer Beauharnois Construction Co., Beauharnois, Que., 1927-29; General Superintendent, Beauharnois Light, Heat and Power Co., 1929-44; Special Engineer representing Department of Munitions and Supply in Chalk River atomic energy project, Montreal, Que. from 1944-45; President, Wartime Housing Ltd., Toronto, Ont., 1945-46; President, Managing Director and Chief Engineer of The J. P. Porter Company Limited since 1947. Clubs: University Club of Montreal; Kanawaki Golf Club; Thistle Curling Club, Montreal. Societies: Engineering Institute of Canada; Corporation of Professional Engineers of Quebec; American Institute of Electrical Engineers. Recreations: golf, hunting and fishing. Residence: Montreal, Quebec.

Beverley K. Boulton,

President, Managing Director & Chief Engineer,
The J. P. Porter Company Limited.

Thomas Rodgie McLagan O.B.E., . . . born Westmount, Quebec, January 22, 1897. He was educated at Lower Canada College, Montreal; McGill University where he received his B.Sc. Mech. His career began with Laurentide Company, Grand'Mere, Quebec as employment supervisor from 1924 to 1932; partner, Dufresne, McLagan & Associates, Industrial Consultants, Montreal, 1932-39; vice-president and general manager, Canadian Vickers Limited, Montreal, 1939-48; executive vice-president and general manager from 1948-50; president and general manager, 1950-51; appointed to present position, August 1951. He was gunner for the 11th Battery, C.F.A. during World War I, 1914-18. He was invested with O.B.E. 1946. He is a director of the following firms: Canadair Limited: Abitibi Power and Paper Co. Ltd.; Canadian Liquid Air Co. Ltd.; Algoma Steel Corporation, Ltd.; The Royal Trust Company; Foundation Co. of Canada Ltd.; National Drug & Chemical Co. Ltd.; Hilton of Canada Ltd.; Royal Bank of Canada. Member: Canadian Manufacturers Association; Corporation of Professional Engineers of the Province of Quebec; Montreal Board of Trade; Board of Governors, Lower Canada College, (Past Chairman); Governor McGill University; President: Canadian Industrial Preparedness Association; Canadian Shipbuilding & Repairing Association. Clubs: St. James's; University: Royal Montreal Golf; Laval-sur-le-Lac Golf; Canadian; Mount Royal; Garrison (Quebec); Toronto (Toronto); Rideau, (Ottawa); Mount Bruno Country. Society: Phi Delta Theta. His recreations include golf and reading. Married Doris Baillie, June 27, 1927. He has one son, Peter William. Residence: 44 Sunnyside Avenue, Westmount, Quebec.

Thomas Rodgie McLagan, O.B.E.

President & General Manager
Canada Steamship Lines, Limited.

Jules R. Timmins, O.B.E., LL.D., D.Sc.

Vice President
Iron Ore Company of Canada Limited

Jules R. Timmins, O.B.E., LL.D., D.Sc. . . . born in Mattawa, Ontario, on June 6, 1888. He was educated at St. Michael's College, Toronto, and McGill University, Montreal. He served with the Canadian Engineers in World War I. In 1927 he formed the stock brokerage firm of J. R. Timmins & Co., with offices in Montreal, Toronto and New York. In 1935 he became President of Hollinger Consolidated Gold Mines Limited. He is President of Hollinger-Hanna Limited, Hollinger North Shore Exploration Company Limited, Labrador Mining and Exploration Company Limited, Quebec North Shore and Labrador Railway Company and Vice-President of Iron Ore Company of Canada; all of these five companies are associated in the development of the iron ore project in Ungava, Northern Quebec. In addition he is a Vice-President of the Imperial Bank of Canada. Director: Canada Oil Lands Limited; Canadian Petrofina Limited; Fire Insurance Company of Canada; Great Lakes Paper Company Limited; Gunnar Mines Limited; Mining Corporation of Canada Limited; Montreal Locomotive Works Limited; Noranda Mines Limited; Normetal Mining Corporation Limited; Quemont Mining Corporation Limited; The Royal Trust Company; San Antonio Gold Mines Limited; Sogemines Limited; Waite Amulet Mines Limited; Combustion Engineering, Inc., of New York. Residence: 14 Sunnyside Ave., Westmount, Que.

William H. Durrell

Executive Vice-President
Hollinger-Hanna Limited

William H. Durrell . . . born at Portage du Fort, Quebec, on October 31, 1903. He was educated at the Haileybury School of Mines. From 1921 to 1941 he was a partner in the firm of Sutcliffe Company Limited, consulting engineers specializing in mining developments across Northern Canada. From 1941 to 1945 he was in charge of wartime construction in Labrador, including Goose Bay Airport, and work along the sea coast. In 1945 he formed a private company, engaged in both consulting and construction work. In 1947 he was appointed General Manager of Labrador Mining and Exploration Company Limited, Hollinger North Shore Exploration Company Limited, and Quebec North Shore and Labrador Railway Company. Upon its formation, in 1949, he also became General Manager of Hollinger-Hanna Limited, management company for Iron Ore Company of Canada. He became Executive Vice-President of Hollinger-Hanna Limited in 1954. In 1955 he became Vice-President of Quebec North Shore and Labrador Railway Company. He is a Director of various other Canadian Companies. Member: Associations of Professional Engineers of Ontario, Quebec and Newfoundland; Canadian Institute of Mining and Metallurgy, and the Association of Ontario Land Surveyors.

Gordon R. Ball . . . born in Toronto in 1897. He began his banking career at Perth, Ont., during the First World War when the Army discovered he had enlisted while under age. A year later, at 18, he re-enlisted and within a short time he was in action on the Western Front. He was wounded three times and was awarded the Military Medal for bravery. He is possibly the best known of all Canadian bankers in United States financial communities, probably as a consequence of his 23 years' experience in the Bank of Montreal's New York agency, where he was first agent when appointed General Manager in 1947. He is a member of the Dollar Sterling Trade Council; a trustee of the National Industrial Conference Board (U.S.A.); and a member of the Canadian Council of that organization. He was honorary chairman of the Advisory Committee on Overseas Investment, in 1950. He was appointed President of the Bank of Montreal in 1952. He is married and has a son and a daughter.

Gordon R. Ball,

President
Bank of Montreal.

G. Arnold Hart, M.B.E., . . . Born in 1913. He began his banking career 28 years ago in Toronto, subsequently serving at a number of branches there and at the head office in Montreal. In the Second World War he served overseas and retired from the Army as a major and a Member of the Order of the British Empire (Military Division) in 1946. On his return from overseas, he became secretary to the late George Spinney, then president of the Bank of Montreal. Early in 1948, he became assistant superintendent of Alberta branches and in 1949 was made manager of the bank's main office at Edmonton. Two years later he was appointed an agent at the bank's New York office. Then in 1953, he became a superintendent at the head office, and in the following year was appointed an assistant general manager. In April, 1956, he was made deputy general manager, and, on January 1, 1957, became general manager at the age of 43. He is one of the youngest general manager in the 141-year history of the Bank of Montreal.

G. Arnold Hart, M.B.E.,

General Manager
Bank of Montreal

Francis Gilbert Ferrabee

President & General Manager
Canadian Ingersoll-Rand Co. Ltd.

Francis Gilbert Ferrabee . . . born at Montreal, August 25, 1902. He was educated at Lower Canada College, Royal Military College and McGill University where he received his B.Sc. His career began with Ingersoll-Rand Co., Phillipsburg N.J., in September 1924. He then went on the Sales Engineer in Pittsburgh, Pa., in July 1925; Representative at Huntington, W. Va., in January 1925. Ass't to Manager Pittsburgh, Pa., November 1928; General Sales Dept., New York, December 1933; General Sales Manager for Canadian Ingersoll-Rand Co. Ltd., Montreal, Quebec in June 1934; He became a Director in 1937; Vice-President of the Sales Division in 1939; Vice-President and Ass't General Manager in 1941; Vice-President and General Manager in 1942; President and General Manager in 1953. He was made a Director of Ingersoll-Rand Co. (U.S.A.) in 1955. He served as Lieutenant 2nd Regiment R.C.A. (N.P.A.M.) from 1922-24; No. 3 Army Field Workshop, R.C.O.C. (Reserve) 2 i/c and Captain 1939-41; No. 4 Reserve Division Ordinance Workshop, C.O. and Major 1941-43. He was a Director of Compressed Air and Gas Equipment Division, Wartime Prices and Trade Board from 1942-45. Clubs: Engineers; University; Mount Royal; Montreal Racket; Montreal Indoor Tennis; St. George's (Sherbrooke); Mount Bruno Country; Sherbrooke Country. Societies and Associations: Engineering Institute of Canada; Canadian Institute of Mining & Metallurgy; Institute of Administration; Society for Advancement of Management; Machinery and Equipment Manufacturers' Association of Canada (Past Pres.); Canadian Industrial Preparedness Association (Past Director); Montreal Board of Trade (Past President); Canadian Chamber of Commerce (Past Member Executive Committee); Canadian Manufacturers' Association Executive & Administrative Committee); Montreal R.C.E.M.E. Corps Association (Past Chairman); McGill graduates Society (Past President); Delta Upsilon (McGill). Residence: 3424 Simpson Street, Montreal, Quebec and Mount Bruno, Quebec.

George L. Wilcox, B.E.E.

President
Canadian Westinghouse Company Limited.

George L. Wilcox, B.E.E., . . . born in New York, N.Y., January 20, 1915. He was educated at Polytechnique Institute of Brooklyn, New York (B.E.E., 1939). He joined Westinghouse Electric International Company in 1943 and held successive posts as sales manager, vice-president in charge of sales, and executive vice-president from 1953 to 1955. He became president of Canadian Westinghouse Company Limited in 1955. During this year he received the Westinghouse Order of Merit for outstanding management abilities. He is a director of the Toronto Dominion Bank, Polytechnic Research and Development Company and of Canadian Westinghouse subsidiaries. He is also a governor of McMaster University, Hamilton, Ontario. Clubs: The Hamilton (Hamilton, Ont.); The Hamilton Golf & Country (Ancaster, Ont.); The University (New York, N.Y.); The Wall Street (New York, N.Y.); His recreations include fishing and sailing. He married Leah Smallshaw on September 2, 1935. They have one son (George) and two daughters (Leslie and Holly). Residence: The Royal Connaught Hotel, Hamilton, Ontario.

George J. McNamara . . . He served for five years in the Marine Division of the Company and was Manager of the Division for two years. He was named General Manager of the McNamara Construction Company in 1952. In 1954 he was appointed President of the Company. This Company, one of the very few Canadian Construction firms to engage extensively in marine work as well as heavy construction work on land, has dredged millions of yards of sand, mud, glacial till and rock to help bring the St. Lawrence Seaway and Power Projects into existence.

George J. McNamara

President
McNamara Construction Company Limited

Harold S. McNamara . . . he served in the field on some of the Company's largest construction projects before being named General Manager of the Quebec subsidiary Cartier Construction Limited, in 1953. Two years later in 1955, he was promoted to the position of Vice President and General Manager of the McNamara Construction Company Limited.

Harold S. McNamara

Vice President & General Manager
McNamara Construction Company Limited

Charles Fowler Williams Burns

Chairman
Burns Bros. & Co. Limited
Burns Bros. & Denton Limited.

Charles Fowler Williams Burns . . . born Vancouver, B.C., Sept. 27, 1907. He was educated at Upper Canada College, 1916-21; Trinity College School, 1921-26; University of Toronto, 1926-28. Came to Toronto, in 1915. Floor Member, Campbell Stratton, Toronto 1929-31; investment dealer, R. A. Daly & Co., Toronto, 1931-32; President Chas. Burns & Co., Toronto, Jan., 1932, which was later enlarged by inclusion of the late Latham Burns and name changed to Burns Bros. & Company, Sept, 1932; He is governor, University of Toronto, Trinity College and Trinity College School. He entered R.C.A.F., Aug. 1, 1941, and was demobilized at the conclusion of hostilities with the rank of Wing Commander. He is Chairman Burns Bros. & Co. Limited; Burns Bros. & Denton Limited; Chairman of the Board, Burns Bros. & Denton Inc., New York; Senior Vice-President and Director, Crown Life Insurance Company; President: Royal Agricultural Winter Fair; Director: Canadian Breweries Limited; Chartered Trust Company; The General Accident Assurance Company of Canada; Huron Forest Products Ltd.; Eastern Steel Products Ltd.; The Monarch Knitting Company Limited; Wool Combing Corporation of Canada Ltd.; Maple Leaf Gardens, Limited; Scottish Canadian Assurance Corporation; The Ontario Jockey Club Limited: Clubs: Toronto; York; Toronto Hunt; Ontario Jockey (Director); University; Halifax. Societies: Zeta Psi Fraternity; A.F. & A.M. (Harcourt Lodge). Recreations: swimming, tennis and riding. Married: Janet Mary Wilson Ottawa, Ont., February 23, 1934; has one son, Herbert Michael and two daughters, Joan Harrison and Janet Mary Cairine. Residence: Kingfield Farms, King, Ont.

David S. Beatty,

President
Burns Bros. & Co. Limited
Burns Bros. & Denton Limited.

David S. Beatty . . . born in Toronto, Ontario, May 11, 1915. He is President of Burns Bros. & Denton Limited, Burns Bros. & Company Limited. Vice-President Burns Bros. & Denton, Inc., New York. He is a Director of: Aga Steel Radiator Co. of Canada, British Columbia Oil Lands, Canadian Equity Insurance Company, Devon-Palmer Oils Limited, Milton Brick Co. Limited, Pronto Uranium Mines Ltd., United Stationery Co. Ltd. Governor: Havergal College, Upper Canada College, Toronto Stock Exchange. Recreations: fishing, music, nature study. Clubs: Albany, Toronto, Granite, Empire, Glen Major Fishing, Toronto Cricket, Skating and Curling Club. Married: Ann Elise Ross in Sault Ste Marie, Ontario on October 14, 1939. Has two children David Ross and Barbara Elise. Residence: 268 Lytton Boulevard, Toronto, Ontario.

Philip Louis Pratley D.Eng., M. Inst. C.E., M.E.I.C., . . . born December 4, 1884 in Liverpool, England. He was educated at the Liverpool Institute; Universities of Victoria and Liverpool (B.Sc. B. Eng.). Came to Canada in February 1906. He was a draughtsman with Montreal Locomotive and Machine Company in February 1906; draughtsman Dominion Bridge Company Lachine 1906-1908; chief designer for the Quebec Bridge Board Montreal, 1909-10; Designing Engineer, St. Lawrence Bridge Company, 1910; Assistant Designing Engineer and later Designing Engineer, Dominion Bridge Company Co., Montreal, 1912-20. Engineer of Bridges, Grand Trunk Railway Arbitration, 1920-21; Consulting Engineer in partnership with Lt.-Col. C. N. Monsarrat, 1921-40. In 1939 was awarded the degree of Doctor of Engineering by the University of Liverpool. Designed a number of Canada's important bridges which include Jacques Cartier Bridge, Montreal, Isle of Orleans Bridge, Quebec, Canadian Portion of Thousand Islands Bridge, Lions Gate Bridge, Vancouver, B.C., Burlington Skyway High Level Bridge, near Hamilton, Ont., Angus L. McDonald Bridge Halifax, N.S., Second Narrows Bridge, Vancouver, B.C., Niagara Arch Bridge and various other notable structures. He was also Canadian Engineer on such International Bridges as Blue Water Bridge, Sarnia-Port Huron, Ambassador Bridge, Windsor-Detroit, Ogdensburg International Bridge. He was retained by the St. Lawrence Seaway Authority as Consulting Engineer on the raising of the Jacques Cartier Bridge, South Approach; as foundation Consultant for the International Bridge crossing South Channel of the St. Lawrence river at Cornwall; and as Consulting Engineer for a new High Level Bridge crossing North Channel, St. Lawrence river, Cornwall. Clubs: University (Montreal); Esperanto (Montreal). Married: Hilda Marion Webster September 15, 1911. They have two sons. Residence: 5 Thornhill Ave., Westmount, Quebec.

Philip Louis Pratley, D.Eng.,

Consulting Engineer

William Gardner Miller . . . born Osaka, Japan (U.S. citizen by birth), August 3, 1905. He was educated at Shady Side Academy, Pittsburgh, Pa.; Stevens Institute of Technology, Hoboken, N.J. (M.E., 1927). 1927-28, student engineer, Stone & Webster, Boston, Mass.; Asst. Production Manager, Jackson Engineering Corporation, Tulsa, Okla., 1928-32; Project Engineer, Alco Products Division, American Locomotive Company, New York, N.Y., 1932-34, 1937; Production Manager, Witt Ice & Gas Co., Los Angeles, Cal., 1935-36; Engineer in Charge, Alco Products Division, American Locomotive Company, Paris, France, 1937-39; Staff of V.P. Manufacturing, American Locomotive Company, New York, N.Y., 1939-45; Supt. Diesel Manufacturing Division, American Locomotive Company, Schenectady, N.Y., 1945-47; Asst. to Vice-President Locomotive Division, American Locomotive Company, Schenectady, N.Y., 1947; Manager American Locomotive Company, Auburn, N.Y., 1948-50; Exec. Asst. to Chairman and President, American Locomotive Company, New York, N.Y., 1950-51; Exec. Vice-President, Montreal Locomotive Works Ltd., Montreal, Que., 1952-53; President Montreal Locomotive Works Ltd., Montreal in 1954. He served with Manhattan Units, 101st Cavalry, New York National Guard, 1933-34, 1937. Member Executive Council Canadian Chamber of Commerce, Member Council Montreal Board of Trade, Director Montreal Boys' Association, Director Machinery and Equipment Manufacturers' Association of Canada. Clubs: Saint James's; University; The Mount Bruno Country Club Inc.; The Laurentian Lodge Club; The Hermitage Country; The Mohawk (Schenectady, N.Y.); University (New York, N.Y.). Societies: St. George's Lodge No. 6, F.A.M. (Schenectady). Recreations: Golf and skiing. Married: Florence Mary Hornsby, formerly of London, England, December 10, 1938; has one son and one daughter. Residence: 76 Belvedere Place, Westmount, Que.

William Gardner Miller,

President,
Montreal Locomotive Works, Limited.

James Muir, D.C.L., LL.D.

Chairman and President
The Royal Bank of Canada

James Muir, D.C.L., LL.D. . . . born in Peebles, Scotland. He was educated in Public and High Schools at Peebles. On July 17, 1907 he joined the Commercial Bank of Scotland, Ltd., in Peebles. In 1910 he joined the Chartered Bank of India in London. He entered the Royal Bank of Canada at Moose Jaw, Sask., on January 30, 1912. He was transferred to Supervisor's Department in Winnipeg in March 1916. On December 19, 1916, he was appointed Accountant at Winnipeg, Grain Exchange Branch. He was transferred to Head Office on December 28, 1917. On March 2, 1923, he was appointed Inspector at Supervisor's Department, Winnipeg. On October 19, 1925, he was appointed Assistant Supervisor at Supervisor's Department in New York. He was appointed Manager at Winnipeg on April 2, 1928. On December 30, 1931, he returned to Head Office as General Inspector and on December 10, 1935, he was made Assistant General Manager. He was appointed General Manager on December 4, 1945. On April 15, 1947, he was elected a Director and on October 19, 1948, elected a Vice-President. He was elected President on October 18, 1949 and Chairman and President on December 14, 1954. He is Vice-President and member of the Executive Committee of the Montreal Trust Company, director and member of Executive Committee, Algoma Steel Corp., Ltd. Director: Canadian Pacific Railway; The Capital Investment Corp. of Montreal Ltd.; Northwest Nitro-Chemicals Ltd.; the Scotsman Publications Ltd., Edinburgh; Sogemines Ltd.; Standard Brands Inc.; Transoceanic Development Corp. Ltd.; Metropolitan Life Insurance Company; Trust Corporation of Bahamas Ltd.; Westcoast Transmission Co. Ltd., Calgary. Director and Vice-President, The Royal Bank of Canada Trust Company. Governor: Lower Canada College; Dalhousie University; Montreal General Hospital; The Royal Edward Laurentian Hospital; and Governor and Member of the Executive Committee, Royal Victoria Hospital, Montreal. He is Freeman of the Royal and Ancient Burgh of Peebles, Scotland, 1952; Life Member, The National Trust for Scotland, 1954; Warden of Neidpath, Scotland, June 19, 1957; Elected Honorary Chief Eagle Ribs of the Blood Indian Tribe of the Blackfoot Confederacy in Alberta, July 1954; appointed to the 5-man Investment committee of the Canada Council, April 1957. Clubs: Royal & Ancient Golf Club of St. Andrews; St. James's; Montreal; Mount Royal; Mount Bruno Golf & Country; The Brook (New York); Manitoba Club (Winnipeg); Mattawin Fishing; Seigniory; Royal St. Lawrence Yacht; Laval-sur-le-Lac Golf; Toronto; York (Toronto); Rideau (Ottawa). Married: Phyllis Marguerite Brayley, Sept. 27, 1919. They have one daughter. Residence: 3495 Holton Ave., Montreal, Que.

Kenneth Middleton Sedgewick

General Manager
The Royal Bank of Canada

Kenneth Middleton Sedgewick . . . born at Middle Musquodoboit, Nova Scotia, on March 7, 1911. Educated at High school in Nova Scotia. He joined the Royal Bank of Canada at Middle Musquodoboit, N. S., in 1929. He was transferred to Truro and Halifax branches, Supervisor's Department, Halifax, and Canadian Credits Department at Head Office in Montreal. He was appointed Assistant Manager at Toronto Branch in 1936. In 1941 he was appointed Inspecting Officer, Supervisor's Department, Halifax. He was appointed Manager of the Truro Branch in 1941, Manager of the Halifax Branch in 1943, and Manager of the Montreal Branch in 1946. He was appointed Assistant General Manager, Head Office, in 1949, and Chief Administrative Officer in Toronto of Ontario branches in 1951. On December 6, 1956 he was appointed General Manager. Clubs: Royal Montreal Curling; Montreal Club; St. James's; Toronto Golf; York Club; The Toronto Club; Canadian Club of Montreal; Forest and Stream; Mount Bruno Golf & Country; Mount Royal; Royal Montreal Golf; Seigniory. Recreations: Golf and Curling. Married: Beatrice Margaret Brophey on September 18, 1937. They have one son, James Millar. Reisdence: 3010 Breslay Road, Montreal, Que.

Arthur Ferdinand Mayne . . . born in Drayton, Ont., on January 12, 1909. Educated at Drayton Public and Continuation Schools. He started with the Royal Bank of Canada at Drayton on November 1, 1925. He later served in Galt, Ont., and Toronto, Ont., branches, the Supervisor's Department, Toronto, and the Credits Department at Head Office, Montreal. He was appointed Inspector in the Supervisor's Department at Calgary in 1941. He returned to Head Office as Inspector of Foreign Branches in 1943, in which capacity he travelled extensively in the West Indies and Central and South America. He was appointed Supervisor of Foreign Branches in 1945; General Inspector in 1946; Assistant General Manager on November 30, 1948 and Associate General Manager on February 9, 1955. Clubs: St. James; Royal Montreal Golf; Royal Montreal Curling; Montreal Amateur Athletic Association, Mattawin Fishing; Montreal Skeet. Recreations: Fishing, hunting, curling, golf, skeet shooting. Married: Helen Mary Dunnigan on September 4, 1934. They have one son, Patrick James. Residence: 444 Elm Ave., Westmount, Que.

Arthur Ferdinand Mayne

Associate General Manager (Non-Domestic Business)
The Royal Bank of Canada

Lewis Eric Reford, B.A., . . . born Montreal, Quebec, December 12, 1900. He was educated at Rugby School, England; Royal Military College, Kingston, Ont.; McGill University, where he received his B.A. in 1921; Oxford University, New College (B.A.). He joined the Robert Reford Co. Ltd., in 1924, becoming Vice-President in 1929 and President in 1946. He was Councillor for the City of Montreal from 1944-47, 1947-1950 and 1950-54. Member of Council, Montreal Board of Trade, 1937-38; President, Shipping Federation of Canada, 1943-45. Hon. President, Quebec Division, Navy League of Canada. He is President of Mount Royal Rice Mills Ltd. and Hunting Steamship Company, Canada, Limited. Director: Canada Northwest Land Co. Ltd. Clubs: Mount Royal; University; Montreal. His recreations including riding and fishing. Married Katharina Nigolaivena, September 1927. They have two sons and one daughter. Residence: 6 Redpath Place, Montreal, Quebec.

Lewis Eric Reford, B.A.,

President
The Robert Reford Co. Ltd.

Desmond Arthur Clarke,

President,
Clarke Steamship Company Limited.

Desmond Arthur Clarke .. born Toronto, Ontario, January 9, 1892. He was educated in public schools; Collegiate Institute; Loyola College. Upon leaving school he commenced his career in the business of the family the Gulf & Paper Co.; organized Clarke Steamship Company Limited, The Clarke Trading Company Limited and North Shore Construction Company Limited, becoming president. In 1921 he founded and became President of Clarke Steamship Company. Early in 1941 he was appointed Director General of Shipbuilding. In 1943, he resigned as Director General of Shipbuilding and became Special Assistant to the Right Honourable C. D. Howe. In 1944 and again in 1945 he was General Chairman of the Federation of Catholic Charities Campaign. In 1946 the Order of the British Empire was given to him. In the same year he became a director of St. Mary's Hospital. In 1951 he was made a director of the Montreal City & District Savings Bank. In that same year he became a Knight of Magistral Grace of the Sovereign and Military Order of Malta, and in 1954 Pope Pius XII conferred upon him the Knighthood of St. Sylvester. Also in 1954 he was Chief Warden of St. Patrick's Parish in Montreal. In 1955 he was elected Chairman, St. Mary's Hospital $5,500,000 Building Fund. He is also president of Terra Nova Steamship Company Limited, and Magdalen Islands Transportation Company Limited. Vice President of Lower St. Lawrence Transportation Company Limited; Labrador Fisheries Company; Quebec-Newfoundland Equipment & Supply Co. Ltd. Director: Gulf Ports Steamship Co. Ltd.; North Pioneer Steamship Co. Ltd.; La Traverse Rivière-du-Loup-St. Siméon Limitée; St. Lawrence Sea Products Ltd.; L. T. Blais Ltée; Chairman of La Traverse Rivière-du-Loup- St. Siméon Limitée. Married: Aline Paradis, of Quebec, June 21, 1916; has two sons and one daughter.

Stanley Desmond Clarke, B. Sc.,

Vice President,
Clarke Steamship Company Limited.

Stanley Desmond Clarke, B.Sc. .... born at Quebec on December 18th, 1917. He was educated at Quebec High School, Quebec, Loyola College, Montreal, Royal Military College, Kingston, Ont., Queen's University, Kingston, Ont., where he received his B.Sc. in Mechanical Engineering. From July 1939 to December 1939 he was with Swan Hunter & Wigham Richardson Ltd. He served with the Canadian Army in Canada, Europe and North Africa from January 1940 to September 1945; was demobilized with rank of Lieutenant-Colonel. From October 1945 to March 1946, he was Assistant to Superintendent, Clarke Steamship Company; April 1946 to February 1950, Operating Manager. In March 1950 he was appointed General Manager of Clarke Steamship Company and associated companies. In September 1956, he was elected Vice President of the Company. President: Gulf Ports Steamships Co. Ltd.; North Coast Steamship Co. Ltd.; North Shore Construction Company Ltd.; Quebec Newfoundland Equipment & Supply Co. Ltd. Vice-President: The Charlevoix-Saguenay Navigation Company: Director: Terra Nova Steamship Co. Ltd.; North Pioneer Steamship Co. Ltd.; Magdalen Islands Transportation Company Limited; The Lower St. Lawrence Transportation Company Ltd.; La Traverse Riviere-du-Loup St. Simeon Limitee; Ungava Transports Limitee; The Clarke Trading Company Limited; Labrador Fisheries Limited. Married: Josefina Delgado y Angulo in Havana Cuba, February 27, 1949. Has two sons, Desmond and Donald, and one daughter, Rosemary.

344

Charles Sydney Frost, M.C., . . . born Argyle, Yarmouth County, Nova Scotia, 27 November 1893. He was educated at Yarmouth Academy, N.S. He began his career with The Bank of Nova Scotia, as a junior clerk, in Yarmouth, N.S., in 1908; Accountant, St. John's Newfoundland, 1914; Manager, Fogo, Newfoundland, 1919; Asst. Manager, St. John's Newfoundland, 1921; Winnipeg, Manitoba, 1926; Manager, Saskatoon, Sask., 1931, Saint John N.B., 1938; Supervisor, Toronto, Ont., and Saint John, N.B., 1941-46; Assistant General Manager, Toronto, Ont., 1946. General Manager, 1949; elected a Director, December 1950 and Vice-President in July 1951; Executive Vice-President, December, 1954; President, June 1956. He served in First World War with Royal Newfoundland Regiment with ranks of Private to Captain, 1914-19; awarded Military Cross, 1918. He is a Director of Imperial Life Assurance Company of Canada; Cosmos Imperial Mills Ltd., Toronto General Trusts Corporation; J. Spencer Turner Co. Ltd. Clubs: The Toronto; York; Granite; National, Toronto Golf; Royal Canadian Military Institute. His recreations include golf and fishing. He married Gertrude R. Hains July 12, 1921. They have two sons and one daughter: C. Sydney, Jr., Robert, Vivian E. Residence: 216 Dunvegan Road, Toronto, Ontario.

Charles Sydney Frost, M.C.,

President,
The Bank of Nova Scotia.

F. William Nicks . . . born in Winnipeg, Manitoba, 9, October 1906. He was educated at St. John's School, Winnipeg, Manitoba. He joined the Bank of Nova Scotia, Winnipeg, 1923; Accountant, Halifax, N.S., 1937; Accountant Montreal, P.Q., 1939; Assistant Manager, Halifax, N.S., 1942; and Assistant Manager, Toronto, Ont., 1944; an Assistant Supervisor, Saint John, N. B., 1946; Manager Halifax Branch, 1946; Manager, Montreal Branch, 1949; Manager, Toronto Branch, 1950; Assistant General Manager, Toronto, 1952; appointed General Manager of the Bank, 1954; elected a Director, January 1957, and a Vice President, September 1957. He is a Director of National Trust Company Limited, The Canada Life Assurance Company and Past President of The Canadian Bankers' Association. Clubs: Halifax (Nova Scotia); The Toronto, National; Royal Canadian Yacht. Residence: 2 Bayview Wood, Toronto, Ontario.

F. William Nicks,

Vice-President & General Manager
The Bank of Nova Scotia.

James Gilmore

Partner

Milne, Gilmore & German

James Gilmore . . . born in Scotland. He received basic and technical education and shipyard training in Scotland. He came to Canada in October 1928, at which time he was employed by Canadian Vickers Limited, Montreal. He was appointed Naval Architect, Canadian Vickers Limited, in 1942. He remained with the firm until 1946 when he joined German & Milne as a Naval Architect. In 1950 he became a partner in the firm. Member: Corporation of Professional Engineers of Quebec; Engineering Institute of Canada, Institution of Naval Architects, England. Society of Naval Architects and Marine Engineers, New York. Clubs. Engineers Club of Montreal; Beaconsfield Golf Club Inc. Residence: 97 Drayton Road, Pointe Claire, Que.

W. Harold Milne,

Partner

Milne, Gilmore & German

W. Harold Milne . . . born in Scotland. He was educated in Scotland and England. He came to Canada in November 1917 to the Imperial Munitions Board, Ottawa. Following this he was associated with several other firms, including Canadian Allis Chalmers, Ltd., Wallace Shipyards, (now Burrard Drydock), Canadian Vickers, Limited, Saint John Drydock and Shipbuilding Co. Ltd., Montreal Drydocks Limited. He then became a partner in the firm of German and Milne in 1936; Technical Adviser to Department of Munitions and Supply, Shipbuilding Branch, Ottawa. Member: Corporation of Professional Engineers of Quebec; Engineering Institute of Canada; Society of Naval Architects and Marine Engineers, New York; Institution of Engineers and Shipbuilders in Scotland; North East Coast Institution of Engineers and Shipbuilders, England. Clubs: Mount Stephen (Montreal); Laurentian (Ottawa); Seigniory Club, (Montebello). Residence: 42 Anwoth Road, Westmount, Quebec.

J. F. Vaughan . . . born in Hamilton, Ontario. Graduating from Westdale Collegiate in Hamilton, he spent a year with a firm of accountants before joining the Royal Canadian Navy in 1942. Upon his discharge in 1946 with the rank of lieutenant in the executive branch, he returned to Hamilton to complete his studies for his chartered accountants degree, which he obtained in 1950. He joined Port Weller Dry Docks Ltd. in 1950 as office manager. From 1951 he served as secretary-treasurer of the Company until 1956 when he was appointed general manager at the age of 36. He was appointed a director of the Company in 1958. Member: Institute of Chartered Acountants; St. Catharines. (Ont.) Club; The Gyro Club of St. Catharines. Director: Niagara Peninsula Sanitorium. Hobbies: gardening and woodworking. He is married and has one son. Residence: Lakeshore Road, St. Catharines, Ontario.

J. F. Vaughan

General Manager
Port Weller Dry Docks Limited

Ernest John Hunter, B.Sc., J.P. . . . he was educated at Oundle and later entered University where he obtained his Bachelor of Science Degree. After graduating he served in the Design and Drawing Offices at Wallsend Shipyard following which he joined the staff of Barclay Curle & Company Limited first in their engineering department and later in their ship repairing department. In 1939 he returned to Wallsend Dry Docks Department as an Assistant Manager, becoming General Manager in 1943. In 1945, he was appointed a Director of Swan, Hunter & Wigham Richardson Ltd. In 1957, he was appointed Chairman of the Company. He is also Chairman of The Hopemount Shipping Company Ltd., and M. W. Swinburne & Sons Ltd. He is a Director of Barclay, Curle & Company Ltd.; The Glasgow Iron & Steel Co. Ltd.; The Wallsend Slipway & Engineering Co. Ltd.; Mercantile Dry Dock Co. Ltd.; Tyne Tanker Cleaning Co. Ltd. He is President-elect of the North East Coast Institution of Marine Engineers and Shipbuilders. He is a Past President of the Shipbuilding Employers Federation; Past Chairman of the Tyne Shipbuilders Assoc.; North East Coast Shiprepairers Assoc., which Assoc. he represents on the Grand Council of the Federation of British Industries. Vice-President: British Employers Confederation. Member: Institution of Naval Architects; Institution of Marine Engineers; Institution of Shipbuilders and Engineers in Scotland; of the Executive Board of The Shipbuilding Conference; Lloyds General Committee; Research Council of British Shipbuilding Research Assoc.; Tyne Improvement Commission. Employers representative on the Northern Regional Board for Industry. Part time member of North Eastern Electricity Board. Justice of the Peace. Liveryman of the Worshipful Company of Shipwrights. Freeman of the City of London.

Ernest John Hunter, B.Sc., J.P.

Chairman
Swan, Hunter & Wigham Richardson, Ltd.

Neil John McKinnon

President,
The Canadian Bank of Commerce.

Neil John McKinnon . . . born in Cobalt, Ont., Jan. 17, 1911. He entered the Canadian Bank of Commerce at Cobalt, Ont., in 1925; Inspector, Head Office, Toronto, 1937; Assistant Manager, Toronto Branch, 1939; Assistant General Manager, Head Office, 1945; General Manager, 1952; Vice-President and Director, 1954; President, 1956. He is also President of The Dominion Realty Company Limited; Director: The Canada Life Assurance Company; Western Assurance Company; British America Assurance Company; Brazilian Traction, Light and Power Company Limited; National Trust Company Limited; Trustee, Hospital for Sick Children, Toronto. Clubs: Toronto, Rosedale Golf, Mount Royal (Montreal), Rideau (Ottawa). Recreation: Golf. Married: Phyllis Adelaide Cowie, May 3, 1941; has one daughter and one son. Residence: 116 Dunvegan Road, Toronto, Ontario.

Jeffery Page Rein Wadsworth

Vice President & General Manager,
The Canadian Bank of Commerce.

Jeffery Page Rein Wadswarth . . . born in Toronto, Ontario, July 27, 1911. He was educated at Lakefield Preparatory School and Upper Canada College. He joined The Canadian Bank of Commerce in Port Credit, Ontario, in 1928; Inspector's Department, Head Office, Toronto, Ont., 1934; Assistant Manager, Hamilton, Ontario, 1943-45; Assistant Manager, Toronto, Ont., 1945-49; Regional Superintendent, Calgary, Alta., 1950-53; Assistant General Manager, Head Office, Toronto, Ont., 1953-55; Assistant General Manager, Montreal, Que., 1955-56; General Manager, Head Office, Toronto, Ont., 1956 to date. He was elected Vice President and Director, 1957. He is also a Director of Dominion Realty Company Limited; Governor, Lakefield Preparatory School, Havergal College, Toronto. Clubs: Toronto; Toronto Golf; Engineers (Toronto); Mount Royal (Montreal); St. James's (Montreali; Ranchmen's (Calgary); Hamilton. His recreations include golf, skiing, sailing and fishing. Married: Elizabeth Cameron Bunting in Toronto, Ontario, on September 23, 1940. They have one daughter Page. Residence. 484 Russell Hill Rd., Toronto, Ont.

T. Graeme McLintock, M.B.E. . . . born at Glasgow, Scotland, on March 6, 1920. He was educated at Rugby and Cambridge, where he was graduated in Economics and Law in 1940. He joined the Indian Army and served throughout the Second World War in the Middle East and Italy and rose to the rank of Major. He joined The British Petroleum Company Ltd., in 1946 and since then his career has been chiefly associated with distributing and marketing. Before assuming his present post, he was Manager of pricing and economics, coordination branch in London, England. He is Vice-President and Managing Director of BP Canada Limited, Montreal; Director of British Petroleum Company of Canada Limited, and of BP Refinery Canada Limited. He is married and has two children. Residence: 637 Carleton Avenue, Westmount, Que.

T. Graeme McLintock, M.B.E.

Vice-President and Managing Director
BP Canada Limited

Alastair F. Down, O.B.E., M.C., T.D., C.A. . . . He was born at Kirkcaldy, Fife, Scotland, on July 23, 1914. He was educated at Edinburgh Academy, Scotland, 1922 to 1927 and Marlborough College, Wiltshire, England, 1927 to 1932. After qualification as a chartered accountant, he joined The British Petroleum Company Ltd., in London, England. He served in Palestine (now Israel) from 1938 to 1940; Iran, from 1945 to 1947; London, from 1947 to 1953; and came to Canada as the firm's representative in 1953. During World War II, he served in the Western Desert, Egypt, from 1940 to 1944 and was made Captain, then Major and Lieutenant-Colonel. In 1944, he was with the 8th Army Headquarters in Italy. In 1945, he was with N.W. Europe, Headquarters First Canadian Army (full Colonel). He was awarded the O.B.E., M.C. Territorial Decoration; Knight Commander Order of Orange Nassau with Swords and was mentioned in dispatches twice. He is President of British Petroleum of Canada Limited; President, BP Exploration (Canada) Ltd., Toronto; President, BP Canada Ltd., Montreal; President, BP Refinery Canada Ltd.; Director, Triad Oil Co. Ltd. He is married and has three children. Residence: 112 Buckingham Avenue, Toronto, Ont.

Alastair F. Down, O.B.E., M.C., T.D., C.A.

President
British Petroleum Company of Canada Limited

George Wesley Bourke, B.A., F.I.A., F.S.A.

President
Sun Life Assurance Company of Canada.

George Wesley Bourke, B.A., F.I.A., F.S.A., . . . born in Westport, Ontario on October 23rd, 1896. He was educated at Kingston and Montreal schools and McGill University from which he graduated in 1917 with a B.A. degree and the Anne Molson Gold Medal for Mathematics and Physics. He served with distinction and was awarded the Military Medal in France during World War 1, but was severely wounded. He first worked for the Sun Life Assurance during the summers of 1915 and 1916 in his student days. He joined the permanent staff of the company in 1919 as a member of the Actuarial Department. In 1924 he was named Chief of the Mathematical Department; in 1929, assistant Actuary. He was appointed General Manager in 1944, and in 1946, Managing Director. He was appointed Vice-President and Managing Director in 1947, and on February 14th, 1950, was elected President. He is a Fellow of the Institute of Actuaries of Great Britain (F.I.A.) and a Fellow of the Society of Actuaries (F.S.A.). He is Provincial Vice-President (Quebec) for the American Life Convention; a director of the Life Insurance Medical Research Fund (1956-57), and a Trustee of the S. S. Huebner Foundation for Insurance Education. He formerly held the position of Vice-President of the Actuarial Society of America, and on two other occasions was elected a Member of the Council. He is a past director of the Life Insurance Association of America, Institute of Life Insurance, Past President of the Canadian Life Insurance Officers Association. Member of the Board of Directors; Canadian Pacific Railway; Bank of Montreal; Royal Trust Company; Howard Smith Paper Mills Limited; Imperial Chemical Industries of Canada. Also a member of the Canadian Board of the Phoenix Assurance Company of London, England, and a Director of the Acadia Insurance Company. He is a Governor of McGill University and a Member of the Advisory Board of the Montreal General Hospital. Member: Mount Royal Club: University Club; Royal Montreal Golf Club; Seignory Club. Married: Beatrice Mitchell in 1920 They have three sons. Residence: 774 Upper Lansdowne Avenue, Westmount, Quebec.

Alistair Matheson Campbell, M.A., F.I.A., F.S.A.

Director and Executive Vice-President
Sun Life Assurance Company of Canada.

Alistair Matheson Campbell, M.A., F.I.A., F.S.A., . . . born on July 3rd, 1905, in Strachur, Argyllshire, Scotland. He was educated at Inverness Royal Academy and Aberdeen University, graduating in 1927 with the degree of M.A. with first class honors in mathematics. He joined the Sun Life Assurance Company of Canada on July 21st, 1928. He was appointed Chief Clerk in 1930, Assistant Actuary in 1934, and Associate Actuary in 1940. He became Actuary of the Company in 1946, Assistant General Manager and Actuary in 1947, Vice-President and Actuary in 1950, and Executive Vice-President and Director in December 1956. In 1939 he was loaned to the Foreign Exchange Control Board to organize the Boards insurance branch and in 1940 he enlisted in the Royal Canadian Artillery, where he served until 1945, receiving his discharge with the rank of Captain. He is a past president and member of Officers Committee of the Canadian Life Insurance Officers Association; a Fellow of the Institute of Actuaries of Great Britain; a Governor and Fellow of the Society of Actuaries, and past President of the Canadian Association of Actuaries, member of the executive committee and Board of Management, and a past vice-president of the Canadian Red Cross Society, Quebec Division. In November 1956 he was awarded the Canadian Red Cross Honorary Membership, highest award given by the divisional Red Cross. Member: Mount Royal Club; University Club; Royal Montreal Golf Club. Married: Barbara Hampson Alexander on April 2nd, 1948. They have three daughters and one son. Residence: 3660 The Boulevard, Westmount, Quebec.

Albert C. Ashforth . . . born at Toronto, Ontario, on March 6, 1893. He was educated at Palmerston School and Harbord Collegiate, Toronto. He commenced his career as a Junior with the Bank of Hamilton, Toronto, in 1909. From 1910 to 1921, he was Junior at the Dominion Bank, Toronto. He was promoted to General Manager's Secretary in 1921, and in 1929 was made Supervisor. In 1934 he was appointed Manager of the Main Office, and in 1946, Assistant General Manager, Head Office. He was appointed General Manager in 1948, Vice President and Director in 1951 and President in 1955 of the Toronto-Dominion Bank. He is 1st Vice President of the Canadian Chamber of Commerce, and Honorary Treasurer of the St. John's Convalescent Hospital, Newtonbrook, Ontario. Director: Canada Life Assurance Co., Toronto; Union Carbide Canada Ltd., Toronto. Member: Investment Advisory Board; The London & Lancashire Insce. Co. Ltd., Toronto; and Advisory Committee of the Boy Scouts Assn. Married: Annetta Lillian Ross on September 5, 1921. They have two sons. Societies: A.F. & A.M.; Past Master, Rowland Lodge, Mount Albert, Ont., 1932; Member of the Zetland Lodge, Toronto, and the University Chapter, Royal Arch Masons. Clubs: Toronto Club; Granite (Toronto); National (Toronto); Rotary Club of Toronto; Past President, Lambton Golf & Country Club; Canadian (Toronto); Past Chairman, Board of Trade Club; former Member of Council, Board of Trade. Recreations: Golf and Curling. Residence: 18 Glenallan Rd., Toronto, Ont.

Albert C. Ashforth

President
The Toronto-Dominion Bank

Allen Thomas Lambert . . . born Regina, Saskatchewan, December 28, 1911. He was educated at Victoria Public and High Schools. He began his career as a junior clerk with the Bank of Toronto in Victoria, B.C., in 1927. Subsequently served in Vancouver, Brockville and Montreal. He then became Manager in Yellowknife, N.W.T., in 1946; Inspector, Winnipeg, Manitoba, 1947; Supervisor, Head Office, Toronto, 1949; Asst. Manager, Main Office, Montreal, 1950; Superintendent, Head Office, Toronto, 1953; Asst. General Manager, Toronto, 1953; General Manager, The Toronto-Dominion Bank, Toronto, 1956; Vice President & Director, 1956. He served with Royal Canadian Navy, as a Lieutenant from April 1943 to October 1945. He is Vice President & General Manager of the Toronto Dominion Bank; Director: Toronto Mental Health Clinic, Canadian Equity Insurance Co. Ltd., The Canada Permanent Trust Co. Clubs: Toronto; Toronto Golf; Granite; Toronto Board of Trade. Recreations: golf, curling. Married: Marion Grace Kotchapaw, in Winnipeg, Manitoba on May 20th, 1950. They have one son and one daughter. Residence: 103 St. Leonard's Avenue, Toronto 12, Ontario.

Allen Thomas Lambert

Vice-President & General Manager
The Toronto-Dominion Bank.

A. Sidney Dawes, M.C., B.Sc.

Chairman
Atlas Construction Limited

A. Sidney Dawes . . . born in Lachine, Que., Dec. 5, 1888. He was educated at Montreal High School and received his B.Sc. in 1910 from McGill University. His career began with Canadian Westinghouse Company, Hamilton where he served two years apprenticeship course. Two years contracting in Saskatoon and then joined Atlas Construction Limited, Montreal, in 1914. On the declaration of World War 1, enlisted in Canadian Field Artillery, going to France in May, 1915; he was twice wounded and then promoted Captain in 1917. he was awarded MC and appointed Major, 55th Battery, in March 1918. On demobilization, rejoined Atlas Construction Limited, who either in their own name or in that of a subsidiary company, have carried out the construction of the Montreal Water Intake; Montreal Aqueduct; Section 6 of the Welland Canal which included the Syphon Culvert and many others. He was President of the Builders' Exchange from 1927 to 1930. Served on Council: Montreal Board of Trade, 1933-34; Montreal Protestant School Commission, 1934-37; Councillor at Large, Canadian Lawn Tennis Association, 1939-46; President: Canadian Amateur Ski Association, 1945-47; President, Canadian Olympic Association, 1947-53. He was elected Member, International Olympic Committee at Stockholm in 1947. He is also Chairman of Anglin-Atlas Limited; President: Atlas Winston Limited; Vice-President: Atlas Construction (Toronto) Limited. Clubs: Mount Royal; St. James's; Forest and Stream; Mount Bruno Country; Murray Bay Golf; Indoor Tennis; Montreal Flying; Canadian; Montreal Board of Trade; Red Birds Ski; Montreal Skeet. Societies: Engineering Institute of Canada; Corporation of Professional Engineers of Quebec; Art Association of Montreal. Recreations: Golf, tennis, fishing, hunting and skiing. Married: Grace Elspeth Paterson, Oct. 11, 1919; one daughter. Residence: 1725 Cedar Ave., Montreal, Quebec.

John G. Bourne

President
Atlas Construction Limited

John G. Bourne . . . born in Montreal, Que., in 1918. He was educated at Selwyn House School, Westmount High School, McGill University. He joined the Royal Bank of Canada in 1935 where he was employed until 1939. In 1945 he joined Atlas Construction Ltd. From 1939 to 1942 he served with the 1st Bn. The Black Watch (RHR) of Canada in Canada and the United Kingdom. From 1942 to 1944 he was with the First Special Service Force as Lieutenant-Colonel Commanding a Battalion. Served in Aleutian Islands, Italy and Southern France. Rejoined Militia in 1946 and assumed command The Black Watch (RHR) of Canada in 1952. He retired in 1955. Clubs: Royal Montreal Golf; St. James's (Montreal); Indoor Tennis; United Services; Murray Bay Golf; Royal St. Lawrence Yacht. Married: Joan Elspeth Dawes on October 10, 1942. They have one son and one daughter. Residence: 25 Ramezay Road, Westmount, Que.

Walter G. Ward . . . born in Peterborough, Ontario. He joined Canadian General Electric in 1931 on production work. After serving his apprenticeship in the Instrument and Standards Laboratory and completing the Company's Engineering Test Course, he took leave of absence to attend McGill University to obtain his Electrical Engineering Degree. He served as a Lieutenant Commander in the Royal Canadian Navy during World War 11, and was mentioned in dispatches in the Normandy Invasion. He rejoined the Company in 1945 as Manager of the Electronic Equipment Section. He was appointed Manager of the Major Appliances Operation in Montreal in 1952. General Manager of the Appliance Department in 1954, then General Manager of the Wholesale Department in 1957. Also in 1957 he was appointed General Manager, Apparatus Department, Peterborough, Ontario. Member: Association of Professional Engineers of Ontario; Institute of Radio Engineers; Naval Officers Association.

Walter G. Ward

General Manager — Apparatus Department
Canadian General Electric Company Limited.

Robert Douglas . . . born at Strathclair, Manitoba. Graduated as an electrical engineer in 1938 from the University of Manitoba. Following his graduation he joined Canadian General Electric and the Company's well known test training course. Following wartime service as a Captain in the Royal Canadian Corps of Signals in England, North Africa, and the Continent, he re-joined Canadian General Electric in 1945 at its Head Office in Toronto. He was appointed Marketing Manager in the Apparatus Department in 1955 following wide experience in Management positions in Application and Sales Engineering functions. He is a member of the association of Professional Engineers of Ontario, and Associate member of the American Institute of Electrical Engineers, and a member of the Engineering Institute of Canada. He is also a member of the Executive Committee of the Canadian Electrical Association.

Robert Douglas

Marketing Manager — Apparatus Department
Canadian General Electric Company Limited.

J. A. Bénard,

President
Neyrpic Canada Ltd.

J. A. Bénard . . . born in France. He is a graduate engineer of the Ecole Polytechnique de Paris, France (1928). For two years thereafter he acted as a consultant for the Persian Navy. Following this he specialized in marine aids, lighthouse installations, harbours and airport construction. He then became associated with BBT in France during which time he became President of the firm. While in this post he had to deal with coal washeries, oil refineries and scientific instruments. He came to Canada in 1949. He is now Vice-President of Beaconing Optical and Precision Materials Co. Ltd.; Vice-president of SIDO Ltd., and has been President of Neyrpic Canada since its organization in 1955.

E. Pariset

General Manager
LaSalle Hydraulic Laboratory

E. Pariset . . . is a graduate of Ecole des Ingenieurs Hydrauliciens de Grenoble, France. He received his degree in 1947 as a Hydraulic Engineer. He began his career at this time when he joined the Neyrpic Laboratory in Grenoble. In 1952 he was promoted Engineer-in-chief in charge of hydro-electric projects at the same laboratory. He has been responsible for a large number of projects, namely: Donzere Mondragon; Montelimar; Serre Ponson in France as well as others in Brazil, Argentina, Greece and the Belgian Congo. He came to Canada in 1955, and as General Manager of the LaSalle Hydraulic Laboratory, was responsible for all the studies and researches including the St. Lawrence Seaway Scale Model.

R. Hausser . . . is a graduate of from Ecole des Ingenieurs Hydrauliciens de Grenoble in France. He received his degree in 1950 as a hydraulic engineer. The same year he joined the Neyrpic Laboratory in Grenoble, France. He had previously graduated in Mathematics at the University in Grenoble. Outside of France, he worked in Brazil and Pakistan on river problems and in Indonesia on hydro-electric projects. His other studies were on a large number of scientific and technical problems: Impulse turbines, hydraulic transportation of solids, water intakes for ships, thermal power houses and floor protection and sewage systems. He is now engineer-in chief for the LaSalle Hydraulic Laboratory.

R. Hausser

Engineer-in-Chief
LaSalle Hydraulic Laboratory.

William Harrison, Terry . . . born Philadelphia, Pa., U.S.A., December 29, 1906. He was educated at Episcopal Academy; William Penn Charter School, Union College; Schenectady, New York, U.S.A. He began his career in Levelman, Quebec with the Saguenay & Chibougamau Railroad Construction Dept., Chicoutimi, Quebec, in 1928; in 1929 he was Asst. Res. Engineer for the Canadian National Railways Construction Department, Shawinigan Falls, Quebec; in 1930 he was Asst. Div. Engineer for Canadian National Railways, Maintenance & Way Department, Montreal, Quebec; in 1931 he was assistant to plant manager, Gulf Oil Refinery Co., Philadelphia, Pa.; he worked at various construction companies in Montreal from 1932-1933; founded Credit Guide Ltd., Montreal, Quebec in 1933; from 1934-1938 he was salesman for Watson Jack & Co., Montreal, Quebec; founded and became President of Terry Machinery, Montreal, Quebec in 1938. He is also a Director of Terry Machinery Company (B.C.) Ltd.; Terry Machinery Company (Ont.) Ltd.; Terry Industries Limited. Clubs: Seigniory; Mount Royal Tennis; M.A.A.A. Society: Psi Upsilon Fraternity. Among his recreations are aqualung, skin diving, swimming, tennis, flying. Married: Hazel Mae Howe in Three Rivers, Quebec on June 29th, 1936; they have two sons. Residence: R.R. No. 2, Ste Therese, Quebec.

William Harrison Terry

President
Terry Machinery Company Limited.

Murray William Hayes,

Vice-Chairman
Executive Committee of the Montreal City Council

Murray William Hayes . . . born at Sherbrooke, Quebec. He was educated at Westmount, Que. public schools and after serving as a private with a tank battalion during World War I, he entered McGill University Law School from which he graduated in 1921. He never practiced law, but joined his father's firm, Sheet Metal Products Company Limited, and at 27, was one of the youngest sales managers in the country. He founded the Verdun Guardian-Observer and is president of Hayes Industries Limited, a position held since the company's formation in 1942. From 1948 to 1950 he was Executive Vice-President of Mount Royal Dairies, and is still a director. In 1951 he first bought W. J. Keating and Son Limited, and a few months later, its chief competitor, a British firm called Durham Industries. He amalgamated the two companies under the name of Hayes, Durham Forgings Ltd., makers of marine hardware, wood and steel blocks, shackles, etc., and sold the company to Quebec Steel Limited in 1954. He is a director of The Canadian Manufacturers' Ass'n., Montreal Branch, which appointed him a "C" Councillor, in 1954. He was appointed Vice-Chairman of the Executive Committee of the Montreal City Council in 1957. He married Dorothy Mead of Montreal in 1921. They have two sons and four grandchildren. He was President of the N.D.G. Conservative Association between 1930 and 1937. Member: Montreal Board of Trade; Canadian Legion. Clubs: Pasadena Golf and Country; Shawbridge Country; St. George's; University. Residence: Montreal, Quebec.

R. L. Dunsmore,

Chairman
Montreal Port Council

R. L. Dunsmore . . . was born at Seaforth, Ont. He received his early education in St. Thomas, Ont., after which he obtained his B.Sc. degree in civil engineering from Queen's University, Kingston, in 1915. During the first World War, Mr. Dunsmore served as a major with the Royal Canadian Engineers. He was awarded the Military Cross for Gallantry. In 1919 he joined the Imperial Oil Limited as assistant engineer, and for many years he was engaged in engineering and petroleum refinery operations in many parts of Canada and in Peru, South America. During the second World War, Mr. Dunsmore served as Director of Fuel Oil for the Royal Canadian Navy with the rank of Commander. He was also appointed assistant Director of Plans. In 1949 he became president of Champlain Oil Products Limited, Montreal, retired from that office in October 1958, although he is still a director of the board of that Company. In November, 1958 he was appointed a director of the Canadian Broadcasting Corporation. Mr. Dunsmore is a past president of the Montreal Board of Trade, a past Vice-President of the Engineering Institute of Canada, and a past chairman of the Halifax Branch and Montreal Branch.

Frank P. Zeidler . . . was elected Mayor of Milwaukee in 1948; was re-elected for another four-year term in April, 1952; and was re-elected to a third four-year term in 1956.

FAMILY BACKGROUND: Mayor Zeidler was born in Milwaukee on September 20, 1912. The Mayor's older brother, Carl F. Zeidler, was a former Mayor of Milwaukee who enlisted in the United States Navy during his term of office and was lost at sea during World War II in 1942 at the age of 34.

The Mayor and his wife, Agnes have six children ranging in age from nine to eighteen.

EDUCATION: Mayor Zeidler graduated from the Grand Avenue School in Milwaukee in 1925 and from West Division High School in 1929. He attended the University of Wisconsin and also Chicago and Marquette Universities.

From the time he took office in 1948, the Mayor worked vigorously to help push the St. Lawrence Seaway legislation through the Congress.

AWARDS: Mayor Zeidler has received several awards for distinguished civic service. In 1948 he received a national award from the Junior Chamber of Commerce as one of the ten outstanding young American men. On December 12, 1956, he was chosen as the recipient of the 1956 Good Government Award by the Milwaukee Junior Chamber of Commerce. In 1956 the United States Civil Defense Council presented an award to Mayor Zeidler for outstanding work in civil defense.

HONORARY DEGREE: On June 13, 1958, the University of Wisconsin conferred upon the Mayor the Honorary Degree of Doctor of Laws.

MEMBERSHIPS: Mayor Zeidler was named a member of the United States National Commission for UNESCO in 1953 and renamed to this commission in 1956. He is a member of the national sociological fraternity, Alpha Kappa Delta, and is also an honorary member of Alpha Phi Omega. He holds a membership in the Wisconsin Academy of Sciences, Arts and Letters, and also one in the American Academy of Political and Social Sciences.

Honorable Frank P. Zeidler

Mayor
City of Milwaukee, Wisconsin

Harry C. Brockel . . . born in Chicago, Illinois, 1908. Become associated with the Milwaukee Board of Harbor Commissioners in 1926, and on 1936, was appointed Secretary tf the Board. Appointed Municipal Port Director in 1942. As chief executive officer of the Milwaukee Board of Harbor Commissioners, is in charge of harbor administration and the development and operation of Milwaukee's municipal port facilities. During World War II, served as a member of the U.S. Coast Guard Reserve, specializing in port security operations, Milwaukee being the third port of the United States to receive a Coast Guard shield of honor for effective port security. Has been active in promoting the St. Lawrence Seaway project and many other phases of Great Lakes shipping and harbor development. Author of numerous published articles on harbor, waterway and shipping topics. August, 1954, appointed by President Eisenhower as member of the 5 man Advisory Board, St. Lawrence Seaway Development Corporation. He holds numerous awards for public service. OFFICES HELD: President, American Association of Port Authorities, 1948-49; Vice-Chairman, Wisconsin Deep Waterways Commission, 1948-55; Chairman, Great Lakes Compact Commission, State of Wisconsin, 1955-; Vice-Chairman, The Great Lakes Commission, (interstate compact Great Lakes states) 1955-57; Secretary, Great Lakes Harbor Assn., 1942-52; Treasurer, 1954-; Chairman, Governor's Committee for the St. Lawrence Seaway Project, State of Wisconsin, 1952-57; Chairman, Milwaukee Port Security Council; National Vice-President (1951) Propeller Club of the U.S.; State Director, Water Transport Section, Wisconsin Civil Defense Organization; Director, Water Transport Section, Milwaukee Civil Defense and Disaster Committee; Director, National Rivers and Harbors Congress; Director, American Association of Port Authorities. Holds membership in numerous transportation, civic and professional bodies.

Harry C. Brockel

Municipal Port Director
Port of Milwaukee, Wisconsin

Fred P. Hudon,

President
Blaiklock Bros. Limited

Fred P. Hudon . . . New Hartford, Conn., November 15, 1900. He was educated at St. Mary's and New Hartford High School; Post College, Waterbury, Conn. He came to Canada in 1924. Began as Eastern Divisional Manager, Premier Vacuum Cleaner Co., which post he held from 1926 to 1934. From 1934 to 1936 he was Eastern Canadian Distributor, for Apex Rotarex Corp., Cleveland, Ohio. 1936 to 1945 he was Sales Specialist for Canadian General Electric Co.; Distributor (Sole): Bendix Automatic Appliances of South Bend, Ind.; Admiral Corp. of Chicago, Simplex, Ill.; Vornado, Toronto; Easy Washing Machine Co., Toronto; Quaker Manufacturing Co. of Chicago, 1945-1954, covering eastern Canada. During World War II services given voluntarily to all Victory Loan Campaigns (nine), addressing groups in public squares, industrial plants and public gatherings. Has also voluntarily worked on Federated Charities, Canadian Red Cross, Salvation Army; Joint Hospital Fund and Rehabilitation Institute Drives. Served with O.T.C., 1918-20, Camp Holibird, Maryland. He is President of Blaiklock Bros. Limited; president, Hudon-Robinson Ltd. Member: Montreal Board of Trade. Club: Mount Stephen. Recreation: World Travelling. Hobby: Color photography. Married Phyllis Naomi McLean, November 15, 1928. Residence: 5540 Queen Mary Rd., Montreal, Que.

M. Harold Robinson,

Vice-President,
Blaiklock Bros. Limited.

M. Harold Robinson . . . born Prescott, Ontario December 20, 1910. He was educated in Public and High Schools. He began as a junior with the Royal Bank of Canada, Prescott Ontario in 1928; later became Branch Manager, serving in Ontario and Quebec branches as well as in Head Office, Montreal. He resigned from the bank in 1953 and entered into partnership with Fred P. Hudon, acquiring Blaiklock Bros. Limited, Customs Brokers. He is Vice-President and Director, of Blaiklock Bros. Limited; Vice-President and Director, Hudon-Robinson Ltd.; Director Affiliated Customs Brokers (Montreal) Ltd. Member: Montreal Board of Trade. Club: Beaconsfield Golf. Recreation: golf. He married Patricia Jordan, April 23, 1940. They have two sons, **Richard H.** and Ross J. Residence: 4385 Mariette Avenue, Montreal, Quebec.

John Stewart Proctor . . . born Vancouver, B.C., July 14, 1904. He was educated at Boy's Central School, Victoria, B.C., Victoria High School, Victoria, B.C.; Victoria College, University of British Columbia. He joined the Bank in Victoria, B. C., in 1922, being transferred to Toronto five years later. He gained experience in a number of branches in Ontario including the Main Toronto Branch until his appointment as Manager of the Main Branch, in Montreal, in 1943. He was appointed Assistant General Manager of the Bank in 1947, General Manager in 1953 and was elected a Director of the Bank during the same year. In 1954 he was elected Vice President and became President of the Bank in 1956. He is also a Director of Interlake Tissue Mills Co. Limited, Merritton, Ont. Clubs: Toronto; St. James's; Montreal; Engineer's (Toronto); The Badminton & Racquet (Toronto); Montreal Indoor Tennis; Recreation: tennis. Married: Kathleen Allan Colpman on April 17, 1929. Has one daughter Dianne Mary. Residence: 277 Oriole Parkway, Toronto, Ont.

John Stewart Proctor

President
Imperial Bank of Canada.

E. J. Friesen . . . born in Rosthern, Saskatchewan. He joined the Imperial Bank as a junior in the Rosthern Branch in 1920. Continuing service in Western Canada, he was appointed Assistant Manager of the Main Winnipeg Branch in 1937. He became a Supervisor at Head Office in 1945, and was appointed Manager of the Main Office in Montreal in 1947, Assistant General Manager of the Bank in 1950, General Manager in 1956. He was elected a Director and a Vice President of the bank in November, 1958. He was succeeded as General Manager by Mr. H. W. Thomson.

E. J. Friesen

Vice-President
Imperial Bank of Canada.

Honourable L. G. "Archie" Lavigne,

Mayor
Cornwall, Ont.

The Chief Magistrate of the "Seaway City" of Cornwall, Ontario, is one of the most active men on the Canadian municipal scene. With Cornwall attracting increasing international attention because of her strategic location (headquarters of the St. Lawrence Seaway Authority, site of the St. Lawrence Power Development), it is not uncommon for L. G. "Archie" Lavigne to play host to a world leader, preside over a city council meeting and attend to complaints about a break in a water main — all in one day. Born in Cornwall in 1917, Mayor Lavigne was the youngest Chief Magistrate in Cornwall's history when he assumed office in August, 1957. He received his early education at the Nativity Boys' School and the Cornwall Collegiate and Vocational School, followed by studies at the University of Ottawa. Mayor Lavigne joined the Canadian Army at the outbreak of war in 1939, serving with the 4th Field Regiment of the Royal Canadian Artillery. He served overseas until the end of hostilities in 1945, and was wounded in action in Holland. After demobilization, Mr. Lavigne opened a grocery business in Cornwall and ten years later added a real estate business to his enterprises. He served on the Cornwall City Council for nine years before becoming Mayor. Mayor Lavigne is married to the former Myrtle Steward, of Morewood, Ontario, and has two sons: Philip, 8, and William, 11. A brother, Albert Lavigne, is a former Federal Member of Parliament.

Honourable Louis Quevillon

Mayor
Salaberry-de-Valleyfield

Hon. Louis Quevillon . . . born in Montreal West, March 23, 1902, son of Mathias Quevillon and Hermeline Binette. His family moved to Salaberry-de-Valleyfield in 1908. Until he was 12, he attended primary school and continued his commercial studies until he was 16 at the Valleyfield Seminary. Mr. Quevillon is a fruit and vegetable dealer. Member: Knights of Columbus (fourth degree); St. Jean Baptiste Society; St. Vincent de Paul Society; life member of the Champlain and Dollard des Ormeaux Guards and Zouaves Pontificaux. He is also co-director of the Fruit and Vegetable Dealers of Montreal. Alderman for Maisonneuve from 1941-1950, elected Mayor of the City in January 1954. Clubs: Moose; Valleyfield Golf; Valleyfield Boat. Married Miss Adela Trepanier of Valleyfield in 1924.

Brigadier James Arthur deLalanne, B.A., C.A., C.B.E., M.C. (with Bar) . . born Montreal, Que., January 26, 1897. He was educated in Westmount Schools; Lachute Academy; McGill University (B.A. 1919). He began his career with Pirelli Cables, Conduits Limited following graduation. Qualified as Chartered Accountant in 1923. Military Service, World War I; joined Princess Patricia's Canadian Light Infantry as Private, in 1915. Subsequently commissioned in the field and served as Lieutenant and Captain in 60th Canadian Infantry Battalion and 5th Canadian Mounted Rifles Battalion. Wounded in Action three times. Awarded Military Cross and Bar. World War II he rejoined Active Army in 1940 as Major; held various staff appointments; promoted Brigadier, 1943; appointed Vice Adjutant General, 1945. Awards: Commander of the Order of the British Empire; Order of the White Lion (Czechoslovak Republic). Governor, McGill University; Alderman, City of Westmount; Member: Protestant Committee of the Council of Education, Province of Quebec, Montreal Advisory Board, Chartered Trust Company; President, Institute of Chartered Accountants of Quebec (1952-53); President, The Graduates' Society of McGill University (1950-52); President, Rotary Club of Westmount (1939-40); Westmount Municipal School Commissioners (former chairman); President, Canadian Rugby Union (1939-40); Past President and Life Member, Quebec Amateur Hockey Association; former Vice-President, Montreal Amateur Athletic Association. Clubs: University (Montreal); Royal Montreal Golf; Montreal Badminton and Squash. Married: Midred Pollock Eakin, June 11th, 1924; has one son. Residence: 683 Lansdowne Ave., Westmount, Quebec.

Brigadier James Arthur deLalanne, B.A., C.A., C.B.E., M.C. (with Bar),

President,
Pirelli Cables, Conduits Limited.

Ottorino Sarcoli . . . born in Cairo, Egypt, on September 11, 1911. He was educated in British Schools, Singapore, Malaya and Oxford, England. He graduated at University of Rome, Italy, in Chemistry. He joined Pirelli SpA Milan, Italy. From 1936-50 Manager, Hard Rubber and Plastic Division; 1950-56, Chief, Plastic Research and Development Laboratories, Milan, Italy. In 1957 he was appointed General Manager, Pirelli Cables, Conduits Limited, St. Johns, Quebec. Clubs: St. Johns Golf Club; Club of Montreal. Sports: Fishing, Hunting and Boating. Married: has two sons and one daughter. Residence: 188 Blvd. Montcalm, St. Johns, Quebec.

Ottorino Sarcoli,

General Manager,
Pirelli Cables, Conduits Limited.

Argue Martin, Q.C.

Chairman
Hamilton Harbour Commissioners

Argue Martin, Q.C. . . . Chairman of The Hamilton Harbour Commissioners, is senior member of Messrs. Martin & Martin, Barristers & Solicitors of Hamilton, Ont. At one time he was an Alderman of the City of Hamilton and member of the Ontario Legislature. He is presently a Governor of Trinity College School and of McMaster University.

Peter James McCulloch

Vice Chairman
Hamilton Harbour Commissioners

Peter James McCulloch . . . Vice-Chairman of the Hamilton Harbour Commissioners, is Secretary of White Supply Company Limited. He has been with White Supply Company for 35 years. He was an Alderman of the City of Hamilton, Ont., for 13 years and was elected President of the American Association of Port Authorities in 1957.

Clifford William Morgan, B.Sc., P.Eng. . . . General Manager and Secretary of the Hamilton Harbour Commissioners, was, prior to 1957, District Engineer at Toronto, Ont., for the Harbours and Rivers Engineering Branch, Department of Public Works. A graduate of Queen's University, his engineering experience includes over 21 years service with the Federal department engaged in harbour construction and development.

Clifford William Morgan, B.Sc., P.Eng.

General Manager and Secretary
Hamilton Harbour Commissioners

J. Edmund McLean . . . Member of the Hamilton Harbour Commissioners is a Hamilton, Ont., executive of the Consolidated Truck Lines Limited, with experience in waterfront operations over the past 25 years. He is a former player of the Hamilton Tiger Cats football team, and was later coach of the Wildcats.

J. Edmund McLean

Member
Hamilton Harbour Commissioners

Robert Dickson Harkness D.S.O., M.C., B.Sc.

President
Northern Electric Co. Ltd.

Robert Dickson Harkness, D.S.O., M.C., B.Sc., . . . born Osaka, Japan, December 23, 1892. He was educated at Queens University, Kingston Ontario, where he received his B.Sc. in 1913. He began his career with Northern Electric & Manufacturing Company in Montreal in 1911 in the manufacturing department. Successively he became assistant cable salesmanager, Montreal; district manager, Winnipeg; telephone contract manager, Montreal; general commercial manager; vice-president, general manager, director in 1938. He was elected President in 1948. He served as private to colonel in the Canadian Army during World War 1 1914-18; as a reserve, 1936-42. He was awarded Distinguished Service Order, Military Cross, 1914-15 Star; Comdr. Brother Order St. John of Jerusalem. Honorary Doctor of Law, Queens University, Kingston, Ontario, 1958. He is a Director of Howard Smith Paper Mills Ltd., Consolidated Mining and Smelting Company of Canada Ltd., Bell Telephone Co. of Canada, Royal Bank of Canada, Montreal Trust Co., Dominion Bridge Co. Ltd., Dominion Engineering Works Ltd., Dominion Sound Equipments Ltd., North American Telegraph Company, Sun Life Assurance Co.; advisory committee Northern Assurance Co. Ltd., Member: Defence Research Board, Can., 1947-50, 1953-56; board management Montreal General Hospital; gov. Montreal Tech. Inst., Trustee Queens University, Kingston, Ontario, President, Canadian Electrical Manufacturers Association, 1957. Associations: Engineering Institute of Canada and Corporation of Professional Engineers of Quebec. Clubs: University, St. James's, Mount Royal, Seigniory, Mount Bruno Country, Forest and Stream. Married: Fue Bryden Leitch, October 13, 1920; has one son, Robert Hugh. Residence: 59 Forden Avenue, Westmount, Quebec.

Martin P. Murphy

Executive Vice-President
Northern Electric Co. Ltd.

Martin P. Murphy . . . Born in Halifax, Nova Scotia, on April 6, 1899. He was educated at Westmount High School and McGill University, Montreal, Quebec. He joined Northern Electric Company Ltd., in the wire and cable engineering department in 1921. From 1928 to 1935 he was Telephone Contract Manager. In 1936 he was appointed Vice-President and Managing Director of Amalgamated Electric Corporation and held this position until 1947 when he was made Assistant General Manager (Commercial) Northern Electric Co. Ltd. In 1948 he was appointed Vice-President and General Manager, Vice-President and Managing Director, on June 1, 1951 and Executive Vice-President, on October 1, 1956. He served overseas with the Canadian Field Artillery, C.E.F., from 1917 to 1919. He was President of the Montreal Junior Board of Trade in 1933; Montreal Board of Trade from 1953-54; Canadian Electrical Manufacturers' Association in 1946. Director: Dominion Sound Equipments Ltd. Clubs: Lambton Golf and Country (Toronto); Granite (Toronto); St. James' (Montreal); Mount Royal (Montreal); Royal Montreal Curling; Royal Montreal Golf. Married: Jean McLauchlin in 1924. They have three sons, Martin P. Jr., John F. and Ross G. Residence: 66 Aberdeen Avenue, Westmount, Quebec.

J. Arthur Savoie . . . born at St. Justin, Quebec. Educated at the Seminary of Three Rivers, Quebec, and Laval University, Quebec, where he graduated in law in 1914. Upon graduating he came to St. Vincent de Paul, just north of Montreal, where he practised as notary for several years. In 1933, he was elected Mayor of St. Vincent de Paul for a two-year term. In 1937, he was elected President of the Montreal Chamber of Notaries. He entered government administration first as vice-president of the former Montreal Tramway Commission and then as general manager of the Quebec Liquor Commission. When the Province of Quebec expropriated Montreal Power and Beauharnois in 1944, he was appointed commissioner. Four years later, in 1948, he was made vice-president, and in 1955, was appointed to the presidency of Hydro-Quebec. Member: Administrative Board of the University of Montreal; Council of Public Education of the Province of Quebec (Catholic Committee). He is also a governor of the Montreal Junior Chamber of Commerce. Residence: Outremont, Que.

J. Arthur Savoie

President
Quebec Hydro Electric Commission

Félix Guibert, . . . President, Bédard-Girard Limited, Electrical Contractors (Est. 1927), 117 Lagauchetiere St., West, Montreal 1, P.Q. President, Lacote Realties Limited, Montreal; Born Plainfield, New Jersey, May 23, 1903, son of Félix and Marie (Marlot) Guibert, both ot France. Educated: Académie Girouard, St. Hyacinthe, P.Q.; Ecole Technique, Montreal. With Collyer and Brock, Ltd., 1916-1921; Lord Electric Incorporated, New York, 1922; Bédard-Girard Ltd., Montreal, 1928; successively held the positions of manager, vice-president and president. Served during the last World War as supervisor of Electric installations in various war industry plants, R.C.A.F. air fields and in naval construction. Member, Chambre de Commerce de Montréal; Member, Montreal Builders Exchange and past president of the Electrical Contractors Section; Member, Corporation of Master Electricians of the Province of Quebec. Clubs: St. Denis (Montreal); St. Lawrence Kiwanis. On August 8, 1931 he married Mathilde, daughter of Emile and M. (de Sylva) Saint-Loup, both of France; they are the parents of four children, (André, Louis, François and Marie). Roman Catholic. Recreations: fishing, hunting, Residence: 651 Stuart Ave., Outremont, P.Q.

Félix Guibert

President
Bédard-Girard Limited

Raymond Q. Armington

General Manager
Euclid Division of General Motors

Raymond Q. Armington, . . . General Manager of General Motors' Euclid Division at Cleveland, Ohio, is one of five brothers, all of whom contributed to the development and progress of the company that was an outgrowth of a crane and hoist manufacturing business founded by his father at the turn of the century. After graduation from Ohio State University as an industrial engineer, Mr. Armington worked as a time study engineer with two major rubber companies in Akron prior to joining Euclid Road Machinery Company, which was incorporated in 1931. He became Vice President and General Manager of the company in 1937 and served in that capacity until his election as President in 1951. During this period Euclid grew from a relatively small manufacturer to a leading position in the earthmoving equipment industry, with its main plants in Cleveland and a manufacturing subsidiary in Great Britain. Production and plant facilities today are more than ten times as large as they were in 1946 and the new Hudson Plant scheduled for production in 1959 represents another 66% expansion. When General Motors acquired the Euclid Road Machinery Company in 1953, Mr. Armington became head of the new Euclid Division. He also serves as a director of the Cleveland Union Bank of Commerce, Euclid Crane and Hoist Company, the Cleveland Chamber of Commerce and the Better Business Bureau. He is a member of the Society of Automotive Engineers, the Union Club and the Kirkland Country Club.

A. Neil Lilley

President
McColl-Frontenac Oil Company

A. Neil Lilley, President of McColl-Frontenac Oil Company Limited, was born on October 28, 1905 in San Francisco. He was graduated from Lawrenceville School and attended Princeton University.

Mr. Lilley joined The Texas Company in 1933 as a bulk plant clerk and trainee. He was engaged in sales work on the West Coast until 1942. He served as an officer in the U.S. Air force for three and a half years and upon his return to The Texas Company he entered the foreign operations.

He was made Assistant Manager in 1946 of the French Company, Societe des Raffineries de Petrole de la Gironde, became Manager in 1947, and Vice President and Stockholders' Representative in 1949. On October 1, 1949, Mr. Lilley was appointed Texaco's General Manager of Foreign Operations — Eastern Hemisphere, with headquarters in New York, and he was elected a Vice President on December 7, 1951, and a Director of the Company in September, 1954.

Mr. Lilley resigned as Vice President and Director of The Texas Company in December, 1957, and was elected President of McColl-Frontenac Oil Company Limited, a Canadian subsidiary of Texaco's.

Mr. Lilley was married in 1935 and is the father of two children.

Reginald Charles Pearse ... born at Ipswich, England, on February 15, 1903. He was educated at Ipswich Public, High and Technical Schools. In 1918 he was apprenticed to Ransomes & Rapier, Mechanical Engineers, Ipswich. In 1924, he was a Draughtsman with Cocksedge Bros., Structural Engineers, Ipswich. From 1925 to 1929 he was Designer Draughtsman, Stothert & Pitt, Crane Builders, Bath. He left England in 1929 to join Dominion Bridge as a Mechanical Designer. 1930 to 1940 he worked as Production Supervisor, General Foreman, Mechanical Superintendent; 1940-43, organized and managed Dominion Bridge Co.'s Ordnance Plant, Vancouver, making Vickers-Armstrong Anti-Aircraft Guns; 1944, Assistant Works Manager, Montreal; 1945-53, he was Works Manager, Montreal; In January, 1954, he was made Assistant Manager, Ontario Division and in July, 1954, appointed Vice-President and Manager. On January 1, 1959, he was appointed President of Canadian Vickers Limited. Director: Canadian Institute of Steel Construction. Member: Ontario Executive Committee, Canadian Manufacturers' Assoc.; Toronto Board of Trade. Clubs: National and Royal Canadian Yacht, Toronto; Engineer's Club, Montreal. Married Elizabeth Elsie Newell in 1936. They have two daughters. Residence: 20 Lambert Crescent, Toronto 18, Ont.

Reginald Charles Pearse,

President
Canadian Vickers Limited

Stuart M. Finlayson . . . born in Montreal, Que. He joined Canadian Marconi Company in January, 1919, as an Apprentice Engineer. In October 1920, he entered McGill University, Montreal, graduating in 1924 with Degree of B.Sc. (E.E.). In 1928 he was appointed Factory Manager; 1934, Assistant to the General Manager; 1937, Deputy General Manager; 1945, General Manager; 1951, President. From 1936 to 1945, he served with Reserve Army in "B" Corps Signals. He was promoted to command Unit in March, 1943. He retired with rank of Lieutenant-Colonel in May, 1945. He is a Director of John Inglis Company Ltd., Toronto, and English Electric Co. of Canada Ltd., Toronto. He is Alderman of the Town of Hampstead, Que.; President of The Montreal Children's Hospital; Governor of the Royal Victoria Hospital; Past President of The Montreal Board of Trade.

Stuart M. Finlayson

President
Canadian Marconi Company

367

J. D. Houlding,

Vice President & General Manager
R.C.A. Victor Co. Ltd.

J. D. Houlding . . . Vice-President and General Manager of RCA Victor Company, Ltd., commenting on the St. Lawrence Seaway undertaking, emphasized the very vital role electronics has played and will continue to play in the smooth operation of the Seaway. Among other things, Mr. Houlding visualized "the setting up of an electronic system of comprehensive seaway traffic control whereby maximum usage of the Seaway will be realized in the face of increasing seaway traffic".

Mr. Houlding was born in London, Ontario, and educated at the University of Western Ontario. He served as a Radar Officer on loan to the Royal Navy from 1943 to 1945. He was also on loan to the Department of Defence Production in 1952.

G. M. Bergson

Manager, Marine Sales & Services
R.C.A. Victor Co. Ltd.

G. M. Bergson . . . since joining RCA Victor Company, Ltd., in 1953, has specialized in the marine electronic field. On the St. Lawrence project, Mr. Bergson opines: "The Seaway has made obsolete the existing Canadian canal boat fleet. This will be replaced — during the next ten years or so — by a fleet of larger and more efficient vessels requiring increased numbers of marine electronic instruments. In meeting this demand the continued growth of the Canadian electronic industry is assured."

Winnipeg-born Mr. Bergson attended the University of Manitoba and McGill University. In World War II he served with the Canadian Armed Forces for three-and-a-half years. Mr. Bergson presently holds the rank of major in the Reserve Army.

William S. Mather, B.Sc. (C.E.), LL.D., D.C.L. . . . born at Oshawa, Ontario, in September, 1885. He was educated at public and high schools at Kenora, Ontario, before going to McGill University, Montreal. While attending University, he worked with the Canadian Pacific Railway during the summer months in various capacities and upon graduation in 1908, he joined the railway company. He became resident engineer at Winnipeg in 1910 and transferred to the operating department in 1912. From then until May, 1933, when he was appointed assistant to the Vice-President at Montreal, he served at Kenora as superintendent, assistant General Superintendent at Vancouver, and as General Superintendent at Moose Jaw and Calgary. One year after he was made assistant to the Vice-President, he returned west as General Manager of western lines, Winnipeg, Sept. 1934. He was appointed operating Vice-President at Winnipeg in 1942 and President of the Company in March, 1948. He became Chairman in May, 1955. He is also Chairman of Canadian Pacific Steamships and Canadian Pacific Airlines. He is Vice-President and Director: Consolidated Mining and Smelting Co. of Canada. Director: C. P. Express Co.; West Kootenay Power and Light Co.; Canadian Marconi; Royal Trust Co.; Calgary & Edmonton Corp. Ltd.; Toronto, Hamilton and Buffalo Railway; Scottish Trust Co.; and other companies. Member: Advisory Committee of Canadian Standards Association; director, Canadian Forestry Assoc.; Hon. President, Montreal Division, Navy League of Canada and honorary chairman, Canadian Paraplegic Assoc. (Que. Div.). Clubs: Mount Royal and University, Montreal; Rideau (Ottawa; Manitoba (Winnipeg); Assiniboine (Regina); Vancouver. He was created a Knight of Grace of the Order of St. John of Jerusalem, in December, 1952. Married Maynard Cruickshank of Moose Jaw, Sask. They have one son and one daughter.

William A. Mather, B.Sc., (C.E.), LL.D., D.C.L.

Chairman
Canadian Pacific Railway Company

Norris Roy Crump, M.E., D.Eng., D.C.L. LL.D., D.Sc., . . . born at Revelstoke, B.C. on July 30, 1904. He was educated in public schools, Vancouver; high schools, Revelstoke; Purdue University, Lafayette, Ind., U.S.A.; (B.Sc. 1929, M.E. 1936). He became a machinist apprentice Motive Power, Field, B.C., on September 9, 1920. He subsequently held posts of increasing responsibility. He became assistant superintendent, Motive Power and Car Department, Winnipeg, Manitoba, on January 1, 1941. Appointed: Assistant to Vice-President, Montreal, on May 11, 1942; General Superintendent, Ontario District, Toronto, on October 1, 1943; Assistant General Manager, Eastern Lines, Toronto, on January 1, 1946; Vice-President and General Manager, Eastern Lines, Toronto, on January 1, 1947; Vice-President, Eastern Region, Toronto, on August 19, 1947; Vice-President with jurisdiction over all lines, Montreal, on April 12, 1948; elected a Director of the C.P.R. on February 14, 1949; Vice-President and Member of Executive Committee on May 4, 1949; elected President of the Company on May 4, 1955. Director: C.P.R.; Canadian Pacific Air Lines; Canadian Pacific Express Company; Canadian Pacific Steamships; Consolidated Mining & Smelting Co. of Canada; Dominion Atlantic Railway Co.; Midland Simcoe Elevator Co.; Minneapolis, St. Paul & Sault Ste. Marie R.R.; Northern Alberta Railway; Seigniory Club Community Assoc. (Pres.); Scottish Trust Co.; Shawinigan Falls Terminal Railway; T. H. & B. Railway; Toronto Terminals Railway; Vancouver Hotel Co.; Bank of Montreal; Mutual Life Assurance of Canada; Royal Exchange Assurance. Governor: McGill University; Royal Victoria Hospital, Montreal. Trustee: Corp. of Bishop's University, Sherbrooke, Que. Advisory Committee: School of Business Administration, University of Western Ont., London; Canadian Standards Association, Ottawa; Conservation for Canada, Foundation Corp. He is a member of numerous organizations and clubs. Married Stella Elvin, Uhrichsville, Ohio, August 23, 1930. They have two daughters. Residence: 12 Kilburn Crescent, Montreal, Que.

Norris Roy Crump,
M.E., D.Eng., D.C.L., LL.D., D.Sc.

President, Member of Executive Committee, Director
Canadian Pacific Railway Company

T. J. Walsh,

Chairman of the Board
Walsh Construction Company

T. J. Walsh . . . he graduated from St. Mary's College, St. Mary, Kansas, in 1906. The same year he started with Walsh Construction Company and worked as laborer, foreman, superintendent and manager. From 1912 to 1916, he was Vice-President of the Company. He was President of Walsh Construction Company from 1916 to 1946 and directly supervised many large railroad construction projects over a period of years. He has always been very active in management of all the Company's operations. He has also been Chief Executive of many associated contracting groups where Walsh Construction Company has operated, including construction of the Grand Coulee Dam. He was appointed Chairman of the Board of Walsh Construction Company in 1946.

W. A. Durkin,

Chairman of Executive Committee
Walsh Construction Company

W. A. Durkin . . . from 1906 to 1912, he was engineer on all classes of railroad and heavy construction. He joined Walsh Construction Company in 1912 and served as Foreman, Superintendent, Engineer and Manager on various construction jobs, including underpinning, foundation work, building, pile driving, etc. From 1921 to 1928, he was District Manager of Walsh Construction Company. From 1928 to 1946, he was Vice-President and Manager of Construction on tunnels, shafts, bridges, buildings, pile driving, dock work, dams, and industrial plants. From 1946 to 1952, he was President of Walsh Construction Company. He was appointed Chairman of the Executive Committee in 1953.

T. J. Walsh, Jr. . . . he graduated from Notre Dame University in 1935. From 1930 to 1935 he worked for Walsh Construction Company between school period as laborer, time-keeper, and foreman. From 1935 to 1937, he was Foreman, Assistant Superintendent, and Shift Superintendent on coffer-dam, concrete and excavation work on Grand Coulee Dam. From 1937 to 1940, he was Foreman and Assistant Superintendent on cofferdam, excavation concrete and tunnels, Queens Midtown Vehicular Tunnels and Water Supply, City of New York. From 1940 to 1941, he was Superintendent, U. S. Army Cantonment. From 1941 to 1942, he was Assistant Project Manager, U. S. Army Foreign Base. From 1942 to 1945, he was Officer, Construction Battalion, U. S. Navy. From 1945 to 1952, he was Vice-President, General Supervisory Capacity, of Walsh Construction. He was appointed President of Walsh Construction in 1953.

T. J. Walsh, Jr.,

President
Walsh Construction Company

J. J. Walsh . . . he graduated from Brown University, Providence, R.I., with a B.A., in 1932. From 1934 to 1941, he was Assistant Superintendent and Assistant Job Manager, Consolidated Builders, on construction of Grand Coulee Dam. From 1941 to 1942, he was Assistant Job Manager, Walsh-Driscoll Company, on construction of the United States Army Base in the Caribbean, a project covering the erection of military bases on Trinidad and other West Indian Islands and in South America. From 1943 to 1946, he was Executive Assistant of Walsh-Kaiser Company, Providence, R.I. This project included both the building of the Providence Shipyard and the construction of ships for the United States Maritime Commission. From 1946 to 1947, he was Project Manager, Walsh Construction Company, Contract Representative of War Assets Administration for the disposal of surplus property at four supply depots. From 1948 to 1950, he was a Special Representative for the Company and was appointed Vice-President in 1953. From 1955 to 1958, he was Chairman of the St. Lawrence Contractors Association, Massena, New York.

J. J. Walsh,

Vice-President
Walsh Construction Company

J. J. Murphy,

Vice-President
Walsh Construction Company

J. J. Murphy . . . he graduated from the University of West Virginia and New York University. From 1929 to 1930, he was employed in general field survey and construction engineering on various construction work. From 1930 to 1940, he was Engineer, Superintendent and General Superintendent on various construction projects including highways, bridges, dams, tunnels, railroads, sanitary sewers with Walsh Construction Company. From 1940 to 1946, he was Superintendent of Construction, Camp Edwards, Mass., U. S. Army; U. S. Naval Dry Docks, Brooklyn, New York; U. S. Naval Munition Depot, Earle, N. J.; and bridge and railroad construction in Kentucky, C. and L. Railroad. From 1946 to 1947, he was Assistant in charge of Operations, War Assets Administration for disposal of surplus material. From 1948 to 1949, he was General Superintendent, Downsville Dam, City of New York. From 1949 to 1951, he was General Superintendent, East Delaware Tunnel, Board of Water Supply, City of New York. From 1951 to 1952, he was Assistant Project Manager, U. S. Steel Fairless Works, Morrisville, Pennsylvania. From 1953 to 1955, he was Project Manager, New York State Thruway, Harriman Newburgh Section. In 1955 he was Project Manager, Bethlehem Steel Company Plant Extension Sparrows Point, Maryland. In 1955 he was appointed Vice-President of Walsh Construction Company. From 1957 to 1958, he was Vice-President in charge of Long Sault Dam Construction.

Alex L. Simpson,

Superintendent and Project Manager
Walsh Construction Company

Alex L. Simpson . . . From 1935 to 1937, he was Superintendent of Tunnels, Los Angeles Aqueduct, L. E. Dixon Co., Pasadena, Calif. From 1937 to 1938, he was Superintendent, Potrero Shaft, Los Angeles Aqueduct, Metropolitan Water Dist., Banning, Calif. From 1938 to 1939, he was Superintendent, Shaft 1A, NY.. Aqueduct, Shea-Kaiser Co., Bronxville, N.Y. From 1939 to 1942, he was Superintendent, Shaft 5, New York Aqueduct, Walsh Construction Company, Plattekill, N.Y. From 1942 to 1943, he was Shift Superintendent, Brooklyn Dry Docks, Walsh-Steers Co., Brooklyn, N.Y. From 1943 to 1946, Assembly Superintendent, Shipyard, Walsh-Kaiser Co., Providence, Rhode Island. From 1946 to 1947, he was General Superintendent, Alcoa Rolling Mill, Walsh Construction Company, Iowa. From 1947 to 1949, he was General Superintendent, and Project Manager, Rock Creek Tunnel, Dixon-Arundel Corp., California. From 1949 to 1952, he was Project Manager, Neusa Dam, Bogota, Colombia, Winston-Raymond Company. From 1952 to 1955, he was General Superintendent in Charge, Niagara Power Tunnel, Perini-Walsh Cos., Niagara Falls, Ontario. In 1956 he was made General Superintendent and Project Manager of Walsh Construction Company and was in charge of the building of the Long Sault Dam at Massena, New York.

Kenneth C. Griffith . . . From 1933 to 1934, he was junior engineer, City of Portland, Oregon. From 1934 to 1943, he was field engineer and Assistant Superintendent for Walsh Construction Company on heavy construction dams, tunnels, dry docks and pipe lines. From 1943 to 1946, he was with the Executive Office C. B. Maintenance Unit 555 located in Panama with activities in Ecuador, Peru, Colombia, Nicaragua and Galapagos Islands. From 1946 to 1948, he was self employed in general contracting. From 1948 to 1949, he was Project Engineer, Walsh Construction Company, Construction of Steel Plant. From 1949 to 1952, he was self employed in general contracting. From 1953 to 1956, he was Superintendent of Construction with Walsh Construction on pipe lines, bridges and heavy construction. From 1956 to 1957, he was Project Manager, Lachine Section of the St. Lawrence Seaway, for Walsh Construction Company. He was appointed Manager of Walsh-Canadian Construction Company Ltd., in 1957.

Kenneth C. Griffith,

Manager
Walsh-Canadian Construction Company Ltd.

Thomas H. Reid . . . was born at Brooklyn, N. Y., November 14, 1901, the son of Thomas F. and Jennie M. (Howard) Reid. He was educated in the public and high schools of New York City and subsequently graduated as a Mechanical Engineer from the School of Science and Technology, Pratt Institute, Brooklyn, N. Y. Later he completed a special 2 year night course in business law at Brooklyn Law School. He entered business with The Texas Company at New York and after special training in all phases of the oil business, became assistant to the Educational Director. It was his duty to gather, edit and publish numerous company publications including the instruction booklets for the company's school for employees. This work brought him into direct contact with the printing industry. In 1923 he left the oil industry to devote his time to taking part in the development of the offset lithography industry. In 1929 he came to Montreal to introduce this new form of printing. He became assistant to the General Manager of the Ronalds Company at Montreal handling production of the letterpress department as well as setting up a lithographing department. He later became a Vice President of the Ronalds Company and was mainly responsible for the conversion of the company into a publication printing type of Company. During World War II he served as an officer with the 15th (R) Armoured Regiment, (6th Hussars). Later he was associated with the sales departments of the Gazette Printing Company and the Maclean-Hunter Publishing Co. In 1957, in company with W. D. Boulton, a former Maclean-Hunter associate, organized Reid and Boulton Publishing Company, publishers of this volume "St. Lawrence Seaway and Power Projects". He has edited and produced two other books dealing with Canada's economic growth. In 1943 he married Marion E. Topp and they have two sons. Resides at 4417 Madison Ave., Montreal. Member, Montreal Board of Trade, Canadian Legion.

Thomas H. Reid

President
Reid & Boulton Publishing Company

J. Edouard Simard, D.C.Sc.

President & Managing Director
Sorel Industries Ltd.

J. Edouard Simard, D.C.Sc., . . . is President and Managing Director of Sorel Industries Ltd., Vice-President and Director of Marine Industries Ltd. and Branch Lines Ltd. He is Chairman of the Board of Reynolds Aluminum Co. of Canada Ltd. and Sicard Inc. His directorates include Canada Paper Co.; Canadian Shipbuilding & Ship Repairing Association; Dominion Stores Ltd.; Donnacona Paper Co. Ltd.; Engineering Products of Canada Ltd.; Hilton of Canada Ltd.; Howard Smith Paper Mills Ltd.; Sicard Industries Inc., Watertown, N.Y.; Sincennes McNaughton Lines Ltd.; Société d'Administration et de Fiducie; Sorel Steel Foundries Ltd. He is a member of the Corporation of Technicians of the Province of Quebec. Born at Baie St. Paul, he was educated there and at Mont St. Bernard, Sorel. His clubs are the Montreal Reform; Canadian Railways; Grunt; Nautique de Sorel (Director and Treasurer); Anglers Association of Quebec; Mount Stephen; The St. Maurice Valley Fish and Game Association, of which he is a Director. He is a member of the Knights of Columbus. His recreations are fishing and hunting.

A. Ludger Simard, O.B.E., D.Sc.

President and Managing Director
Marine Industries Ltd.

A. Ludger Simard, O.B.E., D.Sc., . . . President and Managing Director, Marine Industries Ltd., is also President of Sorel Steel Foundries Ltd., Sorel, Que., Branch Lines Ltd.; Richelieu Knitting Inc., and A. L. Simard Inc. He is a Director of Sorel Industries Ltd.; Engineering Products of Canada Ltd. and Canadian Bronze Co. Ltd. Born in Baie St. Paul, Que., he was educated at Baie St. Paul College. In addition to other honors, he was also the first Canadian to receive the Ordre du Mérite Maritime, France. He is a member of the Canadian Manufacturers Association; Canadian Credit Men's Trust Association; Canadian Chamber of Commerce; Canadian Shipbuilding and Ship Repairing Association. Mr. Simard is a member of the Knights of Columbus and of the Mount Stephen Club, Montreal. His recreations are fishing and hunting.

J. Arthur Simard, O.B.E., D.C.Sc., . . . is Chairman of the Board of Marine Industries Ltd., Sorel Industries Ltd. and Sorel Steel Foundries. He is also President of Administration & Co.; Sincennes McNaughton Lines Ltd.; and United Towing & Salvage Co. Ltd. Mr. Simard is also a Director of Bathurst Power & Paper Co. Ltd.; Canada Northern Power Corp. Ltd.; Canadian Celanese Ltd.; Labrador Mining & Exploration Co.; Massey-Harris-Ferguson Co. Ltd.; North American Elevators Ltd.; Power Corp. of Canada Ltd.; Royal Petroleum Corp., N.Y.; Sherwin-Williams Co. of Canada Ltd.; Sorel Dock & Stevedoring Co. Ltd., and Southwestern Oil & Refinery, Corpus Christi, Texas. He was born in Baie St. Paul, Que. and received his education there. He is a Governor of Notre Dame Hospital, Montreal, and is a member of the Reform Club, Canadian, St. Denis, Mount Stephen, Seigniory and Laval-sur-le-Lac. His recreations are hunting and fishing.

J. Arthur Simard, O.B.E., D.C.Sc.

Chairman
Marine Industries Ltd.

Louis N. DeRome, . . . Managing Director, Dredging Division of Marine Industries Ltd., is a Director of the company and of Royalmount Construction Ltd. He was born in Quebec City and educated at the Quebec Seminary and the Commercial Academy. He is a member of the Knights of Columbus and his clubs are the Mount Stephen; Laval-sur-le-Lac; Royal Quebec Golf and the Canadian Club of New York. His recreations are golf and fishing.

Louis N. DeRome

Managing Director, Dredging Division
Marine Industries Ltd.

Arthur Surveyer,
B.A., B.A.Sc., C.E., D.Eng., LL.D., M.E.I.C.,

Partner,
Surveyer, Nenniger and Chenevert.

Arthur Surveyer, B.A., B.A.Sc., C.E., D.Eng., LL.D., M.E.I.C.
. . . born in Montreal, Quebec. He was educated at College Ste. Marie and Ecole Polytechnique, Montreal; Ecole d'Industrie des Mines du Hainault, Belgium. B.A.; B.A.Sc.; C.E.; D.Eng., Rensselaer Polytechnic Institute; Doctor "honoris causa" Montreal University. He is a partner in the consulting engineering firm of Surveyer, Nenniger and Chenevert of Montreal. The firm specializes in technical and financial investigation for industrial corporations, banks and investment; undertakes the design and supervision of industrial works, waterpower developments, waterworks filtration plants, bridges and general construction. He was President of the Engineering Institute from 1924 to 1925. Chairman Chignecto Canal Commission in 1931. Director Chromium Mining and Smelting Corporation; Confederation Development Corporation; Canadian International Investment Trust; The Shawinigan Water and Power Co.; Credit-Foncier Franco-Canadian. Member: Canadian Council for Industrial and Scientific Research 1917-1924; National Research Council of Canada, 1942-1948; Federal Advisory Committee of Reconstruction; St. Lawrence Waterway Board of Engineers, 1946; Strait of Canso Engineering Board, 1948-1949; Royal Commission for the National Development of Arts, Letters and Science, 1949-1951. Societies: Member, Engineering Institute of Canada; Corporation of Professional Engineers of the Province of Quebec; American Society of Civil Engineers; American Economic Association and American Management Association. Clubs: Universite de Montreal; Cercle Universitaire de Montreal; Mount Royal (Montreal); Royal Montreal Golf; University (New York). Residence: Chateau Apartments, 1321 Sherbrooke St. W., Montreal, Que.

Emile Nenniger, C.E., M.E.I.C.,

Partner,
Surveyer, Nenniger and Chenevert.

Emile Nenniger, C.E., M.E.I.C. . . born in Berne, Switzerland, July 4, 1901. He was educated at Art and Crafts School, Berne; Burgdorf-Cantonale. He was Designing Engineer for Q. Schreck, Berne, from 1921 to 1923 and for Arthur Surveyer and Company, Montreal, from 1923 to 1936. He became a partner of Arthur Surveyer and Company in 1937 and a partner of Surveyer, Nenniger and Chenevert in 1947. He has been associated with numerous projects among which are: the design of storage dams on Commissioner Lake for the Quebec Pulp and Paper Company and Hydro-Electric Power plant at Westbury for Sherbrooke, Que.; study of the effects of the operation of the Beauharnois Power plant on the water levels of the Montreal Harbour for Shipping Federation of Canada; study of cost of developing 500,000 H.P. Hydro-Electric plants, Carillon; valuation of Hydro-Electric Power plants at Grand'Mere, La Gabelle, St. Narcisse, St. Alban and Disraeli for the Shawinigan Water and Power Company; prepared the winning design for Montmorency Falls Bridge Competition for a reinforced concrete arch bridge, inaugurated by Quebec Department of Public Works and Labour in 1925; in charge of structural design of such buildings as J. B. Baillargeon Express Company, Viel School, New Method Laundry, Chapel Loyola College, all of Montreal; consultant for Chromium Mining and Smelting Corp.; study of the economic possibilities of establishing an electric pig iron industry at Three Rivers, Que., for the Shawinigan Water & Power Co. Member: Montreal Committee on Engineering Features of Civil Defence sponsored by the Engineering Institute of Canada; Association of Consulting Engineers; Swiss National; Corporation of Professional Engineers of Quebec; Canadian Institute of Mining & Metallurgy; Engineering Institute of Canada; American Concrete Institute. Married: Sophie Friedel Widmer, July 1923; one son. Residence: 21 Surrey Gardens, Westmount, Quebec.

J. Georges Chenevert, B.A.Sc., P.Eng., M.E.I.C. . . born in Montreal, Quebec, March 19, 1900. He was educated at Ste. Brigitte and Mount St. Louis Colleges, Montreal; Ecole Polytechnique, Montreal University, Montreal (B.A. Sc., Civil Engineer, 1923). He has been associated with numerous projects among which are: Supervision of Construction of such buildings as, Dupuis Freres, Themis & Hermes, St. Pierre Church, Montreal; Notre Dame de Grace Church, Hull, P.Q., Sanitorium de l'Immaculee-Conception, Ste. Agathe des Monts, P.Q. Consultant for the Canadian International Paper Co. on the design of a 20 M.D.G. rapid sand filtration at Gatineau, P.Q. and 30 M.D.G. Water Pre-Treatment Plant at Hawkesbury, Ont.; Official representative of the Corporation of Prof. Engs. of Quebec in connection with the revision of the Building Code of the City of Montreal; in charge of design and supervision of intercepting sewer and sewage pumping station of 500 C.F.S. capacity in the City of Quebec for Department of Public Works, Canada; in charge of design of 1,000 H.P. high pressure steam power plant and of 2,000,000 gallons per year alcohol plant in Gatineau, P.Q.; responsible for design of electrical and mechanical layouts of many important buildings for industrial, commercial and religious institutions; in charge of construction of radio station at Senneterre and Parent for Defence Construction Ltd. He was appointed arbitrator and expert in various important court cases. Clubs: Cercle Universitaire; Societies: Corporation of Professional Engineers of Quebec, Engineering Institute of Canada, Director of Association of Consulting Engineers of Canada; Canadian Institute on Sewage and Sanitation; President, American Society of Heating and Ventilating Engineers (Montreal Chapter). Member: Montreal Chamber of Commerce; Canadian Engineering Standards Association for Concrete and re-inforced concrete. Married: Therese Cadieux, September 24, 1929; they have one son. Recreation: golf. Residence: 536 Outremont Ave., Outremont, Quebec.

**J. Georges Chenevert,
B.A.Sc., P.Eng., M.E.I.C.,**

Partner,
Surveyer, Nenniger and Chenevert.

P. H. Desrosiers . . . In 1916 he joined La Fonderie du Peuple Ltee., in Joliette, Quebec and later joined Joliette Steel Company Limited as Secretary-Treasurer, a position which he held until 1918. He was later associated with Joliette Castings and Forgings Ltd., until 1923. From 1923 to 1925, he was Sales Manager of Stinson Reeb Builders Supply Limited in Montreal. In 1925 he returned to Joliette to reorganize the Joliette Steel Plant under the name of Joliette Steel Limited, becoming Managing Director. In 1932 he was appointed Managing Director of Sorel Steel Foundries Ltd., Sorel, Quebec, a position he held until 1946 when he was made Executive Vice-President of Joliette Steel Division, Dominion Brake Shoe Company Limited. He is also Executive Vice-President of the Manitoba Steel Foundry Division of Dominion Brake Shoe. In addition he is President of P. H. Desrosiers Enterprises Ltd., LaSalle Builders Supply Ltd., National Builders Supply Ltd., LaSalle Products Ltd., Val Royal Building Materials Ltd., Gavard Builders Supplies Division, and Ciment Fondu Lafarge (Canada) Ltd. He is Executive Vice-President of J. A. Laferté Ltd., and a Director of Sorel Mill & Builders Supply Ltd. Member: Foundrymen's Association; Canadian Mining Institute; Canadian Institute of Mining & Metallurgy; American Institute of Mining Engineers; Canadian Good Roads Association.

P. H. Desrosiers

Executive Vice-President,
Joliette Steel Division and Manitoba Steel Foundry Division
Dominion Brake Shoe Company Limited

Donald Gordon, C.M.G., LL.D.

Chairman and President
Canadian National Railways

Donald Gordon, C.M.G., LL.D. . . . born in Oldmeldrum, Scotland, on December 11, 1901. He was educated at public schools in Scotland and Canada. He entered the employ of the Bank of Nova Scotia, Toronto, Ont., in 1916, as a clerk. Four years later he was transferred to Head Office, and in 1924 to the inspection staff. In 1926 he became Assistant Chief Accountant and in 1930, was made Assistant Manager of the Toronto branch. In 1935 he was appointed to the post of Secretary of the newly established Bank of Canada. Three years later, in 1938, he was appointed Deputy Governor. When World War II came in 1939, he was instrumental, along with the Governor of the Bank of Canada, in working out the principles of exchange control and the administrative machinery which grew into Canada's Foreign Exchange Control Board. He was the Alternate Chairman of the Foreign Exchange Control Board in 1939. Chairman of the Wartime Prices and Trade Board in 1941; on loan from 1941 to 1947, returning to the Bank of Canada and the Foreign Exchange Control Board; appointed Director of the Industrial Development Bank on its creation in 1944; appointed Executive Director of the International Bank for Reconstruction and Development in 1948; and on January 1, 1950, he was appointed President of the Canadian National Railways and Chairman of the Board of Directors, and Director of Trans-Canada Air Lines. For his outstanding wartime services he was honored in 1944 with the award of the Companion of the Order of St. Michael and St. George, and in 1947 Queen's University conferred upon him the honorary degree of LL.D. In 1952 the University of Western Ontario also conferred upon him an honorary degree of LL.D. He is an Honorary Member, Vimy Branch (Que., No. 47), Canadian Legion, B.E.S.L. Married: Maisie Barter, 1926 (Deceased, 1950); secondly, Norma Hobbs in 1953. He has three sons. Residence: Chateau Apts., 1321 Sherbrooke St. W., Montreal, Que.

Edgar Philip Rees, C.M.G., M.C.

Director
Furness Withy & Co. Ltd.

Edgar Philip Rees . . . born Cardiff, Wales, June 28, 1896. He was educated in England and Wales. He commenced with the present company in 1912. General Manager, New York Office, for ten years previous to coming to Canada in 1945; appointed Director, 1945. Director, Deputy representative of British Minister of War Transport, New York, 1939-45. He is presently Director of Furness Withy & Co. Ltd.; President, Furness Montreal Ltd.; Director: Manchester Liners Ltd.; Cairn Line of Steamships Ltd., and President Shipping Federation of Canada since 1948. Clubs: St. James's (Montreal); Mount Royal; Montreal Club; Down Town Athletic; New York. Married: Natalie Goddard, in Peterborough, England in 1921; has one daughter. Residence: 540 Argyle Avenue Westmount, Quebec.

James Patrick Boyle, O.B.E. . . . born at Montreal, Que., on February 2, 1897. He was educated at Montreal Public and High Schools. Commenced business career in 1911 with Shipping Federation of Canada (Inc.) and remained until 1925. He was appointed Manager, Montreal office of J. F. Whitney Company, 1924 to 1935. He organized present firm in 1936. President: Canadian Overseas Shipping Ltd. Director: Federation of Catholic Charities. President and Director: Catholic Sailors' Club. Clubs: Country (St. Lambert); Gyro (Montreal); Mount Stephen; Montreal; Thistle Curling; M.A.A.A. Society; Knights of Columbus. He married Mary Edna, daughter of the late Alexander Bissett, Montreal, on April 20, 1925. They have two sons. Residence: 3501 Montclair Ave., Montreal, Que.

James Patrick Boyle, O.B.E.,

President
Shipping Limited

Melvyn Graham Angus, B.Com. . . . born in Stratford, Ont., on January 19, 1911. He was educated at Stratford Collegiate Institute; University of Toronto, (B.Com.) On graduation from University in 1932, he entered the Dominion Mortgage & Investments Association, Toronto; he was made Assistant Secretary-Treasurer in 1935; he resigned in 1936 to become associated with his brother in Angus & Company, Members of Toronto and Montreal Stock Exchange. In 1941, he went to Nova Scotia as Director of Clark Ruse Aircraft Limited, which was formed to carry out wartime overhaul and repair of aircraft for Eastern Air Command. At the end of World War II, he returned to Montreal and entered the shipping business. He is Vice-Chairman of Canadian Shipowners Mutual Assurance Association. Past President, Canadian Shipowners Association. Director, Hayes Steel Products Ltd., Merriton, Ont., 1936-40. Director, The Legare Company Limited, Quebec, 1936-41. Society: Phi Kappa Sigma Fraternity. Clubs: Montreal—St. James's Montreal; University; Montreal Badminton & Squash. Toronto — National; R.C.Y.C. He married Ada Madeline Hutchison in 1936. They have one son and two daughters. Residence: 699 Aberdeen Ave., Westmount, Que.

Melvyn Graham Angus, B.Com.

President
Lunham & Moore Shipping Limited

Marvin H. Gluntz,

Executive Vice President
H. C. Downer & Associates, Inc.

Marvin H. Gluntz . . .Executive Vice President, H. C. Downer & Associates, Inc., 619 Perry-Payne Building, Cleveland 13, Ohio. Entered U.S. Naval Academy from Toledo, Ohio, in 1926. Commissioned Ensign, U. S. Navy in 1930. Received M. S. in Naval Architecture and Marine Engineering, Massachusetts Institute of Technology, 1935. Was stationed at various naval shipyards on both East and West Coasts, also on Guam. Advanced Management Course at Harvard, 1948. Served as Industrial Manager, Ninth Naval District in Chicago, Illinois, 1954-1957. Retired from the Navy after 27-½ years. Married; three children. Author of several articles, mostly in the field of shipbuilding.

Carlton E. Tripp,

Vice President and General Manager
H. C. Downer & Associates, Inc.

Carlton E. Tripp . . . Graduated from U. S. Naval Academy in Class of 1942 and served in the U. S. Marine Corps through 1946. Obtained M.S.E. in Naval Architecture and Marine Engineering from the University of Michigan in 1949. Worked for Ingalls Shipbuilding Corporation Pascagoula, Mississippi, 1950 and 1951 in Machinery Scientific Section and joined H. C. Downer & Associates in 1951. Appointed to present position in 1955. Member of Society of Naval Architects and Marine Engineers. Written several marine technical articles for publication. Married and has one child.

Kenneth L. Hales . . . born in Ohio in 1899. He was educated in primary schools and at Oberlin College. In 1924 he travelled for a feed manufacturing firm over the entire State of Ohio. He went to Chicago in 1927 as Superintendent of a malt house casualty of prohibition, where he rebuilt the property to operating condition. Following a sojourn as Manager of a 1,000 acre estate in Northern Illinois, he returned to Chicago in 1934 where he represented multiple line insurance organization. The next 10 years was filled with intensive sales effort and promotion, including wet marine activity. This contact introduced him to the oil industry. A lack of service facility in the Chicago Harbor catering to the oil industry indicated opportunities in this field. From a humble start of one second hand tug boat he has developed equipment to where the present Harbor Line fleet is effectively serving the interests of not only the oil industry but other users as well. The insurance phase of his business is continuing under the management of his son.

Kenneth L. Hales

President
Chicago Towing Company

Anker L. Christy . . . born in the State of Washington. Educated in primary schools, Montana State College, graduating in 1920 with degree in Mechanical Engineering. During World War I, he spent 18 months in France serving as convoy officer, inspector of shop equipment, and Captain in charge of an overhaul park of the Motor Transport Corps. After graduating from college, he joined Worthington Pump and Machinery Corporation in New Jersey and attended night school at New York University where he received Masters degree in Business Administration in 1924. In 1928, he accepted position with Pure Oil Co. of Chicago where he worked until 1954 when he retired to form his own company, Transportation Engineers. In this capacity he has served as consulting engineer in the design and construction of barges, terminals and pipe lines, and has assisted in the planning and supervision of several large projects on the Eastern seaboard. In 1956, he was Civilian Consultant to the Commanding Officer of the U.S. Army Petroleum Distribution Command in the building of the military pipe line and terminals across France and spent the summer in Europe on that job.

Anker L. Christy

Vice-President
Chicago Towing Company

Wilbrod Bherer, C.R.

President,
Geo. T. Davie & Sons, Ltd.

Wilbrod Bherer . . . born in St. Fidele, Charlevoix County, August 11, 1905. He was educated at Ste-Marie College in Montreal where he obtained his B.A. He studied law at the Laval University in Quebec. He began his law career with the firm of Rochette & Gosselin in Quebec. He was appointed to the Bar in July 1930 and was associated with Mr. Paul Drouin, C.R. On February 5, 1945, he was made Queen's Council. He is associated with the law firm of Bherer, Juneau & Cote. He is also a director of several other companies. Clubs: Garrison Club; Cercle Universitaire, Kiwanis Club. He married Francoise Pruneau in 1931. They have one daughter, Helene. Residence: 79 rue d'Auteuil, Quebec.

Maurice Paquet

General Manager
Geo. T. Davie & Sons, Ltd.

Maurice Paquet . . . born at Lauzon in the County of Levis, January 22, 1912. He was educated at the St. Joseph College at Lauzon and graduated in 1927. He commenced his career as an office clerk with Geo T. Davie & Sons, Ltd., in 1929. His hobbies include golf, fishing and hunting. He married Carmelle Beaulieu in 1935. They have one daughter and three sons. Residence: Lauzon, Quebec.

Charles Barnes, J.P., . . . born at St. John's, Newfoundland in 1896. Served in Canadian Army overseas in World War 1 1914-1918. He is President and General Manager of Barnes Investigation Bureau Ltd., with Head Office in Montreal, Quebec. He is a former mayor of Pointe Claire, Quebec; former director of Montreal Police Department; past President of Chief Constable Association of Canada, Past President Province of Quebec Police and Fire Chiefs' Ass'n; Past President of Canadian Police A.A.A.; Past President of A.A.U. of C; Director of Civil Defense World War II. Member: International Ass'n. Chiefs of Police, Washington, D.C.; International Ass'n of Fingerprints and Identification; Better Business Bureau; Board of Trade, Montreal and Toronto; Canadian Legion, B.E.S.L. Club: Montreal Kiwanis. Married: has two sons (John Charles and Donald Andrew). Residence: 144 Coolbreeze Avenue, Lakeside, Que.

Charles Barnes, J.P.,

President
Barnes Investigation Bureau Ltd.

Jean Pierre St. Arnaud . . . born October 4, 1924 in Montreal, Quebec. He was educated at Notre Dame College, Montreal. He began his business career with St-Arnaud & Bergevin Ltd., Customs Brokers, International Freight Forwarders; Warehousemen; Cartage Contractors, in 1943. He held positions in various departments and was appointed Export Manager, 1949; Appointed Assistant to the President in 1953; He is currently Secretary-Treasurer of the Company. Member: Canadian Exporters' Ass'n.; Canadian International Freight Forwarders' Ass'n.; Dominion Chartered Custom House Brokers Ass'n.; Montreal Board of Trade; Chamber of Commerce of Montreal; Canadian Warehousemen's Ass'n.; Quebec Transport Ass'n. Clubs: Traffic Club and St. Denis Club. Recreations: Golf, fishing, hunting and yachting. Married: Lucie Beliveau May 8, 1954, in Montreal. They have one son, Louis. Residence: 4030 Lacombe Ave., Montreal, Que.

Jean Pierre St-Arnaud

Secretary-Treasurer
St. Arnaud & Bergevin Ltd.

Frank B. Peterson

President
Montreal Shipping Company Limited

Frank B. Peterson . . . born in Montreal, P.Q. He began his business career with the Canadian Pacific Railway in 1939. During World War II he was on loan to the Ministry of War Transport of the United Kingdom. After spending a short time with Saguenay Terminals Ltd., he joined Montreal Shipping Company Limited in 1948. He was appointed Vice-President and Director in 1953 and assumed the position of President in 1957. Member: Montreal Chamber of Commerce; Board of Management Southwestern Y.M.C.A.; National Council Y.M.C.A. Clubs: Engineers Club of Montreal; Country Club of Montreal. Hobbies: Golf and fishing. Residence: 1657 Fayolle Avenue, Crawford Park, Quebec.

James L. Thom

Vice-President
Montreal Shipping Company Limited

James L. Thom . . . born in Paterson, New Jersey. He moved to Montreal, Que., shortly thereafter. He worked briefly during the early days of World War II on vessels of the Canadian National Steamship fleet. He joined Montreal Shipping Company Limited in 1943 as Secretary to the Vice-President. In 1946, he formed James L. Thom, Inc., in New York City to represent the liner interests of the Montreal Shipping Company Limited and the New York firm preceded Canadian Chartering (New York) Limited which is now a subsidiary of the Montreal Shipping group. He returned to Montreal in 1951 as Executive Assistant to the President. He is an Associate of the Institute of Chartered Shipbrokers of London, England. Director: Montreal Sailors' Institute; Montreal Boys' Association. Member: Montreal Board of Trade. Clubs: St. James's; Montreal Amateur Athletic Association; Rideau, Ottawa. Hobbies: Squash; Skiing. He is married to Eugenia McCaw of Diamond Point, N.Y. Residence: 3940 Cote des Neiges Road, Montreal, Que.

Thomas Francis Rahilly . . . born Diorite, Michigan, October 6, 1892. He began his business career with D. S. S. & A. Railway, Michigan in 1908. 1913-16 Algoma Central Railway; Algoma Eastern Railway, 1917-19; Algoma Steel Corp. Ltd., Sault Ste Marie, Ont., 1920-43; Vice-President and General Manager, The Toronto Iron Works Limited, 1945; Appointed President in 1946. He was elected President of Canada Iron Foundries Limited in 1951. He is a Director of The Bank of Nova Scotia, Dominion Foundries & Steel Limited, John Wood Industries Limited, Canadian Refractories Limited and Walworth Company. He is also a Director of the subsidiary companies of Canada Iron Foundries Ltd. Clubs: Rideau (Ottawa); St. James's (Montreal); Granite (Toronto); York (Toronto); Seigniory (Montebello); Sault Ste. Marie (Sault Ste. Marie). Married Violet Kennedy, February 15, 1915; has four sons. Residence: 1855 Kenilworth Road, Town of Mount Royal, Montreal 16, Quebec.

Thomas Francis Rahilly

Chairman and President
Canada Iron Foundries Ltd.

Welsford Allen Marshall . . . born Ottawa, Ontario, January 29, 1912. He is a graduate of Queen's University, B.Sc., 1937. He began his business career with Dominion Structural Steel Limited in 1930. He was a Major with R.C.E.M.E., from 1939-1945, World War II. He was appointed President of Dominion Structural Steel Limited in 1953. Clubs: Laurentian Club, Ottawa; Mount Stephen Club, Montreal; Engineer's Club, Montreal; Dunany Golf and Country Club, Dunany, Quebec. Married: Dorothy Edith Williams, March 20th, 1953; has three children. Residence: 2170 Hanover Road, Town of Mount Royal, Montreal 16, Quebec.

Welsford Allen Marshall

President
Dominion Structural Steel Limited.

Whitham Taylor-Bailey, M.C., B.Sc.,

Chairman of the Board
Dominion Bridge Company Limited

Whitham Taylor-Bailey . . . born Montreal, Que., March 7, 1891, son of William and Margaret (Murphy) Taylor-Bailey. Educated: McGill University, Montreal, Que. Commenced with Dominion Bridge Company, 1908. In addition to being Chairman of the Board of Dominion Bridge Company Limited, he is also Vice-President, Dominion Engineering Works Ltd.; Eastern Canada Steel & Iron Works Ltd.; Director: Royal Bank of Canada; Robert Mitchell Co. Ltd.; National Drug & Chemical Co. of Canada; Wabasso Cotton Co. Ltd.; Woods Mfg. Co. Ltd.; Sheraton Corp. of America; Sheraton Ltd. and Steel Company of Canada. Married Janet Boden of Lancaster, Ont., 1916. Clubs: Mount Royal; University; Royal St. Lawrence Yacht; St. James's. Society: Engineering Institute of Canada. Recreation: sailing. Presbyterian. Residence: 214 Senneville Road, Senneville, Que.

Lieut.-Col. Alfred Henry Cowie, M.C., V.D., M.Eng.,

Vice-President and Managing Director
Dominion Bridge Company Limited

Lieut.-Col. Alfred Henry Cowie . . . born Liverpool, Eng., Feb. 19, 1890, son of Elizabeth E. (Rorke) and Henry J. Cowie. Educated: Wallasey Grammar School and Liverpool University, M.Eng. Joined Dominion Bridge Company Limited 1910. Served in various departments until 1925, when appointed Assistant General Manager; later, in 1934, was appointed Manager, Eastern Division. General Manager, Wartime Merchant Shipping Limited during organizational period in 1941, and subsequently its Vice-President. Member, Executive Committee, Canadian Standards Association for a period of 15 years and, for his services, appointed honorary life member, 1951. He was one of the organizers of the Canadian Welding Bureau and Chairman of its Administrative Board from its inception in 1947 until the end of 1950. Member Council, Montreal Board of Trade, 1949-51. Served in World War I, 1914-19. Awarded Military Cross and Bar. Rejoined Canadian Grenadier Guards after World War I and was promoted to Lieut.-Col.; he commanded the unit, 1928-31; appointed Honorary Lieut.-Colonel, 1956. In addition to being Vice-President and Managing Director of Dominion Bridge Company Limited, Lachine, Que., he is also Director, Dominion Engineering Works Ltd.; Eastern Canada Steel & Iron Works Ltd. and Robb Engineering Works Ltd. Married Gretchen Irene Clarke (now deceased), daughter of the late D. R. Clarke, 1922; has one daughter. Clubs: University; St. James's; Forest and Stream. Societies: Engineering Institute of Canada; Corporation of Professional Engineers of Quebec; Canadian Standards Association. Recreations: golf and fishing. United Church of Canada. Residence: 30 Redpath Place, Montreal, Que.

Hubert Gray Welsford . . . born San Jose, Cal., July 16, 1895, son of Herbert Richard and Ada (Gray) Welsford. Educated: Winnipeg public schools. With Dominion Bridge Co., Winnipeg, 1911-15; Lieut., R.F.C. and R.A.F., 1916-19; M.B.E. (Mil.); Returned to Winnipeg, 1919, with Dominion Bridge Co.; Sales Engineer with Dominion Bridge Co., Montreal, 1921-23; Assistant General Manager, Dominion Engineering Works, Montreal, 1923-26; appointed General Manager, 1926; Vice-President, 1938; President, 1951. Member, Executive Committee, Canadian Chamber of Commerce, 1943-48; Member, Montreal Board of Trade. Member, Defence Research Board, Ottawa, 1952-55. In addition to being President of Dominion Bridge Company Limited, he is also President and Managing Director, Dominion Engineering Works Ltd., Montreal, Que.; President and Managing Director: Dominion Engineering Company Limited; Director: Canadian Pratt & Whitney Aircraft Co. Ltd.; Shawinigan Water & Power Co.; Consolidated Mining & Smelting Co. of Canada Limited; and Canadian Pacific Railway Company; Director, Montreal Trust Company; Trustee, Bishop's University. He is also a life member of the Engineering Institute of Canada. Married Jean Thomson Stavert, Feb. 16, 1927, daughter of Sir William Stavert, K.B.E.; has one son and one daughter. Clubs: Mount Royal; St. James's; Royal Montreal Golf; Mount Bruno C.C.; Laurentian Lodge; Forest & Stream. Recreations: golf, skiing. Residence: 32 Ramezay Road, Westmount, Que.

Hubert Gray Welsford, M.B.E. (Mil.),

President and Director
Dominion Bridge Company Limited

Robert S. Eadie . . born Ottawa, Ont., Aug. 29, 1895, son of the late Rev. Robert Eadie and Flora (Stewart) Eadie. Educated: Ottawa Collegiate Institute and McGill University (B.Sc., 1920 (Civil Engineering), M.Sc., 1922). After graduation held position of lecturer in Department of Applied Mechanics at McGill University until 1924, when he joined the staff of Dominion Bridge Co., Ltd., Lachine; was made Designing Engineer, 1935; Assistant Chief Engineer, 1937; Chief Engineer, Eastern Division, 1944; appointed Vice-President and Manager, Eastern Division, 1951. Active for a number of years on several technical committees of Canadian Standards Association and now 1st Vice-President, Director and Member of Executive Committee; Member, Engineering Institute of Canada, served as Vice-President, 1947 and 1948. Member, Corporation of Professional Engineers of the Province of Quebec. Served in Canada and Overseas with Canadian Engineers, 1916-19. In addition to being Vice-President and Manager, Eastern Division, Dominion Bridge Company Limited, he is also Vice-President and Director, Robb Engineering Works Ltd.; President and Director, Canadian Overseas Projects Limited. Married Vera Grace Adams, daughter of the late Frank W. Adams, Victoria, B.C., 1920; has two sons. Clubs: St. James's; University (Montreal) and Canadian. United Church of Canada. Residence: 4380 Mayfair Avenue, Montreal, Que.

Robert S. Eadie, M.Sc.,

Vice-President and Manager, Eastern Division
Dominion Bridge Company Limited

Harry Winford Morrison

President
Morrison-Knudson Company, Inc.

Harry Winford Morrison . . . born in Tunbridge Township, Dewitt County, Illinois, on February 23, 1885. He was educated at common schools and high school. At the age of 14 he became a waterboy on a construction job to relocate a railroad in Illinois. Three years later he was employed as timekeeper of the construction contracting firm of Bates & Rogers of Chicago. He worked his way up from axman to draftsman and superintendent, with the Reclamation Service of the U.S. Dept. of the Interior. In March 1912 he resigned from the government's service to establish a partnership with Morris H. Knudson as a firm of construction contractors. In 1923 the partnership of Morrison-Knudson was incorporated under the laws of Idaho as Morrison-Knudson Company. In 1929, he became active organizer of a group of western companies known as Six Companies Inc., to compete for the construction of Hoover (Boulder) Dam on the Colorado River . . . an epochal construction feat and a highly profitable one as it was completed two years and two months ahead of schedule. Morrison-Knudson was reincorporated in 1934 as a corporation of Delaware, with Messrs. Knudson and Morrison continuing in control as principal owners. He has been the Company's chief executive officer since November, 1943. Subsidiaries are located in Latin America, Central America, England, Middle and Far Eastern countries, Australia and New Zealand. Degrees: D.Sc. (Honorary) University of Idaho; Doctor of Laws (honorary) University of Portland, Oregon. He is Life President of Idaho Chapter, Associated General Contractors. The Moles, construction contractors's society of New York, conferred on him its annual award for achievement of a non-member. The Beavers, a constructors' assoc. of the western U.S. presented him with an award for distinguished achievement in his profession. Honorary life member of Idaho Professional Engineers.

John B. Bonny,

Vice-President and General Manager
Morrison-Knudsen Company, Inc.

John Bruce Bonny . . . born February 8, 1908 in San Francisco. He graduated from the University of California with a degree of Bachelor of Science. In 1931, while operating his own construction business (J. B. Bonny, Inc.) in the Northwest, he was hired by H. W. Morrison, President of Morrison-Knudsen Company, Inc. to head the new Los Angeles office in charge of southwestern district operations. In 1943 he was made vice-president of the corporation. In 1947, then the youngest of seven vice-presidents, he became general manager and moved to the headquarters of Morrison-Knudsen Company in Boise, Idaho. In this post he is very active and travels extensively in the United States and foreign countries covering the operations of Morrison-Knudsen and subsidiaries. He is chairman of the board of The H. K. Ferguson Company, which he was principally instrumental in adding to the list of more than 40 subsidiaries of Morrison-Knudsen Company, Inc. He is president of Morrison-Knudsen de Sonora (Mexico) and vice-president of several other Latin American subsidiaries; chairman of the operating committee of Atlas Constructors, the five-company joint venture building North African air bases.

Louis R. Perini . . . born in 1902. At an early age he started in the construction business with his father's firm, B. Perini & Sons, Inc., formed as a corporate company in 1917. His father died in 1924 and his brothers and himself took over the administration of the company, at which time he became President of the company. The Perini Corporation, by which name the parent company has become known controls one of the largest construction organizations in the world. The company was active on the American side in the building of the St. Lawrence Seaway and Power Projects, which included the Robert Moses Power Dam at Massena, New York, for the Power Authority of the State of New York. Louis Perini and his wife Florence have seven children. Mr. Perini makes his headquaters at Framingham, Mass.

Louis R. Perini

President
Perini Corporation

Albert R. Berry . . . born at North Andover, Massachusetts, on March 18, 1902. He was educated in public schools, Phillip Andover, Tufts College Mechanical and Civil Engineer. He was employed by General Motors and Department of Public Works. He enlisted in the Army World War II in 1942, Officers' Candidate School, Officer and Troop Commander of Company Battalion Regiment and Group. Branch of Service: Corps of Engineers; Theatre of Operation — E.T.O. He was awarded 5 battle stars and 2 bronze stars. In 1946 he was Director of Construction Supply and Real Estate, Veterans Administration and Troop Reserve under General Bradley, in Washington, D.C. 1948-49, General Superintendent, Coal Division, Perini Corporation; 1949-55, Project Manager, Jim Woodruff Dam; 1952-58, Vice-President, Perini Corporation; 1953-58, Director of Perini Quebec, Inc.; 1955-58, Project Manager Barnhart Island Power Plant, joint ventures of Perini, Walsh Morrison-Knudsen, Kiewit & Utah. 1958 — Project Manager Grass River Lock — joint ventures of Perini, Walsh, Morrison-Knudsen, Kiewit, & Utah.

Albert R. Berry,

Vice President,
Perini Corporation.

Anton P. Nelson

President
Wacker Warehouse Company

Anton P. Nelson . . . born in Denmark in 1894. He formed and is President of the Star West Cartage Company, Chicago, Illinois, since 1913; organized and is president of Gary Warehouse Company, Gary, Indiana since 1929; In 1933 he organized and is the President of Jefferson Park Warehouse, Company, Chicago; He organized and is president of Wacker Warehouse Company, Chicago since 1951; He is president of the Illinois Motor Truck Operators Association. He is Illinois State vice president of the American Trucking Association, also serving as a member of the Executive Committee; He is a director of the Contract Carriers Conference of the American Trucking Association and past chairman of above Conference. He served as chairman of the Appeal Board of the Office of Defence Transportation on Distribution of Motor Truck Equipment. Member: Illinois Warehousemen's Association, Chicago Association of Commerce and Industry, Traffic Club of Chicago, Advisory Board on Truck Tires for the Office of Price Administration. Married: Jane B. Patchell, in 1916. They have two children Virginia Mae and Dorothy Jane. Residence: 707 North Spring Street, LaGrange Park, Illinois.

Henry Golden Marsh

President & Treasurer
Chicago Stevedoring Company

Henry Golden Marsh . . . born in Chicago on July 25, 1909. He was educated at De Pau University from 1927 to 1931. He has been a Warehouseman since 1931. He was associated with the Railway Terminal & Warehouse Company in Chicago from 1931 to 1943. He was acting secretary of the Federal Emergency Warehouse Association of Chicago, and also assistant secretary Illinois Association Merchandise Warehousemen from 1943 to 1946. He has been owner of Henry G. Marsh Company since 1946. Since 1957 he has been President and Treasurer of the Chicago Stevedoring Company, Inc. He is the past director of the Chicago Transportation Club and of the Traffic Club of Chicago, Michigan Shores. Member: Illinois Association Merchandise Warehousemen, Chicago Association of Commerce & Industry-Executive Committee; Industrial Traffic Council, National & Chicago real estate boards, Importers Association, Phi Kappa Psi fraternity. Married: Elizabeth Jean Martin in November 1936. They have two children Jean Anne and George Martin. Residence: 2236 Beechwood Avenue, Wilmette, Illinois.

George F. McLaughlin . . . born in 1901, son of Geo. D. McLaughlin one of the owners. He graduated from Yale in 1922. In 1932 he was appointed President of Wakem & McLaughlin, Incorporated, merchandise warehousemen, distributors, bottling plants in bond and tax paid, financing and fiduciary agents of Chicago, Illinois. He is also Vice-President and Treasurer of W. F. McLaughlin & Co. Manor House Coffee importers and roasters. He is a member of Onwentsia Club, Lake Forest, Illinois.

George F. McLaughlin

President
Wakem & McLaughlin, Inc.

Frances E. Berg (Miss) . . . known in private life as Mrs. Frank Joseph Sherman. She was born in 1898. She started employment at Wakem & McLaughlin in 1912. She trained in all phases of warehousing under able tutorship of J. Wallace Wakem founder of the Company and was his Assistant until his death in 1928. She was elected Secretary-Treasurer and General Manager in 1932 and took full charge of all operations of the Corporation. She has added varied services for customers, such as Internal Revenue Bonded Warehouses, U.S. Customs Bonded Warehouses. She built a new 200,000 sq. ft. single story fully mechanized warehouse in order to service large national shippers and storers of varied products.

Miss Frances E. Berg

Secretary-Treasurer and General Manager
Wakem & McLaughlin, Inc.

Hon. Charles Avery Dunning, P.C. (C), LL.D.

Chairman
Ogilvie Flour Mills Co. Limited.

Hon. Charles Avery Dunning, P.C. (C), LL.D., . . . born in Croft, Leicestershire, England. He received an LL.D. (Queens' University, University of Saskatchewan and the University of Montreal) and later an Hon. LL.D. from McGill University. He came to Canada in 1903. In 1910 he became a Director of the Saskatchewan Grain Growers' Assoc., and was Vice-President from 1911-14. He organized the Saskatchewan Co-Operative Elevator Co. Ltd. in 1911. He was appointed Royal Commissioner by the Saskatchewan Provincial Government to investigate the question of agriculture credit and grain marketing in Europe in 1913. From 1911-16 he was a Member of the Canadian Council of Agriculture and Chairman of the Saskatchewan Victory Loan Committee from 1917-19. In 1918 he served as a member of the Canada Food Board. In 1916, 17, 21 and 25 he was elected to the Sask. Legislature. Provincial Treasurer for Saskatchewan, 1916; Minister of Railways, 1917; Minister of Telephones, 1918; Minister of Agriculture in 1919; In 1922 he was called upon to form a Cabinet and assumed the office of Premier, President of the Council, Provincial Treasurer and Minister of Railways. In February 1926, appointed Minister of Railways and Canals in the Dominion Government, following which he was elected for Regina after assuming office; June 1926, resigned with the Liberal Government and re-elected for Regina to the House of Commons in General Election Sept. 1926 when he was also appointed Minister of Railways; Canadian Delegate to the League of Nations in 1928; Minister of Finance, 1929; 1935 re-appointed Minister of Finance and received acclamation as Member of Parliament of Queen's County, P.E.I., in December of same year. In 1939, he was forced to retire from public life due to ill health but is active in the following capacities: Chancellor of Queen's University, Director of the Canadian Pacific Railway, Consolidated Mining & Smelting Co., Consolidated Paper Corporation, Steel Co. of Canada, Bank of Montreal, Royal Trust Co., Sun Life Assurance Co. of Canada and the Bell Telephone Co. of Canada. Chairman of the Canadian Investment Fund Ltd., and Director of the Royal-Liverpool Group. Chairman of the Board of The Ogilvie Flour Mills, Co., Limited.

H. Norman Davis,

President,
Ogilvie Flour Mills Co. Limited.

H. Norman Davis . . born in Birmingham, England. He was educated at private schools in Cheltenham. He came to Canada in 1905 where he joined the Winnipeg Office of the Ogilvie Flour Mills as a junior on November 18th of the same year. Progressing through secretarial duties to city and country ledgers and to the sales department, where he was three years on the road in Manitoba and parts of Alberta. He served the company as Sales Manager at Winnipeg, Manitoba and Medicine Hat, Alberta. In 1927 he was appointed Manager of the Medicine Hat mill and in 1938 became Assistant General Manager at Montreal. He was appointed Vice-President in 1947 and then became President in 1952. He is also President of the Canada Grain Export Co. Ltd.; Lake of the Woods Milling Co. Ltd.; Chairman of the Board of Consolidated Bakeries Limited, Inter City Baking Co.; Director of McGavin Limited, McGavin Bakeries Limited; Catelli Food Products Ltd., and a Member of the Advisory Board of the Northern Assurance Company.

Arthur Atkins . . . born in Newcastle-on-Tyne, England. He was educated at public schools in both England and Canada. He began his career with Ogilvie when he joined the Company at Winnipeg in September 1918 as a Junior. In May 1925 he moved to Edmonton, Alberta, as operator of the mill elevator. From there he was promoted, in 1927, to Superintendent of the Medicine Hat, Alta., country elevator system. In 1938 he became Assistant Manager of the Medicine Hat Division and Manager in 1940. An appointment as Vice-President of Operations brought Mr. Atkins to Montreal in 1947 and 1952 saw his promotion to Vice-President of the Company. He is also a Director of the Lake of the Woods Milling Co. Ltd., McGavin Bakeries Limited, McGavin Limited, Industrial Grain Products Limited and Seaforth Milling Co., Limited. His recreations include shooting, fishing, curling and golfing.

Arthur Atkins,

Executive Vice-President,
Ogilvie Flour Mills Co. Limited.

———————

John Edward Brownlee, Q.C., LL.D., . . . born in Port Ryerse, Ontario, August 25, 1884. He was educated at the Brigden Public and Sarnia High Schools in Ontario and received a B.A. degree from Toronto University in 1908; He graduated in law at Calgary in 1912 and called to the Alberta Bar that year. The University of Alberta conferred upon him a Doctorate of Laws degree in 1930. He was appointed K.C. in 1921; served as Attorney-General of the Province of Alberta, 1921-24; Premier of that Province from 1924-34 as Head of the United Farmers of Alberta political party. In addition to his duties as President and General Manager of the United Grain Growers Limited which he assumed in 1948, he is a Director of the Catelli Food Products Limited and Senior Partner of the law firm of Brownlee & Brownlee in Edmonton. Married: Florence Edy, in London Ont., December 23, 1912; they have two sons John Edy and Alan Marshall. Club: Winnipeg Motor Country. Recreation: Golf. Residence: 4 Donegal Mansions, Calgary, Alta.

J. E. Brownlee, B.A., Q.C., LL.D., (Hon).

President & General Manager
United Grain Growers Ltd.,

Albert Deschamps, C.E., O.B.E., M.E.I.C.

President
Deschamps & Belanger, Limited

Albert Deschamps, C.E., O.B.E., M.E.I.S., . . . was born at Brockton, Mass., U.S.A. November 24, 1891; son of Albert Deschamps of St. Paul, Que. and Victoria (Pain) Deschamps. Educated: Brockton High School, Brockton, Mass. and McGill University, Montreal, Que. Married Cecile Beaudry and has one son and three daughters. Recreations: golf, fishing, hunting. Roman Catholic. Residence: 156 Maplewood, Ave., Outremont, Que.; summer camp at Sixteen Island Lake, Que. After having worked as General Superintendent for Maritimes Bate & McMahan, he started his own business in 1922. Among important contracts carried out are: Loyola College, Montreal; Deaf and Dumb Institute, Montreal; Nazareth Institute, Montreal; St. John's Hospital, Nicolet Hospital; Valleyfield Cathedral; Granby St. Joseph Hospital; Jean-de-Brebeuf College, Montreal. Member National Advisory Council on Manpower. In 1952, elected Director for European Operations for National Defence enterprises, the Paris office being at 12 Monthieu Street. In November 1946, elected alderman for the City of Outremont. Member National War Labour Board Committee. Past President, Canadian Construction Association. He is a member of the following Clubs: Graduate Society of McGill; Montreal Chamber of Commerce; Reform; St. Denis; University (Montreal); Laval-sur-le-Lac Golf; Board of Trade; Cercle Universitaire de Montreal; St. Lawrence Kiwanis (Past President); Seigniory Club (Montebello). Member of Builders' Exchange, Montreal; President, Canadian Construction Association (1946-47) member of Engineering Institute of Canada; member Corporation of Professional Engineers, Quebec.

Paul Dufresne, M.E.I.C., P.Eng., B.A.Sc.

President
Dufresne Engineering Co. Ltd.

Paul Dufresne, M.E.I.C., P.Eng., B.A.Sc. . . . Born at Montreal, Que., on August 17, 1911. He was educated at Valleyfield Seminary, Valleyfield, Que., and Polytechnical School, Montreal (C.E. 1934; B.A.Sc. 1934). He joined Dufresne Construction Co., Ltd., Montreal, in association with his uncle, the late Marius Dufresne, in 1935. He was elected a director in 1936 and became president in 1945 when he purchased the business upon the death of his uncle. He organized Dufresne Engineering Co. Ltd., in 1938 and was elected president in 1945. Member: Engineering Institute of Canada; Corporation of Professional Engineers, Province of Quebec; Canadian Forestry Association; Montreal Board of Trade; Canadian Chamber of Commerce; Chambre de Commerce de Montréal; Chambre de Commerce de la Province de Québec; Montreal Builders Exchange; Canadian Good Roads Association; Canadian Horse Shows Association. He is a Life Governor of the Notre Dame Hospital in Montreal. Clubs: Cercle Universitaire; Mount Stephen; Laval-sur-le-Lac Golf; Surf (Miami). Recreations: riding and fishing. He married Laurette Gariepy on October 7, 1936. They have three daughters. Residence: Westmount, Quebec.

Jean Paul Lalonde, B.A.Sc., P.Eng. . . . He graduated in Engineering from Ecole Polytechnique of Montreal in 1926. He was in the employ of J. M. Eugene Guay, a consulting Engineer, from 1926 to 1936. He was appointed Chief Engineer of the above firm in 1930. In this post he was responsible for the preparation of plans, specifications and supervision with all projects. In 1936 he formed a partnership with Romeo Valois and formed the firm of Lalonde & Valois, Consulting Engineers. He is a member of the Corporation of Professional Engineers of Quebec, the Engineering Institute of Canada, and the Canadian Standard Association.

Jean Paul Lalonde, B.A.Sc., P.Eng.

Partner
Lalonde & Valois.

Romeo Valois, B.A.Sc., M.Sc., P.Eng., . . . graduated in engineering from Ecole Polytechnique of Montreal in 1930. He obtained his Master of Science in Engineering and Business Administration from the Massachusetts Institute of Technology in September 1931. From September 1931 to 1936, he served in the capacity of assistant-director and finally director of works for the Montreal Catholic School Commission. In 1936, in partnership with Jean Paul Lalonde he formed the firm of Lalonde & Valois, Consulting Engineers. He is a member of the Corporation of Professional Engineers of Quebec.

Romeo Valois, B.A.Sc., M.Sc., P.Eng.

Partner
Lalonde & Valois.

Lucien Paquin,

President,
Three Rivers Shipping Co. Ltd.

Lucien Paquin . . . born Three Rivers, Quebec, Nov. 27, 1899. He was educated at schools at Three Rivers, Que.; De La Salle Academy. He was with the Canadian Pacific Railway Company previous to commencing with J. Malone & Co. Ltd., Three Rivers, Que., remaining for twenty-four years; organized the Three Rivers Shipping Co., in 1945. He is President of Three Rivers Shipping Co. Limited, Three Rivers, Que.; Quebec Terminals Ltd.; Stevedoring & Steamship Agents. Clubs: Three Rivers; Three Rivers Curling; Traffic (New York). Recreations: curling, fishing, etc. Married: Margaret Lord in 1925; has three sons and one daughter. Residence: 1425 Blvd. Des Forges, Three Rivers, Que.

Roger Paquin

General Manager
Quebec Terminals Limited.

Roger Paquin . . . born in Three Rivers, Quebec in 1927. He was educated in primary school in Three Rivers and completed his classical studies at Loyola College, Montreal, Que. He graduated in 1948 from Laval University, Quebec City, in Commerce and Business Administration. From 1948-51, he was employed as Manager of Stevedoring Operations in his father's business, Three Rivers Shipping Company Limited, Three Rivers, Que. At the establishment of Quebec Terminals Limited in 1951, he was appointed General Manager of the new stevedoring and steamship agency business. Member: Winter Club; Chamber of Commerce, Quebec City; KI-8-EB Golf Club, Three Rivers; Grunt Club, Montreal. Residence: The Claridge, 220 Grande Allee, Quebec City, Quebec.

Dudley Roy Townsend, O.B.E., . . . born Louisburg, N.S., March 17, 1888. Educated: Louisburg. He began his career with The Royal Bank of Canada and remained with them for twelve years; commenced in the present business after leaving the Royal Bank; appointed Administrator of Ships Stores in 1942. He was made an Officer of the Order of the British Empire on July 1st, 1946. Clubs: Montreal; Union (Saint John). Recreation: fishing. Married: Jessie M. Grant, in Hopewell, N.S., in 1914. He has four sons and two daughters. Residence: 805 Upper Lansdowne Ave., Westmount, Que.

Dudley Roy Townsend, O.B.E.,

President & Director
Townsend Company, Ltd.

Clarence Dudley (Robin) Townsend, B.Com. . . . born at Montreal, Que., on July 6, 1922. He was educated at Westmount High School and McGill University, Montreal. He was appointed Director of Townsend Company Limited in 1949 and Vice-President in 1950. He is also Vice-President and Director of: Townsend Company (Maritime) Limited; Jos. Bianchi and Son Limited; Marine and Industrial Suppliers, representing — The Beldam Packing and Rubber Company Limited, London, England, D. Morgan Rees and Sons Limited, Cardiff, Wales, and Farboil Paints, Baltimore, Maryland. Member: National Assoc. of Marine Suppliers, New York; Montreal Board of Trade; Associate Member Institute of Power Engineers; Montreal Club; Union Club, Saint John, N.B.; Fossils Club of Montreal, Inc. Recreations: Tennis, Skiing, Hunting.

Clarence Dudley (Robin) Townsend, B.Com.,

Vice-President and Director
Townsend Company Limited

397

Herbert James Lorber

Chairman
Rollins Burdick Hunter Co.

Herbert James Lorber . . . born in Chicago, Illinois, August 26, 1892. He was educated at the Edgewater Grade School, Hoyne High School, Crane Tech., attended Northwestern School of Commerce in the evenings for seventeen years. He began his career as bank messenger and general clerk with the Illinois Trust Co., Chicago 1910. Assistant Manager Insurance Clearing House, 1914-16; Office Manager, Moore Case Lyman & Hubbard 1916-17; General Manager and Secretary all branches Rollins Burdick Hunter Co., 1918-26; Vice President George F. Nixson & Co., 1926-31; Special Executive Representative Investors Syndicate 1932-36; Returned to Rollins Burdick Hunter Co. as Secretary-Treasurer in 1936; elected President 1944; elected Chairman of the Board in 1956. He is a director of Rollins Burdick Hunter Co.; Gulf Mobile & Ohio Railroad; Booth Fisheries Corporation; National Foundation for Infantile Paralysis; Transportation Association of America; Goodwill Industries; YMCA University of Illinois; Trustee, Georgia Warm Springs Foundation; Member: Chicago Board of Underwriters; Chicago Insurance Agents Association: Illinois Association of Insurance Agents; Insurance Federation of Illinois. Clubs: Chicago Club, Chicago Athletic Association, North Shore Country Club (Past President); Oakbrook Polo & Hunt Club, Minneapolis Club. Married: Hazel Emrath, September 6, 1916. One daughter, Lucille: Residence: 5555 north Sheridan Road, Chicago, Illinois.

Adrian B. Palmer

President
Rollins Burdick Hunter Co.

Adrian B. Palmer . . . born October 23, 1910. He began his career as a temporary clerk in the office of Rollins Burdick Hunter Co. in 1928. In 1929 he resided in Mexico City, where he attended school. He returned to Rollins Burdick Hunter Co. in 1930 as a junior clerk in the Accounting Division. He spent the ensuing 5 years in various Divisions of the Company in their training program for junior executives. He was elected Vice-President of Rollins Burdick Hunter Co. in 1946; Executive Vice-President in 1952 and President in 1956. During World War II he entered active duty with the Navy in January 1942 and served until the conclusion of the war. LCDR-USNR (ret.). He is a director of Rollins Burdick Hunter Co. and Chicago Crime Commission. He is active in various civic affairs. Clubs: The Chicago Club: The Mid-Day Club; Westmoreland Country Club. Married Gladys Towne in 1937. Has one son, Robert Towne Palmer. Residence: 751 Glendale Drive, Glenview, Ill.

George Inselman . . . is a native New Yorker. He began his insurance career in 1918 with the British and Foreign Marine Insurance Company in New York. He served as manager of the Claims Department, secretary, assistant underwriter and assistant U.S. attorney. In 1939 he joined the Fire Association and became a vice-president before he left to accept an executive position with the Marine Office in 1945. In 1950 he became assistant Manager and was promoted to general manager in December 1954. In January 1955 he was named President. He is Chairman of the Board of the United States P. & I. Agency Inc., director of the Associated Aviation Underwriters; director, American Institute of Marine Underwriters, United States Salvage Association, Inc.; Second vice-president, Board of Underwriters. Member: National Cargo Bureau, Inc., American Bureau of Shipping, American Cargo War Risk Reinsurance Exchange; Director of New York Council of Navy League of the United States. Mr. Inselman has lectured on marine insurance at the Insurance Society of New York and the American Bar Association.

George Inselman

President
Marine Office of America.

Perry M. Fenton . . . born in Chicago, Illinois. He was educated in Chicago's public grade and high schools. He graduated from the United States Naval Academy, Annapolis, Maryland, with a Bachelor of Science Degree in June 1922, and commissioned Ensign U.S.N. He served in destroyers and submarines until resignation of commission as Lieutenant to enter the Insurance business in 1928. He joined the staff of the Marine Office of America in June, 1931. During World War II, while on leave of absence, served as commanding officer of the U.S.S. DANIEL T. GRIFFEN and the U.S.S. MARSH, both ships being engaged in trans-Atlantic convoy duty and as Executive Officer of the Amphibious training base at Fort Pierce, Florida, where the Navy's underwater demolition teams, scouts and raiders and attack boat crews were trained. Commissioned Captain U.S.N.R. He was appointed Assistant Manager of the Western Department in November 17, 1945. Elected Executive Vice-President on October 15, 1957.

Perry M. Fenton

Executive Vice President
Marine Office of America

S. M. Mendelssohn

President
Mendelssohn Brothers (Canada) Limited

S. M. Mendelssohn . . . has been in the Customs Brokerage business since 1924. Member of Dominion Chartered Customs House Brokers Association. Secretary-Treasurer of Canadian Importers and Traders Association, Quebec Branch and also Director of the Dominion Association.

Nathan Mendelssohn

Executive General Manager
Mendelssohn Brothers (Canada) Limited

Nathan Mendelssohn . . . has been in Customs Brokerage business since early 1900. He is one of the charter members and organizers of the Dominion Chartered Customs House Brokers Association and has been Secretary-Treasurer since its inception in the twenties. Secretary-Treasurer both for Montreal Branch and National Organization. Gave up secretary-ship about 1940. He was also a charter member and organizer of Canadian Importers Association and acted as Secretary of the Montreal Branch for some years. Governor of several hospitals, Y.M.H.A. and member of a number of organizations and clubs.

Samuel Gordon Chodos . . . born near the port of Lobau in Lithuania on July 24, 1901. Moved to Canada with his family from South Africa in 1906. He was educated at Dufferin School and Belmont High School in Montreal, and did several years of business and accounting studies at night. His business career started with the Stonewall Jackson Cigar Co. with whom he remained for five years. At the age of 21 he went into business for himself in the operation of a cigar store. In 1925 he opened and operated two gasoline stations adjacent to the Montreal waterfront. In 1931 he entered into partnership with G. Menard in Empire Stevedoring Co. He took over the business in 1934 when his partner retired. He became President of the Company when it was incorporated in 1940. He is also President of Inland Equipment Inc.; Repmont Construction Ltd.; LaSalle Investment Corp. Director: Canpal Trading Co.; Adath Israel Congregation. Governor: Montreal Jewish General Hospital; The Hospital of Hope; Montreal Y.M.H.A. Married Debby Quint in 1924. They have two children.

Samuel Gordon Chodos,

President
Empire Stevedoring Company Limited

Theodore Chodos . . . born at Montreal, Que., in 1927. He was educated at Mount Royal School, Strathcona Academy (Montreal), and Queen's University, Kingston, Ont. He graduated with his B.A. degree in 1947. Throughout his school days he took an active interest in ships and shipping and worked in various capacities with Empire Stevedoring Company Limited. Upon his graduation from University he was appointed Secretary-Treasurer of Empire Stevedoring Company Limited. Since 1950 he has been making annual trips to Western European Countries, the United Kingdom, Finland, and Czechoslovakia calling upon shipowners and operators, and has done a very successful job of selling the services of Empire Stevedoring. He married Reina Schkubel in 1956. They have one child.

Theodore Chodos,

Secretary-Treasurer
Empire Stevedoring Company Limited

Robert John Beaumont,

Chairman

The Shawinigan Water and Power Company

Robert John Beaumont . . . born in London, England in 1883. He was educated in General and Technical Schools in London, England. Was a draughtsman and engineer on design, construction and operation of steam plants and operation of steam plants and sub-stations, London Underground Railways; entered service as draughtsman, The Shawinigan Water and Power Company, 1910; appointed chief draughtsman 1911; general purchasing agent, The Shawinigan Water and Power Company, and of all electrical and manufacturing subsidiaries, 1913; manager, subsidiary electrical distribution companies, 1918; manager, Commercial and Distribution Department, 1931; Assistant General Manager, October 1937; Vice-president in charge of Distribution, 1941; Director, 1947, appointed to present position, December 1950. Connected with Canadian Electrical Association for a number of years as Chairman, Technical Section; appointed Vice-President, 1923, President 1925 and 1926. He is Chairman of the Board and Director of The Shawinigan Water and Power Company; Chairman of the Board and Director, Quebec Power Company, Quebec City; President and Director, The Quebec Railway, Light and Power Company, Quebec City; President and Director, Shawinigan Buildings Limited, Montreal; Vice-President and Director, St. Maurice Power Corporation, Montreal; Director, The Shawinigan Engineering Company Limited, Montreal; Saguenay Electric Company, Montreal. Clubs: Mount Royal, Montreal; St. James's, Montreal; St. Denis, Montreal; Arts (Montreal); Royal Montreal Golf (Dixie, Que.) Life Member: Forest and Stream (Dorval, Que.); The Quebec Garrison (Quebec City); Thetford Mines Golf (Thetford Mines, Que.); Laurentian Club (Province of Quebec). He is married and has one son and two daughters. Residence: 3489 Atwater Ave., Montreal, 25, Quebec.

John A. Fuller,

President

The Shawinigan Water and Power Company

John A. Fuller . . . born in Montreal, Quebec, March 4, 1903. He was educated at Hotchkiss School, Lakeville, Conn.; Princeton University, Princeton, N.J. (B.A. 1924). After graduating was employed in the Security Savings and Trust Company, Portland Oregon. From 1926 to 1936 was employed by Aldred and Company, Montreal, Quebec as Secretary and subsequently Vice-President. In January 1937 was appointed Secretary, Shawinigan Chemicals Limited, being elected Director and Secretary-Treasurer of the company in February 1940. Appointed Vice-President September 1945 and at the same time appointed Vice-President and Director, The Shawinigan Water and Power Company. Was appointed Executive Vice-President January 1950; President December 1950, and President of Quebec Power Company, February 1951. Vice-Chairman, Canadian Council, National Industrial Conference Board Inc. He is President and Director of: The Shawinigan Water and Power Company, Quebec Power Company, Quebec; Chairman and Director: Shawinigan Chemicals Limited, Montreal; Vice-President and Director: Shawinigan Resins Corporation, Springfield, Mass.; Montreal Trust Company, Montreal; British American Oil Company Limited, Toronto; Rolls-Royce of Canada Limited, Montreal; Sun Life Assurance Company of Canada, Montreal; Canada General Fund Limited, Toronto, Ont., Royal Bank of Canada, Montreal; Southern Canada Power Company, Limited, Montreal, Quebec. He is Past President of Royal Canadian Golf Association. Member: Board of Governors, McGill University; Executive Council, Canadian Manufacturers Association; Y.M.C.A. Metropolitan Board; Royal Edward Laurentian Hospital Board. Clubs: University; Mount Royal; St. James's; Royal Montreal Golf; Laurentian Golf (Ste. Agathe). Recreations: golf, skiing. He married Katharine Boyd, 1924; has two sons and two daughters. Residence: 3445 Ontario Avenue, Montreal, 25, Quebec.

Charles Howard Gordon . . . born Montreal, Quebec, September 8, 1902. He was educated at Lower Canada College; Royal Military College; McGill University. He was a designer with Sir W. G. Armstrong & Whitworth, London, England from 1924 to 1925; commenced with Atlas Construction Co. Ltd., in 1925; Was elected Vice-President and Managing Director, which post he retained until 1948. President, Montreal Builders' Exchange, 1949-50. He is now President of Pentagon Construction Co. Ltd., Montreal, Quebec; Director: Brinton-Peterboro Carpet Co. Ltd.; Canadian Bronze Co. Ltd.; Canadian Corporate Management Co. Ltd. Clubs: University, Montreal Racquet, Canadian; Mount Royal, Mount Bruno Golf & Country. Member: Engineering Institute of Canada. Married: Margaret Hall Black in Montreal in 1929. They have two sons and one daughter. Residence: Boisjoli, Saraguay, Quebec.

Charles Howard Gordon, B.Sc.

President
Pentagon Construction Co. Ltd.

Hugh Richardson Montgomery . . . born St. Johns, Quebec, March 25, 1905. He was educated at Bishop's College School, Lennoxville, Quebec; Bishop's University; McGill University; B.Sc. He began his career as a civil engineer in 1929 with Fraser-Brace Engineering Co. Ltd., Paugon Falls, Quebec; Engineer-in-charge, Atlas Construction Ltd., Quebec and New Brunswick, 1930-37; General Superintendent, various locations, 1937-38; Project Manager, Montreal, Quebec, and Gander, Newfoundland, 1938-1948; he was elected director of Atlas Construction Co. Ltd., in 1932; Vice-president in 1940. He left early in 1948 to help found Pentagon Construction Co. Ltd., Clubs: Canadian; University (Montreal); St. George Snowshoe (Westmount). Societies: Psi Upsilon Fraternity (McGill), President of Chapter, 1928-29; Quebec Vice-President, Canadian Construction Association; Graduates Society of McGill University; Engineering Institute of Canada; Corporation of Professional Engineers of Quebec. Recreation: Fishing. Married: Angeline Price Gregory, in Saint John, N.B. on June 25, 1934. They have one son. Residence: 668 Grosvenor Avenue, Westmount, Quebec.

Hugh Richardson Montgomery, B.Sc.

Vice-President, General Manager & Director
Pentagon Construction Co. Ltd.

Hon. T. S. Bushnell,

Mayor
Village of Massena

T. S. Bushnell . . . born Palmyra, New York, December 21, 1889. He was educated at Plainville and Walworth grade schools and Palmyra High School in New York State. He began his career with the New York Barge Canal Survey and was later associated with Barge Canal Contractors from 1907 - 1914. From 1914 to 1929 with the exception of April 1918 to June 1919 he was a Construction Engineer for Aluminum Co. of America. From April to June he was with the U.S. Army Engineers. He held the post of Mayor of the Village of Massena from 1931 to 1935 and again from 1957 to 1959. He was Trustee for the Village of Massena from 1955 to 1957. He was with the Federal Government in the capacity of Engineer from 1938 to 1942. He is a former president of Massena Monday Luncheon Club, Massena Country Club. He also held the post of County and District Commander of the American Legion. He is a registered New York State Professional Engineer and is also a Director of the U.S. Canada Railways.

Francis Lloyd Hosmer,

Supervisor,
Town of Massena, N.Y.

Francis Lloyd Hosmer . . . born Gouverneur, New York, June 18, 1895. Son of Albert Martin and Carrie Mayhew Hosmer. Student Public Schools, private studies in accounting and business administration. Married Emma M. Storr, July 24, 1917. One daughter, Doris, (Mrs. Kenneth Stark). Laborer, Pyrites Mine, Herman, New York, 1913; payroll and accounting clerk, Aluminum Company of America, Massena, New York, 1914-1921; Service World War I, U. S. Army, decorated Purple Heart 1917-1919. Agent Metropolitan Life Insurance Company 1921-1926; Proprietor General Insurance Agency, Massena, New York, 1926-1944; Town Clerk, Town of Massena, New York, 1936-1951; Supervisor, Town of Massena, New York, since 1952. Member of Republican State Committee 1950-1958 from St. Lawrence County. Member First Methodist Church, Massena, New York, American Legion, Disabled American Veterans, Veterans of Foreign Wars, Massena, N.Y., Masons, Odd Fellows, and Monday Luncheon Club, Massena, New York. High Priest-Royal Arch Masons 1958; Chairman, St. Lawrence County Board of Supervisors 1958. Vice President, New York State Association of Towns, 1958. Residence 64 Bishop Avenue, Massena, New York. Office, Town Hall, Main Street, Massena, N.Y.

Walter Francis Harris, . . . born Auburn, Indiana, August 7th, 1890. He was educated at the Auburn High School and Purdue University, Lafayette, Indiana. He came to Canada in May 1914, when he began to work for Crawley & McCracken Co. Limited at Port McNichol, Ontario. After holding various positions he was appointed Vice President in 1921 and later President in 1940. He is also President of Murray's Restaurants Limited and President of Murray-McCracken Co. Ltd. He has been active in trade associations, having been President and later Honorary President of the Canadian Restaurant Association and Vice-President for Canada of the National Restaurant Association.

Walter F. Harris

President
Crawley & McCracken Co. Ltd.

J. Kenneth Cullen . . . born Bromley Township, Ontario, November 4th, 1909. He was educated at St. Alexander College, Ironside, Quebec and St. James College, Kitchener, Ontario. He joined Crawley & McCracken Co. Limited as a camp clerk at North Bay, Ontario, in 1931. He held the positions of Inspector, District Manager, and General Superintendent until 1953 when he was appointed General Manager. In 1956 he was then elected Vice-President and General Manager. Member: Canadian Restaurant Association; Chamber of Commerce; Canadian Institute of Mining and Metallurgy; Rotary Club of Montreal; Canadian Railway Club and various other associations.

J. Kenneth Cullen

Vice-President & General Manager
Crawley & McCracken Co. Ltd.

William Thow

President
J. & R. Weir Limited

William Thow . . . born at Aberdeen, Scotland, on March 23, 1896. He was educated at Graphic School and Gordon's College, Aberdeen. He came to Canada in 1921 and began his business career as Accountant at Dominion Jobbing Co., Toronto, Ont., in 1923, remaining there until 1929. From 1929 to 1930, he was Sales Manager for Gestetner (Canada) Ltd., Montreal. From 1930 to 1935, he was Secretary of J. & R. Weir Ltd., appointed Vice-President in 1935 and assuming the position of President of the Company in 1950. During the first World War he served with the Royal Engineers and Royal Air Force. He is also President of Welding Engineers Ltd., a subsidiary of J. & R. Weir Ltd. He is Author of "Odd Measures"; "Tales of a Songsmith"; "A Cast of Reverie"; "A Sort of Sentiment". He is Governor of the Montreal General Hospital and the Verdun General Hospital. Clubs: Mount Stephen; Montreal Skeet. Recreations: Shooting and fishing. Hobbies: horticulture and rare plants. He married Cora Weir on June 6, 1923. They have two daughters and one son. Residence: 4835 Cedar Crescent, Montreal, Que.

Norman Weir Benson, B. Eng.

Vice-President and Director
J. & R. Weir Limited

Norman Weir Benson, B. Eng., . . . born Montreal, Que., August 24, 1912, son of Gordon Henry Benson (London, England) and Alice May (Weir) Benson of Montreal, Canada. Educated: Kensington School; West Hill High School; McGill University, Montreal, B.Eng. Apprentice, J. & R. Weir Limited, Montreal, 1930; Chief Draughtsman, 1934; Technical Engineer, 1940; Director, 1940; Technical Engineer, Welding Engineers Limited, 1939; Director, 1940; Vice-President, J. & P. Weir Limited, est., 1875, Marine and Industrial of Canada; the Corporation of Professional Engineers of Quebec; Canadian Chamber of Commerce; The Kirk Section, Knox Crescent and Kensington Church; American Society for Metals; Life Member: Montreal Sailors' Institute. Governor: Montreal General Hospital. Chairman: The Society of Naval Architects and Marine Engineers, Eastern Canadian Division. In May, 1958, elected Chairman of The Society of Naval Architects and Marine Engineers, Eastern Canadian Division. In addition to being Vice-President and Director of J. & P. Weir Limited, est.,, 1875, Marine and Industrial Engineering, 33 Nazareth St., Montreal, Que., he is also Director, Welding Engineers Limited. Married, Mary Victoria Brown, daughter of Mr. and Mrs. George Brown, Loughnease, Co. Tyrone, Northern Ireland, June 28, 1947. Clubs: Summerlea Golf; Red Birds Ski; Canadian (Montreal); Graduate Society, McGill University; Grunt Club Inc. (Montreal); Mount Stephen. Societies: A.F. & A.M., The University Lodge, No. 84, G.R.Q. Steward, November, 1956; Royal Albert Chapter No. G.R.Q., R.A.M.; Scottish Rite, Montreal. Recreations: golfing, bowling, skiing. Presbyterian. Residence: 4601 Cumberland Avenue, Montreal, Que.

Guy Tombs, J.B., . . . born Lachute, Que., in 1877. He was educated at Montreal High, Y.M.C.A. schools. He was with the Canadian Pacific Railways Foreign Freight Department, Montreal, from 1892-5, closely thereafter with pioneers of Great Railway, Waterway, Hydro-Electric and Pulp and Paper expansion which included quarter century in Canadian National Railways and Steamships or components. Revived commercial navigation in New York via the Richelieu-Hudson in 1926. He was its Chief Advocate. He was honorary secretary (transit) Can. Div. Aerial League of the British Empire from 1917-18. He was consul of Argentina for eight years prior to World War II. Advisory member Canadian Maritime Commission in 1947; Chairman Montreal Presbytery United Church of Canada 1934-35; President Montreal Sailors' Institute 1935, 1936, 1943; joint chairman Montreal's First Slum Clearance and Housing Committee, 1934-35, continuing for several years as Metropolitan Comm. on Housing and Clearance; Life Governor, British and Foreign Bible Society and Montreal General Hospital and Montreal Children's Hospital; Governor, United Theological College; a founder member of the St. Georges Williams College Corp'n (1948); he has held various positions in railways, ports and industrial traffic associations, Montreal Board of Trade, American Society of Travel Agents, UNICEF, YMCA, AF&AM, Rotary, and welfare agencies. Member: Antiquarian & Numismatic, Montreal Museum of Fine Arts and Vermont Historical Societies. Decoration: Chevalier de Leopold II for Belgian relief work (1919). Author: The Harbour of Montreal, which included support of St. Lawrence Seaway, (1932); One Hundred Years of Erskine Church (1934); The Chambly Canal 1843-1943; many reports and brochures; publisher "Moose and Caribou" 1908, compiler St. Lawrence winter navigation brief (1956)). Member: Mount Stephen Club (Montreal) and Canadian Club (New York).

Guy Tombs, J.P.,

President
Guy Tombs Limited (1921)

Laurence C. Tombs, M.A., D.Sc. P. . . . born Quebec 1903. He was educated at McGill University, New College, Oxford and the University of Geneva. He was a member of the Communications and Transit Section, League of Nations, Secretariat, Geneva, 1930-39, with missions in many European countries; International Commission for the Assistance of Spanish Refugees, Paris and Franco-Spanish border, 1939; consultant with the British Overseas Airways Corporation, London, 1943-44. He was first executive officer and organizer of the International Air Transport Association, Montreal, 1945-46, with missions in Washington, London, Paris and Cairo. He was President of the American Society of Travel Agents Inc., 1953-54, and of Canadian Inter-American Association, 1954-56. He has been the Consul of Finland for the Province of Quebec since 1950; member of Finnish delegation, Assembly of International Civil Aviation Organization (I.C.AO) 1950-52. He was awarded decorations by France, Italy, Panama, the Order of Malta, and two Mexican Citations. Author: "The Port of Montreal" (used by Sir Alexander Gibb in preparing his report which resulted in establishment of National Harbours Boards in 1936); "International Organization in European Air Transport". He is a trustee of the Canadian-Scandinavian Foundation; Life Governor, Montreal General Hospital. Member: Montreal University Club; Montreal Club; Quebec Garrison Club; Scal Club; Traffic Club of Montreal; Transportation Club of Ottawa; Montreal Board of Tarde; Chambre de Commerce du District de Montreal, Chambre de Commerce Française au Canada, Canadian Institute of International Affairs, Canadian Industrial Traffic League. He is also Vice-President and Secretary Treasurer of Davie Transportation Ltd. and Guy Tombs Marine Services Ltd., Montreal.

Laurence C. Tombs, M.A., D.Sc.P.

Vice President & Secty-Treas.
Guy Tombs Limited (1921)

Gordon L. Manning

President & Managing Director
The Office Specialty Manufacturing Company Limited

Gordon L. Manning, . . . President and Managing Director, The Office Specialty Manufacturing Company Limited, manufacturers of office furniture and filing equipment, Newmarket, Ont. Born, Forest, Ont., Dec. 7, 1889, son of the late Nicholas and the late Marie (Langford) Manning, both of Forest, Ont. Educated: public and high schools, Forest; Technical School, London, Ont. Began with the present company in charge of engineering, Jan. 1913; in charge of production, 1920-1930; General Manager, 1933; appointed President and Managing Director. Married Anna Sheridan, daughter of John Sheridan, Brockville, Ont., June 14, 1919; has one son (Wayne). Clubs: National; Granite; Summit Golf and Country. Society: A.F. & A.M. Recreations: golf, lawn bowling and boating. Progressive Conservative. United Church of Canada. Residence: 76 Park Avenue, Newmarket, Ont.

Lloyd Rogers Champion,

President and Managing Director
Champion Savings Corporation Limited

Lloyd Rogers Champion . . . born at Campbellton, N.B., on September 30, 1904. He joined Investors Syndicate, Vancouver, B.C., in 1927; became Vancouver City Manager in 1929; formed Champion Savings Corporation Limited in 1932 and is to date its President and Managing Director. He bought controlling interest in the Prudential Trust Company Limited in 1939 and is Chairman of the Board. He organized Maritime Central Airways Ltd., in 1941 and was President until 1945. He organized Granby Aviation Ltd., in 1943 and was President until 1946. In 1943 he organized Oil Sands Ltd., and is President of the Company. He organized Permanent Agencies Ltd., in 1949 and is still President. He organized Champion Pipe Line Corp., Ltd., in 1951, and Universal Protected Homes Ltd., in 1953 and is still President of both companies. He formed Champion Mutual Fund of Canada Ltd., in 1955 and is still President of that firm. He is also President of Champion & Company Limited. Recreations: golf, fishing and swimming. Residence: Croyden Apts., 3455 Cote des Neiges Road, Montreal, Que.

A. R. Thomson . . . born in New York, N.Y., March 30, 1906; son of James Omond Thomson and Elizabeth (Wilson) Thomson. Educated: Dalziel High School, Motherwell, Scotland; Hamilton Technical School, Hamilton, Scotland. Began with Fred Smith & Company Limited, Quantity Surveyors, Hamilton, Scotland; came to Canada and joined A. F. Byers & Company, Montreal, 1929; became Secretary, Argus Construction Company, Montreal, 1931-35; Estimator of Construction, G. Archambault Limited 1935-37; joined Foundation Company of Canada as Estimator, 1937; appointed Assistant District Manager 1938; District Manager 1940; Vice-President 1950; with Canit Construction Limited as General Manager 1958. Clubs: Mount Stephen; Royal St. Lawrence Yacht; National (Toronto); Montreal Amateur Athletic Association. Recreation: Sailing. Married: Lorraine Taylor, daughter of George Taylor, Westmount, Quebec, 31 January 1948; children: Ian, Anne, Mary, Margaret, James, John David. Residence: 68 Summit Circle, Yestmount, Quebec.

A. R. Thomson

General Manager
Canit Construction Limited

Jean Leman, B.S., P.Eng. . . . born at Montreal, Que., on January 18, 1912. He was educated at College Jean de Breboeuf, Montreal; Massachusetts Institute of Technology (B.S. General Engineering and Business Administration). From 1936 to 1939 he was associated with Shell Oil Company of Canada. From 1940 to 1945, he was Chief Industrial Engineer at Canadair. He was General Manager of St. Lawrence Metal and Marine Works from 1945 to 1949. He was appointed Treasurer, North American Utilities Corp. in 1949; President of Candiac Development Corp. in 1955 and is President, Newmont Development Corp. He was the first Mayor of the Town of Candiac, Que., and is Vice-President of Northam Equipment Ltd.; Director: Sicard Inc.; Sicard Industries; Calalta Petroleums Ltd.; Phillips Oil Co. Ltd.; President and Director: Newmont Development Corp. (affiliated with Candiac). Member: Montreal Board of Trade; Chambre de Commerce; Corporation of Professional Engineers of the Province of Quebec. Recreations: golf, fishing and hunting. Married: Michelle Dupuis of Montreal, Que., on August 10, 1940. They have three children. Residence: 435 Algonquin Ave., Town of Mount Royal, Montreal 16, Que.

Jean Leman, B.S., P.Eng.,

President
Candiac Development Corporation

William G. Maguire

President and Chairman
Panhandle Eastern Pipe Line Company

William G. Maguire . . . born in Franklin Grove, Illinois, on August 16, 1888. For most of his adult life he has been connected with utilities and related industries. His earliest business experience was as a salesman of iron and steel. As early as 1915 he was associated with a group which was working on the development of by-product coke and gas ovens. From 1915 to 1923 he was active in the development of the North American Light and Power Company. In 1928, he left the presidency of St. Louis Gas and Coke Company to form W. G. Maguire & Co., and specialized in the acquisition and sale of utility and related properties. In 1930 he became associated with the Missouri-Kansas Pipe Line Company, then planning a long distance natural gas pipe line system. When a change in the route of the proposed pipe line was necessitated by competitive utility interests, he developed an alternate route, and was responsible in large part, for the formation of Panhandle Eastern Pipe Line Company as an operating subsidiary of Missouri-Kansas Pipe Line Company. Shortly thereafter Panhandle came under control of the Columbia Gas and Electric holding company system, and he led the fight for an independent management for Panhandle and was successful in restoring control to the original founders in 1943. He was elected Chairman of the Board and Chief Executive Officer and has served since then in that capacity.

C. Bruce Beamer

President and General Manager
Provincial Engineering Ltd.

C. Bruce Beamer . . . Following his school years, he provided himself a 15-year background of practical on-the-job experience in industrial maintenance, machinery installation and structural steel erection before becoming a founding partner of Provincial Erectors & Installation Company in 1939. In September 1941, this original partnership was incorporated under the present name, Provincial Engineering Ltd. Under his continued leadership, Provincial Engineering has grown into one of Canada's most prominent industries. As presently comprised, the corporation now operates as three divisions — Industrial Construction, engaged primarily in the erection and equipment installation of ready-to-operate plants . . . a Transmission Tower Division which designs, fabricates and erects power transmission towers . . . and a Crane & Hoist Division manufacturing overhead materials handling equipment. Today the products and services of this company are employed throughout the Dominion of Canada and in many parts of the world.

Leo Elzéar Dansereau . . . born at Montreal, P.Q., November 5, 1910. He was educated at the Seminary of Ste. Therese and the Seminary of Valleyfield, P.Q. In July 1933 he founded Metropole Electric Reg'd. and was manager until 1938. In February 1938 the firm was incorporated under the name of Metropole Electric Inc. and he became its President and General Manager. Member: Montreal Chamber of Commerce. Clubs: Hunting and Fishing Club of the Mountains of Addington Inc.; Laval-sur-le-Lac Golf Club; Outremont Club; Hedrobar Club; Seigniory Club; Islesmere Golf Club; St. Denis Club. Recreations: Fishing, Hunting, Golf, Travelling. Residence: St. Eustache-sur-le-Lac, P.Q.

Léo Elzéar Dansereau

President
Metropole Electric Inc.

Robert Riopelle, B.A.Sc., P.Eng. . . . Born at Montreal in 1920. Graduated from Montreal Technical School in 1940. Graduated Bachelor of Applied Science and Electrical-Mechanical Engineer in 1947. Joined Metropole Electric Inc., in October 1947 as estimator and superintendent. A few months later he was appointed work's manager and chief engineer. In January 1954, he was appointed to the position of Executive Vice President in charge of Engineering and Installations. Member: Engineering Institute of Canada; Corporation of Professional Engineers of the Province of Quebec. Clubs and Associations: Outremont Club; Addington Hunting and Fishing Club; Rosemere Golf Club. Recreations: Fishing and Golf. Residence: Montreal.

Robert Riopelle, B.A.Sc., P. Eng.

Executive Vice President
Metropole Electric Inc.

J. Elgin Armstrong,

President
Armstrong Bros. Company Limited

J. Elgin Armstrong . . . born in Peel County, Ontario. He started the original contracting firm, Armstrong Bros. Construction, in 1928 with his brother, C. Edwin Armstrong, at Brampton, Ontario. The Company started in the crushing and excavation field, and during the 30 years of operation has expanded and is now operating three companies, of which he is President. These other two companies are, Peel Construction Company Limitd and Montcalm Construction, Inc. His main interest, apart from construction, is the breeding and raising of thoroughbred and standardbred horses. He has had horses racing under his colours in Great Britain, The United States and Canada. Both he and his brother were the first owners, other than American owners, to win the Hambletonian classic. Their mare, Helicopter, won this race in 1953 at Goshen, New York. He is a Director of the Ontario Jockey Club and a member of the Executive of the Canadian Trotting Association and a director of the Ontario Road Builders Association. He has one son, H. Charles Armstrong, who is Secretary-Treasurer of the three companies.

J. O. Lamontagne

President
J. Lamontagne Limited

J. O. Lamontagne . . . born at Quebec City, Que., November, 1901. Educated: Montmagny, Que. He started in business in 1921 as an architect and was associated with the construction of a number of well known buildings, mostly in eastern Canada. Clubs: Ste. Dorothee Golf; Iroquois Yacht. Married Rita Bergeron of Quebec City and has one son. Catholic. Residence: 2260 Hanover Road, Montreal, Que.

Herbert F. Bruning . . . born in New York City in 1902. He holds an A.B. degree (1925) from Cornell University where he majored in Chemical Engineering. He started with the Company in 1925 as Manager of the Paper Sensitizing Department of the Bruning Chicago Office. In 1930, he became Manager of the Chicago Office and in 1931 was appointed Vice-President. He became President in 1949, when the Company was grossing around $12.8 million a year. In 1957 during his eighth year as President, the Company enjoyed sales of $38 million. He has been very active in the affairs of the reproduction industry. He is Vice-President and a Director of the National Association of Blueprint and Diazotype Coaters, which he helped organize in 1954. He is also a member of the International Association of Blueprint and Allied Industries, which he served as a Director from 1938 to 1939 and Treasurer from 1940 to 1944. Member: Tau Kappa Epsilon; Chicago Club; Cornell Club of Chicago; Indian Hill Club; Sunset Ridge Country Club. His main hobby is growing orchids and his favorite sport is fishing. His family includes his wife, two sons, a daughter, and four grandchildren. Residence: Winnetka, Illinois.

Herbert F. Bruning

President
Charles Bruning Company, Inc.
Charles Bruning Company (Canada) Ltd.

Russell M. Shepherd . . born in Philadelphia, Pa., June 21st, 1916. From 1940 to 1943 he was with the U.S. Department of Agriculture. In 1943, he joined the Government-Sponsored Foreign Broadcast Intelligence Service which monitored broadcasts from Germany and Japan. Assigned to set up a Pacific Bureau for the Service, he followed American troops in Guam and eventually Iwo Jima. In 1945, he was appointed Director of the Division and was instrumental in getting the Government to continue the monitoring service after it had decided to end it. He organized the service on a peacetime basis in 1946, and today it is a unit of the Central Intelligence Agency. In 1955 he organized Charles Bruning Company (Canada) Ltd. He undertook the job of setting up the Canadian Company after spending just a short time with the U.S. Company, the Charles Bruning Company, Inc., manufacturers of Copyflex and Copytron reproduction machines and the materials and one of the world's leading suppliers of drafting, engineering, and surveying instruments and materials. Before starting the Canadian Company, he served the Bruning Company briefly as Assistant to the Administrative Vice-President and as a Company representative in Washington, D.C. He holds a B.A. degree from Swarthmore College and a M.B.A. from the University of Pennsylvania. Member: Graphic Reproduction Association of Toronto; National Club of Toronto; Optical Tooling Engineers Association. Residence: Toronto, Ontario.

Russell M. Shepherd

Vice President & Managing Director,
Charles Bruning Company (Canada) Ltd.

INDEX

A

Akin, John R.	65,	332
Angell, Lester W.	64,	331
Angus, Melvyn Graham		379
Armington, Raymond Q.		366
Armstrong Bros. Co. Ltd.		321
Armstrong, J. Elgin		412
Ashforth, Albert C.		351
Atkins, Arthur		393
Atlas Construction Co. Limited		263

B

Ball, Gordon R.	337
Bank of Montreal	197
Bank of Nova Scotia	216
Barnes, Charles	383
Barnes Investigation Bureau Ltd.	270
Beamer, C. Bruce	410
Beatty, David S.	340
Beaumont, Robert John	402
Bedard-Girard Limited	275
Bénard, J. A.	354
Benson, Norman Weir	406
Berg, Miss Frances E.	391
Bergson, G. M.	368
Bériault, Raymond J.	70
Berry, Albert R.	389
Bherer, Wilbrod	382
Blaiklock Bros. Limited	221
Bonny, John B.	388
Boulton, Beverley K.	335
Bourke, George Wesley	350
Bourne, John G.	352
Boyle, James Patrick	379
B. P. Canada Limited	234
British Petroleum Company Ltd.	234
Brockel, Harry C.	357
Brocklesby, John N. Transport Limited	316
Brownlee, John Edward	393
Brucker, Hon. Wilber	16,	333
Bruning, Chas., Company (Canada) Ltd.		292
Bruning, Herbert F.		413
Burns Bros. & Company Limited		187
Burns Bros. & Denton Limited		187
Burns, Charles Fowler Williams		340
Bushnell, His Honor T. S.		404
Campbell, Alistair Matheson		350
Canada Iron Foundries Ltd.		208
Canada Steamship Lines Limited		182
Candiac Development Corp.		256
Canadian Bank of Commerce		205
Canadian General Electric Co. Ltd.		246
Canadian Industries Ltd.		286
Canadian Ingersoll-Rand Company Limited		202
Canadian Marconi Company		298
Canadian National Railways		215
Canadian Overseas Shipping Ltd.		318
Canadian Pacific Railway Company		282
Canadian Vickers Limited		190
Canadian Westinghouse Company Limited		238
Canamont & Canit Construction		264
Canit Construction Limited		280
Castle, Lewis G.	19,	330
Champion, Lloyd Rogers		408
Champion Savings Corporation Ltd.		255
Chenevert, J. Georges		377
Chevrier, Hon. Lionel		66
Chicago Stevedoring Co. Inc.		283
Chicago Towing Company		210
Chodos, Samuel Gordon		401
Chodos, Theodore		401
Christy, Anker L.		381
City of Cornwall		230
City of Milwaukee		288
City of Valleyfield		250
Clarke, Desmond Arthur		344
Clarke, Stanley Desmond		344
Clarke Steamship Co. Ltd.		220
Cornwall, City of		230
Cowie, Lieut.-Col Alfred Henry		386
Crawley & McCracken Company Limited		304
Crump, Norris Roy		369
Cullen, J. Kenneth		405
Cullen Stevedoring Company Limited		211

D

Dansereau, Léo Elzéar	411
Davie, Geo. T., & Sons Ltd.	284
Davis, H. Norman	392
Dawes, A. Sidney	352
de Lalanne, Brig. James Arthur	361
de Rome, Louis N.	375
Deschamps, Albert	394
Desrosiers, P. H.	377
Dewey, Thomas E.	68
Diefenbaker, Prime Minister John G.	15, 329

D (continued)

Dominion Brake Shoe Company Ltd.	232
Dominion Bridge Company, Limited	227
Dominion Wire Rope Ltd.	189
Dondero, George A.	69
Douglas, Robert	353
Down, Alastair F.	349
Downer, H. C., & Associates, Inc.	213
Dufresne, Paul	394
Duncan, James S.	20,	330
Dunning, Hon. Charles Avery		392
Dunsmore, R. L.		356
Durkin, W. A.		370
Durrell, William H		336

E

Eadie, Robert S.	387
Eisenhower, President Dwight D.	13
Elizabeth II, Her Majesty, Queen	11
Empire Stevedoring Company Limited	305
Euclid Division, G.M.C.	198

F

Fenton, Perry M.	399
Ferrabee, Francis Gilbert	338
Finlayson, Stuart M.	367
Fjell-Oranje Lines	318
Friesen, E. J.	359
Frost, Charles Sydney	345
Fuller, John A.	402
Furness, Withy & Company, Limited	301

G

Gavsie, Charles	67
Gayport Shipping Limited	309
General Motors Corp. (Euclid Division)	198
Gilmore, James	346
Gluntz, H. Marvin	380
Gordon, Charles Howard	403
Gordon, Donald	378
Griffith, Kenneth C.	373
Guibert, Félix	365

H

Hale, Lucius M.	64,	332
Hales, Kenneth L.		381
Hamilton, Port of		241
Harkness, Robert Dickson		364
Harrill, E. Reece	64,	331
Harris, Walter F.		405
Hart, G. Arnold		337
Hausser, R.		355
Hayes, Murray William		356
Hees, Hon. George	17,	329
Hosmer, Francis Lloyd		404
Houlding, J. D.		368
Hudon, Fred P.		358
Hunter, Ernest John		347

I

Imperial Bank of Canada	249
Inselman, George	399
Iron Ore Company of Canada	184

J

| Joliette Steel Division | 232 |

K

| Kerr Steamships Limited | 312 |

L

Lalonde, Jean Paul	395
Lalonde & Valois	262
Lambert, Allen Thomas	351
Lamontagne, J., Ltd.	322
Lamontagne, J. O.	412
Lavigne, His Honor L. G.	360
Leman, Jean	409
Lessard, Jean-Claude	65,	332
Lilley, A. Neil		366
Lorber, Herbert James		398

M

Maguire, William G.		410
Malcolm, P. E. R.	65,	333
Malone, J. C., & Company Limited		291
Manitoba Steel Foundry Division		232
Mannin, Gordon L.		408
Marine Industries Limited		174
Marine Office of America		295
Marler, Hon. George		67
Marshall, Welsford Allen		385
Marsh, Henry Golden		390

Martin, Argue	362
Massena, Town of	296
Massena, Village of	297
Mather, William A.	369
Mayne, Arthur Ferdinand	343
McColl-Frontenac Oil Co. Limited	253
McCullough, Peter James	362
McKinnon, Neil John	348
McLagen, Thomas Rodgie	335
McLaughlin, George F.	391
McLean, J. Edmund	363
McLintock, T. Graeme	349
McNamara Construction Co. Limited	258
McNamara, George J.	339
McNamara, Harold S.	339
Mendelssohn Brothers (Canada) Ltd.	323
Mendelssohn, Nathan	400
Mendelssohn, S. M.	400
Metropole Electric Inc.	308
Miller, William Gardner	341
Milne, Gilmore & German	223
Milne, W. Harold	346
Milwaukee, City of	288
Miron & Freres Limited	188
Montgomery, Hugh Richardson	403
Montreal Locomotive Works Limited	204
Montreal, Port of	266
Montreal Shipping Company Limited	307
Morgan, Clifford William	363
Morrison, Harry Winford	388
Morrison-Knudsen Company, Inc.	200
Moses, Robert	21, 331
Muir, James	342
Murphy, A. G.	65, 332
Murphy, J. J.	372
Murphy, Martin P.	364

N

Nelson, Anton P.	390
Nenniger, Emile	376
Neyrpic Canada Limited	186
Nicks, F. William	345
Northern Electric Company Limited	243

O

Oettersagen, M. W.	64, 331
Office Specialty Manufacturing Company Ltd.	320
Ogilvie Flour Mills Co. Limited	310
Oliver, Donald William Graham	70

P

Palmer, Adrian B.	398
Panhandle Eastern Pipe Line Company	244
Paquet, Maurice	382
Paquin, Lucien	396
Paquin, Roger	396
Pariset, E.	354
Paterson, N. M., & Sons Limited	237
Pearse, Reginald Charles	367
Pentagon Construction Company Ltd.	212
Perini Corp.	194
Perini, Louis R.	389
Peterson, Frank B.	384
Pirelli Cables, Conduits Limited	281
Place, Edward R.	64, 332
Porter, J. P. Company Limited	180
Port of Montreal	266
Port Weller Dry Docks Ltd.	314
Pratley, Philip Louis	341
Pratley, P. L. Consulting Engineer	272
Proctor, John Stewart	359
Provincial Engineering Ltd.	302

Q

Quebec Hydro-Electric Commission	224
Quevillon, His Honor Louis	360

R

Rahilly, Thomas Francis	385
R.C.A. Victor Company, Ltd.	313
Reed, Shaw & McNaught	248
Rees, Edgar Philip	378

Reford, Lewis Eric	343
Reid, Thomas H.	373
Riopelle, Robert	411
Robert Reford Company Limited	214
Roberts, Bennett John	18, 330
Robinson, M. Harold	358
Rollins Burdick Hunter Co.	319
Royal Bank of Canada	193
Russell Construction Limited	233

S

Sarcoli, Ottorino	361
Saunders, Robert Hood	71
Savoie, J. Arthur	365
Sedgewick, Kenneth Middleton	342
Shawinigan Water and Power Company	217
Sheperd, Russell M.	413
Simard, A. Ludger	374
Simard, J. Arthur	375
Simard, J. Edouard	374
Simpson, Alex L.	372
Sincennes-McNaughton Line Ltd.	306
Snell, Bertrand H.	68
St-Arnaud & Bergevin Limited	273
St-Arnaud, Jean Pierre	383
St. Laurent, Rt. Hon. Louis Stephen	66
Sun Life Assurance Company of Canada	300
Surveyer, Arthur	376
Surveyer, Nenniger & Chenevert	254
Swan, Hunter & Wigham Richardson, Limited	196

T

Taylor-Bailey, Whitham	386
Terry Machinery Company Limited	242
Terry, William Harrison	355
Thom, James L.	384
Thomson, A. R.	409
Thow, William	406
Three Rivers Shipping Company Limited	290
Timmins, Jules R.	336
Tombs, Guy	407
Tombs, Guy Limited	252
Tombs, Laurence C.	407
Toronto-Dominion Bank	222
Town of Massena	296
Townsend, Clarence Dudley	397
Townsend Company Ltd.	236
Townsend, Dudley Roy	397
Tripp, Carlton E.	380

U

Uhl, Hall & Rich	274
United Grain Growers Limited	278
Utah Construction Company	218

V

Valleyfield, City of	250
Valois, Roméo	395
Vaughan, J. F.	347
Village of Massena	297

W

Wadsworth, Jeffery Page Rein	348
Wakem & McLaughlin, Inc.	317
Walsh Construction Company	206
Walsh, J. J.	371
Walsh, T. J. Jr.	371
Walsh, T. J. Sr.	370
Ward, Walter G.	353
Weeks, Hon. Sinclair	22, 329
Weir, J. & R., Limited	257
Welsford, Hubert Gray	387
West, C. W.	65, 333
Westriver Ore Transport Limited	226
Wilcox, George L.	338
Wiley, Senator Alexander	69
Wilson Shipping Corporation	226
Winnipeg Grain Exchange	276

Z

Zeidler, His Honor Frank P.	357

PHOTO CREDITS

Capital Press Service, Canadian Pacific Railway Co., International Press Limited, Canadian Newspaper Service Limited, William Notman & Son, Gaby of Montreal, Moffett, Chicago, Rice, Montreal, Gaby, Herb Nott & Co. Ltd., Milne Studios Limited, Nakash, Ashley & Crippen, Blank & Stoller Ltd., Trans-Canada Press, Ballard & Jarrett, Jon Nestor, Royal Studio, Press Service Bureau of Canada Registered, Associated Commercial Photographers Ltd., James Hardy, Toronto, Rapid Grip and Batten Limited, Who's Who in Canada, Blackstone Studios Inc., Confederation Life, Turners (Photography) Ltd., Elliott & Fry Ltd., Garcia Studio, Madison Geddes, Geraldine Carpenter, Scott's Studio, Goff Studios, André Studios, John E. Platz Studios, Wal-Mir and Company, Marin Studios Limited, Merrill Chase, E. Gendron, Drummond Photos, Fabian Bachrach, Basil Zarov, Studio Jac-Guy, Rialto Photo Studios, J. H. March, The William Kensit Studio, Eaton's Portrait Studio, Perc Powell, Richard Arless Associates, Joseph Shumilo, Rose Hamilton, Shelburne Studios, Bob Wyer, Varkony, Notman Collection — McGill University and Maclean's Magazine, New York Hydro, Ontario Hydro, City of Montreal.

Printed and bound by
Harpell's Press Co-Operative, Gardenvale, Que.